W9-CXS-350

Formwork
for Concrete

FORMWORK FOR CONCRETE

By M. K. HURD

Prepared with the assistance of
R. C. BALDWIN, under direction of

ACI COMMITTEE 622, FORMWORK FOR CONCRETE
(now redesignated Committee 347)

JOSEPH R. PROCTOR
Chairman

JOHN H. BANKER
PAUL S. BARTON
F. H. BEINHAUER
H. P. CERUTTI
N. L. DOE
HARRY ELLSBERG
JACOB FELD
DAVID E. FLEMING
VANCE J. GRAY

ROBERT C. JOHNSON
VICTOR F. LEABU
DONALD R. PEIRCE
A. H. PILLING
PAUL F. RICE
O. G. SHARRAR
P. R. STRATTON
WILLIAM R. WAUGH
WILLIAM H. WOLF

Special Publication Number 4

AMERICAN CONCRETE INSTITUTE
DETROIT

This third edition contains revisions to agree with ACI 347-68 "Recommended Practice for Concrete Framework," which appears in the Appendix beginning on p. 323. All form design tables, examples, and data on lumber have been revised to conform with PS 20-70, "Voluntary Product Standard for Softwood Lumber."

Third Edition
First Printing
Copyright © 1973 by the American Concrete Institute
P.O. Box 4754, Detroit, Michigan 48219
Printed in the United States of America
All rights reserved

Library of Congress Catalog Card Number 73-77438

The drawings in this book are typical designs and should not be used as working drawings. They are intended to be helpful in the preparation of complete formwork plans which should be adapted to local conditions and should conform with legal requirements. In no way is the book able to, or intended to, supplant the qualified designer or engineer to whom formwork planning should be entrusted.

Limitations of space and time have made it impossible to show all of the methods, materials, and products available for formwork construction. Omission of any item, therefore, should not be regarded as a judgment that it is unsuitable or inferior.

FOREWORD TO THE THIRD EDITION

Even though it was evident in 1968 when the revised second edition of this work was being prepared that changes in United States lumber standards were in the offing, resolution of the controversial changes by the lumber industry did not come soon enough to get the results into our second edition. Not until late in 1970 was the new PS 20-70 "Voluntary Product Standard for Softwood Lumber" formally adopted, and many months later lumber began coming into the market manufactured to the new dimensions specified in that standard. This third edition of *Formwork for Concrete* has been completely revised to reflect changes in the lumber standard, and to make use of the most recent (1971) working stress values for lumber recommended by the National Forest Products Association. All design examples, design tables, and design data for lumber have been revised to conform to the new dimensions and stresses. The design tables of Chapter 7 have been expanded to cover four different strengths of lumber, rather than two as in earlier editions. Additional minor changes include the updating of numerous referenced documents.

Revisions have been reviewed by ACI Committee 347, whose continuing cooperation is greatly appreciated. Committee membership at the time these revisions were completed included:

VICTOR F. LEABU
Chairman

ROBERT R. ANDERSON	JOHN A. GUSTAFSON
MARTIN W. BOLL	ROGER S. JOHNSTON
PETER D. COURTOIS	ROY H. OLSEN
THOMAS J. CROWLEY	CHARLES F. PECK
JACOB FELD	PAUL H. SOMMERS
DAVID E. FLEMING	WILLIAM R. WAUGH

Peter D. Courtois again served as chairman of the subcommittee directly responsible for reviewing revisions. Computer calculations for the new design tables were contributed by William Phillips and by Superior Concrete Accessories, Inc.

Detroit
April 1973   M. K. Hurd

FOREWORD TO THE SECOND EDITION

The first edition of *Formwork for Concrete* appeared in 1963, at the same time that the first ACI Formwork Standard, ACI 347-63, was adopted. The book was written as a how-to-do-it manual for form designers, contractors, engineers, and architects, following guidelines established by Committee 347 (formerly designated Committee 622) in the Standard. In July of 1968, a revised "Recommended Practice for Concrete Formwork, ACI 347-68" was adopted and this second revised edition has been prepared to take cognizance of changes in the Committee 347 recommendations. Retaining the freely illustrated format of the first edition, *Formwork for Concrete* continues to emphasize safety, efficiency, and economy in planning and building formwork. Completely new tables of the sectional properties of plywood and new design tables for plywood form members have been substituted because of changes in product standards for softwood plywood made since the first edition was released.

Revisions for the book were reviewed and approved by Committee 347, in much the same manner that the original draft of the book was reviewed, and the cooperation of this highly capable group is greatly appreciated. Committee membership during the review process included:

WILLIAM R. WAUGH
Chairman

MARTIN W. BOLL	ROY H. OLSEN
GEORGE F. BOWDEN	EDWARD J. O'REILLY
PETER D. COURTOIS	JOSEPH R. PROCTOR, JR.
L. B. CROSSING	PAUL F. RICE
THOMAS J. CROWLEY	LYNN M. ROSS
WILLIAM R. DAVIS, JR.	HARRY L. SCOGGIN
JACOB FELD	WILLIAM H. WOLF
DAVID E. FLEMING	GEORGE J. ZIVERTS

VICTOR F. LEABU

Peter D. Courtois was chairman of the subcommittee guiding revision of the book, and Joseph R. Proctor, Jr. headed the subcommittee which originated the new draft of the Formwork Standard.

Detroit
April 1969   M. K. Hurd

FOREWORD TO THE FIRST EDITION

Born of a concern for improving the safety and quality of formwork for concrete construction, ACI Committee 622 (since redesignated Committee 347) was organized in 1955. With the basic goal of developing a specification for the design and construction of formwork, the committee first published results of its studies of lateral pressure on formwork and of existing form construction practices. Under the leadership of Harry Ellsberg, the committee culminated 5 years of work with the publication in March, 1961, of a recommended practice for formwork. That report, with subsequent revisions, has been adopted this year as an ACI standard.

When the major committee report was completed, it was recognized that much more must be said to provide a how-to-do-it manual useful to form designers, contractors, engineers, and architects. It was then that the American Concrete Institute decided to undertake the preparation of such a formwork manual, following the guide-lines established by the committee report, and under the continuing direction of the committee's formwork authorities.

The entire preparation of this volume has been an exercise in cooperation of the highest order. The Concrete Reinforcing Steel Institute, which had previously contemplated publication of a similar work, turned over its file of information. The Portland Cement Association permitted use of material previously issued in its booklet on forms for architectural concrete. Other trade associations, together with the producers and suppliers of forms, formwork materials, and accessories, contributed generously of information regarding their products and specialties. Form builders, form designers, architects, and engineers shared experience and opinion in discussions which have contributed much to the preparation of this book. Information has also been derived from existing books and periodicals, many of which are cited in the text. The ACI staff offered continuing support in many ways. It is impossible to specifically acknowledge all contributions, but credits for direct contribution of illustrations are listed at the close of the text.

The book has benefitted greatly from the guidance and fine cooperation of Committee 622. A special editorial subcommittee was appointed to shoulder major responsibility for reviewing the manuscript during its preparation. This group included Paul Barton, Harry Ellsberg, Robert C. Johnson, V. F. Leabu, Paul Rice, and O. G. Sharrar. All members of Committee 622 were given the opportunity to review the complete manuscript; many were tireless in their response with constructive suggestions and criticism. Joseph R. Proctor, who assumed chairmanship of the committee early in 1961, was particularly helpful in organizing the talents and energies of the committee in support of the project, and both Chairman Proctor and P. R. Stratton made substantial direct contributions to preparation of the manuscript.

M. K. H.

Detroit
March 1963

CONTENTS

CONTENTS

CONTENTS

CONTENTS

CONTENTS

1:INTRODUCTION

FORMWORK DEVELOPMENT has paralleled the growth of concrete construction throughout the twentieth century. As concrete has come of age, and has been assigned increasingly significant structural tasks, form builders have had to keep pace. The increasing acceptance of concrete as an architectural medium today presents the form builder a new range of problems in the development of appropriate sheathing materials and maintenance of rigid tolerances.

At one time lumber was the predominant form material, but developments in the use of plywood, metal, plastics, and other materials, together with the increasing use of specialized accessories have changed the picture. Formwork was formerly built in place, used once, and wrecked. The trend today is toward increasing prefabrication, assembly and erection by mechanical means, and continuing reuse of the forms. These developments are in harmony with the increasing mechanization of production in other fields.

Not all of the important ideas are new, however. As early as 1908, members of the American Concrete Institute (then called the National Association of

1-1 Turn-of-the-century techniques in form building shown in this photo of work at the Cincinnati Zoo. Concentration of workmen and tools high in the structure is representative of the built-in-place technique that has been supplanted today in large degree by prefabrication.

1

1-2 Assembly line production of form panels typifies trend toward prefabrication in the industry today. Whether factory-built, as this picture shows, or made by the contractor in his own shop, as much of the formwork as possible is assembled before arriving at the job site.

Cement Users) were debating the relative merits of wood and steel formwork at their annual convention. At the same meeting they heard a colleague proclaim the advantages of modular panel forming that could be adapted for most any job, had its own connecting hardware, and was good for extensive reuse. By 1910, steel forms for paving were being produced commercially and used in the field (Figure 1-3). Steel forms for underground structures were marketed even earlier. Continuing refinement of basic ideas like these represents another area of formwork progress.

There are wide variations in details of forming practice from one country to another, and likewise considerable variation locally from one region of the United States to another. It was earlier hoped that this book could be made international in scope, matching the international character of the American Concrete Institute. However, such a task proved too formidable to undertake. It has been necessary to limit the scope to a comprehensive report on current practices and principles of design and construction in the United States and Canada. Suggestions for formwork economy have been based on conditions in these countries. In areas where labor costs are low in relation to the price of construction materials, many of these ideas will not have the same validity.

Whether form building is an art or a science remains an open question; the best answer probably is that it combines important elements of both. There is certainly no substitute for the skill and sense of "know-how" that come with experience. Yet many engineering principles can be brought to bear—improving the safety, quality, and economy of formwork.

One objective of this book is to make available in convenient, concise form much of the available existing knowledge that will be useful in planning, constructing, and using formwork. In no way will it supplant the experienced designer or builder; it can, however, give him considerable help by bringing together a multitude of properties, design data, and construction suggestions for convenient reference in a single volume. For the architect-engineer, it offers an improved opportunity for masterly execution of detail in concrete through a better understanding of the problems and possibilities in form building. For the novice, the book will serve as an introduction to many common forming practices, explaining basic principles of design and encouraging a rational rather than rule-of-thumb approach.

With this audience in mind, the text first establishes the basic objectives in form building:

Quality—in terms of strength, rigidity, position, and dimensions of the forms

Safety—for both the workers and the concrete structure

Economy—the least cost consistent with quality and safety required

Cooperation and coordination between engineer-architect and the builder or contractor are necessary to achieve these goals. How the structure can be designed with economy of formwork in mind, as well as the relationship of contractor to engineer or architect, are described in a preliminary chapter. Over-all planning for profitable construction with formwork in mind is covered in the next section, directed particularly to the problems of the contractor.

The text then divides into three main categories: (1) the detailed planning or design of forms; (2) the form building stage; and (3) using the forms. Design principles and methods are explained as simply as possible, and an entire chapter of design tables has been included to save many calculations. Materials and proprietary products for forming are described as fully as space permits. Suggestions for form construction cover both buildings and bridges, and an entire chapter is devoted to special requirements for architectural work. The section on using the forms covers

1-3 Steel forms developed for street paving were first marketed more than 60 years ago. A 1909 construction scene shows their early application. This and other basic ideas in formwork have undergone continuing development and improvement.

1-4 Present-day formwork is tailored to demanding construction requirements such as those met in building the 60-story reinforced concrete towers of the Marina City project in Chicago. Fiber-glass-reinforced plastic forms climbed to the top of the circular core for a total of 60 uses. Tower cranes moved up inside the cores ahead of the forms, and work followed on the slab and column structure of the floors below.

care and maintenance, inspection, reshoring, and winter work.

The following sections on tunnels, mass concrete, shells, domes, and folded plates deal with special forming problems encountered in building these structures. Non-standard techniques of concreting—slip forming, prepacked aggregate, shotcreting, and others—are discussed in terms of unusual requirements they present for formwork. Since many of the terms encountered in formwork practice are local or regional, or relate to the vocabulary of special trades, a glossary has been included.

Throughout the book, the term "formwork" has been employed in its broadest sense to include the total system of support for the freshly placed concrete—form sheathing plus all supporting members, hardware, and necessary bracing. The book has been intentionally limited to cast-in-place concrete with the only exception being discussion of precasting work done as an option by the concrete contractor at or near the job site. Discussion of concrete construction practices is limited to items that have a direct bearing on the formwork requirements.

The entire text follows recommendations established by ACI Committee 347, Formwork for Concrete, in its report on formwork. That document, now a standard of the American Concrete Institute, is included verbatim in the appendix of this volume.

2:GENERAL OBJECTIVES IN FORMWORK BUILDING

FORMS ARE THE TOOLS and dies of concrete construction. They mold the concrete to the desired size and shape and control its position and alignment. But formwork is more than a mold; it is a temporary structure that supports its own weight and that of the freshly placed concrete as well as construction live loads including materials, equipment, and workmen. The form builder is concerned with more than simply making forms the right size; his objectives are three-fold:

Quality—to design and build forms accurately so that the desired size, shape, position, and finish of the cast concrete are attained.

Safety—to build substantially so that formwork is capable of supporting all dead and live loads without collapse or danger to workmen and to the concrete structure.

Economy—to build efficiently, saving time and money for the contractor and owner alike.

Economy is a major concern since formwork costs may range anywhere from 35 to 60 percent of the cost of the concrete structure. Savings depend on the ingenuity and experience of the contractor. Judgment in the selection of materials and equipment, in planning fabrication and erection procedures, and in scheduling reuse of forms, will expedite the job and cut costs. The architect or engineer can also do much to help save formwork cost by keeping the requirements of formwork economy in mind when he is designing the structure.

In designing and building formwork, the contractor should aim for maximum economy without sacrificing quality or safety. Short-cuts in design or construction that endanger quality or safety may be false economy. If forms do not produce the specified surface finish, for example, much hand rubbing of the concrete may be required; or if forms deflect excessively, bulges in the concrete may require expensive chipping and grinding. Obviously economy measures that lead to formwork failure also defeat their own purpose.

How Formwork Affects Concrete Quality

Size, shape, and alignment of slabs, beams, and other concrete structural elements depend on accurate construction of the forms. The forms must be built to correct dimensions, must be sufficiently rigid under the construction loads to maintain the designed shape of the concrete, must be stable and strong enough to maintain large members in alignment, and must be substantially constructed so they can withstand handling and reuse without losing their dimensional integrity. The formwork must remain in place until the concrete is strong enough to carry its own weight, or the finished structure may be damaged.

The quality of surface finish of the concrete is affected by the material of the form. For example, if a patterned or textured finish is to be secured by use of a textured liner, the liner must be properly supported so that it will not deflect and cause indentions in the concrete surface. A correct combination of form material and oil or other parting compound can contribute materially to eliminating air holes or other surface imperfections in the cast concrete.

Formwork Safety

Among the accidents and failures that occur during concrete construction, many are formwork failures, which usually happen at the time concrete is being placed. A system of formwork filled with wet concrete has its weight at the top and is not basically a stable structure. Generally some unexpected effect

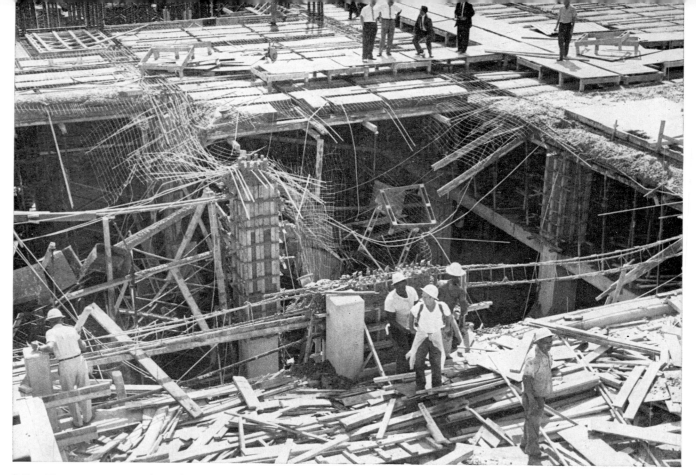

2-1 The contractor must know how to build formwork safely and must not take undue risks for the sake of economy; otherwise he may not only defeat his own purposes, but bear responsibility for loss of life. This formwork collapse caused 15 injuries and one death as well as extensive property damage and construction delays.

causes one member to give way, then others become overloaded or misaligned and the whole formwork structure collapses. Nevertheless, good practice in designing and constructing formwork, and in handling and using it, can provide safety as well as efficiency.

An interesting aspect of formwork failures is that often the same design, or even the same form, has been used several times with no mishap. In some cases this may be just a matter of luck. Perhaps the formwork is not well braced diagonally, but fortunately no strong lateral loads occur and there is no accident. Then in another bay, presumably under the same conditions, the concrete piles up a little too fast against a bulkhead, or several concrete buggies all come to a stop at the same time, and the forms unexpectedly collapse. Another cause may be minor differences in the assembly details resulting in localized weakness or overstress.

Causes of Failures

Premature stripping of forms, resulting from a desire for economy, premature removal of shores, and careless practices in reshoring have caused numerous failures or deficiencies in the completed concrete structure. Improper stripping and reshoring may cause

sagging of partially cured concrete and development of fine hairline cracks which in later years create a serious maintenance problem. Inadequate size and spacing of reshores may lead to a formwork collapse during construction as well as to damage of the concrete structure. Proper practices to forestall damage of this type are discussed in Chapter 10 under stripping and reshoring (p. 214).

In addition to the problems presented by stripping and reshoring, there are several causes of failure arising from the initial design, erection, and assembly of the formwork. The forces that cause forms to fail are usually not simple cases of vertical overloading. Of course this does occur at times, as when an extra load of concrete is dumped into an already filled area of a slab form, or there is a concentration of equipment or material on one section of a form. The more frequent causes of formwork failure, however, are other effects that introduce lateral force components or induce displacement of supporting members.

Inadequate Bracing

Inadequate cross bracing and horizontal bracing of shores is one of the factors most frequently involved in formwork accidents. Investigations of cases involving thousands of dollars of damage show evidence that the damage could have been prevented or held to a minor amount if only a few hundred dollars had been spent on diagonal bracing for the formwork supports. Consider the two cases that follow:

The main exhibition floor of the New York Coliseum collapsed when concrete was being placed in 1955. Forms for the floor slab were supported on two tiers of shores. Bottom shores were wood 4x4's, capped with horizontal 4x4's and cross-braced horizontally. Adjustable metal shores were placed directly over the 4x4 posts to form the second tier. There was little diagonal cross-bracing or horizontal bracing on the adjustable shores. At the time of the collapse there were eight or nine motorized buggies transporting concrete to the area, and about 700 cu yd of concrete had been placed by 2:00 P.M. Apparently a horizontal thrust developed through the combined effect of the movement and sudden stopping of the buggies, dumping of concrete, operation of concrete agitating machines, and other activities on the floor.

Following an investigation, the district attorney for New York County stated: "If there had been sufficient diagonal, horizontal, and end bracing of the temporary supporting structure, the collapse could have been prevented entirely or, at worst, its area held to a minimum." After the accident, new two-tier shoring in the coliseum was braced horizontally and diagonally on both tiers.

Improper lateral bracing of the formwork was blamed for a roof form collapse in a Toronto subway in 1961. The facing material of the roof slab form was ⅝-in. plywood in the shape of an arch, fastened to wood stringers and supported by a series of built-up wood transverse frames. The frames were supported on adjustable shores, set on an intermediate slab, with a corresponding set of shores beneath the intermediate slab. There was no diagonal bracing between the frames or shores, and the frames were not braced against longitudinal movement.

A bulkhead at one end of the section was braced against longitudinal movement but, as the concrete was placed, the load against the bulkhead caused the bracing to deflect, permitting movement of the bulkhead. Apparently this movement caused some of the jack shores to slip or tip and the whole form collapsed.

When a failure occurs at one point, inadequate bracing may permit the collapse to extend to a large portion of the structure and multiply the damage. For example, suppose a workman accidentally rams his wheelbarrow into some vertical shores and dislodges a couple of them; this may set up a chain reaction that brings down the entire floor. One major objective of bracing is to prevent such a minor accident or failure from becoming a disaster.

Vibration

Forms sometimes collapse when their supporting shores or jacks are displaced by vibration caused by passing traffic or the movement of men and equipment on the formwork, or the effect of vibrating concrete to consolidate it. In one case, forms for a roof deck were supported on extensible jacks, without diagonal bracing. While concrete was being placed, some of the shoring jacks were vibrated out of plumb by concrete buggies running on duck boards, and the form collapsed. In another case, a second-floor form supported by two tiers of pipe shores 30 ft high, and braced horizontally at mid-length, failed while concrete was being vibrated. Although vibration was the initial cause in these cases, it is evident that lack of diagonal bracing was the factor that permitted complete failure.

2-2 High shoring with a heavy load at the top is vulnerable to eccentric or lateral loadings. Diagonal bracing improves the stability of such a structure, as do guys or struts to solid ground or completed structure.

2-3 Formwork collapsed at New York Coliseum where rapid delivery with power buggies introduced lateral forces at the top of high shoring.

Unstable Soil Under Mudsills, Shoring Not Plumb

Formwork should be safe if it is adequately braced and constructed so all loads are carried to solid ground through vertical members. But the shores must be set plumb and the ground must be able to carry the load without settling. Shores and mudsills must not rest on frozen ground; moisture and heat from the concreting operations, or changing air temperatures, may thaw the soil and allow settlement that overloads or shifts the formwork.

Inadequate Control of Concrete Placement

The temperature and rate of vertical placement of concrete are factors influencing the development of lateral pressures that act on the forms. If temperature drops during construction operations, rate of concreting often has to be slowed down to prevent a buildup of lateral pressure overloading the forms. If this is not done, formwork failures may result.

Failure to regulate properly the rate and order of placing concrete on horizontal surfaces or curved roofs may produce unbalanced loadings and consequent failures of formwork.

When Formwork Is Not at Fault

It is natural, when forms and slabs collapse during concreting, to assume that the formwork was at fault. This is not always true; the collapse of one four-story concrete structure was thought at first to be caused by form-support failure, but later investigation showed

that some of the exterior wall columns were not on the solid rock assumed in the design plans. A column settled, became inoperative, and the slabs collapsed. Other cases have been reported in which slabs collapsed due to weakness caused by duct openings at high-stress points. When lower floor slabs collapse they carry upper floor forms with them, and the situation sometimes looks like a formwork failure until an analytical investigation is made.

Well designed and strongly constructed formwork can withstand some unusual loads. When a crane boom collapsed during the casting of an upper floor of a concrete apartment building in New York City (1959), the boom fell across the working deck and wrapped itself over both sides of the building. Despite the impact of the falling boom, the forms and supporting shores were undamaged, and concreting operations were resumed 2 days later after some minor repairs.

Lack of Attention to Formwork Details

Even when the basic formwork design is soundly conceived, small differences in assembly details may cause local weakness or overstress leading to form failure. This may be as simple as insufficient nailing, or failure to tighten the locking devices on metal shoring. Other details which have caused failures are inadequate provisions to prevent rotation of beam forms where slabs frame into them on one side; inadequate anchorage against uplift for sloping form faces; or lack of bracing or tying of corners, bulkheads, and other places where unequal pressure is found.

Planning for Safety

Safety begins in the planning and management of a project, and all bids should include allowance for the cost of supervision, equipment, and procedures that will assure safety for workmen and structure. Good safety planning is good profit planning because it gets work done in a controlled and supervised, rather than haphazard, manner.

To make sure forms are correctly designed and strong enough for the expected load, rational analysis rather than rule of thumb is advisable.

Supervision and Inspection

The most effective means of achieving safety in the use of forms is to have competent supervision during erection and concreting. Supervisors must see that formwork is constructed exactly as designed, following a safe erection procedure so that no members are temporarily overloaded. A form designer should be consulted whenever a field change seems called for in the falsework or forms or in the erection procedure.

If forms have been designed with no anticipation of unusual construction loads or eccentric loads due to placing sequence, the job superintendent must make sure no such loads ever are imposed on the formwork. He must be instructed as to the maximum rate of rise of concrete for which the form has been designed and must make sure this rate is not exceeded. Formwork drawings prepared for field use should give the superintendent full information on these factors.

Platforms and Access for Workers

Sound engineering in the planning stage by engineers working with experienced field personnel can develop safety measures for the protection of everyone on the job. Any high construction job requires a method of access and a work area or work platform. Long ladders to the tops of piers or falsework should have rest or passing platforms that will also serve to stop a serious fall. In some types of structures, particularly bridges, it is necessary to provide special scaffolds or equipment for stripping deck and pier forms. Safety signs and barricades should be erected to keep unauthorized personnel clear of areas in which erection or stripping is underway.

Control of Concreting Practices

Rate and sequence of concrete placing should follow any limitations shown on the formwork drawings. Concrete should not be placed until formwork for a given section is completed. In addition, an attempt should be made to place concrete so that unbalanced form loadings are avoided; for example, in beam and

2-4 Following form collapse in one area, increased diagonal bracing was added to all remaining shoring for the New York Coliseum. Bottom lift of shoring for forms that collapsed is being rebuilt (center background).

2-5 Stair tower with seven landings for access to high wall off-rock forming. Scaffold with safety railings is attached to forms.

of crushed stone. There is a limit to the unusual problems that can be guarded against, but if formwork and shores are assembled in a strong, stable structure, there is less chance for complete failure under even the most severe conditions. If shores rest on substantial mudsills and are diagonally braced in two directions, an earth slippage or washout might cause shifting or sagging, but there is less chance of a full collapse. Just how far to go in guarding against the "unexpected" is a matter of over-all economics, experience, and local conditions. But, at the very minimum, the objective should be to so construct the form that localized failures or accidents will not trigger a complete and disastrous collapse.

Shoring and Reshoring

Workers should be instructed to install shores plumb and wedged securely so that each carries its share of the load. A bent jack or defective timber may be able to support only a fraction of the design load and should not be used. When concrete is placed in one section of a form, it may cause upward movement in another section. Shores then may come loose or shift

slab construction, fill the beams first and then work outward equally on both sides in placing the slab.

Improved stability can be obtained in a column-and-slab structure by concreting the columns at least a day ahead of the deck. Hardened concrete in the columns adds stiffness to the formwork structure during concreting of the slab. Job specifications frequently require advance casting of columns so that they can take their shrinkage before the floor is placed. Any extra cost occasioned by this procedure may be offset by the easier casting of the columns before the reinforcing bars for the slab are set.

Form watchers should be on the job during concreting wherever there is danger to personnel or to the structure from forms failing or distorting during placement. Extra shores or other material and equipment that might be needed in an emergency must be available.

Improving Soil Bearing and Bracing

If there is doubt about the bearing quality of the soil, it can be compacted, stabilized by tamping in a lean portland cement mortar, or covered with a layer

2-6 Steel scaffolding tower with stairs for access to formed areas has numerous landings for rest or passing, which will also break a serious fall. Wooden platforms and scaffolds with railings are also in use.

out of plumb unless they have been securely fastened. Alert, continuous form watching during concreting should be routine practice so that problems like these can be met as soon as they arise.

The contractor should keep forms and shores in place long enough to develop sufficient concrete strength to prevent hairline cracks or failures in the concrete. He will be guided by the local code, job specifications, or the engineer. In some cases, when forms are stripped for reuse, reshores are installed to support the concrete until it attains full strength. Such reshoring must be done very carefully, and foremen should understand that reshores must not be wedged in so tightly as to cause a stress reversal that might crack the concrete. (See p. 217 for reshoring recommendations.)

Relationship of Architect, Engineer and Contractor

Generally design of the concrete structure and specifications for its size, strength, and appearance are the responsibility of the architect-engineer,[*] while planning and design of the formwork, as well as its construction, are the contractor's responsibility. It is desirable to leave the contractor as much freedom as possible to use his ingenuity in planning the formwork and concreting procedures. Practically speaking, however, the architect-engineer usually considers it necessary to include some minimum specifications for forming practices to assure that the structure will be completed to his satisfaction. The contract documents and specifications for any job should clearly indicate relationships between the contractor and the engineer-architect so that each knows his area of authority and responsibility.

Plans and specifications must first give the contractor a complete description of the structure so that he can develop an efficient plan for formwork. In addition to the obvious structural dimensions, such points as the following may be needed:

Inserts, waterstops, built-in frames for openings, holes through concrete, and similar requirements where work of other trades will be attached to or supported by formwork.

Concrete surface finishes described in measurable terms. Tolerances for plumb, level, size, thickness, and location.

Number, location, and details of all construction joints, contraction joints, and expansion joints.

Live load used in design of the structure.

Locations and details of architectural concrete.

Chamfers if required, or if prohibited, on beam soffits or column corners.

Basic geometry of special structural shapes such as free-form shells.

Camber if required for slab soffits or structural members.

If camber is desired for slab soffits or structural members to compensate for elastic deflection and/or deflection due to creep of the concrete, the contract drawings must so indicate and state the amounts. Measurement of camber attained should be made *after* initial set and *before* decentering.

Where architectural features, embedded items, or the work of other trades will change the location of structural members such as joists in one-way or two-way joist systems, such changes or conditions should be indicated on the structural drawings.

In addition to this full description of the required structure, criteria for and some details of the forming practices will be specified, depending in part on the type of structure being erected. General minimum requirements should be stated to assure the owner and his architect or engineer that the formwork will provide adequate support during concreting and until the concrete has gained sufficient strength to permit form removal. The following items should be clearly covered in the engineer-architect specifications and drawings: (a) by whom the formwork will be designed; (b) by whom, when, and for what features formwork will be inspected; and (c) what approvals will be required for formwork drawings; for the forms before concreting and during concreting; and for form removal and reshoring; and who will give such approvals.

Among the details of forming and construction practices that may have to be specified are the following:

Location and order of erection and removal of shoring for composite construction, complex structures, and permanent forms.

---

* The terms engineer-architect and architect-engineer are used interchangeably in this text to designate: the architect, the engineer, the architectural firm, the engineering firm, the architectural and engineering firm, or other agency issuing project drawings and specifications and/or administering the work under project specifications and drawings.

Stripping time (in terms of strength of field-cured concrete) and reshoring requirements; decentering sequence for shells and other complex structures.

Formwork materials and accessories where these are critical to appearance or quality of finished structure.

Sequence of concrete placement for structures where this is critical.

Responsibility for Maintaining and Coordinating Tolerances

As mentioned earlier, tolerances should be specified by the engineer-architect so that the contractor will know precisely what is required and can design and maintain his forms accordingly. The tolerances suggested in this book for various structural members are similar to those specified on important work or major structures by many public agencies and private firms.* In specifying these tolerances or some modifications of them, it should be remembered that specifying tolerances more exacting than needed may increase construction costs or delay the work unnecessarily.

Contractors should establish and maintain in an undisturbed condition until final completion and acceptance of a project, control points and bench marks adequate for their own use and for reference to establish tolerances. (This requirement may be important for the contractor's protection when tolerances are not specified or shown.) The engineer-architect should specify tolerances or require performance within generally accepted limits. Where a project involves particular features sensitive to the cumulative effect of generally accepted tolerances on individual portions, the engineer-architect should anticipate and provide for this effect by setting a cumulative tolerance. Where several types of generally accepted tolerances, i.e., on form, on location of reinforcement, on fabrication of reinforcement, etc., may become mutually incompatible, the engineer-architect should anticipate the difficulty and specify special tolerances or indicate which controls. (See discussion of tolerances for placing reinforcement, p. 207.)

The engineer-architect should be responsible for coordinating the tolerances for concrete work with the requirements of other trades whose work adjoins the concrete construction.

* Designers employed by federal agencies required to follow Building Research Advisory Board recommendations are advised that the BRAB tolerances on formwork are often much more restrictive than those suggested herein.

Preparing a Formwork Specification

The value of careful preparation of formwork specifications has been emphasized by ACI Committee 347 in its "Recommended Practice for Concrete Formwork, ACI 347-68," as follows:

For any concrete structure, the specifications for formwork written by the engineer or architect will have much to do with the over-all economy and quality of finished work. *Such a specification must be individualized for the particular job, must indicate to the contractor exactly what will be expected from him, and must be so written as to result in economy and safety.*

A well-written formwork specification tends to equalize bids for the work, provided each bidder knows that full compliance will be required of the successful one. Unnecessarily exacting requirements may make bidders question the specification as a whole and may render it virtually impossible for them to be sure just what is expected. They may be overly cautious and overbid or not cautious enough and underbid.

A well-prepared formwork specification is of value not only to the owner and the contractor, but also to the field superintendent of the engineer-architect and to the subcontractors for other trades.

Guidance for specification writers is now available in the document "Specifications for Structural Concrete for Buildings" prepared by ACI Committee 301. This ACI Standard, which includes provisions for formwork, is set up as a reference specification which the engineer-architect may make applicable to any building project by citing it in the project specifications. If this document is used to cover basic formwork specifications, the architect-engineer must supplement by designating or specifying individual project requirements.

Design, Inspection, and Approval of Formwork

In most cases the contractor will plan and design the formwork. Except for unusual or complex structures, this is desirable since the contractor is in the best position to evaluate men, materials, equipment, and procedures and arrive at a design that is both structurally sound and adapted to efficient erection and concreting.

Although formwork safety is the responsibility of the contractor, the engineer or architect may require that the form design be subject to his review and/or approval. Architect-engineer approval may be advisable for unusually complicated structures, for structures whose designs were predicated on a particular method of construction, for certain post-tensioned structures, and for structures in which the forms impart a desired architectural finish.

The committee has also called attention to the legal implications of specifying in any set of contract documents, including the plans and specifications, both the method by which the work is to be performed and the results to be accomplished. If the method is specified in detail, then provisions regarding the final results may not be legally binding.

Complex Structures

In the case of structures such as shells, arches, or folded plates, with the complexity of designing formwork and planning erection and stripping procedures necessary to guarantee the desired shape, dimensions, and appearance of the concrete, it may be more practical for the engineer or architect who designed the structure to take responsibility for formwork design. If the contractor assumes responsibility for design of formwork for folded plates, thin shells, long span roof structures, and similar space structures presenting complex three-dimensional problems in formwork design, his formwork planners should consult and cooperate with the architect-engineer to make sure the finished concrete will conform to his design. The contractor should receive written approval of such formwork drawings from the architect-engineer.

Permanent Forms

Where metal deck or other material used as a permanent form is also to have permanent structural value, its shape, depth, gage, dimensions, and properties as well as shoring requirements are to be indicated by the architect-engineer in the contract drawings and specifications. The contractor, nevertheless, may be asked to submit fully detailed shop drawings of all permanent deck forms to the architect-engineer for approval.

Composite Construction

The architect-engineer will specify shoring for composite beam and slab construction wherever his design for composite action requires it. He should supervise field-cured cylinder tests of concrete strength, and shores should be removed only after these tests and curing operations indicate to his satisfaction that the recently cast concrete has attained the strength required for the composite action. The procedure for shore removal should be specified in such cases.

Stripping and Decentering

Formwork must remain in place long enough to make sure the concrete is self-supporting and stiff enough to carry its own weight without undue deflection or damage. This is especially important for long span members in flexure. To achieve the necessary strength, either the forms will be left in place for a specified period of time, particularly on small projects where tests are not practicable or where form reuse is not planned; or, preferably for all important projects, the time of removal will be determined by strength of test specimens. In the former case, the architect-engineer will include curing-time requirements in the specifications or refer to applicable codes. If form removal is to be based on strength tests, the architect-engineer should include instructions for the preparation and curing of test cylinders in the specifications and should supervise the testing and determine when it is safe to remove the forms.

In the case of the more complex structures such as shells, arches, and folded plates, to make sure the structure will assume its deflected shape without damage, the decentering and handling procedure for the formwork should be worked out carefully. These procedures should be described in the contract drawings and specifications or, if worked out by the contractor, should be shown on the formwork drawings and approved by the architect-engineer.

Materials and Accessories Related to Finish of Exposed Concrete

If the particular design or desired finish requires special materials, the engineer or architect should indicate in his contract plans and specifications which formwork materials, ties, and other items are required. If internal ties are not acceptable, this should be clearly stated. In the interest of scheduling and economy, the contractor should be permitted to use discretion where quality of finished concrete would not be impaired by using alternate materials and methods.

Finish requirements for concrete surfaces should be precisely described in measurable terms. This may be done by limiting size and number of surface defects. Since some aspects of surface finish such as texture, color, and uniformity are difficult to measure, agreement on finish requirements may more readily be reached by having the contractor submit for approval a sample panel prepared using the proposed form materials and form surface treatments. This panel would then remain on the job as a visual standard of the required finish.

Methods of Measurement and Payment for Formwork

Payment for concrete formwork may be by any one of three methods:

1. It may be included in the lump sum price for the entire job.
2. It may be included in the unit price paid per cubic yard of concrete in place.
3. A separate unit price per square foot of formed area is established.

Regardless of the contractual basis of payment, most contractors keep separate records of formwork cost, particularly for their larger jobs. This serves the dual purpose of maintaining closer control on formwork costs during the job, and also accumulating cost experience data which could be valuable for negotiating any extra work or in bidding future jobs.

When formwork is paid for at a separate unit price, the specifications should clearly state what areas of the formwork, if any, are excluded as pay areas. Some specifications exclude openings such as doors, windows, and pipe blockouts from the area of formwork to be paid for. This represents a problem for the contractor who usually will have to build his form panel continuous across the opening and then attach forms for the opening. Other specifications exclude only openings in excess of a designated size such as 30 sq ft. This latter practice permits normal door openings to be paid for when door bucks are nailed to the main form panels.

Some specifications exclude payment for bulkhead areas; this places the contractor at a disadvantage for two reasons:

Construction joint layout is subject to the owner's approval, and at the bidding stage the contractor cannot always be sure of the owner's intent on joint location.

The pay basis for formed area is usually used for pricing extra work which may have a ratio of bulkhead area to formed area that is substantially different from the main job.

If the contract specifications exclude payment for bulkheads, then they should be fully supported by comprehensive construction joint drawings.

Contracts which specify payment for all formed areas in actual contact with concrete surfaces may prove cumbersome to administer if the structure has numerous keyways, recesses, chamfers, or moldings. A less exacting method of measurement can be achieved by excluding such items when they are either 3 in. or less in depth or 6 in. or less in width.

Where some formed surfaces are likely to be substantially more expensive than others, and their ratio to the total form area is likely to vary during the job, separate pay rates for the two or more classes of formwork should be established.

How the Architect-Engineer Can Reduce Form Costs

With formwork costs ranging up to 60 percent of the total cost of concrete work in a project, the architect and engineer can make big savings possible by considering problems of formwork economy at the same time they design the concrete structure. The main objectives are to obtain maximum reuse of forms and to permit use of standard material sizes with minimum cutting and fitting. Planning a structure that uses simplified ornamentation and surfaces as formed, or with a minimum of finishing, may also yield substantial savings. Frequent changes of dimensions of structural members should be avoided; irregularities of structure intended to save concrete may be expensive rather than economical if they require intricate form construction.

The following design procedure is suggested to help the architect-engineer reduce over-all construction

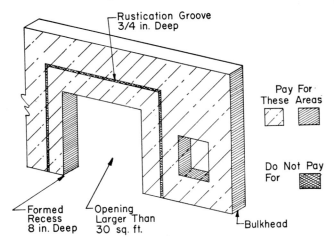

2-7 Suggested basis of measurement of form area for payment purposes: Pay for all formed areas including bulkheads; include area of recesses formed, but deduct areas of openings larger than 30 sq ft on one contact surface. Include formed grooves, keyways, etc., when they are more than 3 in. deep and 6 in. wide.

costs.* Although the detailed suggestions are developed for multistory building construction, many of the principles can be applied in planning other types of structures.

1. Study the framework of the building as a whole. Visualize straight lines of framing with uniform depths, widths, and cross sections.

2. Make freehand framing sketches, comparing various methods.

3. Establish column centers so that they fall in partitions, clear door and window openings, and provide economical framing. Spacings from 14 to 15 ft up to 20 to 25 ft will usually be satisfactory.

4. Select rough preliminary sizes from a design handbook or by rule of thumb.

5. Prepare alternate sketches of any other practical ways of framing the structure and make rough cost comparisons of the various schemes.

6. Select that compromise which achieves the best balance between low cost of the building and minimum interference with desired facilities.

7. Have a sense of comparative values. A stair header has relatively little effect on the over-all cost, but a line of spandrel beams on many stories can become a large item.

8. Visualize the form construction as the final building plan is made.

(a) For economy, keep beams and columns simple, without haunches, brackets, widened ends, or offsets. Eliminate cut-outs that save a little concrete but add complication and expense to the formwork.

(b) Keep beam widths, beam depths, slab thicknesses, column sizes, and story heights constant for several floors, or all floors if possible, so forms can be reused from floor to floor without alteration. Vary strength if necessary by varying the amount of reinforcing steel.

(c) Where column sizes must be changed, reduce one dimension at a time, and continue the same size for several floors. Keep column spacing uniform throughout the building as much as possible to simplify reuse of formwork.

(d) To simplify formwork intersections, make joists and beams the same depth if possible over an entire floor.

(e) Plan dimensions with sizes of commercially available materials in mind. Establish column and beam widths, beam depth, and distances between beam faces so that standard widths of lumber or plywood can be used as much as possible. (Remember that the slab forms may be cut short of the actual clear distance between beam faces to allow for a closure strip or other detail to facilitate assembly and stripping.)

(f) Where ready-made forming systems such as one-way or two-way joist systems are used, design should be based on the use of one standard size wherever possible.

9. Coordinate the structural design with the architectural design. Room sizes can usually be varied

2-8 Highly complicated formed surface illustrates an unreasonably expensive form necessitated by designer's attempt to save concrete.

a few inches to accommodate the structural design.

10. Coordinate architectural features, depressions, and openings for mechanical or electrical work with the structural system for maximum economy to the over-all job. Variations in the structural system caused by such items should be shown on the structural drawings. Wherever possible make depressions in the tops of slabs without a corresponding break in elevations of the soffits of slabs, beams, or joists.

11. Do not require formed foundation walls and footings when an earth form will stand.

12. Permit composite construction with repetitive, intricate elements precast as a contractor's option.

The Practical Approach

The architect-engineer may save on his own work as well as in formwork costs if he consults a contractor before completing the structural design. Small changes in design not at all detrimental to the structure may drastically reduce cost. The contractor might suggest and obtain approval for such changes after the contract is let, but more savings are possible (through competitive bidding) if his suggestions can be obtained before the design is finalized.

Where possible, appearance and finish should be specified in a manner that will permit their achievement with simple formwork construction and without much after-finishing. While fine ornamental effects can be achieved by carefully executed formwork, such formwork is expensive and should be avoided if possible. Design of ornamental details should permit the use of standard mill shapes and, to avoid difficulty in stripping, it is best not to recess too deeply into the concrete mass. Judicious selection of precast units for ornamental purposes may also make possible considerable formwork economy.

When structural design is based on the use of some commercially available form unit in standard sizes such as one-way and two-way joist systems, plans and specifications should be drawn up realistically to make use of available shapes and sizes. Some latitude must be permitted for connections of form units to other framing or centering to reflect the tolerances and normal installation practices of the form type contemplated.

It will pay the architect-engineer to become familiar with various types of form construction and to adapt his design to some of the more economical methods where possible. He should keep abreast of current developments in forming materials and techniques. New materials, accessories, and prefabricated formwork components may enable him to secure a better concrete structure at lower cost.

3:OVER-ALL PLANNING

FORMWORK IS THE STOCK IN TRADE of the concrete contractor, and how he handles it can make or break the profitability of a concrete job. To achieve minimum cost in the construction and use of formwork, it must be treated as an integral part of the total job plan. The over-all construction sequence must be planned to use formwork in the most efficient manner and to permit the optimum investment in formwork to meet schedule requirements. Availability and cost of local labor and materials should also be considered is developing the plan.

For his own protection, a contractor should plan formwork and job sequence at the time of making a bid. Failure to study a job thoroughly enough to arrive at the most efficient plan probably will cause loss of the contract. Even worse, to receive a contract in reply to a bid based on a superficial analysis, and then to find that some aspect of the assumed plan is impractical so that actual costs will be much higher than anticipated, can be disastrous financially. Advance planning will also help to insure the unqualified safety of personnel engaged in formwork and concrete placement and the integrity of the finished structure.

Development of a Basic System

The formwork plan must be adapted to the layout of the concrete structure and to a practical construction sequence. Each job will have some feature or combination of features that will tend to establish, more or less automatically, the basis of an efficient formwork plan. These features may exist in the design of the building, in site conditions, or in other factors. The most efficient system can be determined initially through analysis of placing schedules and stripping time requirements, but practical limitations will be imposed by *accessibility* and *site conditions* and by the *capacity of equipment available to handle form sections and materials*. Among the other major factors to be considered are:

1. Capacity of mixing and placing equipment

2. Construction joints (if specified) which limit size of lifts or placement units
3. Form construction details and facilities for form building
4. Reuse of forms as affected by stripping time and other requirements
5. Relative merits of job-built, shop-built, and ready-made forms
6. Type of surface on which formwork is supported (concrete, sand, clay, wet, frozen, etc.)
7. Reshoring requirements if multistory construction is involved
8. Weather—its influence on protection requirements and stripping time, which will in turn affect reuse and reshoring practices

Compare Alternate Methods

Different basic objectives, or alternative plans and methods for achieving the same objective, should be examined in detail so that over-all costs can be compared. Initial form construction costs, savings through reuse, and costs of setting and stripping are compared to arrive at the lowest-cost formwork plan. In addition, for each plan a comparison should be made of the estimated number and types of rigs, hoists, and other equipment required, and the efficiency with which concreting crews, reinforcing crews, and others will fit into the schedule. In determining total cost for each plan, allowance must be made for preparation and familiarization time at the beginning of the project and finishing up "loose ends" at its conclusion.

Examine Form Plan in Relation to Total Job

After selecting the most efficient plan, the contractor should review his formwork plan along with the specifications to make sure there are no special requirements or conflicts that would make some detail of his plan or intended form design impractical. He also should review the plan in relation to the whole project to make sure that other site activities will not interfere with transport of form sections, cause placing delays, or otherwise upset the schedule so that much of the plan's efficiency is lost on the job. The concrete contractor's schedule may have to be adjusted to the schedules of other trades, and this should be taken into account. The critical path method of scheduling can be advantageously used to coordinate complex projects.

Key Areas of Cost Reduction

Economy in formwork construction must be achieved within the basic limitations of safety and quality of construction discussed in Chapter 2. Three major areas of cost reduction will be discussed in some detail in the following pages:

Planning for maximum reuse
Economical form construction
Efficient setting and stripping practices

Savings in first cost of forms must be balanced against other objectives to achieve the least cost on a per use basis. A form designed for maximum reuse may have to be stronger and more expensive than one designed for a single use, but it can save a great deal on the total form investment. Extra features that make erection and stripping easier will add to original form costs, but labor savings may outweigh the extra cost.

It is poor economy to strive for minor savings that can cause big losses elsewhere. For example, increasing design stresses beyond safe limits usually results in small over-all savings while greatly increasing the risk of damage and severe loss. Careless assembly or cheap materials might save a little in form cost but cause much expensive hand finishing of the concrete afterwards.

Planning for Maximum Reuse

The plan or procedure to be followed in getting maximum reuse of forms will vary greatly depending on the conditions of the individual job. Generally the sooner the forms can be stripped, the more economical and practical it becomes to schedule many reuses of a form. Thus specifications or local code requirements for stripping and reshoring are an important factor in planning form reusage.

Minimum investment in forms is achieved by constructing the least number of forms required for a smooth work flow and then reusing these forms as often as necessary until the job is completed. Since the stripping time for the sides of a beam or header is much shorter than for the bottom, it is often economical to build fewer side forms and plan on early stripping and frequent reuse of the side panels while the bottom forms are left in place. Chimneys, towers, and cylindrical or rectangular concrete cores for multistory buildings can be built quickly and inexpensively using slip forms or climbing forms that are reused for many lifts from bottom to top of the structure.

Mass concrete which has a gradually changing cross section can be built using rugged cantilever form panels that are raised and reused for lift after lift. Piers for bridges or viaducts are frequently cast by repeated use of a form or series of forms, while building columns can use the same forms over and over if the

3-1 Tower crane works within recess in multistory building under construction. Small batching and mixing plant near base of crane discharges concrete to crane bucket as nearby trucks unload. Careful planning is required to make best use of small ground area, maintaining steady flow of materials and equipment as the job progresses.

3-2 Reuse of large form sections must be planned in terms of equipment available for handling them. A special lifting beam was provided to make possible the movement of this large bridge pier form without dismantling.

building designer has had the foresight to make columns the same size or with few dimensional changes. Ready-made modular panels can be moved from one job to another and are adaptable to many different types of structures.

The amount of work involved in reusing a form may depend on whether it has to be disassembled for stripping and reuse. In some cases the form can be moved intact. This is inherent in slip forms, of course, and may be possible with climbing forms or with pier forms that can be lifted off the pier by a crane and set into position at the next pier.

More often the form must be taken apart and moved section by section. This may be required by the shape of the concrete structure which makes it impossible either to loosen the form or to withdraw it without taking it apart. Or it may be that the weight of the whole form is beyond the capacity of the rig and handling equipment, so it must be transported in sections.

Traveling forms (Chapter 15) eliminate much of the disassembly and reassembly in reusing formwork. In long barrel construction, for example, it is possible to build the barrel arch form and shoring as a unit with a roller-equipped base. At stripping time the form is lowered from the concrete and simply rolled forward to the next position; this sequence is repeated until the full length of the barrel has been cast. Wood or steel shoring alone may be assembled and braced in units that can be shifted from bay to bay as forms are moved for reuse. Such shoring units must of course be rugged enough to withstand any extra handling

and moving stresses and are practical only where conditions and equipment available permit easy, safe handling.

Developing a Practical Reuse Plan

A minimum number of different forms is established by the number of different shapes, sizes, and combinations of concrete members in the structure. Where the same size, shape, or combination is repeated there is an opportunity for reuse, but placing schedule, stripping time, and other factors related to a specific job make it impractical to take advantage of all theoretical opportunities to reuse forms. Thus, if the same size column appears 100 times in a building, theoretically all of these columns could be cast by reusing one form 100 times, but this would not permit a smooth work flow and would extend the construction over an unreasonably long time.

In most cases it is necessary to make a detailed study of work flow and construction sequence to decide on a practical number of reuses that will result in a fast, smooth, efficient job with lowest over-all cost. In simpler cases it may be possible to see immediately the number of forms required and the number of reuses that can be planned. Divide the total structure into unit areas and mark on a key plan the days for erecting forms, setting steel, installing mechanical and electrical work, and placing concrete. Experiment with various sizes of area to maintain steady progress. This will determine the reuse of forms.

Comparing Reuse Schemes

In comparing different schemes, the contractor may calculate the size and number of forms required in each case and find the ratio of form contact area to total area of formed concrete structure. This ratio is an indicator of over-all reuse efficiency, although it does not necessarily indicate the number of reuses of a particular form in the plan. In comparing two plans, where one has more reuses than the other, the contractor should take into account the time and cost of repairs and reconditioning between uses. Forms often have to be cleaned between reuses, and a vibrating tool, for example, may damage the contact surface of a form so that a panel must be replaced before the form can be reused.

Economical Form Construction

In evaluating different schemes to get maximum reuse of forms and an efficient construction sequence, the contractor must make an estimate of form construction cost for each plan. He also may choose between building the forms himself and buying or rent-

ing them. One plan may require many forms while another uses fewer forms of a more expensive type. A reasonable cost estimate requires a practical construction plan to determine which is more economical.

Job-Built Forms

When non-reusable forms are to be built in position on the job, the contractor plans to use inexpensive materials that are easy to transport, handle, and shape in the field. Reusable forms must be more durable, made of strong materials that can withstand continuing usage, and usually must have added features that make them easy to handle and to assemble.

Materials and Hardware

In choosing ties or inserts, the initial cost is not as important as the labor involved in their installation and form stripping. In considering the type of materials to be used in construction of the forms, the contractor will keep in mind materials on hand and compare with the economics of purchasing or renting new materials. Thus, if large quantities of 2x4 studs are available, it may prove more economical to use them, spaced closer together, than to purchase 2x6's.

Using plywood panels for large surfaces usually saves money (as compared with board sheathing) because there is less assembly work, and with fewer

3-3 Panel system at the left built by the contractor in his own shop does the same job as the ready-made panels on the right. Contractor must make a careful cost comparison to determine which method is more economical for him on a given job.

joints in the form surface less concrete finishing is required after the forms are removed.

The contractor may have to choose between partially absorptive form materials like standard plywood and dressed lumber that produce a slight texture; hardboard, plastic, plastic-coated plywood, or metal forms that produce smooth surfaces; or purposely rough wood forms that produce a distinctive texture. Specifications must be carefully studied and possibly discussed with the architect-engineer to see just what effects he wishes.

Better grades of lumber and plywood can be counted on for minimum waste and to a great extent are reusable, but sometimes a saving can be made by purchasing a lower grade of lumber and culling at the building site. Whether this saves in over-all cost depends on how much labor must be expended in the culling and in cutting and splicing to get maximum use of material. The decision may depend on the location of the job and the supply available.

Where good materials are required, a saving can be made by obtaining materials for the current job that can be reused on future jobs. Thus it may be economical to invest in high grade reusable panels, sections, materials, and hardware and prorate only a part of their cost to the current job.

Where to Construct Forms

In most jobs the contractor has a choice of building forms in position on the job, setting up a special shop or assembly area on the site, or building all the forms in a central shop and shipping them to the site. For many jobs the greatest efficiency in working conditions and in the purchase and use of materials and machinery is obtained by fabricating form sections in a central carpentry and welding shop maintained by the contractor at his headquarters. The cost of transporting form sections to the site may make this plan uneconomical if the shop is located too far from the job, and of course, if form sections are too large for shipping, they must be built at the site. At times, however, space on the site is so limited that off-site fabrication is the only feasible method.

For small jobs, or where forms must be fitted to the terrain, it may be economical to cut and assemble at the point of installation where cut-and-try methods can be used, in spite of the waste which usually occurs under such conditions. Most job-site form building, however, will benefit from special working conditions and equipment. A shop or at least a sheltered area can be set up and equipped with power tools and assembly benches. If necessary a platform can be built alongside the shop for assembly of large form

3-4 Dock wall form subject to many reuses. Steel beams used as wales may have a long service life beyond this particular project.

sections. The job-site shop should be located so that form materials can be conveniently stored near the shop and where there is access for transport equipment to pick up the finished form sections.

Possible savings through reduced waste of material and better productivity of labor are usually in direct ratio to the amount of work which can be shop-performed. Shop fabrication reduces problems of planning and control since supervision is easier if the only work done at the point of installation is assembly of forms.

Estimating Form Building Costs

Before a formwork plan is actually chosen and the forms designed in detail, a rough estimate of formwork construction cost should be made. It is possible to determine roughly the number of board feet of timber necessary to produce a square foot of contact area by examination of similar types of forms used in previous work. Allow for waste material cut off as well as wales, scabs, strongbacks, and other materials at-

3-5 Footing forms built in place to conform to irregular rock surface

tached to the form. Multiplying by the expected price per board foot of lumber gives an estimated basic material cost per square foot of contact area. For this rough estimate, plywood is sometimes considered to cost twice as much per square foot as unfinished lumber. Material such as steel beams and heavy timbers on hand in the contractor's yard which will have value after the job is finished should be priced at a "use charge" that is a percentage of their original value.

Average labor cost for constructing forms may be available from records. If not, a simple analysis of crew and operations may be converted to manhours per square foot. The price per manhour should be a weighted average of expected labor rates of foremen, journeymen, apprentices, and helpers in addition to other crafts that may be directly involved in construction of the form.

To the foregoing labor and material figures must be added allowances for hardware and other miscellaneous materials as well as the cost of receiving and handling materials onto the site and the cleanup or preparation of used material. The total cost must be divided by expected reuses to make a direct comparison between alternate formwork plans.

Purchased or Rented Forms

The contractor's estimated cost for building forms may be compared with bids or estimates from suppliers who will build the forms for him or who will rent prefabricated forms. Many contractors find ren-

tal of forms for specific usage permits them better flexibility in regulating the volume of work they are able to assume. Passing on the risk, investment cost, and some of the management responsibility to a formwork subcontractor may make the whole operation go more smoothly. Consideration of cash flow may influence the decision; since items such as column molds, fasteners, spacers, and ties will be included or will be offered by the supplier on a rental basis, the contractor can eliminate an investment in such stock items.

The contractor may find that consulting with form suppliers will help develop an imaginative approach to formwork planning that will save time and cost.

A careful analysis of all formwork required may show that the contractor can economically build some of the forms while others should be obtained from specialists. Those intended for a large number of reuses, for example, which must withstand much handling, may be purchased from a supplier of prefabricated steel forms. The purchase price or rental of the forms plus any handling or preparation expenses should be figured on a per square foot of formed area basis to make a valid comparison with other alternatives.

Setting and Stripping

The cost of setting forms in place and subsequently stripping them from the concrete is an important factor, and substantial savings can be made by design and planning provisions that make erecting and stripping easier and faster. The full benefit of a plan for reuse of forms can only be realized if the forms can be stripped and re-erected without too much lost time and if the form is not wrecked in the process. Therefore designing for easy handling and disassembly is essential. The total formwork plan should, if possible, permit repetition of the same functions to increase the crew efficiency as the job progresses.

Formwork can be assembled with metal clamps or special wedge pin connections that are secure, yet easy to assemble and disassemble. Handles or a wood strip nailed to the form give workers a means of grasping the form side so they can pull it away from the concrete and thus eliminate or minimize the need for prying it loose. Lifting eyes and other hardware make it easy to transport the form sections from one placing location to the next. Scaffolding and platforms to make both erection and stripping more convenient and safe for workers should be part of the formwork plan.

Erecting and Stripping Cost Factors

In comparing the expected erecting and stripping costs for various formwork plans, estimates may simply be based on manhours per square foot as shown by previous experience with similar types of forms. A more detailed comparison might be made through an analysis of crew size, specific operations, and time from start of stripping of a form until it is ready for the next placement, but this would be justified only for the major forms on a job, including those with a large number of reuses.

Total time in hours multiplied by the number of men in the crew gives the total expected manhours. The contact area formed at each placement divided by the estimated manhours gives a production rate in square feet per manhour. This figure should reflect average conditions over a representative period and therefore should include allowance for delays resulting from poor weather, equipment breakdowns, and other causes. Any miscellaneous expense normally incurred should be allowed for, including the cleaning and oiling of forms between uses.

Many formwork plans will anticipate raising a form and locating it by inserts in the previously placed concrete or using inserts as a means of anchoring, lifting, or attaching it. Ties, spacers, and other hardware items also may be left in the concrete. So allowance must be made for hardware lost or left in place in the concrete plus other non-reusable material expended during the process of placing and removing the forms.

Other Costs Affected by Formwork Plan

The ultimate objective in selecting a formwork plan is to achieve good, safe performance at the lowest over-all cost for the whole project. Since formwork cost is often a large part of the total cost of erecting a concrete structure, it is easy to assume that a plan that produces the lowest total formwork cost also will result in the lowest over-all cost for the total concrete work. However, the other cost factors in a concreting project, including the efficiency of concreting, reinforcing, and concrete finishing crews, and the use of cranes, hoists and other equipment, are affected by the formwork plan, and could be the deciding factors between two alternate plans. Possible effects of the formwork plan on job costs outside of the concrete contract must also be considered.

Crew Efficiency

Advance planning eliminates confusion and delay in the field, where it is most costly. Where maximum reuse of forms is emphasized, every operation must be scheduled precisely to sustain effective continuity of employment of craftsmen on the site.

The contractor must decide on a reasonable day's work for setting forms and placing concrete. It is poor economy to force a fast pace over short periods with intermittent stoppages, causing concreting, form stripping, and reinforcing crews to keep each other under pressure between delays. True economy comes from a smooth daily repetition of the same operation. If a reasonable schedule is planned, and allowance made for familiarization, each crew will become fast and efficient; the superintendent will be able to concentrate on scheduling of men and materials, and fewer panic situations will arise to disrupt schedules and lead to errors. In the long run the job will be completed faster and at lower cost.

Concreting

The ease and speed of placing concrete is related to the planned sequence and to some extent to the choice of form design. High lifts in wall construction may save money in setting and stripping forms but make placing and vibrating difficult. High rates of placing may require a heavier form to withstand the loads, and conversely placing rate is limited by the form design.

If the planned placing schedule will not permit the concreting crew to spend a full day on the job, the contractor is faced with a choice of:

(1) Increasing the placing schedule by making forms and lifts larger or using more forms with fewer reuses.

(2) Making other assignments available to the concreting crew to take up the slack.

(3) Allowing for less than full effectiveness on the job.

Size of placement units may be predetermined by construction joint specifications; if so, the contractor should plan changes only in consultation with the architect or engineer.

Bar Setting

Crews installing reinforcing steel will be used most efficiently if their work can be scheduled to fit the concreting sequence without causing lost time in either the concreting or bar setting schedule. Where possible, if the form design can permit the reinforce-

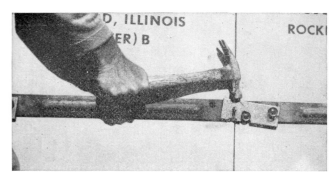

3-6 Hardware details may have an important effect on stripping and erection costs. Ties and panel connections of this panel system were designed to cut labor costs.

ment to be preassembled before installing, it may enable the reinforcing crew to work under more favorable conditions, and they can work at their own pace without lost motion. Their work then can be scheduled ahead of form setting, so that forms can be set one day and concrete placed the next, thus speeding the schedule and possibly increasing the number of form reuses.

Other Trades

The contractor's plan should coordinate the work of other trades, such as electrical and mechanical, with the concreting schedule, not only to permit these other trades to perform their work efficiently but to minimize interruptions in placing.

Cranes and Hoists

One object of planning should be to use cranes and hoists efficiently so that there are just enough on a project to keep the work going smoothly. The amount of time that a crane is tied up in moving and erecting formwork will determine the extent to which it may be available for other work on the project. If this "free" time is too little, then an extra crane will be required for other operations. Careful scheduling of material handling plus a form erection sequence that requires the least movement about the project site will save crane time. Mobile cranes must have access to and from the job, and it may be necessary for the contractor to schedule the placing sequence so that one bay is left open to permit crane and concrete truck movement until the last form is set in place. This access requirement may influence formwork design, requiring large shores spaced some distance apart.

One approach to efficient use of cranes is to determine what cranes are necessary for other functions, then see if a formwork plan can be established that will permit use of one of these cranes for erecting forms during otherwise idle time. It may be worthwhile limiting the size of form sections to the capacity of the largest crane that the contractor owns or would have on the site for other purposes. Or, if a very heavy crane is needed for lifting and placing form sections, it may be possible to so schedule its use that it can handle all heavy work on the project, and thus some small truck-mounted crane may be used for the rest of the work. Or it may be possible to use a single crane for all functions, including handling of forms and materials, and placing concrete.

In some cases traveling cranes already installed in a building may be used to position forms, thus freeing mobile cranes for other work. Some jobs are planned to complete elevator and stair towers early in the schedule so that they can be used for moving men and materials.

Planning Example

The example * below illustrates step by step the thinking involved in following many of the planning principles which have just been explained. The steps in working out the formwork plan for a bridge involving a large number of piers are similar to many other kinds of work where sequence, reuse, and careful coordination of all operations are important.

The bidder has received plans for the bridge illustrated in Figure 3-7 and proceeds to make his over-all plan for its construction. The job is to be bid in February with good prospects of an immediate award and the completion date set for September of the following year. Since a substantial liquidated damage charge may be levied in event of running past the completion date, an early finish is mandatory.

Working backward, for the moment, bidder reasons that he should allow 4 to 5 months for erecting the superstructure and that erection in the spring is preferable to such work during winter months. Starting erection in early spring and assuming deck concreting may commence a month or so before the steel erection is complete, the job can be finished within allowable time. This leaves 12 months for the excavation and concrete substructure.

Since considerable site preparation and excavation is necessary before pier footings may be constructed, it is decided that concreting cannot be carried out on any kind of production scale till around July 1. Rainy spring conditions may also influence this decision. Further, severe winter conditions may render concreting after November erratic and too costly to be practical. Therefore, bidder concludes that schedule demands that substructure be started and essentially completed during the months of July to October with allowance of approximately one month to "tail out" the top pier strut placement which may lag because of the time required for the supported form to remain in place. This leaves approximately 17 weeks to place all

---

* This example is based on material which appeared in an article by Joseph R. Proctor in the ACI JOURNAL, June 1962, *Proceedings* V. 59, No. 6, pp. 779-802.

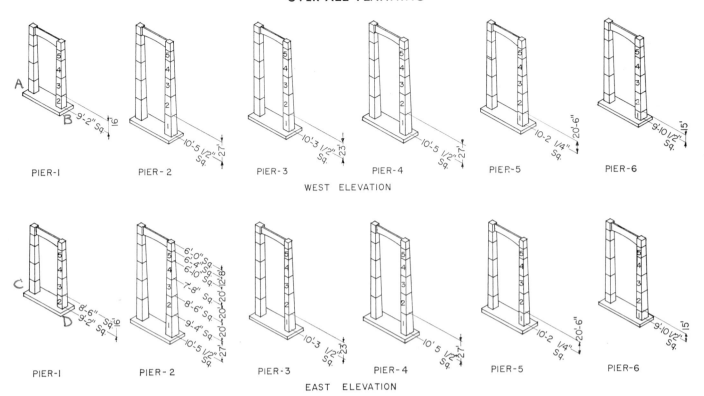

3-7 Dimensions and required lifts of piers for the bridge discussed in the planning example. Each row of piers carries two traffic lanes.

the concrete except for a few tail-out lifts on the pier struts. Assuming a 5-day week with some holidays and miscellaneous delays, there are less than 80 work days available.

Since the footing forms depend on the excavation and suitability of the sides of the excavation as forms, they are not subject to reuse analysis and probably will be built in place. The bidder assumes sufficient lead may be attained in June so that shaft concrete may start on July 1. There are 58 shaft placements on the piers to be accomplished if the construction joint layout is used as drawn. This would require almost 95 cu yd daily placement. The ideal situation is to find that set of circumstances which would permit one crew to be placing concrete regularly all day every day while a crew of carpenters and one of reinforcing steel workers were continuously employed preparing the forms for concrete. This is rarely obtained and provision must be made for rainy days or other contingencies which would throw the sequence off schedule.

Shaft forms in this hypothetical case may be stripped the day after placing while the supported strut forms must be left in place 14 days.

Trial Plans

Since so many variables are involved, it is necessary to adopt a trial plan which fits the circumstances and then compare it to any alternative ideas which may evolve. Many of these comparisons and the subsequent discard of alternatives are accomplished without detailed work due to the ability and experience of the estimator. However, in cases where all the factors are not so clearly seen, it is necessary to evaluate each detail of an alternate plan. As a result, the bidder may decide the advantages of working through the winter and completing the work ahead of schedule outweigh the added cost of attempting steel erection during cold and stormy weather.

The bidder could consider requesting a change in construction joint spacing with the thought that perhaps 30-ft lifts instead of 20-ft lifts would reduce the cost per square foot of stripping and placing the forms and obtain a smoother use of his form handling equipment.

In this case the bidder is not inclined to request a change in the details shown on the plans as he feels they present a very workable construction sequence as is. The pier shafts have a uniform batter on four sides with the construction joints spaced exactly the same except where shaft meets footing. This joint varies with the terrain in which the footing is placed. The contractor therefore sees that, instead of a form which is raised up the pier as it is constructed, necessitating a change in cross section at each lift, he can use a set of forms for each lift and move them laterally from pier to pier. Thus he can eliminate costly changing of the form's dimensions at each lift and can increase the number of uses without sacrificing speed. He deduces that due to the batter he can devise a form which may be stripped by loosening at the corners and raising up and over the completed concrete; upon tightening the corners again, it may be set down on the next pier shaft. This feature will reduce the time a rig must be tied up with one form and thus free it for other operations. A form requiring removal of four panels individually and then reassembling them on the ground would obviously require excessive rig time.

To be removed in the proposed manner, the form must be designed without internal tie rods. This calls for a stronger wale system and some sort of corner fastener which can carry the large loads and yet is easily released. Further, this plan is feasible only if access between piers is easily negotiated by the cranes. On a water job where forms would have to move from pier to pier by barge, this scheme might be impractical, and the more conventional method using a set of forms which rise

3-8 Rig time may be saved by designing a form that can be stripped as a unit and set in place on the next pier to be concreted. Corners are loosened for stripping, then tightened again before form is set for next lift. Batter of piers facilitates this approach.

from lift to lift for each pier would appear more economical. This decision may be largely influenced by the number of uses such a form would have. With a small number of piers but with relatively large number of lifts per pier, greater economies may be realized by sacrificing speed and modifying the form for each lift to permit greater number of uses.

Crane Size

The size of the crane available for this job is now scrutinized to determine its suitability. The contractor proposes to have two 1½ cu yd draglines on the job for the excavation phase. These will adapt themselves readily to the tentative forming method. A rough weight calculation is made on the tentative form size and found to be well within the capacities of these cranes. Suitable boom lengths are available to allow removal

of the forms in one piece for all except the top lift. In this case the rig can reach the form but could not lift it over the completed concrete. Therefore it is decided to design the form so that one side may be detached for this lift in order that it can be removed from around the completed concrete shaft. This additional operation must be evaluated in deciding the time required to move a form.

Analysis is made of each operation involving rig time to determine the activity of the rigs available. It is found that one rig will be tied up with the form move for one pier lift (two shafts) most of the day. Concreting this one lift involving approximately 100 cu yd will take about one-half shift counting setup time, moving, etc. This will permit occasional use of one of the rigs for setting reinforcing cages and other miscellaneous operations. From this analysis it appears the rig requirements for the scheme contemplated will be in reasonable balance.

However, further analysis of various miscellaneous operations brings out the desirability of having a general purpose rig such as a small truck crane for small jobs. These may include building forms, handling material, and fabricating reinforcing cages. Production operations of the large cranes for moving forms and concreting preclude using these pieces of equipment for any operations which take them away from the pier shafts during the critical forming period. Therefore it is decided to use the truck crane to fabricate the resteel into cages for individual lifts so that the cage may be delivered to the pier ready to set into place as soon as the form is removed from the previous lift.

Efficient Scheduling

In cases like this where maximum reuse of the form is emphasized, every operation must be scheduled precisely so that the form may be stripped and reset as soon after concreting as possible. Otherwise it will be difficult to sustain continuity of effective employment of the various crafts involved. Ideal production rates are attained when crews can be set up to do the same operation day after day; that is, one crew concreting or preparing to do so every day, one crew stripping and setting forms, one crew fabricating and placing reinforcing cages, etc.

As shown earlier, the concreting schedule presumes one 95 cu yd placement per day and this requires the time of the rig and concrete crew for little more than half a shift. The rig may be used on other operations but the bidder must review how effectively the concrete crew may be employed for the remainder of the shift. It is found that there are other operations on the job requiring labor that these men may do when not concreting, so no allowance for less than full effectiveness needs to be taken.

Planning Form Sizes

To meet this schedule as outlined so far, all operations should be checked thoroughly to assure smooth timing. The lateral movement of the forms from one pier to another must be planned to minimize moving time. Figure 3-7 shows that the highest piers, measured from footing elevation, are No. 2 and 4 whose first lifts are 27 ft high. The first lift of Pier 3 is 23 ft, of Pier 5 is 20.5 ft, and of Pier 6 is 15 ft. The first lift on Pier 1 corresponds to the second lift on the others and is only 16 ft high. All other lifts are 20 ft except the last shaft lift, which is 12 ft high for all piers.

It is tentatively decided to make one set of two shaft forms specifically for each of Lifts 2, 3, 4, and 5. These will fit their respective lifts for all piers without modification except Lift 2 on Pier 1. The form for Lift 2 should, therefore, be made 20 ft high with a removable section 4 ft high at the bottom to be removed for Pier 1 only. Lift 1 should be made 27 ft high with removable sections 4, 2.5, and 5.5 ft high. Allowance must be made therefore for additional work on the first lift of each pier to modify the form for the varying heights. Such extra work may be cut down by establishing a sequence which permits the greatest number of uses of each size of Lift 1 before a section is taken out. This would mean starting with Pier 2E, moving to No. 2W, then to Pier 4E, and last to Pier 4W before the 4-ft section is removed. Now 23 ft high, it proceeds to No. 3E and so forth until it is down to 16 ft on Pier 6. Careful planning of other work may make it possible to revamp the flow for successive lifts so that forms may start at one end of job and move from one pier to the next adjacent pier without leap-frogging.

Cost Estimate

On the basis of the procedure outlined, the bidder then checks costs for shaft forming. A complete set of forms for the two shafts of one pier would permit approximately 12 uses for each form. However, if forms were provided for only one shaft of a pier, approximately 24 uses could be obtained. It should be reasonable to assume that if the carpenter crew could move the forms for a given lift on two shafts in one work shift they would be able to prepare two different lifts using a single set of shaft forms in the same time. Since all the piers are close together, the move between placements would be inconsequential. Therefore, it is decided to provide one set of forms for a single shaft, consisting of one lift 27 ft high, three lifts 20 ft high, and one lift 12 ft high. This totals about 3400 sq ft of form area.

For reasons of job expediency, necessary durability because of the large number of uses, and the importance of rigidity to simplify alignment problems, the bidder decides to purchase a steel form from a fabricator specializing in custom-made formwork. This set of forms costs $10.00 per sq ft or $34,000.00. The total contact area in the shafts is 71,000 sq ft, which means an average of 21 uses or $0.48 per sq ft direct form cost.

Stripping and erection of one lift of this shaft form is estimated to take a crew of five men, a foreman, operator, and oiler half a shift to have ready to place concrete. To average this out for the varying sizes, assume 3400 sq ft divided by five lifts equals 680 sq ft per lift or 680/(8 men × 4 hr) equals 21 sq ft per manhour. Costs are summarized in Table 3-1.

To stay within proposed estimate, two forms will be moved every day and two forms will be filled every day. Five forms

have been provided so that a slight margin is allowed for minor delays or difficulties which may arise. If we had provided a set of forms for a pair of shafts, the form cost would have doubled with no advantage substituted to produce an offsetting reduction in the place and remove cost.

Pier Strut Forming

All struts at the top of the piers are identical, but the engineer requires the supporting formwork to remain in place for 14 days. Since vertical forms may be stripped in 1 day it is important to minimize the money tied up in forms for a longer period. Therefore, the contractor decides to provide a form which is composed of two separable parts—the supporting section and the sides. The sides of a pier strut represent approximately 650 sq ft of contact area so that this form at $10.00 per sq ft would cost $6500. Two such forms would permit a crew to work on one every day, but the additional $6500 cost would be unwarranted as the completion time of the job will be determined by the stripping time of the supported form. Casting one strut a day would also throw the job out of balance with the schedule established by shaft placement. Therefore, one form for the sides of a pier strut is purchased and it will be used 12 times. This form will require more manhours to prepare but it should not tie up a crane more than about half a shift moving from one pier to another.

The supported form which must serve 12 piers and remain in place on each for 14 days would obviously be a bottleneck if only one were provided. It is anticipated that a strut could be cast every other day allowing one full day to prepare the side form. However, only one top shaft lift form is provided for 24 lifts so obviously this schedule could not be maintained. Let us assume then that the one strut side form will permit placing once every 4 days. With the requirement of leaving the supported form in place for 14 days, this would require 14 divided by 4 or say four forms. Table 3-2 shows estimated costs for strut forming.

3-9 Prefabricating reinforcing steel in cages for single shaft lift is important to maintaining proposed construction schedule on this bridge pier job.

TABLE 3-1: FORMING COST ESTIMATE

	LABOR	LABOR + MATERIAL
	per sq ft of form area	per sq ft of form area
Forms, purchase price	—	$10.00
Site handling	$1.00	1.00
Cleaning, oiling, etc.	1.00	1.00
Total	$2.00	$12.00
	per sq ft of formed surface	per sq ft of formed surface
Above costs prorated over 21 uses gives:	$0.10	$0.57
Place and remove cost at 21 sq ft per manhour ($3.75)	0.18	0.18
Miscellaneous hardware, etc.	0.12	0.15
Total	$0.40	$0.90

Scheduling

Since there are 12 strut placements for four forms, it can be readily seen that, with three uses for each form at 15 days in place, it will take approximately 45 days from the time of placing the first strut concrete to the last. Since there is one shaft form for the top lift and 24 shafts it follows that there will be a tail-out period of approximately 45 − 24 or 21 days after shaft concreting is completed. This tail-out period plus a corresponding buildup period at the start to get "work-wise" are important considerations affecting the operating cost of the job. The unit costs of the formwork may be unaffected, but analysis of operating costs determined by the duration of the job should be made to assure that maximum over-all economy is being realized by the formwork method selected. The work days allocated to the pier concrete are now itemized as follows:

> 5 days–buildup to get shaft placements started and work "bugs" out of form handling methods
> 58 days–of placing in 2 shaft lifts per working day
> 6 days–miscellaneous delays
> 3 days–due to unforeseen sequence and other problems
> 21 days–tail-out of strut pours
> ‾‾‾‾
> 93 days ÷ 5 working days per week = 19 weeks (approximate)
> 19 Saturdays
> 19 Sundays
> 2 holidays
> ‾‾‾‾
> 133 days

133/7 = 19 weeks, which is consistent with the tentative allowance (p. 22) requiring "approximately 17 weeks to place all concrete with the exception of a few tail-out placements on the pier struts."

3-10 Over-all progress on pier shaft construction depends on scheduling the use of a single set of shaft forms. Piers in the foreground are one lift high with reinforcing set for the next lift. Intermediate piers are at the second lift stage, while remote piers are at the third and higher lift levels.

TABLE 3-2: PIER-STRUT FORMING COST ESTIMATE

	Side form, cost per sq ft of formed surface		Supported form, cost per sq ft of formed surface	
	Labor	Labor + material	Labor	Labor + material
Form cost *	$0.17	$1.00	$1.00	$5.00
Place and remove cost at 10 sq ft per manhour ($3.75) (5 sq ft per manhour, supported form)	0.38	0.38	0.75	0.75
Miscellaneous hardware, etc.	0.05	0.12	0.15	0.25
Total	$0.60	$1.50	$1.90	$6.00

* Side form costs $10.00 per sq ft plus $2.00 labor per sq ft based on form area. These figures divided by 12 uses give tabulated values per sq ft of formed area.

Supported form costs $12.00 per sq ft plus $3.00 labor per sq ft based on form area. These values divided by 3 uses give tabulated costs per sq ft of formed area.

Recheck Plan Details

Now that the schedule has been worked out and the general plan developed, the bidder must go back over each step to check out the details of the form design. Reinforcement details should be checked to make sure that there is no conflict with the form placing method and that the assumption of fabricating in cages of one-lift units is feasible. Ladders and catwalks for access to and on the forms must be provided. Provision for cleanout holes must be made as well as installation of working platforms for concrete crews and their equipment. Safety features figure prominently here as men work considerably more effectively when they are unconcerned over their personal safety.

Details of corner connections, aligning devices, and handling hooks or slings must be made to assure fast action of removing and erecting form to permit the production rates assumed. Specifications on chamfer, rustication strips, finish, anchor bolts, and other embedded items must be investigated to be sure they are consistent with the proposed form plan. Then the design must be rechecked to verify the sizing of structural members. (This is more pertinent to cases where the form is designed and built by the contractor.) The weight of the form is then rechecked to ascertain if it is still within the capacity of the lifting rig. Provisions for separating the form to remove it from the top shaft lift must be worked out as well as the connections for the cut-off sections of the first lifts in order to attain the production rates assumed.

A re-evaluation of other construction operations which will be in progress during this period is necessary to determine if any will adversely affect the forming operation. Unusual foundation problems in one or more piers might, if not recognized early enough, throw the schedule out of sequence which invariably results in the contractor having to build or purchase more forms. It can readily be seen from the cost details shown above how a reduction in the number of uses will influence the unit costs.

The materials used in the form and the question of whether to buy the form fabricated elsewhere or build on the job determine how much of a job mill will be provided for miscellaneous carpentry.

4: MATERIALS, ACCESSORIES, PROPRIETARY PRODUCTS

SELECTION OF MATERIALS suitable for form-work should be based on maximum economy to the contractor, consistent with safety and the quality required in the finished work. Only a few decades ago the story of formwork materials could have been written very simply—boards, posts, and nails, oil for coating, wire and band iron for ties. Forms were for the most part built in place on the job, were torn down after a single use, and salvage was limited to individual boards or timbers. This practice is still representative of areas where labor costs are low and industrial technology is not greatly advanced. However, in the United States, rising labor costs and the increasing awareness of the precision and economy attainable with mass production have changed the formwork picture radically in recent years.

Prefabricated, reusable form panels and shoring units have become standard items of construction equipment; the number and variety of tying, fastening, and bracing accessories seem to increase almost daily. New materials have been adapted to form construction, and new ways to use conventional materials have been found. The introduction of plywood for sheathing has alone been responsible for major changes in form planning and building. Plastics, glass fiber, steel, the light metals, and rubber, both as raw materials and in patented, prefabricated shapes have simplified the forming of concrete to meet the challenges of contemporary architectural demands.

The purpose of this chapter is to provide as complete as possible a description of the various products and materials currently in use for formwork. In the case of patented panels, shoring, ties, and other accessories, some generalizations have been made because of the enormous number of individual items. The illustrations have been selected as representative of a class of items, and their inclusion does not imply superiority of the product pictured. It is recognized that there is significant variation from one country to another in the materials and manufactured devices available and in use for formwork; however, it has been necessary to limit the present discussion to United States practice.

Lumber

Practically all formwork jobs, regardless of the varied or exotic form materials that may be used, require some lumber. Although the species, grades, sizes, and lengths vary geographically, the local supplier will advise what material and sizes are in stock or promptly obtainable, and the designer or builder can proceed accordingly. Frequently the choice of lumber species is a question of local availability and cost; usually there are several kinds that will serve equally well for a given job. Any lumber that is straight and structurally strong and sound may be used for formwork, although the wide distribution and abundance of softwoods make them generally most economical for all types of formwork. The softwoods are usually lighter in weight and are easier to work, though not all species are truly softer than the so-called hardwoods. Hardwood caps and wedges may be introduced where additional strength across grain is needed.

Partially seasoned stock is usually used for formwork, since fully dried lumber swells excessively when it becomes wet, and green timber will dry out and warp during hot weather, causing difficulties of alignment and uneven surface. Old and new boards should not be used together in the same panel if uniform finish is important. Although final choice of wood for forming will depend on the local market, the following brief description of some of the commonly used woods may be of value.

Kinds of Lumber

Southern yellow pine and Douglas fir, sometimes called Oregon pine, are widely used in structural concrete forms, and are equally suitable for architectural concrete. They are easily worked and are the strongest in the softwood group. Both hold nails well and are durable. They are used for sheathing, studs, and wales, and Douglas fir is sometimes used for milled wood forms. Douglas fir is appreciably lighter in weight and a little softer than southern pine. Southern yellow pine has moderately large shrinkage, but stays in place well when properly seasoned. The choice between the two should be primarily one of cost, as the differences between them are generally small.

California redwood is used to some extent for structural concrete forms and is an excellent material for many uses. It is not recommended for architectural concrete work, however, because of its tendency to stain the concrete. Even for studs and wales, redwood is not suitable as the stain may drip onto an exposed surface when the wood is wet.

Western hemlock is comparable to Douglas fir as form lumber and may generally be used wherever Douglas fir or southern pine is used, although it is not quite as strong. The species of hemlock growing on the Pacific coast should not be confused with eastern hemlock which is not generally considered suitable for architectural concrete forms, although it is used for structural concrete.

Northern white, Idaho white, sugar, and ponderosa pines are excellent woods for architectural concrete forms. Since they are not so abundant as Douglas fir and southern pine and are used for purposes for which the latter are not so well suited, they are not generally economical for forms except for special uses. Because the white pines are soft and straight grained, they are especially well suited for run moldings and milled forms for ornamentation. The white pines stay in place well, as they are not inclined to warp and twist. This characteristic is especially desirable for forms made up of an assembly of milled pieces, as they will remain tight and will insure sharp detailing. Norway pine and eastern spruce have many of the qualities of the white pines and may be used, providing satisfactory grades can be obtained.

Occasionally, form lumber contains sufficient tannin or other organic substances to cause softening of the surface concrete. For example, the Corps of Engineers has reported [12] * some failures of mass concrete to harden where it was in contact with forms made of *new* ponderosa pine. When this condition is recognized it can be remedied by treating the form sur-

* Numbered references appear at the end of the chapter.

4-1 Dimension lumber and plywood are much in evidence in this construction view of a four-story parking structure. Adjustable horizontal and vertical shoring are also being used.

faces with whitewash or lime water before applying a form oil or coating. The condition also disappears after one or two reuses of the form.

Lumber Finish and Sizes

Lumber which has been surfaced in a planing machine to attain smoothness of surface and uniformity of size is called "dressed" lumber. The surfacing may be on one side (S1S), two sides (S2S), two edges (S2E), a combination of sides and edges (S1S1E, S1S2E, S2S1E) or on all four sides (S4S). Dressed lumber is generally used for formwork, because it is easier to handle and work, but rough sawn boards and timbers may be used in bracing and shoring, or as a form surfacing material to secure a special texture effect in the finished concrete.

Minimum sizes of both rough and dressed lumber are specified in the American Softwood Lumber Standard, PS 20-70.[17] Lumber is commonly referred to by its nominal size, which at one time was the same as the rough sawn measurements. However,

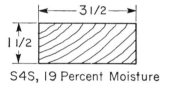

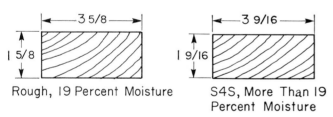

4-2 Specified actual size of a 2x4 for different moisture contents and finishes

under PS 20-70 adopted in 1970, dimensions were changed in an attempt to equate green and dry lumber. Minimum sizes for green lumber are selected so that as moisture is lost it becomes the same size as dry lumber. Rough lumber is now generally required to be ⅛ in. thicker and ⅛ in. wider than its finished counterpart.

Table 4-1 shows actual dimensions and cross section properties of American Standard lumber at 19 percent moisture content. Actual, not nominal, sizes must always be used for design. Values of Table 4-1 can be safely used with either dry or green lumber.

The length of lumber ordered, when this can be specified, should be such that it can be used to the best advantage with little waste. The most common

lengths commercially available range up to 20-24 ft in even-numbered increments of 2 ft. Sheathing can be ordered in random lengths, as it generally has to be cut, and short pieces can be worked in. Joists, studs, posts, beam bottoms, and other members where exact dimensions are required should be ordered in the nearest commercial length which equals or is a multiple of the span or height required. Floor joists, for example, which are to span 5 ft 6 in. can be ordered in 12-ft lengths for the least waste. Care in specifying lengths cuts down on the number of short ends that are wasted.

Quantities of lumber are generally spoken of in terms of board feet, or feet board measure, variously abbreviated as bd ft, ft bm, or fbm. The board foot is a measure of quantity, *based on nominal dimensions,* equal to 144 cu in. or a board 1 ft square and 1 in. thick. These units are used in estimating and paying for formwork lumber.

Sheathing Boards

Tongue-and-groove boards are used for sheathing where smoothness of surface is an important consideration. "Matching" of the boards—that is, fitting the tongue into the groove of the adjacent board—improves alignment of the sheathing and also prevents loss of mortar through the joints.

Shiplap boards are used to some extent in place of tongued-and-grooved stock. The finished surface obtained is less smooth, but greater reuse is sometimes possible because there is less chance of splitting the edges when stripping. Square-edged boards are also used where a rougher finished surface is either desirable or permissible, but some leakage between boards can be expected.

Stress Grading and Working Stresses

Stress-graded lumber provides material of designated and assured strength so that formwork structures can be designed to safely carry anticipated loads. Detailed requirements which lumber must meet to qualify for a stress grade are published by various manufacturers' associations in conformance with the American Softwood Lumber Standard, PS 20-70. Because of regional differences in grading practices and strength characteristics of different species, the grade designation alone is not a sufficient indicator of lumber quality for the user.*

* For example, select structural dimension lumber of Eastern spruce has an allowable bending stress of 1500 psi, while select structural Douglas fir has 2100 psi, and mountain hemlock has 1750 psi for the same grade.

TABLE 4-1: PROPERTIES OF AMERICAN STANDARD BOARD, PLANK, DIMENSION AND TIMBER SIZES COMMONLY USED FOR FORM CONSTRUCTION

Based on data supplied by the National Forest Products Association

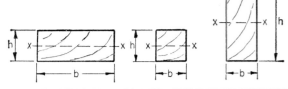

X — X = neutral axis

Nominal size in inches, bxh	American Standard size in inches, bxh S4S* 19% maximum moisture	Area of section $A = bh$, sq in.		Moment of inertia, in.⁴ $I = \frac{bh^3}{12}$		Section modulus, in.³ $S = \frac{bh^2}{6}$		Board feet per linear foot of piece
		Rough	S4S	Rough	S4S	Rough	S4S	
4x1	3½x¾	3.17	2.62	0.20	0.12	0.46	0.33	⅓
6x1	5½x¾	4.92	4.12	0.31	0.19	0.72	0.52	½
8x1	7¼x¾	6.45	5.44	0.41	0.25	0.94	0.68	⅔
10x1	9¼x¾	8.20	6.94	0.52	0.32	1.20	0.87	⅚
12x1	11¼x¾	9.95	8.44	0.63	0.39	1.45	1.05	1
4x1¼	3½x1	4.08	3.50	0.43	0.29	0.76	0.58	5/12
6x1¼	5½x1	6.33	5.50	0.68	0.46	1.19	0.92	⅝
8x1¼	7¼x1	8.30	7.25	0.87	0.60	1.56	1.21	⅚
10x1¼	9¼x1	10.55	9.25	1.11	0.77	1.98	1.54	1 1/24
12x1¼	11¼x1	12.80	11.25	1.35	0.94	2.40	1.87	1¼
4x1½	3½x1¼	4.98	4.37	0.78	0.57	1.14	0.91	½
6x1½	5½x1¼	7.73	6.87	1.22	0.89	1.77	1.43	¾
8x1½	7¼x1¼	10.14	9.06	1.60	1.18	2.32	1.89	1
10x1½	9¼x1¼	12.89	11.56	2.03	1.50	2.95	2.41	1¼
12x1½	11¼x1¼	15.64	14.06	2.46	1.83	3.58	2.93	1½
4x2	3½x1½	5.89	5.25	1.30	0.98	1.60	1.31	⅔
6x2	5½x1½	9.14	8.25	2.01	1.55	2.48	2.06	1
8x2	7¼x1½	11.98	10.87	2.64	2.04	3.25	2.72	1⅓
10x2	9¼x1½	15.23	13.87	3.35	2.60	4.13	3.47	1⅔
12x2	11¼x1½	18.48	16.87	4.07	3.16	5.01	4.21	2
2x4	1½x3½	5.89	5.25	6.45	5.36	3.56	3.06	⅔
2x6	1½x5½	9.14	8.25	24.10	20.80	8.57	7.56	1
2x8	1½x7¼	11.98	10.87	54.32	47.63	14.73	13.14	1⅓
2x10	1½x9¼	15.23	13.87	111.58	98.93	23.80	21.39	1⅔
2x12	1½x11¼	18.48	16.87	199.31	177.97	35.04	31.64	2
3x4	2½x3½	9.52	8.75	10.42	8.93	5.75	5.10	1
3x6	2½x5½	14.77	13.75	38.93	34.66	13.84	12.60	1½
3x8	2½x7¼	19.36	18.12	87.74	79.39	23.80	21.90	2
3x10	2½x9¼	24.61	23.12	180.24	164.89	38.45	35.65	2½
3x12	2½x11¼	29.86	28.12	321.96	296.63	56.61	52.73	3
4x4	3½x3½	13.14	12.25	14.39	12.50	7.94	7.15	1⅓
4x6	3½x5½	20.39	19.25	53.76	48.53	19.12	17.65	2
4x8	3½x7¼	26.73	25.38	121.17	111.15	32.86	30.66	2⅔
4x10	3½x9¼	33.98	32.38	248.91	230.84	53.10	49.91	3⅓
6x3	5½x2½	14.77	13.75	8.48	7.16	6.46	5.73	1½
6x4	5½x3½	20.39	19.25	22.33	19.65	12.32	11.23	2
6x6	5½x5½	31.64	30.25	83.43	76.26	29.66	27.73	3
6x8	5½x7½	42.89	41.25	207.81	193.36	54.51	51.56	4
8x8	7½x7½	58.14	56.25	281.69	263.67	73.89	70.31	5⅓

* Roughdry sizes are ⅛ in. larger, both dimensions.

The allowable unit stresses for stress-grade lumber and comprehensive recommendations for their engineering application are summarized in the "National Design Specification for Stress Grade Lumber and Its Fastenings."[2] The factor of safety represented in these allowable stresses is about 2½. To be sure that stress grades are obtained, check the lumber for proper grade mark, grade stamp, or certification of quality by a recognized, competent grading and inspection agency.

Because allowable stresses depend on so many factors including the species of wood, grade, size of cross section, moisture content, and duration of loading, it is impossible to recommend a single set of working stresses for formwork design. Table 4-2, showing the range of stresses assigned to several species of wood, plus stress values for construction grade and No. 2 lumber 4 in. and less in thickness and in width, gives an idea of the wood strengths available. Values of Table 4-2 are stresses recommended for normal duration of loading (continuous throughout 90 percent of the life of the structure) using wood with a moisture content no more than 19 percent (partially seasoned). According to the definitions of PS 20-70, wood with 19 percent or less moisture is *dry*, all other is *green*. For green lumber or lumber wet during use, such as form sheathing, allowable stresses must be decreased as indicated at the bottom of Table 4-2. Since wood possesses the ability to absorb large overloads for short periods, adjustments for duration of loading are also provided.

Following the principles outlined by ACI Committee 347 for the purpose of arriving at working stresses, formwork can be divided into two classes:

Class I: forms for light construction, single use, or very limited reuse

Class II: forms for any heavy construction where danger to life and property are great, or any forms for which continuing or prolonged reuse is planned.

For Class II formwork, the suggested working stresses are the same as the allowable unit stresses recommended in the National Design Specification. Representative values for different species are given in Table 4-2. For Class I formwork, a 25 percent increase in these stresses may be made because of the short duration of loading. No increase is permitted in the modulus of elasticity.

Sheathing boards are not ordinarily available in stress grades. Stress values for sheathing may be approximated by comparison with face appearance of

TABLE 4-2: REPRESENTATIVE WORKING STRESS VALUES (PSI) FOR LUMBER AT 19 PERCENT MOISTURE CONTENT *

Derived from National Design Specification for Stress Grade Lumber [2] and from recommendations of American Plywood Association

PROPERTIES / SPECIES AND GRADE	Extreme fiber bending †	Compression ⊥ to grain	Compression ∥ to grain	Horizontal shear ‡	Modulus of elasticity
EASTERN SPRUCE					
Range, all grades	200-1785	255	425-1200		1,100,000-1,400,000
No. 2, 4x4 and smaller	1050	255	700	140	1,200,000
Constr., 4x4 and smaller	775	255	800		1,100,000
SOUTHERN PINE					
Range, all grades	275-2750	345-475	600-2150		1,400,000-1,900,000
No. 2, 4x4 and smaller	1250	345	850	180	1,400,000
Constr., 4x4 and smaller	1050	345	1150		1,400,000
DOUGLAS FIR-LARCH					
Range, all grades	275-2450	385-455	600-1850		1,500,000-1,900,000
No. 2, 4x4 and smaller	1450	385	1000	185	1,700,000
Constr., 4x4 and smaller	1050	385	1150		1,500,000
CALIFORNIA REDWOOD					
Range, all grades	200-2300	270-425	150-2150		900,000-1,400,000
No. 2, 4x4 and smaller	1400	425	1000	160	1,300,000
Constr., 4x4 and smaller	800	270	550		900,000
HEM-FIR					
Range, all grades	225-1650	245	500-1300		1,200,000-1,500,000
No. 2, 4x4 and smaller	1150	245	800	150	1,400,000
Constr., 4x4 and smaller	825	245	925		1,200,000
REDUCTION FOR MOISTURE CONTENT GREATER THAN 19 PERCENT: Use percentage shown (also applies to wood used wet)	86 **	67	70	97 §	97 **
INCREASE FOR SHORT TERM LOAD, permitted for Class I formwork	25%	25%	25%	25%	0
PLYWOOD SHEATHING USED WET, Plyform B-B, Class I		(Bearing on face)			
short term load	2000	285	—	75 ††	1,600,000
permanent load	1600	230	—	60 ††	1,600,000

* Normal duration of load as defined by Reference 2.
† Under appropriate conditions, as described in the text, repetitive-member stresses 15 percent higher may be used for normal duration of load.
‡ Based on Sec. 400-E-2 of NDS (Reference 2).
§ For redwood use 94 percent; for southern pine use 90 percent.
** For redwood and southern pine, use 80 percent of bending stress, 93 percent of *E*.
†† Value for rolling shear in plane of the plies; check for rolling shear should be made according to formula on p. 89.

2-in. lumber which is available in stress grades. Working stresses so selected should be reduced as indicated in Table 4-2 to allow for wetting of the sheathing by contact with the concrete.

Among the more widely available species used for formwork in the United States, Douglas fir, Southern pine, and Eastern spruce are frequently specified. Working stresses applicable for commonly used grades of these woods have been used in developing form design tables presented in Chapter 7.

Repetitive Member Stresses

Increased bending stresses are permitted by the National Design Specification in certain cases where a given size of member is used repeatedly in a structure. These "repetitive-member stresses" are 15 percent higher than extreme fiber stresses given in Table 4-2, and may be applied, according to Sec. 200-D-2 of the 1971 National Design Specification: [2]

> ". . . . for the design of members in bending, such as joists, trusses, rafters, studs, planks, decking or similar members that are spaced not more than 24 inches, are not less than 3 in number and are joined by floor, roof, or other load-distributing elements adequate to support the design load."

With proper engineering judgment these stresses may be applied to some formwork. The intent is that they be used where structural continuity provides for load distribution; thus the repetitive-member stresses might be applied to carefully constructed panels whose components are securely nailed or bolted together, as is common with crane-handled panels designed for continuing reuse. They should not be applied in de-

4-4 Controlled gluing is important in the manufacture of plywood. Veneer sheets pass through rollers which apply glue evenly. Each sheet of veneer is then placed with the grain at right angles to that of the plies above and below.

sign of loosely assembled formwork, made for a single use. Application of the 15 percent increase for repetitive members is not recommended in cases where basic stresses have already been increased the 25 percent permitted for short duration loads.

Plywood

Plywood has been increasingly used for form sheathing in recent years. Relatively large sheets of plywood (Figure 4-1) save labor in form building, and the correspondingly large areas of joint-free concrete reduce the cost of finishing and rubbing exposed surfaces. Improved production standards, along with waterproof or moisture resistant glues, have largely overcome the earlier objections that plywood would delaminate when in recurrent or prolonged contact with wet concrete. With proper care and treatment of form surfaces and panel edges, many reuses are possible with plywood sheathing.

Construction; Sizes Available

Plywood is built up of an odd number of thin sheets of wood glued together with the grain of each piece at right angles to the one adjoining it. Grain of the two outside plies is parallel to provide stability. The layers or plies are dried and joined under pressure with glues that make the joints as strong or stronger than the wood itself. Alternating direction of the grain of adjoining layers equalizes strains and thus minimizes shrinkage and warping of the plywood panels.

Softwood plywood, which is used for concrete forms, is manufactured from several species of woods, of which Douglas fir is the most common. Among other kinds of wood used are western larch, redwood, and various species of pine, spruce, fir, and cedar.

The ½-, ⅝-, and ¾-in. thicknesses of plywood in 4x8-ft sheets are most commonly used for formwork, with sheets of ¼-in. plywood frequently used as form liners. A wider range of thicknesses is obtainable when needed (see Table 4-3), but the thicknesses from ¼ to 1 in. are more widely available. In addition to the standard 4x8-ft sheet, 5-ft widths, and lengths ranging from 5 to 12 ft are often available from stock. Some contractors cut the 5-ft width to 2½x10-ft panels, which are easier for one man to handle than the 4-ft width. Table 4-3 shows the weight of 4x8-ft panels of various thicknesses, as well as the weight per 1000 sq ft.

Types and Grades

Softwood plywood is made in two types, *interior* and *exterior;* exterior type is bonded with waterproof glue, and the interior type is bonded with water-resistant glue. Both types are used for formwork, but the exterior type is chosen where maximum reuse is desired. Within each type, panels are made up of several grades of veneer ranging from A to D depending on the freedom of the surface from knots and other defects. Grade B-B commonly used for formwork has

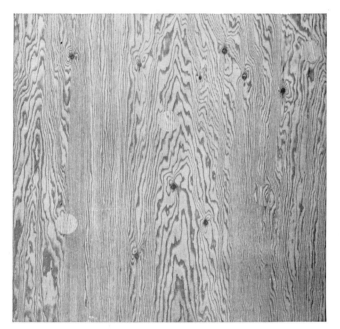

4-5 Surface characteristics of B-B grade plywood commonly used for formwork. Actual size of the piece photographed is 4x4 ft.

both faces of B-grade veneer, which is a smoothly sanded solid-surface sheet with circular repair plugs and tight knots permitted.

Plywood grades and types are defined in commercial standards for the manufacture of plywoods established by the U. S. Department of Commerce.* These same standards also provide that plywood labeled as concrete form grade shall be edge sealed and mill oiled. Mill oiling does not eliminate the need for oiling or coating on the job, but mill oiled plywood gives better service than that which is job-treated only. Edge sealing protects the glue line from moisture. Some form coatings now on the market require an unoiled base; if the use of such a coating is planned, it is important to specify unoiled plywood.

* U. S. Product Standard PS 1-66 for Softwood Plywood—Construction and Industrial, issued by the Product Standards Section, National Bureau of Standards, U. S. Department of Commerce. PS 1-66, adopted Nov. 1, 1966, superseded CS 45-60, CS 122-60, and CS 259-63.

Various grades of plywood may be found to suit different forming needs, but mill oiling and edge sealing are standard practice only for the grades specifically designated for formwork.

Wherever plywood of known structural qualities is required, as is generally the case for formwork, it is a good practice to specify panels carrying the mark of an approved inspection and testing agency, which indicates type and grade, species of veneer, and conformance with the applicable U. S. Commercial Standard. If there is any doubt as to quality of plywood purchased, a certification of type and grade may be requested.

Overlaid (Plastic Coated) Plywood

Overlaid plywood is exterior type (waterproof glue) produced the same as other plywood, but with the addition of resin-impregnated fiber faces permanently fused under heat and pressure on one or both sides. It may be either *high density* or *medium density* as described below. Overlaid plywood is also referred to as plastic coated, but it should be carefully distinguished from plywood which is coated or treated by the user with various plastic compounds.

Translucent or opaque overlays blank out the pattern of grain or knots, and consequently these overlaid plywoods are used where smoothest, grainless surfaces are desirable. Up to 200 reuses in formwork have been reported for overlaid plywood, but such performance depends largely on the care taken in using the forms. The overlay generally improves the abrasion and moisture resistance of plywood, and decreases requirements for form oiling. Some of the high density overlay surfaces may be used untreated, but light oiling usually prolongs their service life. Since the exact nature of the overlay may vary from manufacturer to manufacturer, the producer's instructions should be followed with regard to oiling or treating overlaid plywood.

High Density

The surfacing is hard, smooth, and of such character that further finishing by paint or varnish is not required. The overlay, which may be one or both sides, consists of a cellulose fiber sheet or sheets having no less than 45 percent, by weight, of the laminate of thermosetting resin of the phenol or melamine type. The resin impregnation is sufficient to attach the sur-

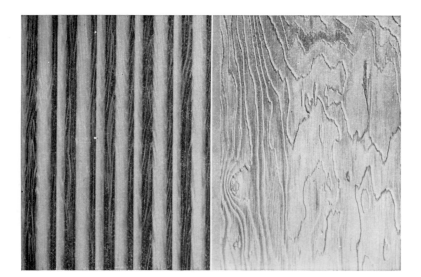

4-6 Pronounced pattern of grooves of varying width and depth in plywood at the left, manufactured especially for formwork. Contoured face of plywood at the right is produced at the mill by removing some of the soft grain growth to accentuate natural swirls and contours.

facing material with a strong bond. The overlay face is usually translucent, showing the natural wood color.

Medium Density

The resin impregnated facing on one or both surfaces of medium density overlaid plywood consists of a cellulose-fiber sheet in which not less than 17 to 22 percent by weight of the laminate is a thermosetting resin of the phenol or melamine type. An integral phenolic resin glue line is applied to one surface of the facing material to bond it to the plywood. The overlay face is of solid color, and there is no consistent show-through of grain. Medium density overlaid plywood is less resistant to abrasion and water penetration than the high density.

Textured Surfaces

A number of textures such as deep, wide striations or realistic wood grain are available in both interior and exterior type plywood panels. The pattern or design on the plywood is reproduced on the concrete to provide one-way or vari-directional patterns for exposed concrete surfaces. The result is functional as well as decorative; textured surfaces may have a marked reduction in light reflection and glare, important in highway structures. The use of textured form panels also cuts down on the otherwise necessary sack and rub finishing, although it is more difficult to match where patching is required. Standard panels and pre-cut squares can be arranged as desired when the forms are constructed, and designers can originate patterns without expensive special forming. Fewer reuses of textured panels are generally obtained than with conventional surfaces.

Strength Properties

Working stresses for plywood are based on the strength properties and basic stresses for wood as determined by the U. S. Forest Products Laboratory. Suggested working stresses for plywood form sheathing are included in Table 4-2 along with working

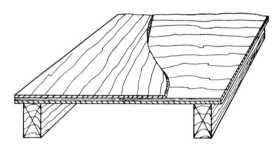

Plywood Used The Weak Way

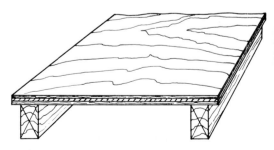

Plywood Used The Strong Way

4-7 Plywood at the bottom—face plies parallel to span —is used the strong way. With face grain perpendicular to the span, the specimen at the top is used the weak way. Most plywood used structurally for formwork has five plies, rather than the three shown in this simplified drawing.

TABLE 4-3: EFFECTIVE SECTION PROPERTIES FOR PLYWOOD (12-IN. WIDTHS)*
FACE PLIES OF DIFFERENT SPECIES FROM INNER PLIES

Sanded plywood, net thickness, in.	Number of plies	Effective thickness for shear all grades, using exterior glue	12-in. width, used with face grain parallel to span				12-in. width, used with face grain perpendicular to span				Approximate weight, lb	
			Area for tension and compression (in.²)	Moment of inertia I (in.⁴)	Effective section modulus S (in.³)	Rolling shear constant I/Q (in.)	Area for tension and compression (in.²)	Moment of inertia I (in.⁴)	Effective section modulus S (in.³)	Rolling shear constant I/Q (in.)	4x8-ft sheet	1000 sq ft
¼	3	0.241	1.680	0.013	0.091	0.179	0.600	0.001	0.019	—	26	800
⅜	3	0.305	1.680	0.040	0.181	0.309	1.050	0.004	0.053	—	35	1100
½	5	0.450	2.400	0.080	0.271	0.436	1.200	0.016	0.115	0.215	48	1500
⅝	5	0.508	2.407	0.133	0.360	0.557	1.457	0.040	0.214	0.315	58	1800
¾	5	0.567	2.778	0.201	0.456	0.687	2.200	0.088.	0.366	0.393	70	2200
⅞	7	0.711	2.837	0.301	0.585	0.704	2.893	0.145	0.496	0.531	83	2600
1	7	0.769	3.600	0.431	0.733	0.763	3.323	0.234	0.682	0.632	96	3000
1⅛	7	0.825	3.829	0.566	0.855	0.849	3.307	0.334	0.843	0.748	106	3300

* Information from *Plywood Design Specification*.[16] Use listed S value in bending calculations, and use I only in deflection calculations.

stresses for lumber. For Class I formwork which is regarded essentially as a temporary structure with short term loads, the working stress values recommended by the American Plywood Association for Class I concrete form grade plywood * are given. For Class II formwork whose design is comparable to that of a permanent structure, these allowable unit stresses have been reduced one-fifth because of the difference in allowable stresses for long term loading. Modulus of elasticity values for both classes of formwork are derived from the basic value for form grade plywood, reduced by one-ninth as recommended by the plywood manufacturers because form sheathing will generally be wet when loaded. For high density overlaid plywood or plywood coated on the job to make it impervious to moisture, higher working stresses would be permissible since the reduction for moisture would no longer apply.

Plywood sheathing acts as a beam, but the plies whose grain runs perpendicular to the span contribute little to the bending strength and stiffness of the panel. Table 4-3 gives the effective section properties for various thicknesses of plywood for two cases—face plies parallel to span of beam and face plies perpendicular to beam span. For a given thickness of plywood panel, I and S are larger when the face grain is parallel to the span of the beam, and this is referred to as using plywood the "strong way." Conversely, plywood with its face grain perpendicular to beam span is said to be used the "weak way." Due to involved

considerations concerning properties of plywood, the effective moment of inertia I divided by distance to extreme fiber c may not equal effective section modulus S (Table 4-3). Therefore, *effective S as tabulated should be used for all bending calculations and I should be used only for deflection calculations.*

Bending Plywood to Curved Surfaces

Simple curves with radii not less than 24 in. can readily be made in plywood form sheathing. Table 4-4 shows minimum bending radii for several thicknesses of panel. Note that shorter radius curves can be obtained when plywood is bent across the grain. Shorter radii than those tabulated may often be developed by wetting and steaming, but this should be done only with exterior type plywood made with waterproof glue. Checking and grain rise may be more prominent with this method.

Best results in bending are obtained when a continuous rounded backing is used, but this may not be required for larger radius curves. In applications where there is abrupt curvature, secure the panel to the shorter radius first. In critical bends, two thin panels often work better than one thick one.

Thick plywood, like solid timber, may also be bent by saw kerfing the inside of the curve. To get a smooth curve the saw cut should not go through the

* This "Class I" is a plywood grade, independent of formwork classes defined in this manual.

TABLE 4-4: MINIMUM BENDING RADII FOR PLYWOOD PANELS *

These radii apply for mill run panels carefully bent. Select pieces with clear, straight grain can be bent to smaller radii.

Panel thickness, in.	Curved across grain	Curved parallel to grain
$\frac{1}{4}$	24 in.	5 ft
$\frac{3}{8}$	36 in.	8 ft
$\frac{1}{2}$	6 ft	12 ft
$\frac{5}{8}$	8 ft	16 ft
$\frac{3}{4}$	12 ft	20 ft

* Based on information published in "Guide to Plywood for Industry," American Plywood Association, Tacoma, Wash., 1967.

last two plies next to the face. Space kerfs so that at the correct radius the cuts will just close up. The finer the saw, therefore, the narrower will be the space on either side of the cut and the smoother the corresponding curve.

Other Framing and Facing Materials

Tempered Hardboard

Hardboard is a board material manufactured from refined or partly refined wood fibers, felted into a panel having a density from 50 to 80 lb per cu ft under controlled combinations of consolidating pressure, heat, and moisture. Both standard and tempered hardboard are produced, but the latter is preferred for formwork. Tempering is the supplemental operation of impregnating the hardboard with materials such as drying oils which are stabilized by baking or other heating after impregnation. Tempered hardboard has improved strength properties, lower rate of water absorption, and improved abrasion resistance.

Effectiveness of hardboard as a form material is controlled not only by the tempering, but by the density of the board and the type of wood "furnish" of which it is made. If a hardboard other than that specifically designated form grade is being selected, it is imperative to follow the *manufacturer's recommendations* as to the grade to be used.

Screen back hardboard has the reverse impression of a screen on the back, produced when a damp or wet mat is hot-pressed into the hardboard and dried in the press. Both the smooth and screen surfaces of tempered hardboard have been successfully used as contact surfaces for forms. Board manufactured with a smooth surface on both sides is not generally recommended for forming use.

Concrete form hardboard is a tempered hardboard which has been given additional processing for improved performance when used as a panel and liner in concrete formwork. Usually made only in $\frac{1}{4}$-in. thickness, it has a factory-applied plastic coating which seals out alkaline water that weakens wood fibers. The coating makes it more abrasion resistant than standard tempered hardboard, and so a greater service life can be expected with this grade. When the special surfacing is outworn, it may be replaced and the hardboard panel kept in use.

If uncoated hardboard is used for forming purposes, a resin-based parting compound is recommended as a sealer to keep moisture from the concrete out of the board.

Used primarily as a form liner or form facing material, hardboard is not a structural material like plywood and lumber and therefore should be applied to a supporting backing of 4-in. or wider lumber. Space between supporting members varies, as accompanying details show, from $\frac{3}{4}$ to $3\frac{1}{2}$ in. Adjoining hardboard sheets should not be tightly butted. To prevent

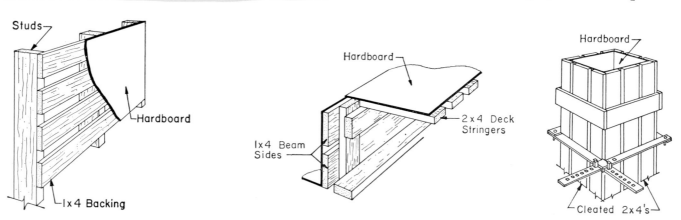

4-8 Typical assembly of wall, beam, and column forms with hardboard sheathing

buckling, joints about the width of a dime are usually left between abutting edges.

Sheets 4 ft wide are available in lengths from 4 to 16 ft, but the 4x8-ft panel is the standard size. The ¼-in. thickness recommended for formwork weighs 1.4 psf. Large sheets cut down the number of seams and thereby reduce finishing costs.

Applications

Hardboard together with 1x4 and 2x4 lumber makes a lining-sheathing surface for wall, deck, column, and beam forms as shown in the several applications sketched. Spacing between the backing boards ranges from ¾ to 3½ in. depending upon the loads imposed on the formwork. Consult manufacturers' recommendations for exact dimensions, and note special requirements for architectural surfaces given in Chapter 11.

The ¼-in. form grade can be bent to a radius of 25 in. without heating or wetting. It can be ordered bent to smaller radii down to 5 in.

Steel

Steel has long been an important material for the fabrication of special-purpose forms; all steel panel systems for general building construction have been successfully fabricated and used; and steel framing and bracing are important in the construction of many wood and plywood panel systems described later (p. 60). Patented steel pan and dome components for slab forming (p. 62) as well as various stay-in-place steel forms are standard construction items, and horizontal and vertical shores of steel are widely used today (p. 69).

Standard and lightweight structural steel members —channels, angles, I-beams, and others—also are finding increasing use in the framing or supporting of formwork, serving much the same purpose as wood members, but often permitting greater spans or heavier loads than would be possible with sawed timber members. A comprehensive listing of steel members available for this purpose will not be attempted here, but several handbooks or manuals [13, 14, 15] will help the form builder to select steel members that may be suitable for his purposes. Tables of allowable loads are shown in these books, and conventional steel design procedures may be followed. The form builder may have to exercise some ingenuity in adapting standard form hardware to steel members.

With reasonable care steel form framing members will last indefinitely and hence be suitable for many reuses; their selection may be determined on the basis

4-9 Hardboard panels used for deck forming. Stringers (2x4's) cleated together in groups of three or four are placed over horizontal steel shoring. Single 2x4's fill out odd spaces. Hardboard panels, 4x8 ft, are then nailed to the stringers. A gap about the width of a dime is left between hardboard panels.

of cost comparisons, or a contractor who has some steel sections on hand may adapt his form design to make use of them. At times steel members do a job that is impossible with other materials; their relatively longer spans make possible considerable saving in materials and labor that would otherwise go into intermediate supports. Consider for example the large beam form shown in Figure 4-10, which has an unsupported length of 42 ft.

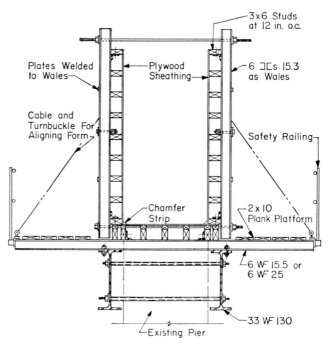

4-10 Steel channels, angles, and wide flange beams were used with wood and plywood in this form for beams up to 6x10 ft in cross section. Unsupported form length ranged up to 42 ft. For beam spans over 42 ft, forms were supported at midspan by a heavy wood bent framed of double 2x12 members.

4-11 Double channels held together at the proper spacing by small welded plates serve as wales for this wall form.

Figure 4-11 shows steel channels in use as wales for a simply framed wall form. The channels are used double, just as wood members would be, with a space between to allow fitting the ties without drilling the members.

Light Metals

Magnesium and aluminum have found rather limited use for forming concrete, although their lightness, favorable strength-weight ratio, and freedom from rust discoloration suggest that additional formwork applications may be developed. Relatively high initial costs for these materials may be offset by reductions in handling and shipping costs as well as by their extended service life.

Aluminum

Pure aluminum is attacked chemically by wet concrete, but a number of aluminum alloys have proved successful in resisting corrosion both from concrete and from the atmosphere. Uses of aluminum in formwork in the United States have been reported on a limited scale thus far; cast aluminum alloy molds are available for making ornamental concrete products and have been used in manufacture of concrete

blocks. Tubular aluminum has been used for form bracing. A successful aluminum pan system for slab forming has been reported, and a horizontal shoring member (described on p. 72) of aluminum has recently been marketed in the United States. Development of other prefabricated aluminum forming products is reported in progress.

Alloys 6061-T6 and 6063-T6, whose properties are given in Table 4-5, are said by aluminum producers to have been successfully used in concrete forms. Initially a rather mild etching takes place on the form surface, and a tough film of the corrosion products develops. This prevents any further attack and also provides a relatively smooth surface for the concrete. Standard form oils used to facilitate stripping of steel forms work satisfactorily on aluminum forms.

Cadmium plated or aluminum hardware or fittings are required wherever these devices are likely to contact the aluminum and wet concrete at the same time. This is to prevent galvanic corrosion caused by dissimilar metals in contact with the wet concrete which serves as an electrolyte.

Magnesium

Magnesium sheet and extrusions have been used to a limited extent in making concrete formwork. Two

TABLE 4-5: TYPICAL MECHANICAL PROPERTIES OF ALUMINUM ALLOYS SUITABLE FOR FORMWORK

Alloy and temper	Ultimate tensile strength, psi	Yield point, psi	Hardness, Brinell number, 50 kg load 100 mm ball	Ultimate shearing strength, psi	Modulus of elasticity, psi *
6061-T6	42,000	37,000	–	27,000	10,300,000
6063-T6	35,000	31,000	73	22,000	10,300,000

* Average value for aluminum alloys.

TABLE 4-6: TYPICAL MECHANICAL PROPERTIES OF MAGNESIUM ALLOYS SUITABLE FOR FORMS

Form of product	Alloy and temper	Ultimate tensile strength, psi	Yield point, psi	Approximate modulus of elasticity, psi
Extrusion	AZ31C-F Comm GR	32,000–38,000	20,000–28,000	6,500,000
Sheet	AZ31B-H10 AZ31B-H11	30,000–40,000	12,000–20,000	6,500,000

types of wall panel forms have been manufactured: one using an extruded and welded magnesium frame with plywood face; the other an all-magnesium form with an extruded frame and $\frac{3}{16}$-in. sheet face. One metal producer has reported development and field testing of a magnesium paving form (Figure 4-12).

Properties of some typical magnesium alloys are shown in Table 4-6. The weight advantage that can be obtained with magnesium, its ease of fabrication, and its freedom from rust discoloration are offset to some extent by attack from the freshly placed concrete whenever it contains calcium chloride or acid base aggregates. An additional protective coating is required to overcome this problem. Magnesium forms must also be protected from galvanic corrosion which is caused by dissimilar metals in contact in the presence of an electrolyte (the wet concrete). Steel or other metal fasteners in contact with the magnesium may be zinc or cadmium plated to prevent galvanic action.

The all-magnesium panel form previously mentioned was fabricated in 2-ft widths with cross bracing members 12 in. on centers supporting the $\frac{3}{16}$-in. magnesium sheet facing. After a relatively short period, according to the manufacturer, faces of the forms deflected between the cross members and took on a permanent set. This problem coupled with chemical and electrolytic corrosion led the manufacturer to discontinue production of the all-magnesium form in favor of one framed with magnesium and faced with plywood. Satisfactory performance with the latter was reported, and the form panel so developed weighed 3 lb per sq ft, compared with 5 lb per sq ft for a similar one framed in steel. Relative cost of magnesium may determine whether this sort of use is increased.

Glass-Fiber-Reinforced Plastic

Glass-fiber-reinforced plastic forms are popularly described both as plastic forms and fiber glass forms, but neither abbreviated term is completely correct. They are truly a combination of materials, up to about one-third being glass fiber. Such forms are finding increasing use in precast concrete construction and in architectural concrete because they produce excellent cast concrete surfaces, minimizing the need for finishing and repair. Only a very light oil coating is required; some successful use has been reported without oiling the forms at all. A seamless surface with little limitation of size or shape is possible.

Thickness of the fiber-glass-reinforced plastic forms

4-12 Experimental magnesium alloy paving forms during field test

has varied from $\frac{1}{8}$ in. for slab material with no external reinforcing to $\frac{5}{8}$ in. for column forms with 3x4's as reinforcement. Dome pans, pictured on p. 65, have been used successfully with a wall thickness of $\frac{1}{8}$ in.

For complex shapes made in small quantity, the forms are constructed by the conventional hand lay-up method used for other reinforced plastics. First a model of plaster, wood, or steel is prepared to the exact dimensions desired. This piece is then waxed, polished, and sprayed with a parting agent to prevent sticking of the resin to the master pattern. Glass mat is then fitted over the model and thoroughly saturated with a brush coat of polyester resin. When the resin has set and the heat dissipated, another layer of glass mat and polyester resin is added, and this process is repeated until the desired thickness is obtained.

An alternate method of building up the forms is to use a spray gun to apply the resin to which chopped strands of glass fiber have been added as the reinforcing material. Often a combination of the two methods is used. Depending on the size and shape of the form, it may be necessary to provide additional stiffening and support by means of built-up ribs, wood struts, steel rods, or aluminum tubing.

If a series of identical forms is required for a job, additional molds can be cast in plaster using the first form prepared as a master pattern. The number of additional molds required is determined by the number of matching form units needed and by the production schedule. Simpler shapes can be mass produced as was the reinforced plastic pan by hot molding in matched metal dies. In the case of the pans where numerous reuses were contemplated, a 10-mil veil of plastic was molded into the contact surface to prevent any "blooming" of the glass fibers to the form surface.

4-13 Workman applying brush coat of polyester resin to glass mat which is supported on mold for curved form member.

With either method of making the forms it is possible to eliminate all joints or seams. When special conditions dictate the building of a form in sections, it is possible to join the units in such a manner that the several sections may later be sealed together at the job site with additional applications of resin and glass fiber to produce a seamless mold.

The materials generally do not lend themselves to field fabrication, however. Careful temperature and

4-14 Fiber-glass-reinforced plastic served as the contact surface for sectional forms used 60 times on the 32 ft diameter core of the Marina City apartment building in Chicago. Eight 9-ft high sections were joined to make the complete circle. The glass-fiber-reinforced plastic face was ½ in. thick, backed by 4x4's on 1-ft centers. Additional bracing was provided by curved double-angle wales and double-channel strongbacks.

humidity controls must be exercised at all times during the manufacture of the forms. For these reasons all glass-fiber-reinforced plastic forms made to date have been fabricated under factory conditions. Most of these forms have been custom made by a number of firms specializing in this work. However, ready-made column and dome pan forms are now available.

Form Lining Materials

The term "form lining" used here includes any sheet, plate, or layer of material attached directly to the inside face of forms to improve or alter the surface texture and quality of the finished concrete. Substances which are applied by brushing, dipping, mopping, spraying, etc. to preserve the form material and to make stripping easier are referred to as form coatings and described in a later section, although some of these "coatings" are so effective as to approximate the form liner in function.

Plywood, hardboard, steel, and glass-reinforced plastic previously described have application as form liners, but emphasis here is placed on other types such as the various plastics, plastic coated metal, paper, cardboard, and fiberboard. One of the few comparative studies available on these newer lining materials was made recently in Australia at the Council of Scientific and Industrial Research Organizations Chemical Research Laboratories.[3, 4]

Various thicknesses of the several lining materials have been tried and various means of attaching the materials to the forms are used. Some adhesives are suitable for attaching liners to both wood and steel forms, or they may be tacked or nailed to wood forms.

Whether the liner is attached to a horizontal or vertical form surface also makes a difference. Thin sheets that can be used satisfactorily as base mats may wrinkle or sag when attached to vertical forms. Thicker layers of lining material generally have greater rigidity and consequently are more adaptable to vertical form surfaces; they also are less subject to accidental damage from vibrators.

Extreme smoothness and relative imperviousness of some of the lining materials give rise to a problem of eliminating air or "bug" holes, particularly when oil or grease is applied. Air bubbles seem to adhere to some of these ultra-smooth surfaces and resist removal by vibration. Wood, plywood, and hardboard form faces do not present this problem to the same extent because the oil or other parting compound tends to be absorbed into the exterior fibers rather than existing as a film on the form surface.

Highly absorptive materials used as form liners have eliminated voids and air pockets on the surface

4-15   Comparison of concrete surfaces cast with internal vibration against different types of material.   The surfaces shown measure 4x12 in., were in a vertical position when cast against: 1. Unoiled steel.   Portions of the surface were pulled out on stripping; 2. Polyethylene liner, unoiled.   Relatively smooth, uniform surface; 3. Epoxy resin coating on steel.   Shows unevenness of coating, a few bug holes; 4. Vaseline coated steel.   Shows unevenness of coating and larger number of bug holes.

of the concrete and improved durability of the concrete surface layer.   However, increased cost and difficulties associated with the use of such materials have prevented their widespread acceptance.

Plastic Form Liners

Either glossy smooth or textured concrete surfaces can be obtained with a variety of plastic formulations including polyethylene sheets and films, polystyrene sheets, and polyvinyl chloride sheets used as form liners.   Portland Cement Association studies [5] indicated that various butadiene styrenes and linear polyethylene gave the most satisfactory performance.

The PCA study, limited to panels precast in a horizontal position, pointed out that it is considerably more difficult to obtain void-free surfaces when they are cast in a vertical plane.   If the plastic is used in a vertical position extra care in vibration is necessary to get rid of entrapped air.   One contractor drilled $\frac{1}{8}$-in. air holes in his plastic forms to allow escape of air. The plastic sheet widely used for concrete molding purposes has a high gloss on one side and a leather-like texture on the other, giving the user a choice as to degree of sheen he wants in his finished concrete. Various patterns can be imparted to the plastic lining material either by positive pressure or by vacuum forming.   The latter method offers some economic advantage since the side of the plastic which contacts the original pattern is opposite the surface which will contact the concrete.   Thus minor imperfections in the pattern are not reproduced, and high quality finish is unnecessary on the model.

The pattern may be of various materials such as wood, plaster of paris, metal, or glass.   Small-diameter holes are drilled through the model at strategic low points in the design.   These holes are incorporated in a vacuum system, usually by placing the model in a pan that has a marginal lip for automatically sealing the edges of the plastic sheet.   After this sheet has been heated above 300F, it is placed over the pan, and the vacuum valve is opened.   Because of the extreme flexibility of the plastic at this temperature, forming over the model is then almost instantaneous.

Model dimensions must provide proper allowance for the thickness of the plastic if small details are to be faithfully reproduced.   Plastic materials that have been used in this forming technique range from a few mils to $\frac{1}{8}$ in. or more thick.   Extremely thin sheets may wrinkle or accidentally puncture or tear.

Plastic liners clean easily and, except for very thin ones, are suitable for numerous reuses.   No form coatings are necessary.   The liner should be clean and dry; improved luster may be imparted to the finished concrete surface by polishing the form with a dry towel and by curing concrete in the form, with a waterproof membrane protecting any exposed concrete.   Thorough vibration is required to break the air bubbles from the formed surface; external vibration may be helpful.   No finishing is needed for surfaces cast against plastic liners.   Although the high-gloss concrete surfaces achieved with some plastic liners may be desirable for interior concrete, they are sometimes vulnerable to crazing and uneven weathering when exposed to the elements.

4-16 Patterned plastic liner, in 17 pieces, each 2 ft square, placed in column form and held in place by chamfer strips on both sides. Column was cast face down, then lifted into vertical position.

4-17 Finished column in erected position. The leather-like texture of plastic contact surface was selected by the architect for this installation to avoid glossiness otherwise attainable with plastic liners.

Rubber Liners

Neoprene and other types of rubber mat have been successfully used as base liners in repetitive factory precasting work. Rubber has in common with the thicker sheet plastic materials a long life and high reuse value. Thus far patterned rubber materials intended for other purposes such as bus platforms or industrial floor mats have been adapted for lining purposes (see picture on p. 229). However, special rubber form linings can be made and used economically if large quantities are desired, or if the patterned liners are made from liquid rubber. The latter method has been used experimentally to produce successful concrete castings.

Vacuum Liners

Vacuum treatment removes water and air bubbles from the surface layer of freshly placed concrete. It is sometimes specified to improve the resistance of a concrete surface to the action of water flowing at a high velocity. The vacuum treatment also improves appearance and durability, but it is generally too expensive to be justified for these latter purposes alone.

The vacuum treatment is achieved on formed surfaces by using a special form liner made of two layers of screen or wire mesh covered by a layer of cloth. The liner is sealed with rubber or caulking material around the edges of the form panel or unit. A series of openings in the form panel backing is connected to the vacuum pump. Individual vacuum areas are usually several feet long and 12 to 18 in. high so that each area may be quickly covered by concrete and vacuum applied while the concrete is quite fresh. One method of vacuum liner construction is shown in Figure 4-18.

Absorptive Form Liners

At one time there was keen interest in the use of absorptive materials for lining forms; wallboard of various compositions, canvas and other cotton cloth, blotter-type paper, and muslin covered chipboard were among the materials successfully used. The absorptive linings proved practical in eliminating voids and other common imperfections on concrete surfaces, and also produced surfaces that were superior in durability and resistance to abrasion.[6, 7]

Several government agencies conducted extensive investigations [8] and contributed to development of various absorptive lining products. Millions of square feet of these materials were used to line vertical or sloping forms for dams, powerhouses, spillways, pumping plants, and other structural and architectural con-

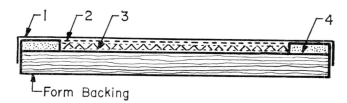

Form Backing

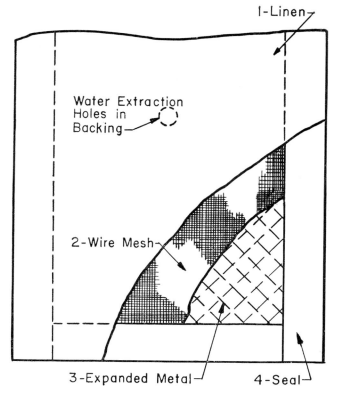

1-Linen

Water Extraction Holes in Backing

2-Wire Mesh

3-Expanded Metal   4-Seal

4-18 One method of constructing a vacuum form lining

crete. In spite of the real advantages obtained with absorbent form liners, high cost, misuse, and difficulty in installation and removal have discouraged their widespread use.

Insulation Used as Form Liner or Form Board

Both thermal and acoustical insulating boards made from such substances as glass fiber, wood fiber, or foamed plastic may be placed in contact with the concrete forms and the concrete cast against them. No oil or parting compound is required; the supporting formwork is easily stripped and the insulating boards remain in place, either bonded to the concrete or held in place by form plank clips. The supplier of these products should advise the user of any possible effects on curing of the concrete.

Some of the insulating board materials are strong enough to serve as permanent forms, replacing conven-

tional deck sheathing. A glass fiber form board, for example, is frequently used where the roof deck is made of gypsum concrete or lightweight aggregate concrete. Normal construction with this form board involves placing the boards, finished face down, on a system of sub-purlins securely welded to a steel structural frame. The whole area is then covered with wire mesh reinforcement and the lightweight roof deck concrete is placed.

Wood fiber form boards commercially available are suitable for support on conventional wood framing and carry normal weight concrete slabs up to 8 inches in thickness. Manufacturers' published recommendations should be followed in setting up spacing of supports for these form boards. The manufacturer should also advise the user of any special curing problems that may arise because the insulating boards remain in place.

Foamed polystyrene plastic board is another insulating material that serves either as a form liner or as a structural or semi-structural form material which stays in place when forms are removed and provides permanent insulation. The hyperbolic paraboloid form shown in Figure 4-21 is an example of this product's use, with a combination of tightened wires and in-

4-19 Installation of glass fiber form boards on supporting steel members preparatory to concreting thin gypsum concrete roof deck

4-20 Wood fiber form boards being installed for deck forming, supported by wood joists. Metal clips hold these planks in place after supports are removed.

4-21 Wires 1 ft apart strung in two directions across a steel frame support foamed polystyrene plank used to form hyperbolic paraboloid shell. A comparable layer of wires spaced at two 2-ft intervals was used on top of planks. High density foamed plastic wedges are inserted between the planks and exterior steel beam to pre-compress the form boards.

sulating board serving as the support for fresh concrete. The same plastic material, sandwiched between necessary reinforcing steel members, can serve as support for shotcreted surfaces during placement (Figure 15-34) and will remain as a permanent insulating core for the completed structure.

Hardware and Fasteners

Nails

Nails and spikes are the most common mechnical fastening used in construction of wood formwork and bracing, and their proper use contributes much to economy and quality of the work. Forms must be substantial and their component parts held together securely, but the use of too large or too many nails should be avoided. The labor required for fabrication, erection, and stripping of forms will be reduced by holding the number of nails to a safe minimum, and by selecting the best types of nails for differing formwork requirements.

Nails and spikes are available in a wide assortment of lengths, wire diameter (gage), kind of head, and kind of point; shanks may be smooth bright, cement coated, barbed, etched, galvanized, etc. Regardless of these several variables, wire nails and the shorter spikes have become standardized in "penny" (*d*) lengths through usage, while the longer spikes are measured in inches. The nominal length is customarily measured from under the head to the tip of the point. Measurements of several types and sizes of nails are shown in Table 4-7, and Figure 4-22 shows the actual size of several 16*d* nails.

Double Headed and Common Nails

Double headed nails are a must for nailing kickers, blocks, braces, and reinforcing for wales—anywhere that considerable holding power is required, and at the same time nails must be removed readily when forms are stripped. Double headed nails can be pulled easily and quickly with a claw hammer or stripping bar without bruising or otherwise damaging the lumber. The size depends on the material to be nailed and the load to be carried. A spike with removable head now available from form hardware manufacturers may be used where loads are heavy.

Common nails are used in assembly of form panels and other components for multiple use, or wherever nails need not be removed in stripping. Their holding power makes them relatively difficult to remove, and their heads leave a more noticeable impression in the concrete than some of the special purpose nails.

Nails for Attaching Sheathing or Liners

For attaching sheathing or lining materials to studs, nails whose heads leave the smallest impression on the finished concrete are generally desired. For built-in-place forms, *box* nails are desirable because the shank is thinner than that of common nails and will pull loose more readily. The size needed depends on the thickness of the sheathing. For nominal 1-in. sheathing or ⅝-in. and thicker plywood, 6*d* nails are recommended. For panel forms common nails of this size are better because such forms must withstand considerable racking and abuse.

Where fiberboard or thin plywood liners are to be attached over sheathing, small nails with thin flat heads such as 3*d* blue shingle nails are desirable. The heads of these nails leave a very faint impression in the concrete, and the small diameter shank pulls out of the sheathing material easily without pulling the head through the lining material.

Holding Power of Nails

The diameter, penetration, surface condition, and metal strength are considerations in determining both the lateral and withdrawal strength of nails and

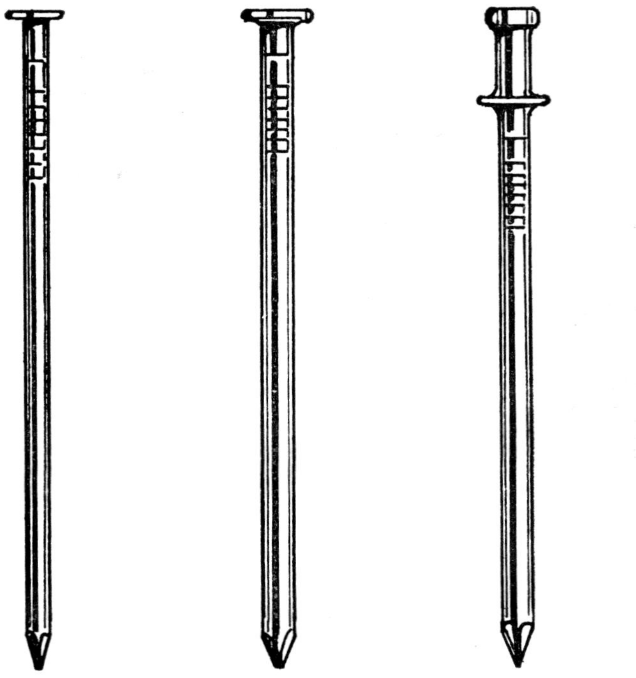

BOX COMMON DOUBLE HEAD

4-22 Actual size of 16-penny nails

spikes. A further variable is the specific gravity of the species of wood into which the nail or spike is driven.

Nailed joints are generally stronger when the nails are driven into the side grain (perpendicular to the wood fibers) instead of into the end grain of the wood. The joint is also stronger if it uses the lateral resistance rather than direct withdrawal resistance of the nail. Comparison of these resistances may be made

TABLE 4-7: NAIL SIZES AND MEASUREMENTS

Size	COMMON NAILS Flat head, diamond point			SMOOTH BOX NAILS Large flat head, diamond point			DOUBLE HEAD NAILS Diamond point, double head		
	Length,* in.	Gage No.	Diameter of head, in.	Length,* in.	Gage No.	Diameter of head, in.	Length under lower head, in.	Gage	Distance between heads, in.
2*d*	1	15	11/64	1	15½	3/16	–	–	–
3*d*	1¼	14	13/64	1¼	14½	7/32	–	–	–
4*d*	1½	12½	¼	1½	14	7/32	–	–	–
5*d*	1¾	12½	¼	1¾	14	7/32	–	–	–
6*d*	2	11½	17/64	2	12½	17/64	1¾	11½	¼
7*d*	2¼	11½	17/64	2¼	12½	17/64	–	–	–
8*d*	2½	10¼	9/32	2½	11½	19/64	2¼	10¼	¼
9*d*	2¾	10¼	9/32	2¾	11½	19/64	–	–	–
10*d*	3	9	5/16	3	10½	5/16	2¾	9	5/16
12*d*	3¼	9	5/16	3¼	10½	5/16	–	–	–
16*d*	3½	8	11/32	3½	10	11/32	3	8	⅜
20*d*	4	6	13/32	4	9	⅜	3½	6	⅜
30*d*	4½	5	7/16	4½	9	⅜	4	5	7/16
40*d*	5	4	15/32	5	8	13/32	–	–	–
50*d*	5½	3	½	–	–	–	–	–	–
60*d*	6	2	17/32	–	–	–	–	–	–

* Length from underside of head to tip of point.

TABLE 4-8: ALLOWABLE WITHDRAWAL LOADS FOR COMMON NAILS AND SPIKES *

Allowable withdrawal loads, lb per in. of penetration of nail or spike into member receiving the point, for common wire nails and spikes driven into the side grain of various softwoods

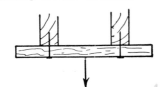

Species of wood	SIZE OF NAIL, d										SIZE OF SPIKE, d									
	6	8	10	12	16	20	30	40	50	60	10	12	16	20	30	40	50	60	5⁄16″	3⁄8″
Redwood (open grain), Engelmann spruce	13	15	17	17	19	22	24	26	28	30	22	22	24	26	28	30	33	33	36	43
Balsam fir and Eastern white pine	14	16	18	18	20	24	25	28	30	32	24	24	25	28	30	32	35	35	38	46
Redwood (close grain) and Pine: red, ponderosa, sugar, and Idaho white	18	21	23	23	25	30	33	35	38	41	30	30	33	35	38	41	45	45	49	59
Eastern spruce	19	22	25	25	27	32	35	38	41	44	32	32	35	38	41	44	48	48	52	63
Hem-Fir, lodgepole pine	20	23	26	26	29	34	37	40	43	46	34	34	37	40	43	47	50	50	55	66
Mountain hemlock	24	27	31	31	34	40	43	47	51	55	40	40	43	47	51	55	59	59	65	78
Douglas Fir-Larch	29	34	38	38	42	49	53	58	63	68	49	49	53	58	63	68	73	73	80	96
Southern pine	34	39	44	44	49	57	61	67	73	79	57	57	61	67	73	79	84	84	93	111

* Data reproduced through courtesy of National Forest Products Association.

NOTES: 1. The above values are for nails driven into seasoned wood or unseasoned wood which will remain wet. If the nail or spike is driven into unseasoned wood which will subsequently season under load, the allowable load is $\frac{1}{4}$ of the tabular value.
2. Nails and spikes should not be loaded in withdrawal from end grain.
3. The allowable withdrawal load for nails in toenailed joints is $\frac{2}{3}$ of the tabular value.

TABLE 4-9: ALLOWABLE LATERAL LOADS FOR NAILS AND SPIKES *

Allowable lateral loads, lb, for common wire nails and spikes driven into the side grain of various softwoods

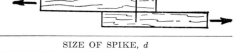

Species of wood	SIZE OF NAIL, d										SIZE OF SPIKE, d									
	6	8	10	12	16	20	30	40	50	60	10	12	16	20	30	40	50	60	5⁄16″	3⁄8″
Redwood (open grain) Cedar: western, northern white Fir, balsam Spruce: Engelmann Pine: Eastern white and western white	41	51	62	62	70	91	101	116	132	146	91	91	101	116	132	146	162	162	189	248
Pine: Idaho white, lodgepole, northern, red, ponderosa, sugar Redwood (close grain) Hemlock: mountain and Eastern Spruce: Eastern and Sitka	51	64	77	77	88	113	126	144	165	182	113	113	126	144	165	182	202	202	236	310
Douglas Fir-Larch Southern pine	63	78	94	94	107	139	154	176	202	223	139	139	155	176	202	223	248	248	289	380

* Data reproduced through courtesy of National Forest Products Association.

NOTES: 1. The above values are based on the assumption that the nail or spike penetrates the piece receiving the point for a distance not less than 14 diameters for species in the first group; not less than 13 diameters for species in the second group; and not less than 11 diameters for species in the third group. When penetration is less than that specified, the allowable load may be determined by straight line interpolation between zero and the tabulated load, except that penetration must not be less than one-third of that specified.
2. The allowable lateral loads for nails or spikes driven into end grain are $\frac{2}{3}$ of the tabular values.
3. If the nail or spike is driven into unseasoned wood that will remain wet or will be loaded before seasoning the allowable load is 75 percent of the tabular values.
4. If metal side plates are used, the allowable loads can be increased 25 percent.

for softwoods with Tables 4-8 and 4-9 which show the resistance of common nailed joints to lateral loads as well as to withdrawal loads. The values tabulated are for one nail. When more than one nail is used, the load carrying capacity of the joint is the sum of the individual values of the nails used.

It is not good practice to place nails in long rows in a tension splice. The end distance and edge distance should be such that objectionable splitting does not occur.*

* No definite distances have been established, but the following may serve as a guide:

Minimum end distance—13 to 20 times nail diameter, at loaded end
Minimum spacing—12 to 15 times nail diameter in direction of load; 5 times nail diameter perpendicular to load direction.

Toenailing

Since withdrawal resistance of nails and spikes driven into end grain is quite low, connections of this type should be avoided where possible. This makes toenailing an important technique for form construction. Toenailing, used in place of end nailing, provides a joint that is equivalent to two-thirds of the allowable withdrawal resistance and five-sixths of the lateral load capacity of nails and spikes driven perpendicular and entirely through the side grain of the wood. Best results are obtained when the toenails are started at one-third the length of the nail from the end of the piece with the nail driven at an angle of approximately 30° to the face of the piece in which it is started.

Cement Coated Nails

The so-called cement coated nails have some obvious advantages for certain types of formwork construction, since a properly applied coating may double the resistance to withdrawal of nails immediately after they are driven into the softer woods. Different techniques of applying the coating as well as different ingredients in the coating make it impossible to pre-

TABLE 4-10: ALLOWABLE WITHDRAWAL LOADS FOR WOOD SCREWS, NORMAL LOAD DURATION *

Allowable load in withdrawal, lb per in. of penetration of threaded portion of screw into side grain of member receiving the point. Approximately two-thirds of the length of a standard wood screw is threaded.

Screw gage	6	7	8	9	10	12	14	16	18	20	24
Screw diameter, in.	0.138	0.151	0.164	0.177	0.190	0.216	0.242	0.268	0.294	0.320	0.372
SPECIES OF WOOD											
Englemann spruce, redwood (open grain)	54	59	64	69	74	84	94	104	115	125	145
Balsam fir, Eastern white pine	57	62	67	73	78	89	99	110	121	132	153
Redwood (close grain) and pine: red, ponderosa, sugar, Idaho white	69	76	82	89	95	109	121	135	148	161	187
Eastern spruce	73	80	86	93	100	114	127	141	155	169	196
Hem-Fir, lodgepole pine	76	83	91	97	105	119	133	148	162	177	205
Mountain hemlock	87	95	103	111	120	136	152	169	185	201	234
Douglas Fir-Larch	102	112	121	131	141	160	179	199	218	237	276
Southern pine	118	130	141	152	164	186	208	231	253	275	320

* Data reproduced through courtesy of National Forest Products Association.

TABLE 4-11: ALLOWABLE LATERAL LOADS FOR WOOD SCREWS, NORMAL LOAD DURATION *

Allowable lateral load in lb for screws embedded to approximately 7 times the shank diameter into the member receiving the point. For less penetration, reduce loads in proportion. Penetration should not be less than 4 times the shank diameter.

Screw gage	6	7	8	9	10	12	14	16	18	20	24
Screw diameter, in.	0.138	0.151	0.164	0.177	0.190	0.216	0.242	0.268	0.294	0.320	0.372
SPECIES OF WOOD Douglas Fir-Larch Southern pine	75	90	106	124	143	185	232	284	342	406	548
Eastern spruce, Hem-Fir, mountain hemlock, Redwood (close grain), Pine: red, ponderosa, sugar, Idaho white, lodgepole, northern	62	74	87	101	117	151	190	233	280	332	448
Fir, balsam Redwood (open grain) Eastern white pine Spruce: Engelmann	48	58	68	79	91	118	148	181	218	258	349

* Based on data provided by the National Forest Products Association.

dict the exact improvement in withdrawal resistance. The increase in withdrawal resistance is not permanent but drops off about half after a month or so.[1]

Nails in Plywood

Nailing characteristics of plywood are much the same as those of solid wood, except that plywood's greater resistance to splitting when nails are driven near the edge is a definite advantage. The resistance to withdrawal of nails in plywood is 15 to 30 percent less than that of solid wood of the same thickness, because the fiber distortion is less uniform than in solid wood. Direction of the grain of face ply has little influence on the withdrawal resistance along the end or edge of a piece of plywood.

Wood Screws

Tables 4-10 and 4-11 show allowable loads on wood screws, both in lateral and withdrawal resistance, for normal loading; these values are subject to increase of 25 percent for short term loading (less than 7 days total duration of maximum load). As in the case of nailed joints, loads given are for one screw, and where more than one screw is used per joint, the total allowable load on the connection is the sum of the allowable loads for the individual screws.

Bolts, Lag Screws, and Other Connectors

Bolts and lag screws are common joint fasteners for heavier formwork construction, and Tables 4-12 and 4-13 showing the strength of such joints have been included for the designer. For information on other more specialized connectors such as the split ring and toothed assemblies, refer to technical literature on timber design such as that listed in this chapter.[2, 9]

Bolt Loads

Tabulated allowable bolt loads are for normal duration of loading, and are subject to 25 percent increase for short term loading (less than 7 days total duration of maximum load) such as might exist in single use formwork. Loads for more than one bolt, each of the same or miscellaneous sizes, are the sum of loads permitted for each bolt. Spacing and end and edge distances of course must be sufficient to develop the full strength of each bolt.

Tabulated loads (Table 4-12) are for a joint consisting of three members, where the side members are

each half the thickness of the main member. For other joint constructions the following adjustments apply.

Side member dimensions: If side members are thicker than half the thickness of the main member (A), no increase in tabulated loads is permissible.

When the side members are less than half the thickness of the main member (B), the tabulated loads indicated for a main member which is twice the thickness of thinnest side members apply. For example, with 2-in. side members and a 10-in. center member, the tabulated loads for a 4-in. center member are used.

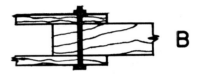

Number of members in joint: When a joint consists of two members (single shear) of equal thickness (C), half the tabulated load for a piece twice the thickness of one of the members is used.

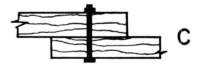

When members of a two-member joint are of unequal thickness (D), half the tabulated load for a piece twice the thickness of the thinner member is used.

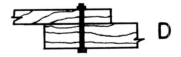

For multiple-member joints other than two or three members (E), of which the pieces are of equal thickness, the allowable load varies as the number of shear planes involved; the allowable load for each shear plane shall be

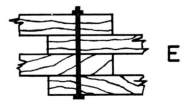

equal to one-half the tabulated load for a piece the thickness of the member involved. Thus, when a joint consists of four members of equal thickness, one and one-half times the tabulated load for a piece the thickness of one of the members applies.

TABLE 4-12: ALLOWABLE LOADS, LB, ON ONE BOLT LOADED AT BOTH ENDS FOR VARIOUS SPECIES OF WOOD, NORMAL DURATION OF LOADING*

Values given are for three-member joints where side members are each half the thickness of the main member. For adjustment of load values for other conditions, see p. 50.

|| indicates load applied parallel to grain of wood
⊥ indicates load applied perpendicular to grain of wood

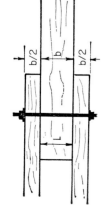

Length of bolt in main member, in.	Bolt dia., in.	DOUGLAS FIR-LARCH (Dense) SOUTHERN PINE (Dense) || grain	⊥ grain	CALIFORNIA REDWOOD (Close grain), DOUGLAS FIR-LARCH, SOUTHERN PINE (Med. grain), SOUTHERN CYPRESS || grain	⊥ grain	DOUGLAS FIR, South, SOUTHERN PINE (Open grain) || grain	⊥ grain	EASTERN HEMLOCK-TAMARACK, CALIFORNIA REDWOOD (Open grain), HEM-FIR || grain	⊥ grain	MOUNTAIN HEMLOCK, WESTERN CEDARS, NORTHERN PINE || grain	⊥ grain	SPRUCE-PINE-FIR, SITKA SPRUCE, YELLOW POPLAR, IDAHO WHITE PINE, EASTERN SPRUCE, LODGEPOLE PINE || grain	⊥ grain	RED PINE, WESTERN WHITE PINE, PONDEROSA PINE-SUGAR PINE, EASTERN WHITE PINE, BALSAM FIR || grain	⊥ grain	COTTONWOOD, EASTERN, ENGELMANN SPRUCE, SUB-ALPINE FIR, NORTHERN WHITE CEDAR || grain	⊥ grain
1½	½	1120	500	960	430	820	370	810	280	750	310	700	270	640	190	530	220
	5/8	1420	570	1210	490	1030	420	1010	310	940	350	870	300	800	210	660	250
	3/4	1700	630	1460	540	1240	470	1210	350	1130	390	1040	330	960	240	800	270
	7/8	1990	700	1700	600	1440	520	1410	380	1320	430	1220	370	1120	260	930	300
	1	2270	760	1940	650	1650	570	1610	420	1500	470	1390	400	1280	280	1060	330
2	½	1406	670	1200	570	1020	500	1050	370	1000	410	920	350	850	250	700	290
	5/8	1860	760	1590	650	1350	560	1340	410	1250	460	1160	400	1070	280	880	330
	3/4	2260	840	1930	720	1640	630	1610	460	1500	520	1390	440	1280	320	1060	370
	7/8	2640	930	2260	790	1920	690	1880	510	1750	570	1620	490	1490	350	1240	400
	1	3030	1010	2590	870	2200	750	2150	550	2010	620	1860	530	1710	380	1410	440
2½	½	1510	840	1290	720	1100	620	1190	460	1200	510	1110	440	1020	310	840	360
	5/8	2190	950	1870	810	1590	710	1640	520	1560	580	1440	500	1330	350	1100	410
	3/4	2780	1060	2370	900	2020	790	2010	580	1880	650	1740	560	1600	390	1330	460
	7/8	3290	1160	2810	990	2390	860	2350	630	2190	710	2030	610	1870	430	1550	500
	1	3770	1270	3230	1080	2740	940	2690	690	2510	780	2320	670	2130	470	1770	550
3	½	1530	1010	1310	860	1110	750	1220	550	1290	620	1190	530	1100	380	910	440
	5/8	2350	1140	2010	970	1710	850	1830	620	1810	700	1680	600	1540	430	1280	490
	3/4	3150	1270	2690	1080	2290	940	2360	690	2240	770	2080	670	1910	470	1580	550
	7/8	3860	1390	3300	1190	2810	1040	2810	760	2630	850	2440	730	2240	520	1860	600
	1	4500	1520	3840	1300	3270	1130	3230	830	3010	930	2780	800	2560	570	2120	660
3½	½	1530	1140	1310	980	1110	870	1220	640	1290	720	1190	620	1100	440	910	510
	5/8	2380	1330	2030	1130	1730	990	1900	730	1980	810	1840	700	1690	500	1400	580
	3/4	3360	1480	2870	1260	2440	1100	2600	810	2560	900	2370	780	2180	550	1800	640
	7/8	4290	1630	3670	1390	3120	1210	3210	890	3060	990	2830	860	2600	610	2160	710
	1	5120	1770	4380	1520	3720	1320	3740	970	3510	1090	3250	930	2990	660	2480	770

Continued

TABLE 4-12 (Continued) : ALLOWABLE LOADS, LB, ON ONE BOLT LOADED AT BOTH ENDS FOR VARIOUS SPECIES OF WOOD, NORMAL DURATION OF LOADING*

Length of bolt in main member, in.	Bolt dia., in.	DOUGLAS FIR-LARCH (Dense) SOUTHERN PINE (Dense) ∥ grain	⊥ grain	CALIFORNIA REDWOOD (Close grain), DOUGLAS FIR-LARCH, SOUTHERN PINE (Med. grain), SOUTHERN CYPRESS ∥ grain	⊥ grain	DOUGLAS FIR, South, SOUTHERN PINE (Open grain) ∥ grain	⊥ grain	EASTERN HEMLOCK-TAMARACK, CALIFORNIA REDWOOD (Open grain), HEM-FIR ∥ grain	⊥ grain	MOUNTAIN HEMLOCK, WESTERN CEDARS, NORTHERN PINE ∥ grain	⊥ grain	SPRUCE-PINE-FIR, SITKA SPRUCE, YELLOW POPLAR, IDAHO WHITE PINE, EASTERN SPRUCE, LODGEPOLE PINE ∥ grain	⊥ grain	RED PINE, WESTERN WHITE PINE, PONDEROSA PINE-SUGAR PINE, EASTERN WHITE PINE, BALSAM FIR ∥ grain	⊥ grain	COTTONWOOD, EASTERN, ENGELMANN SPRUCE, SUB-ALPINE FIR, NORTHERN WHITE CEDAR ∥ grain	⊥ grain
4	1/2	1530	1180	1310	1010	1110	960	1220	700	1290	820	1190	710	1100	500	910	580
	5/8	2380	1510	2040	1290	1730	1130	1910	830	2010	930	1860	800	1710	570	1420	660
	3/4	3420	1690	2920	1440	2490	1260	2710	920	2790	1030	2580	890	2370	630	1970	730
	7/8	4560	1860	3900	1590	3310	1380	3510	1020	3430	1140	3170	980	2920	690	2420	810
	1	5600	2030	4790	1730	4070	1510	4190	1110	3990	1240	3690	1070	3400	760	2820	880
4½	5/8	2380	1640	2040	1400	1730	1270	1910	930	2010	1040	1860	900	1710	640	1420	740
	3/4	3430	1900	2940	1620	2500	1410	2750	1040	2900	1160	2680	1000	2470	710	2040	820
	7/8	4640	2090	3970	1790	3370	1560	3660	1140	3720	1280	3450	1100	3170	780	2630	910
	1	5910	2280	5060	1950	4300	1700	4540	1250	4420	1390	4090	1200	3760	850	3120	990
	1¼	8170	2670	6990	2280	5940	1990	5990	1460	5630	1630	5220	1410	4800	1000	3970	1160
5½	5/8	2380	1650	2040	1410	1730	1380	1910	1010	2010	1230	1860	1050	1710	750	1420	870
	3/4	3430	2200	2930	1880	2490	1720	2750	1270	2890	1420	2680	1220	2470	870	2040	1010
	7/8	4680	2550	4000	2180	3400	1900	3750	1400	3950	1560	3650	1340	3360	950	2780	1110
	1	6080	2790	5200	2380	4420	2080	4860	1520	5040	1700	4670	1470	4290	1040	3560	1210
	1¼	9160	3260	7830	2790	6660	2430	7000	1780	6770	2000	6270	1720	5770	1220	4780	1420
7½	5/8	2380	1480	2040	1260	1730	1290	1910	950	2010	1190	1860	1030	1710	730	1420	850
	3/4	3430	2130	2930	1820	2490	1800	2750	1320	2900	1650	2680	1420	2470	1000	2050	1170
	7/8	4670	2840	3990	2430	3390	2360	3750	1730	3940	2080	3650	1790	3360	1270	2780	1480
	1	6100	3550	5210	3030	4430	2800	4890	2060	5150	2320	4770	2000	4390	1420	3630	1650
	1¼	9540	4450	8160	3800	6930	3310	7640	2430	8040	2720	7450	2340	6850	1660	5680	1930
9½	3/4	3430	1920	2930	1640	2490	1700	2740	1250	2890	1570	2680	1350	2460	960	2040	1120
	7/8	4680	2660	4000	2270	3400	2260	3750	1660	3940	2080	3650	1790	3360	1270	2780	1480
	1	6100	3460	5210	2960	4430	2900	4880	2130	5150	2650	4770	2280	4390	1620	3640	1880
	1¼	9530	5210	8150	4450	6920	4140	7640	3040	8040	3450	7440	2970	6840	2110	5670	2450
	1½	13740	6480	11750	5530	9990	4830	11000	3540	11600	3960	10740	3410	9880	2420	8180	2810
11½	7/8	4680	1980	4000	2060	3400	2170	3750	1590	3940	1780	3650	1530	3360	1230	2780	1430
	1	6090	3240	5210	2770	4430	2780	4900	2040	5150	2570	4770	2210	4390	1570	3640	1820
	1¼	9530	5110	8150	4360	6930	4270	7640	3130	8030	3880	7430	3340	6840	2370	5660	2750
	1½	13730	7200	11750	6150	9980	5740	10960	4210	11550	4800	10690	4130	9840	2930	8150	3400
13½	1	6090	2410	5210	2530	4430	2680	4900	1970	5150	2200	4770	1900	4390	1520	3640	1760
	1¼	9530	4860	8150	4160	6920	4130	7660	3030	8050	3800	7450	3270	6860	2320	5680	2700
	1½	13730	7070	11740	6040	9980	5920	11020	4340	11590	5330	10730	4590	9870	3250	8180	3780

* Data reproduced through courtesy of National Forest Products Association.

TABLE 4-13: ALLOWABLE WITHDRAWAL LOADS FOR LAG BOLTS OR LAG SCREWS, NORMAL DURATION *

Allowable load in withdrawal in pounds per inch of penetration of threaded part into side grain of member holding point.

Shank diameter, in.	0.250	0.3125	0.375	0.4375	0.500	0.5625	0.625	0.750	0.875	1.000	1.125	1.250
SPECIES OF WOOD												
Southern pine	264	312	356	402	443	484	524	601	675	745	815	881
Douglas Fir-Larch	232	274	313	352	389	425	460	528	593	655	716	774
Mountain hemlock	205	242	278	312	345	376	407	467	525	580	633	685
Hem-Fir, lodgepole pine	186	220	252	283	313	341	369	424	476	526	574	621
Eastern spruce	180	213	244	274	303	331	358	411	461	509	556	602
Redwood (close grain) and pine: red, ponderosa, sugar, Idaho white	173	205	235	263	291	318	344	395	443	490	535	579
Balsam fir, Eastern white pine	149	176	202	227	251	273	298	339	381	421	460	498
Redwood (open grain), Engelmann spruce	143	169	194	218	241	263	285	326	367	405	442	479

TABLE 4-13A: ALLOWABLE LATERAL LOAD FOR LAG BOLTS OR LAG SCREWS, NORMAL DURATION OF LOAD, WITH WOOD SIDE MEMBERS

Values shown are total lateral load, lb, per lag bolt or lag screw, single shear.

Thickness of Side Member (inches)	Length of Lag Bolt (inches)	Diameter of Lag Bolt Shank (inches)	Southern pine Douglas Fir-Larch		Eastern spruce, Hem-Fir, mountain hemlock, redwood (close grain) and pine: red, ponderosa, sugar, Idaho white, lodgepole		Redwood (open grain), Engelmann spruce, balsam fir, Eastern white pine	
			Parallel to Grain	Perpendicular to Grain	Parallel to Grain	Perpendicular to Grain	Parallel to Grain	Perpendicular to Grain
1½	4	¼	170	170	130	120	100	100
		5/16	210	180	150	130	120	100
		3/8	240	180	170	130	140	100
		7/16	270	190	190	140	150	110
		½	290	190	210	140	170	110
		5/8	360	210	260	150	200	120
	5	¼	200	190	180	170	160	150
		5/16	280	240	220	190	180	150
		3/8	370	280	260	200	210	160
		7/16	400	290	290	210	230	170
		½	440	290	310	210	250	170
		5/8	530	320	380	230	310	180
	6	¼	230	220	200	200	180	180
		5/16	330	280	290	250	260	220
		3/8	420	320	360	280	290	220
		7/16	510	360	400	280	320	220
		½	600	390	430	280	340	220
		5/8	710	430	510	310	410	250
	7	¼	240	230	210	210	190	180
		5/16	350	300	310	270	280	230
		3/8	450	340	410	310	360	270
		7/16	560	400	500	350	420	290
		½	660	430	560	360	450	290
		5/8	790	470	640	380	510	310
2½	6	3/8	370	280	270	200	210	160
		7/16	430	310	310	220	250	180
		½	470	310	340	220	270	180
		5/8	550	330	400	240	320	190
		¾	620	340	440	240	360	200
		1	790	390	560	280	450	230
	7	3/8	430	330	370	280	300	230
		7/16	570	410	420	300	340	240
		½	650	420	460	300	370	240
		5/8	750	450	540	320	430	260
		¾	840	460	600	330	480	270
		7/8	950	500	680	360	550	290
		1	1070	540	770	380	620	310
	8	3/8	480	360	430	330	380	290
		7/16	630	440	550	390	440	310
		½	770	500	600	390	480	310
		5/8	970	580	700	420	560	340
		¾	1080	600	780	430	620	340
		7/8	1200	630	860	450	690	360
		1	1360	680	970	490	780	390
	9	3/8	520	390	460	350	410	310
		7/16	680	480	610	430	540	380
		½	840	540	750	490	600	390
		5/8	1130	680	860	520	690	420
		¾	1340	740	960	530	770	420
		7/8	1450	760	1040	540	830	430
		1	1640	820	1180	590	940	470

* Data reproduced through courtesy of National Forest Products Association.

Ties

A concrete form tie is a tensile unit adapted to holding concrete forms secure against the lateral pressure of unhardened concrete, with or without provision for spacing the forms to a definite distance apart, and with or without provision for removal of metal to a specified distance back from the concrete surfaces. Twisted wire and band iron were once the chief tying materials, but because of low strength and the labor of assembly and installation, they are today considered acceptable only for the simplest structures. A wide variety of ready-made ties with safe load ratings ranging from 1000 lb to about 50,000 lb have gained general acceptance. They consist of an internal tension unit and an external holding device, and are manufactured in two basic types:

Continuous single member, in which the tensile unit is a single piece, and a specially designed holding device is added for engaging the tensile unit

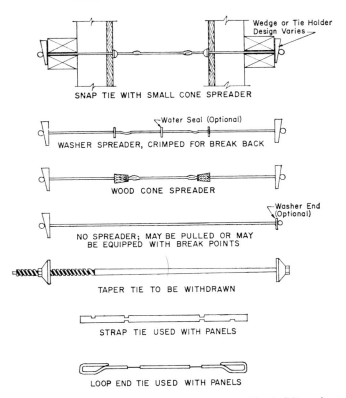

SNAP TIE WITH SMALL CONE SPREADER

WASHER SPREADER, CRIMPED FOR BREAK BACK

WOOD CONE SPREADER

NO SPREADER; MAY BE PULLED OR MAY BE EQUIPPED WITH BREAK POINTS

TAPER TIE TO BE WITHDRAWN

STRAP TIE USED WITH PANELS

LOOP END TIE USED WITH PANELS

4-23 Some typical single member ties. The holding device is shown schematically, since a number of different "wedges" or other devices are available. The taper tie is shown with a threaded end holding device, but for single member ties the holder generally slips over the end "button" of the tie and drops down until the assembly is held tight. Working loads vary depending on the kind of steel, diameter of tie, and details of the fastener. A number of ties like these are available with manufacturers' suggested working loads ranging from about 2500 to 5000 lb.

against the exterior of the form. These ties may be rod, band, channel, or angle in cross section, and may be cut to length on the job or completely prefabricated. Form spreading devices are an integral part of some of these ties as Figure 4-23 shows. Some single member ties may be pulled as an entire unit from the concrete; others are broken back a predetermined distance at a section weakened to facilitate "snapping." Some are cut off flush with the concrete surface.

Internal disconnecting type, in which the tensile unit has an inner part with threaded connections to removable external members which make up the rest of the tensile unit and have suitable devices for holding them against the outside of the form. This type of tie (Figure 4-24) is available with or without spreading devices, and the internal member generally remains in the concrete.

These two types of tying devices are identified commercially by various descriptive names, such as form clamps, snap ties, wedge clamps, coil ties, rod clamps, and the like, but no attempt to differentiate them in detail can be made here. The continuous single member type is generally used for lighter loads, ranging up to about 5000 lb safe load. The internal disconnecting type of tie is available for light or medium loads but finds its greatest application under heavier construction loads.

Safety factors for ties recommended by ACI Committee 347 range from 1½ to 2 based on ultimate strength of the tie.* Since many manufacturers' catalogs show the ultimate load rating for tying devices as well as a suggested working load, a form designer or user can modify suggested loads depending on the safety factor required for a given job. The maximum load on the tie should never exceed the yield point load of the steel, even though the safety factor based on ultimate strength is adequate.

Regardless of the type of tie, the external holding device should have a large enough bearing area so that when the tie is loaded to its maximum safe load, excessive crushing of the wood will not take place. This is explained under tie design on p. 101.

Effect of Tie on Finished Concrete Surface

Wherever the concrete surface is to be visible and appearance is important, the proper type of form tie or hanger which will not leave exposed metal at the concrete surface is essential. Architectural concrete specifications often require that no metal be left closer

---

* Details appear in ACI 347-68 reprinted in the appendix.

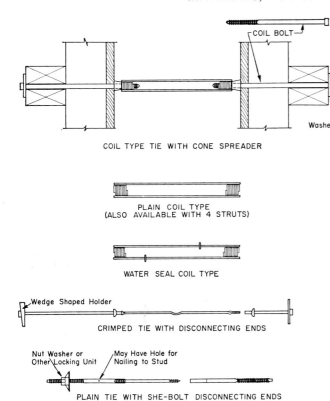

COIL TYPE TIE WITH CONE SPREADER

PLAIN COIL TYPE
(ALSO AVAILABLE WITH 4 STRUTS)

WATER SEAL COIL TYPE

CRIMPED TIE WITH DISCONNECTING ENDS

PLAIN TIE WITH SHE-BOLT DISCONNECTING ENDS

4-24 A few types of commercially available internal disconnecting ties. Either threaded or wedge style external holding devices may be used, depending on the tie details. Water seal and spreader features are available for many of these ties. Suggested working load for the coil-type units ranges from about 6000 to 36,000-lb working load, depending on size and number of struts. The crimped tie is available in a working load range of 3000 to 9000 lb, and the plain disconnecting tie is available in 3000 to 48,000-lb range of working loads. (Data based on manufacturers' statements, but higher or lower strengths may be found since materials and sizes vary.)

than 1½ in. to the surface of the concrete. This requirement can generally be met with either type of tie. However, with the so-called snap tie there is the possibility that break-off will not occur at the specified depth in spite of the weakened tie section.

Where spreader ties are used for exposed work, the spreading device should be of a type that can easily be removed with a minimum of damage to the concrete and that leaves the smallest practicable hole for filling. Spreader cones of wood, plastic, or metal leave a uniform hole for patching. Some wood or plastic spreader cones used with snap ties also permit breaking back ties before the forms are stripped.

A good patch over the tie end, well bonded to adjacent concrete, is essential. If any moisture gets to the tie end, rust stains will gradually appear on the surface of the concrete. Greater depth of breakback

or threaded ends of internally disconnected tie units allow a better chance of bonding the patch which covers the tie, and also a greater factor of safety in case of spalling of the patch. Although the patch remains in place, it may shrink and leave fine cracks through which moisture and rust gradually seep. Special admixtures for the patching grout may improve moisture resistance and adhesion of the patch; non-shrink grouts or dry-pack mortar may also be used.

Water Retaining Structures

The tie used for watertight walls must be leak proof. What constitutes a leak proof tie varies with the head of water retained and the resultant pressure on the concrete surface; under some circumstances no ties are permitted at all. If ties are used, they cannot be pulled completely out of the wall because the resultant hole cannot be grouted watertight. The ends of tie metal should be at least 1 in. back from the wall face, and the holes left by tie ends should be carefully plugged with grout.

The process of breaking back or disconnecting tie ends may loosen the tie in the wall, providing a channel for water seepage. To overcome this problem, some manufacturers have crimped or otherwise deformed the tie to improve bond, and have attached round metal or neoprene washers as waterstops at the middle of the ties.

Anchors

Form anchors are devices used to secure formwork to previously placed concrete of adequate strength; they are normally embedded in concrete during placement. Anchors are also used to support forms by off-rock tying (Figure 4-25). There are two basic parts: the embedded anchoring device, whose design varies with the load to be carried and the strength of concrete in the structure; and the bolt or other ex-

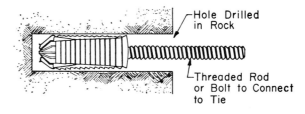

Hole Drilled in Rock

Threaded Rod or Bolt to Connect to Tie

4-25 One of the several available anchors for off-rock tying. The anchor unit is placed in a hole drilled in the rock. When the bolt or external fastener is inserted, it expands the anchor, thus tightening it in the rock. Some rock anchors are designed to be surrounded by grout in the rock cavity.

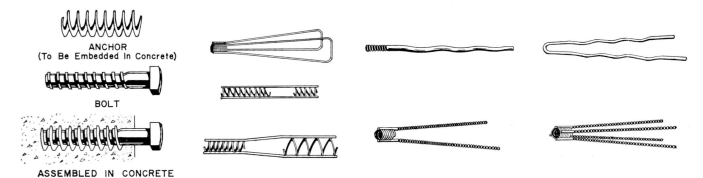

ANCHOR
(To Be Embedded In Concrete)

BOLT

ASSEMBLED IN CONCRETE

4-26 Simple screw anchor (left) showing the two parts of the unit assembled in concrete. Embedded anchorage unit only is shown for several other types of form anchors. Some of these require a bolt like that at the left. The crimped anchor requires an internally threaded bolt connection, and the hairpin shape is suitable for looped tie attachment.

Safe working loads for these devices depend on the strength of concrete in which they are embedded as well as the depth of embedment and the area of contact between the anchor and the concrete. Working load data supplied by manufacturers indicate safe loads from 7000 to 22,000 lb in 400-psi concrete; 9000 to 25,000 lb in 500-psi concrete; and 12,000 to 30,000 lb in 1000-psi concrete (pull-out loads on the embedded anchor).

ternal fastener which is removed after use, leaving a set back hole for grout patching. A number of the various types of anchors now available for embedment in fresh concrete are shown in Figure 4-26.

ACI Committee 347 suggests a safety factor of 1.5 to 3 for form anchors, depending on job conditions under which they are to be used (p. 86). Ultimate strength of anchoring devices in shear and tension is frequently given by manufacturers in sales literature, but their actual *holding power* depends on the strength of the concrete in which they are embedded, the area of contact between concrete and anchor, and the depth of embedment.

Many form anchors are set in the relatively low strength concrete used for massive structures, and development of holding power may be a limiting factor in early reuse of the cantilever forms which the anchors must support.* Some manufacturers' strength data for their anchorage products are based on tests in actual concrete specimens at various low strength levels. Using data of this sort, and with estimated compressive strength of the concrete mix at early ages (3-7 days) tentative selections of anchoring devices needed for a given job can be made (see also mass concrete, p. 260). Specific selections for any large job should be field tested under actual summer and winter working conditions.

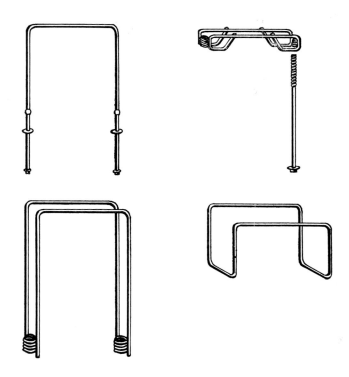

4-27 A few of the many designs of form hangers used to support forms from existing structural members. Applications of these and similar devices are shown in Chapter 9. Actual working loads vary with diameter and strength of the wire or rods used, as well as hanger design details, but some representative values are: for the snap tie hanger (upper left), 4000 to 8000 lb total load; for the hanger at upper right, 12,000 to 18,000 total load; lower left, 6000 to 20,000 lb total load; and for the wire beam saddle (lower right), 2500 to 6000 lb total load. These figures based on manufacturers' suggestions show a probable range of strengths for typical commercially available devices; the user must verify the strength of his own specific selection.

* Of interest in this connection is a study [10] by the Corps of Engineers of the holding strength of a variety of form anchors to determine how soon the forms could safely be removed for reuse. In a mix containing 2.5 bags of Type II cement per cu yd, laboratory tests (presumably at about 70F) indicated that concrete had developed sufficient strength at the end of 3 days to permit anchors of all types tested to withstand a pull of 25,000 lb or more. A later study [11] made at temperatures of 45-50F indicated that adequately designed anchors of either 18 or 24 in. length would provide resistance at 3 days in excess of normally expected loads (for 5-ft lifts) in concrete with a cement content as low as 2.5 bags per cu yd. Use of 30 percent fly ash by solid volume reduced the holding power of anchors appreciably but not below a safe level.

Hangers

There are a number of ready-made devices for hanging forms from steel or precast concrete structural members; such forming may be for the construction of a supported slab, for building the fireproofing required for the steel members, or for construction of a slab composite with beam framing.

A number of different designs are available in ready-made hangers, as shown in Figure 4-27. External holding devices are similar to those used for tie rods. ACI Committee 347 recommends safety factors of 1.5 to 2 for these hanger assemblies, depending on conditions of use (see p. 86). When checking manufacturers' safe load ratings note carefully whether suggested working load is given on a per leg basis or as the total capacity of the hanger.

Soffit Spacers

Soffit spacers similar to the one shown in Figure 4-28 act as a separator and gage between the beam soffit form and a steel member that is being encased in concrete. Two soffit spacers are placed on the beam

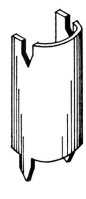

4-28 Soffit spacer placed on beam bottom to maintain correct depth of fireproofing

bottom at each hanger. When the form hanger assembly is tightened, the soffit spacers insure correct depth of fireproofing and aid in keeping the beam bottom rigid.

Form Jacks

Under some field conditions, use of a jack supported on the lower flange of the steel beam may be preferable to hanging the forms. Several devices available for this purpose may also be adapted for use with precast concrete girders.

A similar jacking device (Figure 4-29) is used to hold the bottom members of cantilever form panels at the proper distance from finished wall.

4-29 Typical cantilever form jack to hold bottom members of cantilever form panels at correct distance from finished wall. A similar jack sometimes is used to support forms from the lower flange of steel beams.

Steel Strapping

Steel strapping, ⅝ to 2 in. wide, the same kind of material that has been widely used in packaging, is used for tying column forms, attaching nailing strips to steel form members, suspending forms for fireproofing structural steel, and tying of low foundation walls. Either standard tensioning tools used for packaging applications or special tools developed for forming applications may be used to install the strapping. When forms are stripped, the straps are cut and discarded.

Steel strapping is held fast by a seal device which is closed after the strap has been placed around the column or other member being tied. Because of variations in sealing devices and the tools used to attach them, it is wise to assume that the joint strength may be only about 70 percent of the strap strength, although some tool-seal combinations do give 100 percent of the strap strength in the joint.

Representative breaking strength of some of the "heavy duty" strapping used for concrete formwork is shown below. Both stronger and weaker strappings are available with approximately the same cross sec-

Strap width, in.	Strap thickness, in.	Ft of strap per lb	Average breaking load, lb
¾	0.028	14.0	2300
¾	0.035	11.2	3100
1¼	0.035	6.7	5000
1¼	0.050	4.7	7000
2	0.050	2.9	11,000
2	0.065	2.2	15,500

4-30 Workman is tightening steel strapping around column form (left), and fastening the seal in place on the strapping (right).

tions. A factor of safety of at least 2 (based on 100 percent of breaking strength) is suggested in using steel strapping, and a greater factor may be advisable when worn tensioning tools or inexperienced workmen are on the job.

One thing to guard against is the initial tension that operator may mistakenly put on the strapping before the concrete is placed. High initial tension introduces excessive stress in the strapping and the truss and the form itself. Ideally only enough tension is applied initially to cause the strapping to conform closely at form corners or joints. Placing of the concrete then loads the strapping.

When steel strap ties are to be used, rectangular or square column forms are usually provided with some external supporting members that give extra stability under load and keep the steel strapping from making

sharp or right-angle bends. For columns of 24 in. and larger dimensions, this "trussing" is arranged so that the strapping assumes a nearly circular shape around the outside of the form. Most manufacturers of steel strapping have developed their own spacing and truss designs, and these recommendations should be consulted along with suggestions in this manual for column form design (pp. 103-107) before planning to use strapping.

Column Clamps

Column clamps or yokes encircle column forms and hold them together securely, withstanding the lateral pressure of the freshly placed concrete. Individual parts of the column clamp may be loaded in bending

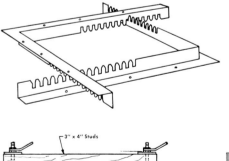

4-31 Some of the lighter column clamps now commercially available. The clamp made of steel strap may be used for heavier loads when appropriate trussing of the column form is provided.

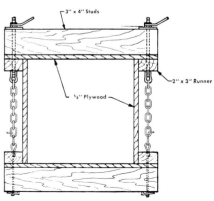

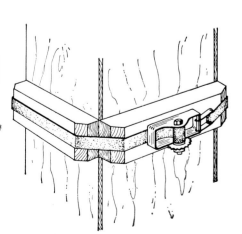

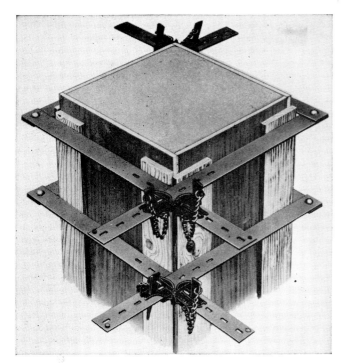

4-32 Hinged bar column clamp typical of heavier clamps produced by several manufacturers

or tension or a combination of the two, depending on details of assembly as explained on p. 104. Several designs are available in ready-made reusable column clamps that are adjustable to a range of column cross section dimensions. Certain clamping devices such as some of those shown in Figure 4-31 are best adapted to shorter columns of small cross section, while other heavier devices are suited to larger cross sections and the greater loads that may be imposed in concreting taller columns.

Figure 4-32 shows a hinged bar column clamp typical of the heavier ones produced by several manufacturers. Two hinged units making up each clamp have all fastening hardware permanently attached; the two parts are laid in place around the column, lock castings are slid together, and the wedge is dropped into the proper slot and tightened with a hammer. Where column forms are in tight quarters, a single bar type, made up of four straight members with attached hardware is used.

Clamps of the type shown in Figure 4-32, or the single bar variation thereof, are available for column sides ranging from about 8 in. to 8 ft. The longer clamps have a thickened cross section at midspan or are reinforced with attached channels.

It is advisable to examine carefully all of the manufacturer's suggestions and recommendations for the use of these clamps. Aside from the obvious dimensional limitations, there may be suggested limits on height and rate of placing concrete when a given type

of clamp is to be used. Clamps may be suggested as suitable for only a limited size of column cross section or a special type of framing.

The manufacturer may not indicate whether his suggested clamp spacing is based on strength and stiffness of proposed column sheathing and framing or strength and stiffness of the clamp itself, or a judicious balance between the two. For any unusual column framing—extra long span of clamp, for example, without intermediate tie, or a non-typical selection of column sheathing—at least a rough check of proposed clamp spacing is desirable. (See column design suggestions, p. 103.) Unless the user has definite data on allowable deflections used by the clamp manufacturer in preparing his recommendations, or has had successful experience with the column forming combination proposed, there may be disappointing results in terms of bulges or bows in columns.

Prefabricated Forms

Prefabricated forms and forming systems have become increasingly important to the concrete contractor as a means of saving both material and labor cost

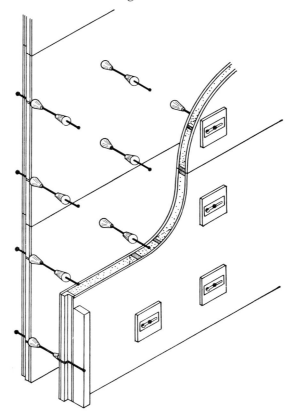

4-33 Cut-away view of form panel of stressed-skin plywood construction with a foamed plastic insulating material between the two plywood faces. Plywood "donuts" serve as bearing plates for tie holders when wales are not used.

4-34A Metal framed plywood panels cross braced with metal and furnished with metal handles. These standard 2 ft wide panels are available in heights up to 8 ft.

4-34B Unframed plywood panels backed by steel braces. This view shows two panels joined by prefabricated metal corner piece.

through the efficiency of mass production. Their flexibility in financing offers attractions to some contractors; the forms may be purchased outright, rented, or sometimes rented with an option to purchase. Manufacturers of the forming systems frequently provide engineering layouts at no additional cost or for a nominal charge. Supervision for erecting the forms may also be provided.

Prefabricated forms are most advantageous where numerous reuses are expected, and they are generally built with added durability to meet this anticipated reuse. However there are some prefabricated forms such as the fiber tubes and void forms intended for a single use, which are destroyed or lost in construction. Other prefabricated forms are built to stay in place as part of the finished structure.

Prefabricated forms may be considered in two groups:

1. *Ready-made forms.* This includes the modular panel systems that are made in relatively small, easily handled units that can be adapted to forming different structural members. Standardized forms suitable for only one kind of structural member, such as column forms or pans for concrete joist construction, are also part of this group.

2. *Custom-made forms.* This group includes special purpose forms built to order, such as tunnel forms, cantilever forms for dams, special forms for bridges, and many others. Although these forms may be made for a single job, they are often reused many times on that job.

Main emphasis in this section is on the ready-made forms which are of more general interest; many of the custom-made forms are discussed in other sections of the book covering the special types of construction for which they are intended. Prefabricated panels made up by the contractor in his own yard or shop are also discussed elsewhere (p. 152).

Panel Forms and Forming Systems

Prefabricated panel forms are generally manufactured in modular sizes, with 2- and 4-ft widths being

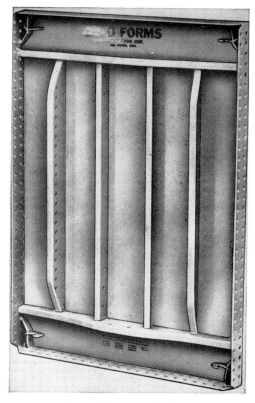

4-34C All-metal panel form available in sizes ranging up to 2x6 ft, either square or rectangular panels.

the most common in heights ranging from 2 to 8 ft. Smaller filler and corner units are of varying sizes. Hardware and ties supplied with form panels vary with the different manufacturers. Ties are similar to those already described (p. 54), but are usually fastened against the panel frame, eliminating wales in the typical installation.

Although the many panel forming systems on the market today vary widely in details, there are four basic types:

1. Unframed plywood panels. Locking and tying hardware are supplied; some panels of this type have attached metal bracing on the back.
2. Plywood panels framed in wood and braced with metal members.
3. Plywood panels set in metal frame, with or without metal bracing on the back.
4. All-metal panels: metal plates welded or bolted to a metal frame.

In addition to these basic types, the relatively new panel form shown in Figure 4-33 uses stressed-skin construction and sandwiches a foamed plastic insulating material between the two plywood faces.

Although these panels were developed primarily for wall forming, many of them are adaptable to slab and column forming, and smaller ones have been successfully used in forming beams. The form user should read carefully the manufacturers' data on these forms and select a system that is suited to his own job conditions. Some are obviously for light construction, while other form panels are so sturdily built that they can be adapted for a variety of forming needs.

Prefabricated panels are most often used for general and light construction where walls range in height from 2 to 24 ft, with particular emphasis on walls ranging from 4 to 10 ft. "Prefab" forms are less frequently used on complicated walls such as curved or battered ones with corbels, but interesting applications for such jobs have been developed (Figures 4-35 and 4-36).

On large jobs where cranes can work to advantage in handling forms, panel forms are "ganged," that is

4-35 Prefabricated forms used for 22-ft bulkhead wall. Although these forms are best suited to simple lower walls, they may be used for more specialized structures. Note, however, the addition of wales and heavy bracing.

4-36 Newly-stripped 50-ft diameter sewage treatment tank built with prefabricated form panels. Small panels made it possible to form the round shape.

4-37 Prefabricated panels ganged in 16x28-ft unit for use in forming high bridge pier

joined together with special hardware provided by the form manufacturer, to form a relatively large wall section. A crane erects, strips, and then moves this large unit to another location for reuse. This is advantageous for high walls where much labor is saved as compared with repeated assembly and disassembly of individual panel components. Size of ganged form units commonly ranges up to 30x50 ft.

Pans and Domes for Concrete Joist Construction

Concrete joist construction is a monolithic combination of regularly spaced joists and a thin slab cast in place to form an integral unit with beams and columns. The joists may be all arranged in one direction within a column bay, or they may be arranged in two directions to create a waffle-like pattern. This type of construction has been conventionally formed with ready-made steel "pans" or "domes" of standard size. Recently other materials, including hardboard, fiberboard, glass-reinforced plastic, and corrugated cardboard, have been adapted to do the same forming job. Some of the firms that supply these forms also subcontract complete erection and removal of the forms, with or without the supporting centering. Other companies only rent or sell the forms.

Joist depths and spacings for one way concrete joist construction were standardized in 1932 by the U. S.

Department of Commerce on the basis of an industry study by a committee of architects, engineers, contractors, and steel form suppliers. That early standard has since been replaced by Voluntary Product Standard PS 16-69, "Types and Sizes of Forms for One-Way Concrete Joist Construction," which establishes standard shapes and dimensions for one-way joist forms of all materials. Standard form widths are 20 and 30 in., and depths are 6, 8, 10, 12, 14, 16, or 20 in. The standard also covers narrower filler forms and tapered end forms to fit varying floor layouts and sizes.

Standard sizes for dome pans used to form grid or waffle slabs are established by the Department of Commerce Simplified Practice Recommendation R265-63, "Forms for Two-Way Concrete Joist Floor and Roof Construction." They are based on 24- and 36-in. modules, the 24-in. size forming 19x19-in. voids with 5-in. ribs between, and the 36-in. size forming 30x30-in. voids with 6-in. ribs. Standard pans are available with void depths from 4 to 12 in. for the 24-in. size, and from 8 to 20 in. for the 36-in. dome forms. Deeper pans of non-standard dimensions are coming into increasing use.

Figure 4-38 shows the different types of standard steel units available for forming concrete joist construction. Since this type of construction is well established with a long record of successful use, it is suggested that the recommendations of established manufacturers be followed in using these forms.

Erection procedures for the support of pan and dome forms are given on p. 178.

The design of these steel pans and domes has recently been duplicated or approximated in other materials. For example, the hardboard pans shown in Figure 4-39 are braced with metal supports set in place on wood supporting members. Constructed of $\frac{1}{4}$-in. hardboard coated with a waterproof plastic, they require a coating of oil or other bond breaker before concrete is placed. The end pan in each row is trimmed to fill out the row to the exact dimension required. Tapered end pans and end closures are provided. A collapsible wood pan-type form has also been used very successfully.

Reusable special molded fiber pans are available in widths from 10 to 30 in. and depths from 6 to 14 in. for use on either solid or open deck centering. The fiber of which they are made is molded under heat and pressure and treated to withstand the effects of weather and wet concrete, but a release agent or form

NAIL-DOWN FLANGE TYPE can be placed, aligned, and nailed from the top side. Simplest to use, but does not generally provide architectural concrete surface.

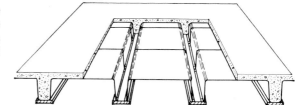

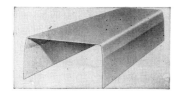

ADJUSTABLE TYPE has no flanges, provides smooth joist bottoms without flange marks. Pans can be removed without disturbing soffits and shore supports.

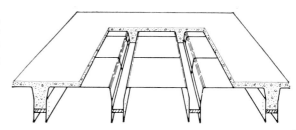

DOME TYPE used for two-way or waffle slabs. This kind of slab design may offer certain structural economies. Flanges are butted at joints, not lapped.

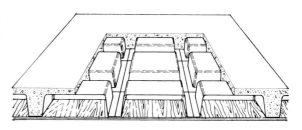

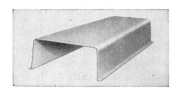

SLIP-IN TYPE is based on the same form as the nail-down type, but uses soffit board between pans to form a smooth joist bottom. Like adjustables, pans can be removed without disturbing soffit supports.

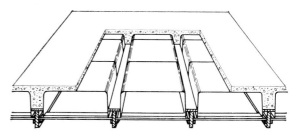

4-38 Typical steel pan and dome forms. One other type, the long pan, is shown in Chapter 9 along with erection details for all types.

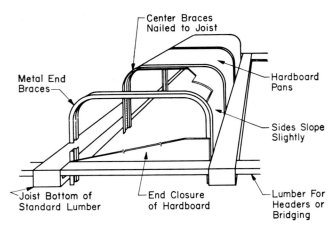

4-39 Assembly detail for hardboard pans made in widths of 20, 30, and 40 in. with depth adjustable from 6 to 24 in.

oil applied before each use facilitates stripping and improves durability. Support chairs and stiffeners are required for most applications of these pan forms. They are suitable for either the nail-down or slip-in systems similar to those shown for steel pans, and can also be adapted to forming two-way joist construction.

Single-use corrugated cardboard box-type special pan or dome form members are also available (Figure

4-40 Molded fiber pans being installed for slab forming

4-41 Assembly of single-use cardboard dome-type forms on a solid plywood deck

4-41). The corrugated board is asphalt- or wax-impregnated, and these forms require no oiling. An interior core of egg-crate style or other design provides bracing. The boxes are shipped flat, pre-slotted and scored, for assembly on the job with tape or stapling machines. They may be either stapled or taped to deck or centering.

Glass-reinforced plastic dome pans (Figure 4-42) are now available as a ready-made stock item, either for sale or for rent. Range of sizes for these reusable forms is considerably greater than that given for steel domes. Clay tile or lightweight concrete filler blocks that remain permanently in the slab structure accomplish much the same purpose as the removable pan and dome forms.

Void and Duct Forms

A number of products have been developed for forming voids and ducts in both slab and beam construction. Laminated fiber tubes equipped with end closures so that concrete will not flow into them are placed near the neutral axis to displace low working concrete, and tied down with wire to prevent floating or lateral movement when the concrete is being placed. These laminated tubes are available in two types: one with a weather resistant ply designed for use in cast-in-place construction in exposed areas; and the other for use where they will be completely protected from weather during storage and use.

Corrugated cardboard members similar in construction to the cardboard pans and domes described above are also available for forming voids, and inflatable rubber tubing has been used for this purpose too. The patented rubber forms, ¾ to 12 inches in diameter, are laid in position and then inflated. A loose wire coil is used to hold the tube in place. Reinforcing mesh laid on top of forms also helps keep them from floating. Form may be tapped with a hammer during placement of slab to vibrate concrete and produce smoother ducts if desired. When the concrete has hardened the form is deflated and withdrawn through bulkhead or edge form of slab. Specially woven nylon or cotton reinforcement governs the way the tube contracts on deflation and thereby aids in breaking bond with the concrete. No form coatings are needed, and little cleanup is required.

Rubber void forms are available up to 60 ft long and can be joined for greater lengths. Greater than 330 ft total length gives excessive friction on withdrawal. Typical inflating pressures range up to 85 psi for smaller sizes, 25 to 33 psi for the medium sizes, and 25 psi or less for larger sizes.

For large diameter sewer and industrial work, above

12 inches and up to 87 inches in diameter, duct formers are made of several plies of rubberized fabric. The hose-like form is open at both ends to contain airtight bulkheads through which air pressure is applied for necessary strength of the form. These large forms are inflated at low pressure sufficient to maintain the shape and carry loads imposed on the form, but without stretching the form material.

Column Forms

Standard forms for round columns are available in both fiber and metal as complete units with no extra fastenings. The fiber tubes are single use items and require only a minimum of external bracing to keep them plumb. Also available is a square column form assembled from panels of galvanized sheet steel backed by ¾-in. plywood and braced against lateral pressure with column clamps described earlier. Ready-made panels (p. 163) are also adaptable for some column forming.

The tubular fiber column form shown in Figure 4-45 is available for columns ranging from 6 to 48 inches in diameter. Standard lengths available are 12 and 18 ft, but greater lengths may be ordered. One manufacturer reports that such forms have been successfully used for continuous placement of columns 40 ft high. Fiber forms can be cut by saw to the exact length desired, and cut sections can be adapted to forming half-round, quarter-round, and obround columns (see p. 168) and pilasters. They are also suitable for encasing steel pipe and other members with concrete. Where the form cannot be slipped over existing piling, piers, or posts that are to be encased, a special double walled version which can be cut for installation is suggested.

The laminated fiber plies are spirally constructed and are available with wax-impregnated inner and outer surface for weather and moisture protection. Where the columns are to be exposed, the inner surface is coated with polyethylene. If the appearance of the columns is critical, a so-called seamless type is available in which fiber plies nearest the inner surface are deckled or scarfed and overlapped to minimize the spiral gaps or seams on the column surface.

No clamps or ties are needed and no form oil is required; since there is no reuse, there is no cleanup. If these forms are left in place, they aid proper hydration of concrete without additional curing procedures. However, it is advisable to strip before placing any critical loads on the columns, in order to detect any voids which may have formed during placement, which would weaken the member.

4-42   Glass-fiber-reinforced plastic pans used for slab forming. Pans shown produced a 19x19x8-in. void, weighed about 7 lb each. A range of other sizes is available.

4-43   Void of hollow box girder is formed by cardboard box assembly placed inside the girder form.

4-44   Inflatable rubber tubing set in place to form heating duct void in floor slab. Loose wire coils are used to hold the inflated duct form in place.

4-45 Fiber tube column forms require only bracing to keep them plumb and a template at the base for accurate positioning.

The fiber tube form can be stripped by making two vertical cuts with a power saw and pulling the form off; or by making a vertical 12-in. cut in the tube with a linoleum knife, then peeling spirally, using a broad bladed tool. With either method, care must be taken to prevent marring the column surface.

Adjustable steel forms for column capitals are made for use with these fiber forms (Figure 4-46). They are similar to the capital portion of the all-steel column forms and are generally a rental item.

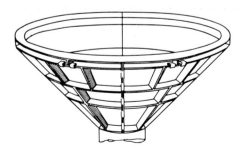

4-46 Typical steel capital form for use with fiber tube column forms

Ready-made steel column forms are assembled in sections, with necessary hardware being provided with the form. Bracing is built into the form so that no column clamps are required, and external bracing is needed only to keep the forms plumb during concreting. The capital is a standard part of the form, and can be adjusted to different depths and diameters.

These forms are manufactured in diameters ranging from 14 in. to 10 ft, with vertical panels 1 to 10 ft high. Some have an access ladder built into the form.

Stay-In-Place Forms

A number of materials used for formwork are left permanently in place, and some become an integral part of the completed structure. Generally described as permanent forms, these may be of the rigid type such as metal deck, precast concrete, wood, plastics, and the various types of fiberboard; or the flexible type such as reinforced water-repellent corrugated paper, or wire mesh with waterproof paper backing. Some of these, such as the void forms (p. 64), have already been described. Insulation board stay-in-place forms were discussed (p. 45) along with form lining materials.

Where the permanent form serves for deck construction, it is generally supported from the main structural members; however it may require additional temporary intermediate supports. The permanent form material may be covered in the engineer-architect specifications for the job, but where it is a contractor's optional item, the manufacturers' specifications and recommendations for use are generally relied upon.

4-47 One of the several commercially available steel column forms, showing (right) the general appearance of the column after stripping

4-48 Corrugated metal forms that stay in place are shown supported on steel bridge girders (right) and on precast concrete girders (left). Preset nails in the concrete members are bent over to hold the steel form in place.

Metal Deck

Ribbed or corrugated steel sheet is used both as a permanent form for cast concrete and as a combined form and reinforcement; in roofs it may be the permanent supporting member for lightweight insulating concrete fills. Where the steel is to provide continuing support or reinforcement it should be galvanized. When it acts only as a stay-in-place form it is generally "black" or uncoated. The high tensile steel used has a working stress around 30,000 psi.

The forms are used for concrete floor and roof slabs cast over steel joists or beams and for bridge decks above high-traffic areas; they also may be used to form the top slab over pipe trenches or other inaccessible locations where it is impractical and expensive to remove wood forms. Metal deck forms can also be set in short lengths between precast joists (Figure 4-48) where shear connectors project from the top of the precast members, or over several spans just as with steel members if there are no stirrups.

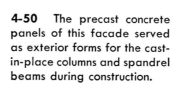

4-49 One type of combined form and reinforcement. Temperature steel is laid on top of this form, but some combinations have temperature steel welded in place as part of the form. Top steel must be provided where slabs are continuous over supports.

When the forming material is installed it is secured in various ways; for example, by clips attached to the top of the joist, or by welding to inserts cast in the concrete members. Varying gages and corrugation styles make these forms usable on clear spans ranging up to 8 ft for 20-gage steel.

Some galvanized steel deck forming materials combine form and positive reinforcing in one piece; this is achieved by deeper corrugations and raised lugs on the corrugations. Transverse wires welded across the corrugations in one such product take the place of temperature steel reinforcing, whereas others require added temperature mesh to prevent shrinkage cracks. Regardless of manufacturers' claims, these products cannot take the place of negative reinforcing bars (top steel) required where slabs are continuous over beam, girder, or wall support.

Wherever metal deck forms are to become a structurally active part of the permanent structure, the architect engineer should take full design responsibility and specify gage, thickness, depth, physical dimensions, and properties, as well as special shoring requirements, if any.

Precast Concrete

Precast concrete panels or units serve as stay-in-place or permanent forms for various structural elements (see also architectural concrete, p. 231, and Section 5.7 of ACI 347-68, reproduced in the appendix

4-50 The precast concrete panels of this facade served as exterior forms for the cast-in-place columns and spandrel beams during construction.

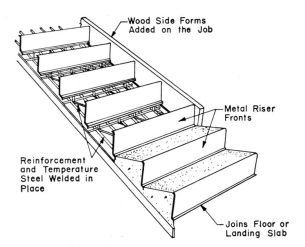

Wood Side Forms
Added on the Job

Metal Riser
Fronts

Reinforcement
and Temperature
Steel Welded in
Place

Joins Floor or
Landing Slab

4-51 Prefabricated metal form for reinforced concrete stairs has metal riser fronts, reinforcement, and temperature steel all welded into a single unit. Soffit form is built in place, and wood side forms are added to this unit. Other designs have permanent metal stringers.

of this book). In some applications these are exposed aggregate panels which produce a specified architectural surface; another type of precast panel provides an abrasion resistant surface for mass concrete. Lightweight concrete dome pans have been used as stay-in place forms for two-way concrete joist systems. Construction applications vary; the precast units may be used as self-supporting form panels, or as form liners to produce a special surface on the concrete.

4-52 Another example of custom-made special purpose forms. This massive steel pier cap form weighing 30 tons is supported on pier columns and temporary steel verticals (foreground).

Special Purpose and Custom-Made Forms Built by Specialists

A number of companies in the United States specialize in building forms for use by the contractor; such forms are built to order for special structures or special construction conditions where ready-made form components or job-built forms are not satisfactory. In many cases it is to the advantage of the contractor to get the service of these experts who not only design the form but may fabricate it in materials not easily handled by the contractor on the job or in his shop.

Various firms specialize in different types of formwork such as that needed for underground structures, mass concrete, bridge work, or architectural ornament. Since many of these forms are for specialized construction techniques or are made of special materials, they are described elsewhere in the book, and only a few examples are shown here (Figures 4-51, 4-52 and 4-53).

4-53 Bottom structure and supporting frame structure for a custom-made watertight column caisson form

Shoring, Scaffolding

A number of patented shoring systems have been developed with adjustable legs which eliminate cutting, close fitting, and wedging. Miscellaneous hardware is available for joining components, attaching T-heads, braces, stringers, and the like. There is also the so-called horizontal shoring which provides a relatively long adjustable span horizontal support for forms. Most of these items are available either for rental or purchase.

When patented shores or methods of shoring are used, manufacturers' recommendations as to load-carrying capacity may be followed, but they should be supported by test reports from a qualified and recognized testing laboratory. Committee 347 has advised reduced values of allowable loads after materials such as these shoring components have experienced substantial reuse. The user must carefully follow the manufacturers' recommendations for bracing and working loads for unsupported lengths. It is well to remember that bracing of shores may be needed to give safety and stability to the entire formwork assembly, although it might not be suggested by the shore manufacturer to increase load carrying capacity.

Vertical Shores

There are several types of adjustable individual shores. The simplest of these, shown in Figure 4-54, is based on a clamping device which permits the overlapping of two 4x4 members. A portable jacking tool is carried by the workman from one shore to another to make vertical adjustments. Special hardware for the top of these shores facilitates joining them to stringers with a minimum of nailing. Typical working load capacity is about 3000 lb, with a safety factor of 4. Exact load ratings will depend on condition and quality of the lumber as well as the unbraced length.

The shore shown in Figure 4-55 is typical of those made of dimension lumber combined with a steel column and adjusting device; working loads range up to 6000 lb. The steel member may be tubular, T-section, or other shape. If tubular it may be filled with concrete. Setting is considered a one-man operation. There is a special jacking device for these shores too, and various fittings and extensions for the top are available including T-heads, L-heads, U-heads. Worn-out wood members often can be replaced with stock lumber to extend the service life. Another advantage of the wood-metal combination is that the shores can be easily braced by nailing to the wood members.

4-54 Shores made of two pieces of dimension lumber are joined by a patented clamping device which permits length adjustments.

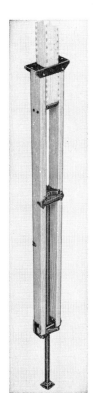

4-55 Typical adjustable shore of wood and metal combined. An extension head is shown at the top, but various other head pieces are available.

4-56 One of the many designs of all-metal adjustable shores. Note nailing brackets for attachment of bracing.

An all-metal individual adjustable shore, sometimes described as a jack shore or simply as a jack, is also available from a number of manufacturers in adjustable heights from about 4 ft to 16 ft. Figure 4-56 shows a typical line of these shores. There are the usual individual variations in fittings and adjusting devices from one product to another. Safe load ratings range from 1500 to 9000 lb, with a safety factor of about 3, depending on type of shore and the length to which it is extended. Metal bracing brackets with holes for nailing wood bracing are provided, and heads of different types are available.

Scaffold-Type Shoring

When tubular steel frame scaffolding was first introduced, it was designed to support the relatively light loads involved in getting men to the work area. Later contractors began to try out the scaffolding as a support for formwork because of the apparent advantages of its modular assembly and system of jacks for leveling and adjusting elevations. As this shoring application became more popular, it was necessary to

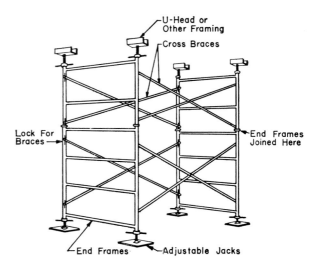

4-58 End frames assembled with diagonal braces to form typical shoring "tower." A number of different designs of end frames, coupling, and bracing details are available from the various manufacturers.

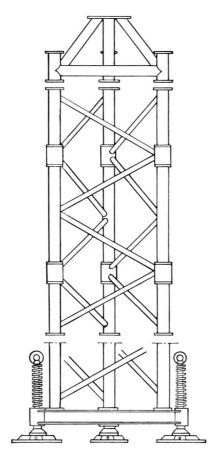

4-57 Tripod shoring towers are available for heavy loading at heights up to 50 ft.

For heavy duty and heights up to 50 ft, tripod shoring towers (Figure 4-57) are available. They consist of a base section, intermediate sections which can be assembled to the desired height, and a bearing member which is attached as the top section. The tripod shoring towers carry up to 33 tons total concentric load at unbraced lengths up to 45 ft.

develop more accurate data on the carrying capacity of scaffold frames, since the loads of concrete and forming materials were much greater than the loads previously supported as straight scaffolding. As a result of this concern for carrying capacity, heavy duty frames were designed and placed on the market specifically for shoring installations.

The Scaffolding and Shoring Institute, working to develop more consistent and reliable data on load capacities of scaffold-type shoring, has developed a standard load test procedure and has made load tests of scaffold-frame components assembled in relatively high towers. Recommendations for erection of scaffold shoring have also been developed by that organization (see p. 185).

Basic components of a scaffold shoring installation are the end frames of various designs and dimensions, which are assembled with diagonal bracing, lock clamps, and adjustable bases in shoring towers that may have flat top plates, U-heads, or other upper members for attaching or fitting to the forms.

4-59 Heavy-duty shoring supports formwork for bridge span. Average working load for this type is 5 tons per leg. Jacks for adjustment are at both top and bottom.

In terms of load carrying capacity, there are three types of tubular steel scaffold shoring:

1. *Standard.* Panel frames available in 2- to 5-ft widths, varying from 2 to 6½ ft high, with various panel designs and bracing details. Average safe working load is 2500-6000 lb per leg.

2. *Heavy-duty.* Tubular panel frames available in 3- to 4-ft widths; 3, 4, 5, and 6 ft high; various designs and bracing and connection details. Average safe working load is 10,000 lb per leg.

4-60 Extra-heavy-duty scaffold shoring supporting 125-ft concrete girders. Working loads up to 20 tons per leg are permitted with this type of shoring. Note steel beam sills mounted on rails to move the shoring after it is lowered.

3. *Extra-heavy-duty.* Has heavier tubular members, more rigid bracing, with components that assemble in 6½ ft high sections. Supports up to 40,000 lb safe load per leg.

Full flights of free-standing sectional shoring, with or without the supported forms, can be moved from one bay to another by skidding, by attaching casters for rolling, or by lifting as shown in Figure 4-61.

Horizontal Shoring

Adjustable beam, truss, or beam and truss combination members which support formwork over a clear span and eliminate intermediate vertical supports are

4-61 Scaffold shoring assembly with forms attached is lifted by crane for reuse at another location.

referred to as *horizontal shoring*. Fixed length metal support beams (either I- or box-type) which span lengths of about 2 to 8 ft, replacing timber ledgers, are sometimes included in this category too. However, the two major adjustable types are:

Telescoping horizontal shores, which are made up of lattice, plate, or box members, or a combination of these. Units support forms for spans of 6 to 30 ft, and have built-in adjustable camber.

Allowable loads range from about 80 to 800 lb per lineal ft, depending on span.

Heavy-duty horizontal shores, which are truss assembly horizontal shores for long span formwork, capable of carrying 500 lb per lineal ft across spans of 15 to 83 ft.

One disadvantage of such shoring is that the high end loads may cause the member to "bite" into supporting timbers unless special bearing plates are provided.

4-62 Installation of typical telescoping lattice-type horizontal shoring

4-63 These telescoping horizontal shoring members are made of aluminum. An I-section fits within the hollow box member.

REFERENCES

1. *Wood Handbook*, prepared by the Forest Products Laboratory, Forest Service, U. S. Department of Agriculture as Agriculture Handbook No. 72, U. S. Government Printing Office, Washington, D. C., 1955, 528 pp.
2. "National Design Specification for Stress Grade Lumber and Its Fastenings," National Forest Products Association, Washington, D. C., 1971 Edition.
3. Roberts, J. A., and Vivian, H. E., "Form Liners for Concreting," *Constructional Review* (Sydney), V. 34, No. 5, May 1961, pp. 21-25.
4. Arber, M. G.; Roberts, J. A.; and Vivian, H. E., "Concrete Form Treatments," *Constructional Review* (Sydney), V. 34, No. 6, June 1961, pp. 27-33.
5. Hanson, J. A., "Plastic Forms for Architectural Concrete," ACI JOURNAL, *Proceedings* V. 56, No. 11, May 1960, pp. 1137-1148.
6. Vidal, E. N., and Blanks, R. F., "Absorptive Form Linings," ACI JOURNAL, *Proceedings* V. 38, No. 3, Jan. 1942, pp. 253-268.
7. Johnson, W. R., "The Use of Absorptive Wall Boards for Concrete forms," ACI JOURNAL, *Proceedings* V. 37, No. 6, June 1941, pp. 621-631.
8. "Tests on Concrete and Mortar Surfaces Cast Against Various Types of Forms and Form Linings," *Technical Memorandum* No. 6-336, Feb. 1952, U. S. Army Corps of Engineers, Waterways Experiment Station, Vicksburg, Miss., 68 pp.
9. *Timber Construction Manual*, prepared by American Institute of Timber Construction, John Wiley and Sons, New York, 1966.
10. "Tests of Anchors for Mass-Concrete Forms," *Technical Memorandum* No. 6-399, Mar. 1955, U. S. Army Corps of Engineers, Waterways Experiment Station, Vicksburg, Miss., 13 pp.
11. Bendinelli, Ralph A., "Tests of Holding Strength of Form Anchors Embedded in Concrete Placed and Cast at Reduced Temperatures," *Technical Report* No. 6-473, Feb. 1958, U. S. Army Corps of Engineers, Waterways Experiment Station, Vicksburg, Miss., 9 pp.
12. "Tests of Form Lumber and Form Oil," *Miscellaneous Paper* No. 6-80, Mar. 1954, U. S. Army Corps of Engineers, Waterways Experiment Station, Vicksburg, Miss.
13. *Light Gage Cold Formed Steel Design Manual*, American Iron and Steel Institute, New York, 1961, 115 pp.
14. *Manual of Steel Construction*, American Institute of Steel Construction, New York, 7th Edition, 1970.
15. "Open Web Steel Joists, Standard Specifications and Load Tables," Steel Joist Institute, Washington, D. C., 1963, 36 pp.
16. "Plywood Design Specification," American Plywood Association, Tacoma, Wash., 1966.
17. "American Softwood Lumber Standard," PS 20-70, U. S. Department of Commerce, National Bureau of Standards, Washington, D. C.

5:LOADS AND PRESSURES

FORMWORK FOR CONCRETE must support all vertical and lateral loads that may be applied until such time as these loads can be carried by the concrete structure itself. Loads on the forms include the weight of reinforcing steel and fresh concrete, the weight of the forms themselves, and various live loads imposed during the construction process. Dumping of concrete, movement of construction equipment, and action of the wind may produce lateral forces which must be resisted by the formwork to prevent lateral failure.

Form design must consider conditions such as unsymmetrical placement of concrete, impact from machine delivered concrete, uplift, and concentrated loads produced by storing supplies on the freshly placed slab. Rarely will there be precise information as to loads that will come on the forms, and the designer must make some safe assumptions which will hold good for conditions generally encountered. The following sections are a guide to the designer for determining the loadings on which to base form design for ordinary conditions normally applicable to structural concrete. Form loadings for other types of concrete—such as mass concrete and tunnel linings—and nonstandard methods of construction or placement are discussed in later chapters.

formwork weight is small in relation to the weight of the concrete plus live load, it is frequently neglected.

If concrete weighs 150 lb per cu ft, it will place a load on the forms of 12.5 lb per sq ft for each inch of slab thickness. Thus a 6-in. slab would produce a dead load of 12.5 × 6 or 75 psf, neglecting the weight of forms. If the same slab were of lightweight concrete weighing 100 lb per cu ft, dead load would be $^{100}/_{12}$ × 6 or 50 psf.

ACI Committee 347 recommends a minimum construction live load of 50 psf of horizontal projection to provide for weight of workmen, equipment, runways and impact. Unusual conditions may justify a smaller allowance than this, but many designers use 75 psf or more for construction with powered concrete buggies. The Scaffolding and Shoring Institute recommends that combined live and dead load used for shoring design should never be less than 100 psf, regardless of slab thickness.

Table 5-1 showing vertical load on forms for various kinds of slabs of varying thickness has been developed using the minimum live load of 50 psf recommended by the committee, and neglecting weight of the forms, which may be added by the designer.

Vertical Loads

Vertical loads on formwork include the weight of reinforced concrete together with the weight of forms themselves which are regarded as dead load, and the live loads imposed during processes of construction (such as workmen and equipment). While concrete may weigh anywhere from 40 to 600 lb per cu ft, the majority of all formwork involves concrete weighing 145-150 lb per cu ft. Minor variations in this weight are not significant, and for these majority cases 150 lb per cu ft including weight of reinforcing steel is commonly assumed for design. Formwork weights vary from as little as 3 or 4 psf to 10 to 15 psf. When the

5-1 Storing or unloading large quantities of material on the formwork may be prohibited by the specifications. If it is necessary to pile up steel and form materials as shown here, the designer must allow for this loading.

TABLE 5-1: VERTICAL LOAD FOR DESIGN OF SLAB FORMS, PSF

Includes weight of concrete and reinforcing steel plus construction live load of 50 psf; weight of formwork not included.

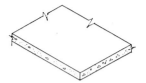

SOLID SLAB CONSTRUCTION

Slab thickness, in.	3	4	5	6	7	8	9	10	11	12
100 lb concrete	75	83	92	100	108	117	125	133	142	150
125 lb concrete	81	92	102	113	123	134	144	154	165	175
150 lb concrete	88	100	113	125	138	150	163	175	188	200

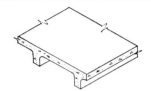

TYPICAL JOIST SLAB CONSTRUCTION

Actual weights and dimensions vary slightly from one manufacturer of forming systems to another.

Depth of steel form		20 in. wide forms				30 in. wide forms			
	Joist width, in.	2 in. slab	2½ in. slab	3 in. slab	Joist width, in.	2½ in. slab	3 in. slab	3½ in. slab	
6	4	89	95	102	4	91	98	–	
	5	92	98	105	5	93	100	106	
	6	94	100	107	6	95	102	108	
8	4	95	101	108	4	95	101	–	
	5	98	104	111	5	98	104	111	
	6	101	107	114	6	100	106	113	
10	4	100	106	113	4	100	106	–	
	5	104	110	117	5	102	108	116	
	6	108	114	121	6	105	111	118	
12	4	107	113	119	4	104	110	–	
	5	111	117	124	5	107	113	120	
	6	116	122	128	6	111	117	124	
14	4	113	120	126	5	112	118	124	
	5	118	125	131	6	116	122	130	
	6	123	130	136	7	120	126	133	

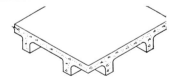

TYPICAL "WAFFLE" TYPE TWO-WAY JOIST SYSTEMS

Actual weights and dimensions vary slightly from one manufacturer of forming systems to another.

Size of "pan" form, in.			Slab thickness above form, in.				
Depth	Outside plan	Inside plan	2	2½	3	3½	4½
4	24x24	19x19	96	103	109	115	–
6	24x24	19x19	109	116	122	128	–
8	24x24	19x19	123	129	135	141	–
	36x36	30x30	111	117	123	130	143
10	24x24	19x19	129	136	142	148	–
	36x36	30x30	120	128	133	139	152
12	24x24	19x19	145	152	158	164	–
	36x36	30x30	133	139	145	152	165
14	36x36	30x30	141	148	154	160	173

5-2 Live load including power buggy and concrete crew. A minimum value of 50 psf for design is suggested; where power buggies are used, 75 psf is more common.

Where slab form members are continuous over several supporting shores, dumping concrete in one "bay" may cause uplift of supporting shores in other bays. Forms must be designed to hold together under such conditions. If the form members are not secured to resist this uplift, they should be built as simple spans.

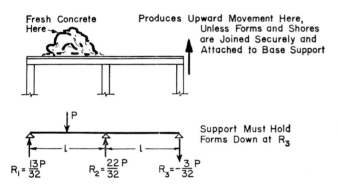

On inclined slabs no steeper than about 45°, the tendency of fresh concrete to slide down the form is resisted by friction between the concrete and the form. However the slab form must be rigidly connected to its supports, and the horizocontal component of the concrete pressure must be resisted by guying or internal or external bracing of the shores (Figure 5-3). In the case of rapidly placed, steeply sloping slabs, backforms are required.

Shoring Loads in Multistory Structures

In multistory work, the shoring which supports freshly placed concrete is necessarily supported by lower floors which may not yet have attained their full strength, and which may not have been designed to carry loads as great as those imposed during construction, even if they were at full design strength.

Therefore shoring must be provided for enough floors to develop the needed capacity to support the imposed loads without excessive stress or deflection. Whether permanent shores or reshores are used at the several required lower floor levels depends on job plans for reuse of materials, but loads to be carried are the same on either permanent shores or reshores, once the lowest floor of shores has been removed. (See Section 2.8.1 of ACI 347-68.)

In any case, shores in the lower stories should be designed to carry the full weight of concrete and formwork posted to them prior to removal of the lowest story of shores supported on the ground or other unyielding support. For rapid multistory work, Committee 347 recommends that shores above the first level be designed for at least 1½ times the weight of a given floor of concrete, forms, and construction loads; in many cases a larger load than this must be supported. More detailed information on analysis of these loads has been presented by Feld,[*] Grundy and Kabaila,[**] and Blakey and Beresford.[***]

Where selective reduction in the number of reshores required for lower floors is made, the size of the shore should be carefully determined so as to assure its adequacy for the loads posted thereon.

In determining the number of floors to be shored to support construction loads above, ACI Committee 347 recommends consideration of the following factors:

1. Design load capacity of the slab or member including live load, partition loads, and other loads for which the engineer designed the slab. Where the engineer-architect included allowances for construction loads, such values should be shown on the structural drawings.
2. Dead weight of the concrete and formwork.
3. Construction live loads involved, such as placing crews or equipment.
4. Design strength of concrete specified.

[*] Feld, Jacob, "Reshoring of Concrete Buildings," *Engineering News-Record*, Oct. 6, 1966, pp. 33, 34; correction published Nov. 10, 1966, p. 6.
[**] Grundy, Paul, and Kabaila, A., "Construction Loads on Slabs with Shored Formwork in Multistory Buildings," ACI JOURNAL, *Proceedings* V. 60, No. 12, Dec. 1963, pp. 1729-1738.
[***] Blakey, F. A. and Beresford, F. D., "Stripping of Formwork for Concrete Buildings in Relation to Structural Design," *Civil Engineering* (Transactions of the Institution of Engineers, Australia,) V. CE7, No. 2, Oct. 1965, pp. 92-96.

5. Cycle time between placement of successive floors.

6. Developed strength of the concrete at the time it is required to support new loads above.

7. Span of slab or structural member between structural supports.

8. Type of forming systems; i.e., span of horizontal forming components, individual shore loads.

Lateral Pressure of Fresh Concrete

Loads imposed by fresh concrete against wall or column forms differ from the gravity load on a horizontal slab form. The freshly placed concrete behaves temporarily like a fluid, producing a hydrostatic pressure that acts laterally on the vertical forms. This lateral pressure is comparable to full liquid head when concrete is placed full height within the period required for its initial set. With slower rates of placing, concrete at the bottom of the form begins to harden and the lateral pressure is reduced to less than full fluid pressure by the time concreting is completed in the upper parts of the form. The effective lateral pressure—a modified hydrostatic pressure—has been found to be influenced by the weight, rate of placement, temperature of the concrete mix, use of retardant admixtures, and effect of vibration or other consolidation methods. How these factors affect lateral pressure will be discussed briefly before considering the magnitude of pressure to be used in form design.

Factors Affecting Lateral Pressure on Forms

Weight of Concrete

The weight of concrete has a direct influence, since hydrostatic pressure at any point in a fluid is created by the weight of superimposed fluid. Liquid (hydrostatic) pressure is the same in all directions at a given depth in the fluid, and it acts at right angles to any surface which confines the fluid. If concrete acted as a true liquid, the pressure would be equal to the density of fluid—150 lb per cu ft is commonly assumed for concrete—times the depth in feet to the point at which pressure was being considered. However, fresh concrete is a mixture of solids and water whose behavior only approximates that of a liquid, and then for a limited time only.

Rate of Placing

The average rate of rise of the concrete in the form is referred to as the rate of placing. As the concrete is being placed, lateral pressure at a given point increases as concrete depth above this point increases. Finally by consolidation, stiffening, or by a combination of the two, the concrete at this point tends to support itself, no longer causing lateral pressure on the forms. The rate of placing has a primary effect on lateral pressure, and the maximum lateral pressure is proportional to the rate of placing, up to a limit equal to the full fluid pressure.

Vibration

Internal vibration tends to consolidate concrete. It also results in temporary lateral pressures locally which are at least 10-20 percent greater than those occurring with simple spading, because it causes concrete to behave as a fluid for the full depth of vibration. Since internal vibration is now a common practice, forms should be designed to withstand the greater pressure. They must also be made tighter to prevent leakage.

Revibration and external vibration are accepted practice for certain types of construction, producing even higher loads on the forms than normal internal vibration, and requiring specially designed forms. External vibration hammers the form against the concrete, causing wide fluctuation in lateral pressure. The frequency and amplitude of external vibration must be adjusted in the field to avoid battering forms to pieces, and yet be sufficient to consolidate the concrete. If maximum vibration that the forms can withstand is inadequate for consolidation, the slump of concrete is usually adjusted upward.

During revibration the vibrator is forced down through freshly placed concrete into layers which have stiffened or nearly reached initial set. Local pres-

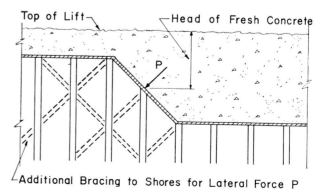

5-3 Simplified drawing of inclined slab form with supporting shores shows diagonal bracing to resist lateral component of pressure.

sures up to 300 psf per ft of head of concrete have been recorded with vigorous revibration. On the whole, however, the effects of revibration and external vibration have not been sufficiently investigated to be expressed in a pressure formula, and therefore *recommendations in this manual are limited to internally vibrated concrete.*

Temperature

Temperature of the concrete at the time of placing has an important influence on pressures because it affects the setting time of concrete. At low temperatures, the concrete takes longer to stiffen and therefore a greater depth can be placed before the lower portion becomes firm enough to be self-supporting. The greater liquid head thus developed results in higher lateral pressures. It is particularly important to keep this in mind when designing forms for concrete to be placed in cold weather or with fly ash replacement or retarding admixtures used in any weather.

Other Variables

Other variables measured at various times which have been found to have an effect on lateral pressures include consistency of concrete, amount and location of reinforcement, ambient temperature, pore water pressure, maximum aggregate size, placing procedures, type of cement, depth of placement, cross section of forms, and smoothness and permeability of the forms. However, with usual concreting practices, the range of these variable effects is generally small and is usually neglected.

Fly ash or other pozzolan used as a cement replacement at low ambient temperature, or with retarding admixtures, has a significant effect on lateral pressure, which must not be overlooked (see p. 79).

Lateral Pressure Values for Form Design

After 50 to 60 years of discussion, laboratory tests, and field investigations, there is still disagreement among engineers, physicists, form-tie manufacturers, and contractors as to the relative importance of the several variables discussed. The question of lateral pressure variation cannot be fully resolved until much more basic research has been undertaken. However, the form planner must adopt safe design assumptions which have proved workable for average conditions on the particular type of job being done, rather than try to outguess field conditions.

It should be understood that the pressure assumption will have an over-all effect on the entire form assembly, and that this assembly is subjected to local load effects quite different from the assumed uniform pressure of the concrete—such as those imposed by swelling of form members, uneven tightening of tie rod assemblies, unpredictable construction activities, and perhaps even by carelessness of construction.

Knowing that a form pressure recommendation with a small margin of safety could result in form failures with the prevailing practices in form construction, ACI Committee 347 studied available data and has made recommendations of lateral pressures * for safe form design. These recommendations cover two cases: (1) maximum lateral pressure on wall forms, with controlled, relatively slow rates of placement, where maximum lateral pressure is limited as concrete begins to set; and (2) maximum pressure on column forms, where the entire form is usually filled in less than the time required for concrete to begin to stiffen. Although pressure at a given point within the form varies with time, exact knowledge of this variation is usually beyond the scope of the designer's need; hence the formulas have been developed to show only the *maximum* pressure used for design.

Wall Forms

For structural concrete ** placed at controlled rates, ACI Committee 347 has developed the formulas below for maximum lateral pressure on the form, for prescribed conditions of temperature, rate of placement, vibration, weight of concrete, and slump. These are working formulas based on presently available experimental data; they are believed practical and are recommended for form design, but no claim is made for their theoretical precision. For walls with R not exceeding 7 ft per hr

$$p = 150 + \frac{9000\,R}{T} \quad \text{maximum} = 2000 \text{ psf or} \atop 150\,h, \text{ whichever is less} \quad \cdots\cdots(5\text{-}1)$$

For walls with R greater than 7 ft per hr

$$p = 150 + \frac{43{,}400}{T} + \frac{2800\,R}{T} \quad \text{maximum} = 2000 \text{ psf or} \atop 150\,h, \text{ whichever is less} \cdots(5\text{-}2)$$

---

* Although Committee 347 has recommended a formula which it believes can safely be used for form design, the scarcity of available test data limits the scope and precision of any such formula. The committee is continuing its pressure studies and has published a field test procedure to standardize and simplify the gathering of further data. Refer to "Testing Program for Lateral Pressure of Concrete," by David E. Fleming and William H. Wolf, ACI JOURNAL, *Proceedings* V. 60, May 1963, pp. 567-574.
** Special formulas for lateral pressures of mass concrete and slip-formed concrete are given in the sections on those techniques. Application of the pressure formula for tunnel work is discussed in Chapter 14. For additional details on the development of these formulas, refer to "Pressures on Formwork," reported by ACI Committee 622, ACI JOURNAL, *Proceedings* V. 55, Aug. 1958, pp. 173-190.

where

p = maximum lateral pressure, psf
R = rate of placement, ft per hr
T = temperature of concrete in the forms, °F
h = maximum height of fresh concrete in the form, ft

These two formulas hold good for internally vibrated structural concrete of normal density, placed at 10 ft per hr or less, and with a slump no more than 4 in. Depth of vibration is limited to 4 ft below the top of concrete surface. Good placing procedures are assumed; for example, vibration is used for consolidation only, not for lateral movement of the concrete.

Table 5-2, based on Eq. (5-1) and (5-2) above, shows the maximum lateral pressures to be used for design of wall forms with varying rates of placement and concrete temperatures ranging from 40 to 90F. Since studs and sheathing are ordinarily uniform throughout their entire height, only this maximum pressure value will be needed for their design. However, wale and tie spacings may be increased near the top of the forms to take advantage of lower maximum lateral pressures there. For example:

A wall form 15 ft high may be concreted at $R = 10$ ft per hr, when the temperature is 60F. Maximum pressure by Eq. (5-2) or from Table 5-2 is 1340 psf. Since this is comparable to fluid pressure up to the time concrete begins to stiffen appreciably, assume that the pressure increases uniformly at 150 psf per ft of depth until the maximum of 1340 psf is reached at a distance 1340/150 or 9 ft below the top of the form. The 1340 maximum is used for design throughout the remaining 6 ft of the form.

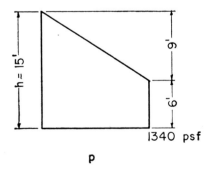

1340 psf

p

In the case of a wall form only 6 ft high, concreted at the same $R = 10$ ft per hr and a temperature of 60F, the limit of 150 h applies since it is less than the value given by the formula. The envelope of maximum pressure then is as shown below.

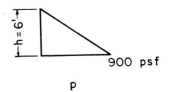

900 psf

p

TABLE 5-2: MAXIMUM LATERAL PRESSURE FOR DESIGN OF WALL FORMS

Based on ACI Committee 347 pressure formulas

NOTE: Do not use design pressures in excess of 2000 psf or 150 × height of fresh concrete in forms, whichever is less

Rate of placement, R, ft per hr	p, maximum lateral pressure, psf, for temperature indicated					
	90F	80F	70F	60F	50F	40F
1	250	262	278	300	330	375
2	350	375	407	450	510	600
3	450	488	536	600	690	825
4	550	600	664	750	870	1050
5	650	712	793	900	1050	1275
6	750	825	921	1050	1230	1500
7	850	938	1050	1200	1410	1725
8	881	973	1090	1246	1466	1795
9	912	1008	1130	1293	1522	1865
10	943	1043	1170	1340	1578	1935

Column Forms

In many types of construction, column forms are small enough that the concrete is placed the full height of the form in a relatively short time. Vibration frequently extends throughout the full height of the form, and resulting maximum lateral pressures are greater than for wall forms. If the full height of column form is filled in less than the time required for the concrete to stiffen appreciably, the pressure is essentially fluid; that is, it increases uniformly from zero at the top of form to a maximum at the base.

The following formula developed by ACI Committee 347 indicates maximum pressure recommended for column form design with concrete weighing approximately 150 lb per cu ft:

$$p = 150 + \frac{9000\,R}{T} \quad \substack{\text{maximum} = 3000\,\text{psf or} \\ 150\,h,\ \text{whichever is less}} \quad \cdots (5\text{-}3)$$

Table 5-3 shows the maximum pressure values given by Eq. (5-3), for concrete temperatures ranging from 40 to 90F. Like the formulas for lateral pressure on wall forms, this too was established on the basis of experimental data and current construction experience. It is recommended for column form design where lifts do not exceed 18 ft. Eq. (5-3) should be used for determining design pressure for forms whose maximum horizontal dimension is 6 ft or less; for all others the wall formulas will apply.

Since the lateral pressure on column forms is comparable to fluid pressure up to the time concrete stiffens appreciably, maximum pressure is assumed to increase uniformly at 150 psf per ft of depth until the maximum as given by Eq. (5-3) is reached. That maximum then remains constant throughout the remaining depth of the form. For example:

> For a 15 ft high column concreted at $R = 10$, temperature of 70F, Eq. (5-3) gives a maximum pressure of 1436 psf. Maximum pressure will occur at a depth of 1436/150 or 9.6 ft below the top of the form, and the maximum of 1436 psf applies for design throughout the remaining depth of form. Column form will be designed for the envelope of maximum pressure shown.

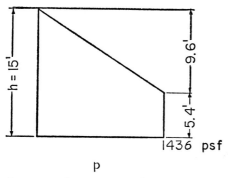

For the same column, concreted at the same rate, but at a temperature of 40F, maximum p by Eq. (5-3) is 2400 psf, which is greater than $150h$ ($15 \times 150 = 2250$ psf), so the latter value represents maximum pressure,

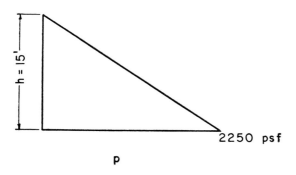

with the distribution shown. Or if this column were concreted at $R = 20$ ft per hr, with the temperature at 70F, Eq. (5-3) gives 2721 psf, again exceeding the limit of $150h$, so the maximum for design would be the same 2250 psf.

Adjustment for Non-Standard Conditions

Both the wall and column form design pressures may be adjusted for certain conditions other than those specified, as explained below.

Weight

For concretes weighing between 100 and 200 lb per cu ft, take a proportionate amount of the maximum pressure value for 150-lb concrete. For instance, if concrete weighs 130 lb per cu ft take $^{130}\!/_{150}$ or 0.87 times the pressure shown for 150-lb concrete.

TABLE 5-3: MAXIMUM LATERAL PRESSURE FOR DESIGN OF COLUMN FORMS

Based on ACI Committee 347 pressure formula

NOTE: Do not use design pressures in excess of 3000 psf or 150 × height of fresh concrete in forms, whichever is less

Rate of placement, R, ft per hr	p, maximum lateral pressure, psf, for temperature indicated					
	90F	80F	70F	60F	50F	40F
1	250	262	278	300	330	375
2	350	375	407	450	510	600
3	450	488	536	600	690	825
4	550	600	664	750	870	1050
5	650	712	793	900	1050	1275
6	750	825	921	1050	1230	1500
7	850	938	1050	1200	1410	1725
8	950	1050	1178	1350	1590	1950
9	1050	1163	1307	1500	1770	2175
10	1150	1275	1436	1650	1950	2400
11	1250	1388	1564	1800	2130	2625
12	1350	1500	1693	1950	2310	2850
13	1450	1613	1822	2100	2490	3000
14	1550	1725	1950	2250	2670	
16	1750	1950	2207	2550	3000	
18	1950	2175	2464	2850		
20	2150	2400	2721	3000		
22	2350	2625	2979			
24	2550	2850	3000			
26	2750	3000	3000 psf maximum governs			
28	2950					
30	3000					

Spaded Concrete

Pressures given by the formulas may be reduced 10 percent if the concrete is spaded instead of vibrated internally.

Effect of Retarders, Fly Ash

Where a retarding admixture * or fly ash or other pozzolan replacement of cement is used in hot weather, an effective value of temperature less than that of the concrete in the forms should be used in the pressure formula. If a retarding admixture or fly ash replacement is used in winter weather, the lateral pressure should be assumed equal to that exerted by a fluid weighing 150 lb per cu ft.

Uplift Due to Lateral Pressure

The lateral pressure of freshly placed concrete will cause uplift where the confining forms are sloping in-

---

* Such admixtures are ordinarily used to produce a setting time equivalent to that of concrete at about 70F.

stead of vertical because the pressure acts at a right angle to the surface confining the concrete. Forms such as for the footings or tank shown in Figure 5-4 must be weighted or tied down to counteract this up-

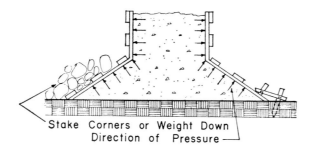

Stake Corners or Weight Down
Direction of Pressure

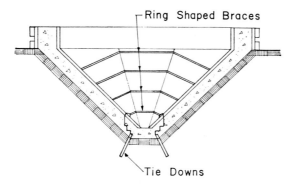

Ring Shaped Braces

Tie Downs

5-4 Inclined forms such as for sloped footing or a tank with sloping walls below grade require tie-downs, weights, or other means of resisting uplift of the freshly placed concrete.

lift effect. For design, pressure is calculated the same as for vertical forms, measuring rate of placing and pressure head (depth) vertically, not along the sloping form face.

Lateral Loads

Forms and shores must be braced to resist all foreseeable lateral loads, such as wind, cable tensions, inclined supports, and dumping of concrete or other impact such as starting and stopping of equipment. Bracing should be provided to withstand the sidesway effects which occur when concrete is placed unsymmetrically on a slab form. In the customary absence of controlling specifications or precise information on lateral loadings that will occur, Committee 347 has recommended that forms be braced for the following minimum lateral loads, acting in any direction:

Slab forms: 100 lb per lineal ft of slab edge, or 2 percent of total dead load on the form (distributed as a uniform load per lineal ft of slab

edge), whichever is greater. Consider only the area of slab formed in a single placement.

Wall forms: wind load of 10 psf or greater if prescribed by local building code; in no case less than 100 lb per lineal ft of wall applied at the top of the form, except for walls less than 8 ft high below grade. Walls of unusual height or exposure should be given special consideration.

Wind loads on enclosures or other windbreaks attached to the forms should be considered, as well as those applied to the forms themselves. For structures such as domes and bins, negative forces due to suction created by the wind on the leeward side of the structure should be considered.

Slab Forms

Minimum lateral load requirements for design of slab form bracing are presented in Table 5-4 for various slab thicknesses. If the formwork is enclosed, as in winter concreting for example, wind load based on local code requirements should be used for bracing design if it exceeds the tabulated minimum.

EXAMPLE: Find the minimum lateral load for design of bracing for a 50 x 100 ft slab, 6 in. thick, 10 ft above grade ($h = 10$ ft).

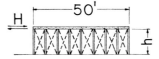

By Table 5-4, H along the 100-ft edge is 100 lb per lineal ft; use for design of members indicated by dashed lines.

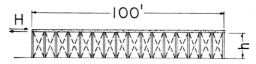

H along the 50-ft edge is 180 lb per lineal ft; use for design of members indicated by dashed lines.

Suppose the same formwork is enclosed, and local building codes call for 25 psf wind force. Wind force applied at slab level would be $h/2 \times 25$ or 125 lb per lineal ft. This is greater than tabulated value of H along the 100-ft edge, and would be used for design of bracing parallel to the 50-ft slab dimension. However, the tabulated H of 180 lb per lineal ft would govern along the 50-ft slab edge.

It must be emphasized that these are only minimum requirements for slab form bracing. When unusual unbalanced loading from unsymmetrical placement of concrete is anticipated, or when impact from starting and stopping of unusually heavy equipment or dumping of concrete can be anticipated, a complete structural analysis of bracing requirements should be made.

TABLE 5-4: MINIMUM LATERAL FORCE FOR DESIGN OF SLAB FORM BRACING

NOTE: Special conditions may require
heavier bracing as noted in text.

H, lb per lineal ft, applied along
edge of slab in either direction

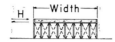

Solid slab thickness, in.*	Dead load, psf*	Width of slab in direction of force, ft				
		20	40	60	80	100
4	65	100	100	100	104	130
6	90	100	100	108	144	180
8	115	100	100	138	184	230
10	140	100	112	168	224	280
12	165	100	132	198	264	330
14	190	100	152	228	304	380
16	215	100	172	258	344	430
20	265	106	212	318	424	530

* Slab thicknesses given for concrete weighing 150 lb per cu ft; allowance of 15
psf for weight of forms. For concrete of different weight or for joist slabs and
beam and slab combinations, estimate dead load per sq ft, and work from dead
load column, interpolating as needed on straight line basis.

TABLE 5-5: MINIMUM LATERAL FORCE FOR DESIGN OF WALL FORM BRACING

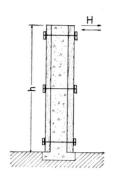

Minimum lateral force, H, lb per
lineal ft, applied at top of wall
form. H may act in either
direction.

Wall height, h, in ft	Committee 347 minimum, 100 lb/ft or 10 psf wind	Wind force prescribed by local code *			
		15 psf	20 psf	25 psf	30 psf
(Above grade)					
4 or less	20	30	40	50	60
6	30	45	60	75	90
8	100	100	100	100	100
10	100	100	100	125	150
12	100	100	120	150	180
14	100	105	140	175	210
16	100	120	160	200	240
18	100	135	180	225	270
20	100	150	200	250	300
22 or more	5.0 h	7.5 h	10.0 h	12.5 h	15.0 h
Walls below grade					
8 ft or less	0	—	—	—	—
More than 8 ft	100	—	—	—	—

* Wind force prescribed by local code shall be used whenever it would require a
lateral force for design greater than the minimums shown.

Wall Forms

Wall forms must be braced laterally to allow for wind or accidental eccentric loadings. If the wind force prescribed by local code exceeds 10 psf, the wind effect is $h/2 \times$ wind; otherwise the minimum wind allowance is $10 \times h/2$. For walls over 20 ft high, either local code wind or 10 psf minimum wind controls; for walls 8 to 20 ft high, either local code wind or 100 lb per lineal ft minimum controls bracing design. For walls under 8 ft high, wind controls. Basement walls 8 ft or less below grade have no specified requirement for bracing, because there is little danger involved, and it is assumed that builders will supply bracing enough to prevent misalignment during concrete placing.

Table 5-5 shows minimum lateral forces recommended for design of bracing for wall forms. These values of course apply to forms where the lateral pressure is carried by ties; if a single-side form is used with concrete supported on the other side against earth or existing structure, bracing or struts will be designed to carry lateral pressure of the fresh concrete, as explained on p. 112.

Other Loads

Imposition of construction loads on the partially completed structure should not be allowed except with the approval of the engineer-architect. If it is necessary to use recently cast concrete areas for storage of materials and supplies, forms, shores, or reshores must be designed to carry this extra load without damage to the concrete.

If the form designer wishes to plan shoring and reshoring in multistory work to take full advantage of the strength of the partially completed structure, he must know or estimate the live load capacity for which the completed structure is designed, and the actual strength of the partially cured concrete. Any

5-5 External form vibrators impose added loads on the forms not provided for in the pressure formula on p. 77, and require heavier form construction; bolted rather than nailed connections may be needed. Mounting plates (top center) receive vibrators as they are moved from one point to another along the form.

temporary loads thus imposed on partially cured concrete should be within a safety factor at least equal to that for permanent loads.

Partially cured concrete deflects more than fully aged concrete of the same compressive strength. Often the critical limit on temporary construction loads will not be the strength but avoidance of excessive deflection, cracking, and inadequately developed bond for splice details of reinforcement. Under additional loads, *many shoring or reshoring systems adequate to support the concrete and formwork will develop negative moments in partially cured concrete areas where there is no negative reinforcing.* Resulting cracks may be objectionable for the life of the building. These problems are discussed in more detail in the section on reshoring, p. 217.

Form designers should be alert to provide for special loading conditions such as walls constructed over spans of slabs or beams which exert a different loading pattern before hardening of concrete than that for which the supporting structure is designed. Where stresses may be induced in a concrete member before it is fully constructed, because of the type of forming or falsework used, the architect-engineer should review design of the member in relation to the proposed formwork support. This condition may occur in heavy flexural members, such as massive bridge pier struts, which are concreted in several lifts. When the first lift has been cast and begins to develop strength, it may become stiffer than the supporting formwork and hence carry some of the load from subsequently concreted lifts.

Structures Designed for Composite Action

Structures or parts of structures which are designed so that the concrete portions act compositely with other materials or with other parts of the structure present special forming problems which should be anticipated in the design of the structure. Requirements for shoring or other deflection control of the formwork should be clearly presented by the engineer in the specifications. Where successive placements are to act compositely in the completed structure, deflection control becomes extremely critical to prevent preloading reinforcing steel before imposition of live load.

Shoring, with or without cambering of portions of the structure during placement and curing of the concrete, should be analyzed separately for the effects of dead load of wet concrete and for the effect of other construction loads which may be imposed before the concrete attains its design strength.

Where camber is specified for previously installed components of the structure, allowance should be made for the resultant preloading of the shores before application of the dead load of concrete.

6:FORM DESIGN

WHEN THE MATERIALS for formwork have been chosen, and the anticipated loading estimated as explained in Chapter 5, the form designer takes up the problem—how to make the form strong enough to carry the anticipated loads safely, and stiff enough to hold its shape under full load. At the same time the builder or contractor wants to keep costs down by not overbuilding the form. Some form builders operate on the basis of their considerable experience, knowing that what worked on a previous job can be adapted to the present situation.

However, with the coming of new materials and new systems in the formwork business, and with mounting demands for efficiency and economy, consistent with safety, it is well to be able to make what is called a rational design; that is, one calculated on the basis of known strengths of materials and the estimated loads that must be carried. On large and small projects alike, careful planning of formwork can save both time and money.

Although increasing numbers of new materials are being introduced for forming, basic support is provided in most cases by wood, plywood, or steel members and the discussions of this chapter will be focused on them. However, the same general principles can be applied to other materials whose strength properties are known.

For extremely heavy loadings, for highly specialized types of construction, or where there is unusual danger to life or property, a complete and precise structural design of formwork may be required. This chapter in no way seeks to replace the structural engineer whose services should be sought when an exact design of formwork is indicated. However, for much common formwork, design based on simplifying assumptions and simplified formulas is completely satisfactory. Thus the purpose here is to present the simplified formulas and assumptions that are commonly used, and to explain the necessary calculations by means of examples. As a further aid, the tables of Chapter 7 have been developed on the basis of these formulas, and it is shown there how size and spacing

of many form members can be determined directly from the tables without calculations.

These design simplifications will also be useful in arriving at a trial design in those cases where a rigorous structural analysis is deemed necessary.

Basic Simplifications

Although there is a need for greater accuracy than is frequently used in formwork design, too much refinement wastes time. Absolute precision in calculation of bending moments, for example, is unwarranted when so many assumptions have to be made as to loads, lateral pressures, quality of materials, workmanship at the site, and other factors. Unless there is unusual control over field conditions, the actual construction will be less accurate than office calculations, perhaps negating the designer's efforts toward precision.

The convenience of modular spacing may also operate to reduce the significance of extremely precise calculations. If there is a 10-ft length of slab to be supported, it will be simpler from a construction point of view to divide it into five 2-ft spans, even though support spacing might be calculated at 26 in. The commonly used large sheets of plywood should be supported at panel edges, and calculated spans are often adjusted to this requirement, rather than holding rigidly to a calculated spacing.

These two considerations—the approximate nature of many of the design assumptions, plus simplified modular approach desirable for actual construction—justify a simplified approach to form design. The following simplifications are used with a few noted exceptions in the suggested form design procedure, and in preparation of the form design tables that follow in Chapter 7.

1. *All loads are assumed as uniformly distributed.* The loads on sheathing, joists, and studs are in fact always distributed, though not always uniformly. Loads on wales, ledgers, etc. are applied at points where the studs or joists bear on them,

83

NOTATION

A = area of cross section, sq in.

b = width of beam cross section, in.

c = allowable timber stress, psi, in compression ∥ to grain

$c\perp$ = allowable timber stress, psi, in compression ⊥ to grain

Δ = deflection, in.

Δ_{max} = maximum deflection, in.

d = net dimension, in., of face under consideration for simple solid wood column; measured parallel to plane of lateral support

E = modulus of elasticity, psi

e = columnar shortening, in.

f = unit stress in extreme fiber in bending, psi

H = horizontal unit shearing stress, psi

h = depth of beam cross section, in.

I = moment of inertia, in.$^4 \left(= \dfrac{bh^3}{12} \right)$

I.D. = inside diameter, in.

L = span, ft

l = span or length, in.

l/d = ratio of unsupported length to least dimension in compression member (shore)

M_{max} = maximum induced bending moment, ft-lb or in.-lb as indicated

M_r = resisting moment, in.-lb ($= fS$)

O.D. = outside diameter, in.

P = total concentrated load, lb

p = lateral pressure or load, psf

r = radius of gyration

S = section modulus, in.$^3 \left(= \dfrac{bh^2}{6} \right)$

s = spacing of members, in.

v = average shearing stress, or average horizontal shearing stress, psi

V = maximum vertical shear, lb (same as end reaction for simple beam)

w = uniformly distributed load, lb per lineal ft

W = total uniformly distributed load, lb ($= wL$)

but it is convenient and generally sufficiently accurate to use an equivalent uniform load for design, so that the spacing and number of point loads can be neglected.* If a preliminary design based on these assumptions appears marginal, it can be rechecked by more exact methods.

2. Beams supported over three or more spans are regarded as continuous, and approximate formulas are used.

3. For beams continuous over two spans, design values for simple spans may be safely used when deflection or bending moment govern the span (this is conservative for deflection). Although this condition prevails for many of the load and working stress combinations common for formwork members, short heavily loaded spans are frequently governed by shear, and one- and two-span beams should be individually checked using the formulas in Table 6-1.

4. Strength of nailed connections is neglected in determining size of main form members. This does not apply when considering splices, braces, brackets, etc.

* If the spacing of point loads exceeds one-third to one-half of the span between supports, fiber stress and deflection should be investigated for the worst loading condition.

Beam Formulas

In general, formwork consists of sheathing to retain the concrete and supporting members necessary to hold the sheathing firmly in place. Direct support for the sheathing is provided by members called studs

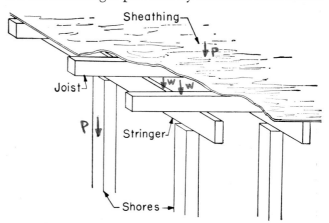

6-1 Parts of typical slab formwork

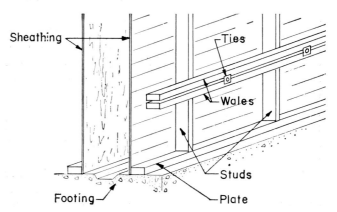

6-2 Typical wall form with components identified. Boards and plywood are both common sheathing material.

in vertical formwork and by joists in horizontal formwork for slabs. Studs are usually supported by cross members called wales, and the joists by stringers. The wales or stringers are held in place by tension members such as tie rods or bolts, or compression members such as shores or posts. The whole assembly may be braced by struts or guys and cables.

Although these basic elements of formwork are referred to as sheathing, studs, joists, wales and stringers,* all (except ties and shores) act structurally as beams. Some are horizontal, some are vertical, and they have different kinds of support, but only a few beam formulas are needed for their analysis.

Table 6-1 shows formulas for shear, bending moment, and deflection for some of the beam conditions

* Many other terms—lagging, girts, rangers, soldiers, bearers, etc.—are applied to these same form members. See glossary of formwork terms in the appendix.

TABLE 6-1: BEAM FORMULAS APPLICABLE FOR FORMWORK DESIGN

BEAM CONTINUOUS OVER TWO EQUAL SPANS, UNIFORM LOAD

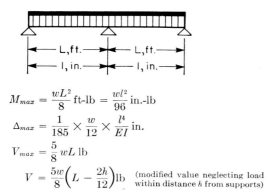

$$M_{max} = \frac{wL^2}{8} \text{ ft-lb} = \frac{wl^2}{96} \text{ in.-lb}$$

$$\Delta_{max} = \frac{1}{185} \times \frac{w}{12} \times \frac{l^4}{EI} \text{ in.}$$

$$V_{max} = \frac{5}{8} wL \text{ lb}$$

$$V = \frac{5w}{8}\left(L - \frac{2h}{12}\right) \text{lb} \quad \text{(modified value neglecting load within distance } h \text{ from supports)}$$

CANTILEVER (FIXED AT ONE END) BEAM, UNIFORM LOAD

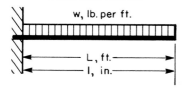

$$M_{max} = \frac{wL^2}{2} \text{ ft-lb} = \frac{wl^2}{24} \text{ in.-lb}$$

$$\Delta_{max} = \frac{w}{12} \times \frac{l^4}{8EI} = \frac{wl^4}{96EI} \text{ in.}$$

$$V_{max} = wL \text{ lb}$$

BEAM OVERHANGING ONE SUPPORT, UNIFORM LOAD BETWEEN SUPPORTS

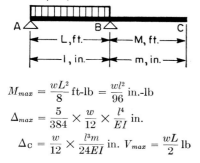

$$M_{max} = \frac{wL^2}{8} \text{ ft-lb} = \frac{wl^2}{96} \text{ in.-lb}$$

$$\Delta_{max} = \frac{5}{384} \times \frac{w}{12} \times \frac{l^4}{EI} \text{ in.}$$

$$\Delta_C = \frac{w}{12} \times \frac{l^3 m}{24EI} \text{ in.} \quad V_{max} = \frac{wL}{2} \text{ lb}$$

SIMPLY SUPPORTED BEAM, CONCENTRATED LOAD AT MIDPOINT

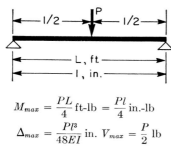

$$M_{max} = \frac{PL}{4} \text{ ft-lb} = \frac{Pl}{4} \text{ in.-lb}$$

$$\Delta_{max} = \frac{Pl^3}{48EI} \text{ in.} \quad V_{max} = \frac{P}{2} \text{ lb}$$

BEAM CONTINUOUS OVER 3 OR MORE SPANS, UNIFORM LOAD (approximate values)

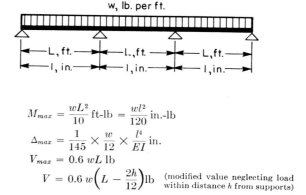

$$M_{max} = \frac{wL^2}{10} \text{ ft-lb} = \frac{wl^2}{120} \text{ in.-lb}$$

$$\Delta_{max} = \frac{1}{145} \times \frac{w}{12} \times \frac{l^4}{EI} \text{ in.}$$

$$V_{max} = 0.6 \, wL \text{ lb}$$

$$V = 0.6 \, w\left(L - \frac{2h}{12}\right) \text{lb} \quad \text{(modified value neglecting load within distance } h \text{ from supports)}$$

SIMPLY SUPPORTED BEAM, UNIFORM LOAD

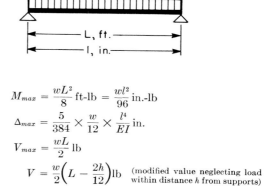

$$M_{max} = \frac{wL^2}{8} \text{ ft-lb} = \frac{wl^2}{96} \text{ in.-lb}$$

$$\Delta_{max} = \frac{5}{384} \times \frac{w}{12} \times \frac{l^4}{EI} \text{ in.}$$

$$V_{max} = \frac{wL}{2} \text{ lb}$$

$$V = \frac{w}{2}\left(L - \frac{2h}{12}\right) \text{lb} \quad \text{(modified value neglecting load within distance } h \text{ from supports)}$$

BEAM OVERHANGING ONE SUPPORT, UNIFORM LOAD

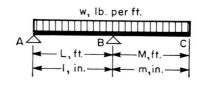

$$M_{max \, A\text{-}B} = \frac{w}{8L^2}(L + M)^2(L - M)^2 \text{ ft-lb}$$

$$= \frac{w}{96l^2}(l + m)^2(l - m)^2 \text{ in.-lb}$$

$$M_B = \frac{wM^2}{2} \text{ ft-lb} = \frac{wm^2}{24} \text{ in.-lb}$$

$$\Delta_C = \frac{w}{12} \times \frac{m}{24EI}(4m^2l - l^3 + 3m^3)$$

$$\Delta_x \left(\substack{\text{at } x \text{ in.} \\ \text{from A}}\right) = \frac{w}{12} \times \frac{x}{24EIl}(l^4 - 2l^2x^2 + lx^3 - 2m^2l^2 + 2m^2x^2) \text{ in.}$$

$$V_{max \, B} = \frac{w}{2L}(L^2 + M^2) \text{lb}$$

most commonly encountered in formwork; these formulas are sufficient for the simplified analysis proposed and explained in this chapter. For conditions that require more exact investigation, standard works on timber design and engineering mechanics are recommended.[1,2]

Design Criteria

Allowable Stresses

Working stresses for use in the design of formwork are discussed in the section on formwork materials, p. 33; these are based on the applicable codes or specifications governing the use of the given material and include appropriate factors of safety. When fabricated formwork units are used, manufacturers' recommendations for allowable unit stresses may be followed if supported by standard tests or by successful experience records.

Formwork is ordinarily thought of as a temporary structure because it remains in place only a short time. As explained in the section on materials, the working stresses recommended for temporary structures are often significantly greater than those for permanent construction. The form designer, in the interest of economy, will want to take advantage of those greater working stresses whenever possible; however, it is also in the interest of economy to get the most possible reuses of form components, and *if a panel or member is to be used many times it cannot properly be regarded as a temporary structure, even though it is loaded temporarily for the job at hand.* With this in mind, ACI Committee 347 has made the following recommendation:

> For forms of a temporary nature with limited reuse, allowable stresses should be those specified in the appropriate design codes or specifications for temporary structures or for temporary loads on permanent structures.
>
> Where there will be a considerable number of form reuses and where forms to be used many times are fabricated from material such as steel, aluminum, or magnesium, it is recommended that the formwork be designed as a permanent structure carrying permanent loads.

Minimum safety factors for accessories are also recommended by Committee 347 as shown in Table 6-2. Safety factors are based on ultimate strength with the provision that the yield point must not be exceeded.

TABLE 6-2: SAFETY FACTORS FOR FORMWORK ACCESSORIES

ACCESSORY	TYPE OF CONSTRUCTION	ACCESSORY SAFETY FACTOR, BASED ON ULTIMATE STRENGTH *
FORM TIE	Light formwork; or ordinary lifts at grade and 16 ft or less above grade	1.5
	Heavy formwork; all formwork more than 16 ft above grade or unusually hazardous	2.0
FORM ANCHOR	Light form panel anchorage only; no hazard to life involved in failure	1.5
	Heavy forms—failure would endanger life—supporting form weight and concrete pressures only	2.0
	Falsework supporting weight of forms, concrete, working loads, and impact	3.0
FORM HANGERS	Light formwork. Design load—including weight of forms, concrete, and 50 psf minimum live load—totals less than 150 psf	1.5
	Heavy formwork; form plus concrete weight 100 psf or more; unusually hazardous work	2.0
LIFTING INSERTS	Tilt-up panels	2.0
	Precast panels	3.0
EXPENDABLE STRAND DEFLECTION DEVICES **—Pretensioned concrete		2.0
REUSABLE STRAND DEFLECTION DEVICES **—Pretensioned concrete		3.0

* Ultimate strengths guaranteed by reputable manufacturers may be used in lieu of tests for ultimate strength.
** These safety factors also apply to pieces of prestressing strand which are used as part of the deflection device.

Deflection

The type of work being done or job specifications will commonly determine what deflection can be allowed. Forms must be so designed that the various parts will not deflect beyond these prescribed limits. Otherwise wavy lines, unsightly bulges, and possibly even cracks (in floor) will mar the appearance of the concrete. The exact amount of deflection permissible depends upon the desired finish as well as the location. A small deflection that might escape notice on a rough textured wall might be most objectionable in a very smooth surface. If surfaces are near eye level, or can be observed from short distances, less deflection can be allowed than in upper stories where irregularities are not so noticeable. Special deflection problems for architectural concrete forms are noted in Chapter 11.

Tolerances for the finished work must be considered in determining allowable deflection of formwork; the deflection must be kept well within the specified tolerance limits for completed construction, since deviations for other reasons must also be allowed for. In the absence of job specifications to the contrary, an acceptable and frequently used value of allowable deflection for structural concrete work is $\frac{1}{360}$ of the span of the formwork member.* Some designers prefer to limit deflection to a maximum of $\frac{1}{16}$ in. for sheathing and $\frac{1}{8}$ in. for other form members. Where the span of the form member is relatively long—5 ft or more—$\frac{1}{4}$ in. deflection is frequently acceptable.

Deflection will govern design where depth of member is small in relation to span, as is often the case with sheathing. Joists, studs, and other members should also be checked for deflection, but more often bending and shear are governing factors in their design.

In the deflection formulas that follow, the factor E, modulus of elasticity, appears. This is a measure of stiffness and has been determined by tests for many construction materials. Note in the discussion of the properties of wood that this factor is different for various kinds of wood; this means that for the same load and same size of lumber, some woods will deflect much more than others.

When wood becomes wet, as is often the case with form sheathing, it becomes more flexible, and this loss of stiffness is reflected in the lower E values recommended for sheathing (p. 33). The larger the E values, the stiffer the wood, and hence the smaller the deflection will be.

The approximate value of maximum deflection for a beam continuous over three or more spans is

$$\Delta_{max} = \frac{w}{12} \times \frac{l^4}{145\,EI} \quad \ldots \ldots \ldots \ldots (6\text{-}1)$$

where Δ_{max} is deflection in inches, $w =$ uniform load, lb per ft, and $l =$ span, in.

If the allowable deflection is $l/360$, substitute that value for Δ_{max}, and solve for l to find the allowable span (in inches) of a form member, with deflection the governing criterion:

$$\frac{l}{360} = \frac{w}{12} \times \frac{l^4}{145\,EI}, \quad l = \sqrt[3]{\frac{12 \times 145\,EI}{360\,w}}$$

$$l = 1.69\sqrt[3]{\frac{EI}{w}} \quad \ldots \ldots \ldots \ldots (6\text{-}2)$$

* The new "Specifications for Structural Concrete for Buildings (ACI 301-72)" limits deflection of form members for architectural concrete to $l/400$ unless otherwise specified.

Similarly, for a simple beam, the maximum deflection in inches is

$$\Delta_{max} = \frac{5}{384} \times \frac{w}{12} \times \frac{l^4}{EI} \quad \ldots \ldots \ldots \ldots (6\text{-}3)$$

Again setting Δ_{max} equal to $l/360$, the allowable span becomes:

$$l = \sqrt[3]{\frac{384 \times 12 \times EI}{5\,w \times 360}}$$

which reduces to

$$l = 1.37\sqrt[3]{\frac{EI}{w}} \quad \ldots \ldots \ldots \ldots (6\text{-}4)$$

If a limiting deflection of $\frac{1}{16}$ or $\frac{1}{8}$ in. has been set, a check should be made to see if that limit has been exceeded.

Bending

Design for bending is based on the allowable or working stress in flexure for the material being used. Allowable flexural stresses for various kinds of lumber, plywood, and other materials are given on p. 33. From Table 6-1, maximum bending moment for a simple beam uniformly loaded is

$$M_{max} = \frac{wl^2}{96} \text{ in.-lb} \quad \ldots \ldots \ldots \ldots (6\text{-}5)$$

and for a uniformly loaded continuous beam (more than three supports)

$$M_{max} = \frac{wl^2}{120} \text{ in.-lb} \quad \ldots \ldots \ldots \ldots (6\text{-}6)$$

where $w =$ uniformly distributed load, lb per ft, and $l =$ span, in.

The resisting moment of the member being designed is

$$M_r = fS \quad \ldots \ldots \ldots \ldots (6\text{-}7)$$

in which $M_r =$ resisting moment in in.-lb; $f =$ allowable stress in extreme fiber in bending, psi; and $S =$ section modulus $(bh^2/6)$, of the member in.³

Since the resisting moment provided must equal or exceed the applied bending moment, the maximum allowable span is determined by equating $M_r = M_{max}$ and solving for l; thus:

$$fS = \frac{wl^2}{96}$$

$$l = \sqrt{\frac{96\,fS}{w}}$$

$$l = 9.80\sqrt{\frac{fS}{w}} \text{ (simple beam)} \quad \ldots \ldots \ldots (6\text{-}8)$$

or

$$fS = \frac{wl^2}{120}$$

$$l = \sqrt{\frac{120\,fS}{w}}$$

$$l = 10.95\sqrt{\frac{fS}{w}} \quad \text{(continuous beam)}\dots\dots(6\text{-}9)$$

The basic flexure formula, $f = M/S$, can be used to check bending stress when all conditions of span and loading are known.

A beam of circular cross section is assumed to have the same strength in flexure as a square beam of equal cross-sectional area.

Concentrated Loads

It must be remembered that the simplified design procedure developed here is based on uniformly distributed loads, although some form members such as wales or stringers or ledgers actually support a group of concentrated loads. This simplification is satisfactory for most cases, but if the spacing of point loads exceeds about one-third to one-half of the span between supports of the beam under consideration, a detailed investigation should be made for the worst loading condition. This should be kept in mind particularly when designing heavy timber or steel members at wide spacing.

Shear

In a loaded beam there is a tendency for one part of the beam to move vertically with respect to an adjoining part; this tendency for movement at right angles to the beam axis is referred to as *vertical shear*. There is also a tendency for fibers to slide past one another in a horizontal direction, parallel to the length of the beam, and this is called *horizontal shear*. Obviously these terms were developed when viewing the beam as a horizontal member, but by thinking of their direction in relation to the axis of the beam, they can easily be applied to beams positioned vertically, such as the studs in formwork.

At any point in a beam, horizontal and vertical shear are of equal intensity, acting at right angles to each other. Uniform materials like steel can resist either type of shear equally well, but a fibrous material like wood does not resist splitting or shearing between the fibers (which are generally parallel to the beam axis) as well as it resists shearing action across the grain. Since the horizontal shearing stress is more critical for wood, and wood has long been one of the major materials for formwork, it is common

when considering shear for formwork design to speak in terms of horizontal shear.

The intensity of horizontal shear within the beam is calculated on the basis of external vertical shear V at the section being considered. In designing formwork, only the section at which V is maximum need be considered. Maximum values of V are shown for beam loading conditions in Table 6-1.[*]

Timber Beams

The maximum shearing stress in a rectangular timber beam is calculated by the formula

$$H = \frac{3V}{2bh}\dots\dots\dots\dots(6\text{-}10)$$

where $V = wL/2$ for simply supported beams of uniform load, and $V = 0.6wL$ (approximately) for a uniformly loaded beam continuous over three or more spans. (L = span, ft; w = uniform load, lb per lineal ft; b = width of beam, in.; and h = depth of beam, in.)

H must not exceed the allowable unit stress in horizontal shear for the species and grade of lumber being used.

If a timber beam does not qualify for shear loading when checked by the foregoing method, design specifications of the National Forest Products Association[1] permit recalculation neglecting all loads within a distance h from either support. In this case V becomes $w/2 (L - 2h/12)$ for a simply supported beam or $0.6w (L - 2h/12)$ for a continuous beam.

Horizontal shearing stress then is:

for simple beam uniformly loaded

$$H = \frac{3w}{4bh}\left(L - \frac{2h}{12}\right)\dots\dots\dots(6\text{-}11)$$

for continuous beam uniformly loaded

$$l = 13.33\frac{Hbh}{w}$$

$$H = \frac{0.9w}{bh}\left(L - \frac{2h}{12}\right)\dots\dots\dots(6\text{-}12)$$

Shearing stress may determine the size of member required where short spans are heavily loaded. It is rarely the governing factor in sheathing, but should be checked for design of other form members. Where spacing of concentrated loads is greater than one-third to one-half of the beam span, it may be necessary to check shear on the basis of point loads, rather than using the equivalent uniform load which is sufficiently accurate for much formwork design.

Steel Beams

Because of the way shearing stresses are distributed, it is assumed that the web of steel beams is the

---

[*] If shear is being checked for other loading conditions, it is helpful to remember that V at any section is equal to the algebraic sum of all vertical forces, both loads and reactions, on either side of the section.

only portion of the cross section resisting shear. If the average unit shearing stress v does not exceed an allowable shearing unit stress, usually 40 percent of the specified minimum yield stress, the beam is safe with respect to shear. The following formula is used:

$$v = \frac{V}{A} \qquad \qquad (6\text{-}13)$$

where V = maximum vertical shear, lb, and A = area of the web of steel section, sq in. (Over-all depth of beam multiplied by web thickness gives area.)

Most steel members large enough to resist flexure are adequate for shear stresses; however, short beams or beams with large loads near the supports should always be checked for shear.

Plywood

Plywood panels are checked for rolling shear in the plane of the plies using the formula

$$v = \frac{VQ}{bI} \qquad \qquad (6\text{-}14)$$

where $V = wL/2$ for simply supported beams and $V = 0.6\ wL$ for beams continuous over three or more spans. The rolling shear constant I/Q is taken from Table 4-3 data.

Bearing

Bearing stress or compression perpendicular to grain will be a factor in design of timber members of formwork. Joists rest on stringers or ledgers—ledgers or stringers may in turn bear on posts or shores—studs bear against wales. All these members must either have sufficient area of bearing on their supports to prevent crushing of the grain of the timbers or a means of adjustment to compensate for crushing. Otherwise the formwork will settle out of position or have undesirable cracks and openings.

Hardwood caps or metal bearing plates may be placed between vertical and horizontal bearing timbers so that the concentrated pressure from the posts may be distributed over a large area of the relatively weaker side grain of the horizontal member.

The allowable unit stresses for compression perpendicular to the grain shown in Table 4-2 apply to bearings of any length at the ends of the beam, and to all bearings 6 in. or more in length at any other location. When calculating the bearing area at the ends of beams, no allowance is made for the fact that, as the beam bends, the pressure upon the inner edge of the bearing is greater than at the end of the beam.

For bearings less than 6 in. long and not nearer than 3 in. to the end of a member, the maximum al-

lowable load per square inch is obtained by multiplying the allowable unit stresses in compression perpendicular to grain by the following factor:

$$\frac{l + \frac{3}{8}}{l}$$

in which l is the length of bearing in inches measured along the grain of the wood. For round washers or bearing areas, use a length equal to the diameter.

The multiplying factors for indicated lengths of bearing on such small areas as plates and washers are shown below.

Length of bearing, in.	½	1	1½	2	3	4	6 or more
Factor	1.75	1.38	1.25	1.19	1.13	1.10	1.00

Bearing Examples

In the following examples, it is assumed that construction grade Douglas fir lumber is used. According to Table 4-2, p. 33, the allowable $c \perp$ grain of the wood is 385 psi for multiple use formwork.

1. Check the bearing stress when ties loaded to 4000 lb have 3½ in. round washers supported against double 2x4 wales. The allowable bearing stress may be increased for any washers 3 in. or more from the end of the wales because the length of bearing is less than 6 in. Multiply the allowable compression perpendicular to the grain by the factor $(l + \frac{3}{8})/l$:

$$385 \times \left(\frac{3\frac{1}{2} + \frac{3}{8}}{3\frac{1}{2}} \right) = 385 \times 1.11 = 426 \text{ psi}$$

This gives the adjusted allowable $c \perp$ grain; if the washer were within 3 in. of the end of the wale, no adjustment would be permitted and the basic value of 385 psi would be used.

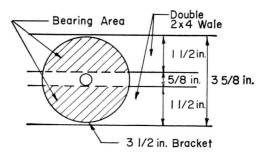

The bearing area is the total area of plate less the ⅝ in. wide strip across the middle which does not contact the wood:

$$\text{bearing area} = \frac{\pi d^2}{4} - (d \times \tfrac{5}{8})$$
$$= \frac{\pi 3.50^2}{4} - 3.50\,(0.625)$$
$$= 9.62 - 2.19$$
$$= 7.43 \text{ sq in.}$$

$$\text{actual bearing stress} = \frac{\text{total load}}{\text{bearing area}}$$
$$= \frac{4000}{7.43} \text{ or } 538 \text{ psi}$$

Since the actual bearing stress of 538 psi exceeds the adjusted allowable $c \perp$ grain, some adjustment should be made. A larger washer might be used to increase the bearing area, or the tie load might be reduced by changing tie spacing or rate of placement.

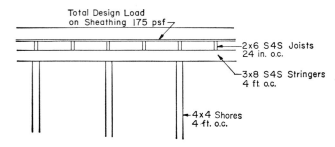

2. Investigate bearing stresses in the slab form shown at points where stringers bear on shores and where joists bear on stringers, again using construction grade Douglas fir. Average shore load is 4 ft × 4 ft × 175 psf = 2800 lb. Length of bearing is 3½ in., which permits an adjusted $c \perp$ grain of 385 × 1.11

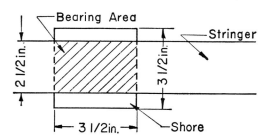

or 426 psi. Contact area between shore and stringer is $2\frac{1}{2} \times 3\frac{1}{2} = 8.75$ sq in. $c \perp$ grain of stringer $= \frac{2800}{8.75} = 320$ psi. Bearing stress is therefore satisfactory at this point.

Now examine the bearing between joist and stringer. Average load transmitted to stringer by joist is 2 ft × 4 ft × 175 psf = 1400 lb. Length of bearing on joist is 2½ in.

$$\text{allowable } c \perp \text{ grain} = 385 \times \left(\frac{l + \frac{3}{8}}{l}\right)$$
$$= 385 \times \frac{2\frac{7}{8}}{2\frac{1}{2}}$$
$$= 443 \text{ psi}$$

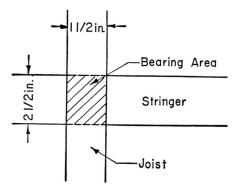

Contact area between joist and stringer is 2½ in. × 1½ in. = 3.75 sq in.

$$\text{actual } c \perp \text{ grain} = \frac{\text{load}}{\text{bearing area}} = \frac{1400}{3.75} \text{ or } 373 \text{ psi}$$

This bearing stress is also within the allowable 443 psi, and so the design is satisfactory with respect to bearing stresses.

Wall, Slab, and Beam Form Design

Design of formwork involves a step by step analysis of sheathing and framing members. The sequence of these design steps depends in large measure on the over-all plan for the job. One procedure is based on working out from the sheathing to the various supporting members, assuming that tie or shore support can be provided wherever the form members need it. This procedure is reversed at times to meet particular job conditions; for example, installation of ties in a wall might be difficult because of heavy reinforcement or tight working space. To meet such a situation the number of ties could be reduced to a minimum by selecting heavy ties at wide spacing and designing other form members to this tie requirement.

If points of support for shores are limited by poor bearing or the need for large open spaces in the work area, long span metal members—so-called horizontal shoring—may be introduced, and other components sized to fit them. If scaffold-type shoring is used, its spacing may first be determined on the basis of loading to its recommended working limit; then joists and stringers are selected to suit this spacing. The latter approach will generally give a design of heavier members at wider spacings than the approach of working out from the sheathing. Using certain materials or accessories already on hand may save money, but they will also influence design of the other formwork parts which must be adapted to them.

Thus it can be seen that there are several different starting points for wall and slab form design. The following suggested design procedures cover these alternatives for various members. However, the accompanying design examples are based on a single set of assumed job conditions, and thus only one of the alternative courses is fully developed for each problem.

Wall Forms

Studs and sheathing are ordinarily uniform throughout their entire height. Wale and tie spacings may be increased near the top of the forms to take advantage of lower maximum lateral pressures there. However, spacing of ties and wales is often kept uniform throughout wall height for convenience of construction and uniform appearance after stripping.

1. *Lateral pressure for design*—From the known conditions of the concreting operation, estimate the maximum design pressure, based on recommendations in Chapter 5.

2. *Sheathing thickness and spacing of its supports* (*stud spacing*)—One of these will be predetermined, based on considerations of material availability, economy, etc.

BENDING CHECK

A. If sheathing thickness is fixed, determine its maximum allowable span, which is the required spacing of studs.
B. If the stud spacing is fixed, calculate the required section modulus S of sheathing to carry the load, and select lumber, plywood, or other material to meet this requirement from Tables 4-1 and 4-3.

DEFLECTION CHECK

A. If sheathing thickness is fixed, calculate maximum allowable span which satisfies deflection requirements.
B. If the stud spacing is fixed, transpose the deflection equation to solve for the required moment of inertia, I. Then select sheathing material to meet this requirement, using Tables 4-1 and 4-3.

SHEAR CHECK

A. If sheathing thickness is predetermined, calculate the maximum span which satisfies shear stress requirements.
B. If the stud spacing is predetermined, solve the appropriate shear equation for: the required cross section area bh, in the case of board sheathing; or I/Q (rolling shear constant) if plywood sheathing is used. Select material to meet the applicable requirement (Table 4-1 or 4-3).

3. *Stud size and spacing of their supports* (*wale spacing*)—One of these will be predetermined and the other calculated to correspond with it. If stud size is first selected, the allowable span of studs will determine wale spacing. In some cases of light construction where wales are omitted, the studs are supported directly by ties, and the stud span determines *tie spacing* instead. If the span of studs is fixed by predetermined tie or wale spacing, stud size will be selected to carry the known load on that span.

BENDING CHECK

A. If the stud size is known, calculate its maximum allowable span, which is the required spacing of wales. Studs are usually assumed continuous over three or more spans, but for low walls where only one or two spans are required, use simple beam formula.
B. If the stud span is predetermined by fixed tie or wale spacing, transpose the basic equation to solve for the required section modulus S, and then select a member with the required S.

DEFLECTION CHECK

A. If the stud size is known, calculate the maximum allowable span which meets the deflection requirements.
B. If the stud span is fixed by predetermined tie or wale spacing, solve the deflection equation for I, and select a member to meet this requirement.

SHEAR CHECK

When a combination of stud size and wale (or tie) spacing have been selected on the basis of deflection and bending requirements, investigate horizontal shear in the stud. If this exceeds the allowable stress, a modification of either size or span must be made.

4. *Wale size and spacing of supports* (*tie spacing*)—Required spacing of supports for wales determines tie location. As in the case of other members, either wale size or support spacing will be preselected and the other designed to correspond with it. Wales are customarily made of double timbers to avoid drilling to accommodate ties. Double members also offer better resistance to warping. Wales are actually loaded with a series of point loads imposed by the studs, but except as noted on p. 84, it is sufficiently accurate to design for an equivalent uniformly distributed load.

With reusable panels composed of studs and plywood the tie spacing is a multiple of the panel width, and wale size may be determined for ties at one, two, or three panel widths. Standard stock or stock on hand will be used at maximum allowable tie spacing.

BENDING CHECK

A. If wale size is known, calculate the maximum allowable span which determines permissible tie spacing.
B. If tie spacing is preselected, solve the equation for S and select wale or wales with this re-

quired section modulus. If double-member wales are being used, note that S will represent the combined section modulus of the two parts.

SHEAR CHECK *

A. If wale size is known, determine the maximum allowable span to meet horizontal shear stress requirements.

B. If tie spacing is known, solve the same formula for *bh,* which is the required area of wale cross section. Select a suitable pair of members to meet this requirement. Remember that *bh* is *total* area of two wale members.

DEFLECTION CHECK

Deflection of wales is seldom critical; a check based on the beam formulas of Table 6-1 may be made if desired.

5. *Tie design* can then be based on total load as explained on p. 101. If the available tie material makes it necessary to space ties closer, wales may be redesigned for this shorter span between supports.

In some cases, the tie to be used is chosen first (for example, using what is already on hand), and tie spacings are then set to load the tie to its safe capacity. Then framing members can be designed to fit tie spacing, in effect reversing the design sequence outlined above.

6. Check *bearing stresses* as recommended on p. 89.

7. *Lateral bracing for wall forms*—From Table 5-5 find the minimum lateral force for which wall form bracing must be designed. Since the force may act in either direction, single side bracing must be designed to take either tension or compression; otherwise bracing should be placed on both sides of the wall.

WALL FORM EXAMPLE

Design forms for 14 ft high wall to be concreted at a rate of 3 ft per hour, internally vibrated. Anticipated temperature of the concrete at placing is 60F. These forms will be used only once, so the working stresses for Class I formwork apply.

Form grade plywood sheathing, 7/8-in. thick, is available in 4x8-ft sheets and 3000-lb ties are on hand. Framing lumber of construction grade Douglas fir is to be purchased as required.

* In design of wales for known stud spacing and tie spacing, the slight additional effort of applying stud loading as point loads instead of equivalent uniform load is usually justified.

Step 1. From Table 5-2 in Chapter 5, maximum lateral pressure for $R = 3$ and $T = 60$ is 600 psf. Assuming that the depth to maximum pressure is $p/150$, the maximum pressure for form design will be as shown:

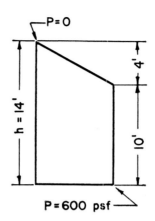

Step 2. *Sheathing* will be same thickness throughout wall height and supports will be uniformly spaced. Since 4x8 sheets of plywood are to be used, supports will be spaced to fall at edges of panels. Use plywood the "strong way," that is with face grain parallel to beam span. In this case, it means placing the 8-ft dimension of the panel horizontally. The panels will act as continuous beams.

CHECK BENDING, considering a 12-in. wide strip of plywood. Maximum allowable span $l = 10.95 \sqrt{\dfrac{fS}{w}}$, by Eq. (6-9). From Table 4-2, f for Class I B-B plyform is 2000 psi when forms are designed for single use. S for 7/8-in. plywood, considering a 12-in. wide strip, is 0.585 in.[3] when face grain is parallel to the span (Table 4-3).

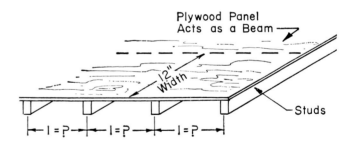

w, loading of the beam, is 600 lb per lineal ft since p is 600 psf and a strip of plywood 1 ft wide is considered. Then substituting in Eq. (6-9)

$$l = 10.95 \sqrt{\frac{2000 \times 0.585}{600}}$$

$$= 10.95 \sqrt{1.95}$$

$$l = 15.3 \text{ in.}$$

This is the maximum allowable span, based on bending strength of the plywood. However, deflection must be checked.

CHECK DEFLECTION, again considering a 12-in. width of the plywood sheathing. Maximum allowable deflection of the sheathing is assumed to be 1/360 of span or 1/16 in., whichever is less. For Δ of $l/360$

$$l = 1.69 \sqrt[3]{\frac{EI}{w}} \quad \dots \dots \dots \dots (6\text{-}2)$$

For Δ of $\frac{1}{16}$ in., substitute in Eq. (6-1) to obtain

$$l = 3.23 \sqrt[4]{\frac{EI}{w}} \quad \dots \dots \dots \dots (6\text{-}15)$$

E for the plywood is 1,600,000 psi by Table 4-2, and I for plies parallel to span is 0.301 in.[4] (Table 4-3). w is 600 lb per lineal ft as in the bending check.
Substituting in Eq. (6-2)

$$l = 1.69 \sqrt[3]{\frac{1,600,000 \times 0.301}{600}}$$
$$= 1.69 \sqrt[3]{803} \quad = 1.69 \times 9.29$$
$$l = 15.7 \text{ in. for } \Delta = l/360$$

Substituting in Eq. (6-15)

$$l = 3.23 \sqrt[4]{\frac{1,600,000 \times 0.301}{600}}$$
$$= 3.23 \sqrt[4]{803} \quad = 3.23 \times 5.32$$
$$l = 17.2 \text{ in. for } \Delta = \frac{1}{16} \text{ in.}$$

CHECK ROLLING SHEAR, using Eq. (6-14) with maximum shear for continuous beam:

$$v = \frac{VQ}{bI} = \frac{0.6 \, wL}{b} \times \frac{Q}{I}$$

From Table 4-2, v (allowable rolling shear stress) = 75 psi; from Table 4-3, $I/Q = 0.704$.

$$75 = \frac{0.6 \, (600) \, L}{12} \times \frac{1}{0.704}$$
$$L = \frac{12 \times 75 \times 0.704}{0.6 \times 600}$$
$$L = 1.76 \text{ ft or } 21.1 \text{ in.}$$

SPACING OF THE STUDS: Deflection of $\frac{1}{360}$ of span governs the maximum support spacing. Studs can be no farther than 15.7 in. apart.

Since the 8-ft panels should have studs at joints between them for support, and since uniform spacing of the studs is desirable, the 8 ft panel can be divided into 7 equal spaces of $\frac{96}{7} = 13.7$ in., which comes within the 15.3 in. allowed for stud spacing. A spacing of studs at 12 in. on centers might be selected if convenience in layout is more important than saving the extra stud.

Step 3. *Stud size* and *spacing of the wales* to support them. Assuming that the 12-in. spacing of the studs is used for simplicity of layout and that 2x4 S4S studs will be used, find maximum span where lateral pressure is greatest, 600 psf. Equivalent uniform load w for design of studs will be maximum lateral pressure in psf × stud spacing in ft:

$$w \text{ (studs)} = 600 \times \frac{12}{12}$$
$$= 600 \text{ lb per lineal ft}$$

$$W_{studs} (lb/ft) = p(lb/ft^2) \times \frac{S}{12} (studs/ft)$$

Points of Stud Support (Wales)

Assuming the studs act as continuous beams, uniformly loaded, check allowable spans for shear, bending, and deflection.

BENDING CHECK: According to Eq. (6-9) the maximum allowable span of the studs $l = 10.95 \sqrt{\frac{fS}{w}}$. $f = 1050 + 25$ percent for short term load = 1313 psi for construction grade Douglas fir (Table 4-2), and S for a 2x4 S4S is 3.06 in.[3] (Table 4-1). Substituting in Eq. (6-9), then

$$l = 10.95 \sqrt{\frac{1310 \times 3.06}{600}}$$
$$= 10.95 \sqrt{6.69}$$
$$l = 28.3 \text{ in.}$$

DEFLECTION CHECK: Allowable deflection is $\frac{1}{360}$ of span or $\frac{1}{8}$ in., whichever is less. Using formulas for continuous beams, for $\Delta = l/360$, the maximum allowable span

$$l = 1.69 \sqrt[3]{\frac{EI}{w}} \quad \dots \dots \dots \dots (6\text{-}2)$$

For $\Delta_{max} = \frac{1}{8}$ in., substitute in Eq. (6-1) to get the maximum allowable span

$$l = 3.84 \sqrt[4]{\frac{EI}{w}} \quad \dots \dots \dots \dots (6\text{-}16)$$

Substituting $I = 5.36$ in.[4], $E = 1,500,000$ psi, and $w = 600$ lb per lineal ft:

For $\Delta = l/360$

$$l = 1.69 \sqrt[3]{\frac{1,500,000 \times 5.36}{600}}$$
$$= 1.69 \sqrt[3]{13,400}$$
$$= 1.69 \times 23.7$$
$$l = 40.1 \text{ in.}$$

For $\Delta = \frac{1}{8}$ in.

$$l = 3.84 \sqrt[4]{\frac{1,500,000 \times 5.36}{600}}$$
$$= 3.84 \sqrt[4]{13,400}$$
$$= 3.84 \times 10.76$$
$$l = 41.3 \text{ in.}$$

SHEAR CHECK: Allowable horizontal shearing stress $H = 185 + 25$ percent = 232 psi (Table 4-2). For a continuous beam, such as the studs being checked

$$H = \frac{0.9w}{bh}\left(L - \frac{2h}{12}\right) \quad \dots \dots \dots (6\text{-}12)$$

where h = depth of beam, in.; b = width of beam, in.; and w is uniform load in lb per lineal ft. Solving for L, the allowable span in ft

$$L = \frac{Hbh}{0.9w} + \frac{2h}{12} \text{ ft}$$
$$l = 13.33 \frac{Hbh}{w} + 2h \text{ in.} \quad \dots \dots \dots (6\text{-}17)$$

A 2x4 S4S has an actual $b = 1\frac{1}{2}$ in. and $h = 3\frac{1}{2}$ in. Substituting, and again using $w = 600$ lb per lineal ft,

$$l = \frac{13.33 \times 231 \times 1\frac{1}{2} \times 3\frac{1}{2}}{600} + 2(3\frac{1}{2})$$
$$= 26.9 + 7.0$$
$$l = 33.9 \text{ in.}$$

SPACING OF THE WALES: Inspection of the maximum span of studs computed above shows that bending governs, and supporting wales must be spaced no more than 28.3 in.

apart where maximum pressure of 600 psf exists. Increased wale spacing is theoretically correct near the top of the form because from the 4 ft depth on up to the top the maximum design pressure declines from 600 psf to zero. In this form, the top wale could be spaced at a greater distance than 28 in. from the adjacent one. However, exact dimensions will be determined from some construction considerations; the top and bottom wales are frequently set about 1 ft from top and bottom of wall forms. Assume 12 in. from top and 8 in. from bottom and work out intermediate spacing on trial and error basis to meet 28-in. spacing requirement for stud supports.

$$W_{wales} \ (lb/f_t) = (sheathing \ load) \times (wale \ spacing)$$

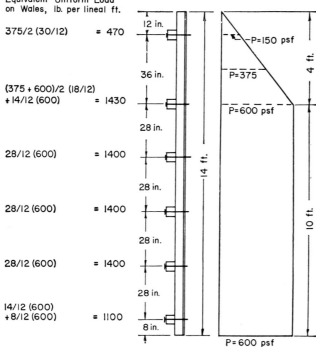

Equivalent Uniform Load
on Wales, lb. per lineal ft.

375/2 (30/12) = 470

(375 + 600)/2 (18/12)
+ 14/12 (600) = 1430

28/12 (600) = 1400

28/12 (600) = 1400

28/12 (600) = 1400

14/12 (600)
+8/12 (600) = 1100

Step 4. *Wale size* and *tie spacing.* Sketch pressure diagram alongside diagram of wale spacing, and determine equivalent uniform load per lineal ft of wale, assuming that each wale carries load on form for half the distance to each adjacent wale. This gives the equivalent uniform load per lineal ft of wale.

Assuming that 3000-lb (safe working load) ties are to be used, the tie spacing will be determined as noted in Step 5 which follows. Wale design can then be developed using the calculated tie spacing of 2 ft. (Refer to Step 5, Tie Design.)

BENDING CHECK: Since both span and loading are known, this is Case B. Substitute fS for M_{max} in Eq. (6-6) and solve for S, required section modulus. (The equivalent uniform load is used although actual wale loading occurs at points where studs bear on wales.)

$$fS = \frac{wl^2}{120}$$

$$S = \frac{wl^2}{120f} \quad \ldots \ldots \ldots \ldots (6\text{-}18)$$

Substituting 1313 psf for f, 24 in. for l and 1430 lb per lineal ft for w,

$$S = \frac{1430 \ (24)^2}{120 \ (1313)}$$
$$= 5.23 \ in.^3 \quad \text{(required section modulus)}$$

Using Table 4-1, p. 32, which shows properties of various sizes of finished lumber, find a section that will meet section modulus (S) requirements. If a double-member wale is used, as is common to avoid drilling of timbers, the computed S is the required section modulus of two members. A double 2x4 wale would be a conventional selection for this type of form and Table 4-1 shows it would more than meet requirements if surfaced on all sides.

$$S = 2 \ (3.06) = 6.12 \ in.^3 \ \text{compared with } 5.23 \ in.^3 \ \text{required.}$$

SHEAR CHECK: Use Eq. (6-12) to check shearing stress in the proposed double 2x4, again assuming equivalent uniform load:

$$H = \frac{0.9w}{bh}\left(L - \frac{2h}{12}\right)$$
$$= \frac{0.9(1430)}{2(5.25)}\left(2 - \frac{2(2.5)}{12}\right)$$
$$= 194 \ psi$$

This is satisfactory when compared with the 231 psi permitted for short term horizontal shear in construction grade Douglas fir. For point loads spaced at greater intervals than half the wale span, a check using actual loads rather than equivalent uniform loading is advisable.

Step 5. *Tie design.* Assume that ties of 3000-lb working load capacity are available and will be used. When wale loading in lb per lineal ft is known at the beginning of Step 4, the tie spacing can then be computed. Not all wales carry the same load; spacing is designed for the heaviest loading and used uniformly throughout the form for convenience in drilling plywood panels, etc. Maximum load per lineal ft of wale is 1430 lb.

$$\frac{\text{tie capacity}}{\text{wale load}} = \frac{3000 \ lb}{1430 \ lb/ft}$$
$$= 2.1 \ ft \ \text{maximum tie spacing}$$

For greater convenience in drilling panels use 2-ft tie spacing. Then go back to complete wale design (Step 4).

$$P_{ties} \ (lb) = w_{wales}\left(\frac{S \ tie}{12} f_t\right)$$

Step 6. *Bearing check:* The points to be investigated in this design would be bearing of studs on wales and bearing between the tie wedges or tie holders and wales. Allowable $c \perp$ to grain of the wood is 1.25×385 or 480 psi for construction grade Douglas fir in this class of formwork (from Table 4-2 p. 33).

Ties: At point of maximum loading, tie load is 1430 lb/ft $\times$ 2 ft, or 2860 lb. Suppose that the tie wedge (tie holder) is irregularly shaped, with about 4½ sq in. actually contacting the 2x4's that make up the wale. Assume also that the length of bearing is no more than 2 in.

Because of this short bearing length, $c \perp$ can be increased from 480 as explained on p. 89, by a factor of 1.19 for 2-in. bearing.

adjusted $c \perp = 480 \, (1.19) = 571$ psi

The actual bearing stress is

$$\frac{\text{maximum tie load}}{\text{bearing area}} = \frac{2860}{4.5} = 636 \text{ psi.}$$

This exceeds the adjusted allowable $c \perp$, and if this tie holder is used some crushing may take place. Since the difference between the calculated and allowable stresses is relatively small, it might be decided to use the wedge anyway. (This would be judged in part on basis of how strict the tolerances are for completed structure.)

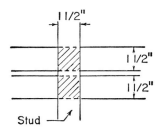

Stud

Studs on wales: The bearing area between studs and wales would be as shown in the drawing. If 2x4 wales S4S are used, the total bearing area is

$$2 \times (1\frac{1}{2} \times 1\frac{1}{2}) = 4.50 \text{ sq in.}$$

Maximum load transferred from studs to wales is maximum uniform stud load × maximum wale spacing, or

$$600 \text{ lb/ft} \times \frac{28}{12} = 1400 \text{ lb}$$

$$\text{bearing stress} = \frac{1400 \text{ lb}}{4.50 \text{ sq in.}} = 311 \text{ psi}$$

Since this is well below the 480 psi value of $c \perp$, no increase in stress for short bearing length need be considered.

Step 7. *Lateral bracing* for this type of form is explained on p. 112.

Slab Forms

There is no single correct sequence for slab form design, since conditions vary greatly from job to job. Once the load that the forms must carry is figured, design may start at any one of several points. The general goal is a balanced form design, one that loads all the parts at or near their safe carrying capacity. Often the preliminary design has to be adjusted to fit the module used in structural design, or it may be modified to improve the "balance" and use materials more efficiently. Where labor costs are high, changes may be introduced to save working time instead of materials.

1. *Design load*—Determine the combined dead and live load for which the forms must be designed, according to suggestions in Chapter 5.

NOTE: The sequence of the following steps has been arbitrarily selected. On one job it might be entirely reversed; on another, the designer might preselect both shores and sheathing, in effect working from both ends toward the middle of the suggested sequence. The individual steps, however, are all needed, and the design following shows how calculations can be made.

2. *Sheathing thickness and spacing of its supports (joist spacing)*—One of the two is chosen on the basis of job conditions or material availability and economy; the other is calculated to correspond with it.

BENDING CHECK

A. If sheathing thickness is fixed, determine its maximum allowable span, which is the maximum spacing of joists.

B. If the joist spacing is fixed, calculate the required section modulus S of sheathing to carry the load, and select lumber or plywood to meet this requirement from Tables 4-1 and 4-3.

DEFLECTION CHECK

A. If sheathing thickness is fixed, calculate maximum allowable span which satisfies deflection requirements.

B. If the joist spacing is fixed, transpose the deflection equation to solve for the required moment of inertia, I. Then select sheathing material to meet this requirement, using Table 4-1 or 4-3.

SHEAR CHECK

Shear stress may govern design of wood sheathing where short spans are used under heavy load. Check to be sure. Plywood sheathing should be checked for rolling shear, just as it is in wall form design.

3. *Joist size and spacing of supports (stringer spacing)*—One of these must be selected arbitrarily and the other designed to correspond with it. In some cases, joists are supported directly on shores, but generally the allowable span of joists will serve to determine the stringer spacing. Joists are generally assumed continuous over three or more spans. (In slab and beam construction, the joist may span between two beam sides with one or no intermediate supports . . . in which case simple beam formula should be used for design.)

BENDING CHECK

A. If the joist size is known, calculate its maximum allowable span; this span is the maximum allowable spacing of the stringers.

B. If the joist span is predetermined by other job conditions, transpose the basic equation to solve for the required section modulus S, and then select a joist with the required S.

DEFLECTION CHECK

A. If the joist size is known, calculate the maximum allowable span which meets deflection requirements.

B. If the joist span is fixed by other job conditions, solve the deflection equation for I and select a member to meet this requirement.

SHEAR CHECK

When a combination of joist size and span (stringer spacing) have been selected on the basis of deflection and bending requirements, investigate horizontal shear in the joist. If this exceeds the allowable stress a modification of either size or span must be made.

4. Stringer size and span (shore spacing)—Depending on job conditions, either the shore spacing or the size of stringer will have been preselected; the other must be designed to correspond. Stringers are actually loaded with a series of point loads from the joists but for most cases an equivalent uniform load is sufficiently accurate for design purposes. In cases of heavily loaded short spans, a shear check using point loads may be desirable.

BENDING CHECK

A. If the stringer size is known, calculate the maximum allowable span; this establishes a maximum spacing of the shores. Double members are frequently used for stringers.

B. If the span of stringers is fixed by predetermined shore spacing, transpose the basic equation to solve for the section modulus S and select a member (or members) with the required S.

DEFLECTION CHECK

A. If the stringer size is known, calculate the maximum allowable span which meets deflection requirements.

B. If the span of the stringers is fixed on the basis of shore spacing, solve the deflection equation for I and select a member to meet this requirement.

SHEAR CHECK

A. If the stringer size is known, calculate the maximum allowable span which can be used and still keep shear stress H below the allowable.

B. If the shore spacing is known, which in effect determines the span of the stringers, then use the simple shear formula to determine the required stringer cross-sectional area, bh.

When these three checks have been made, it will be obvious which criterion governs the stringer design. If shear governs, it may be advisable to recheck the design, using point loads on the stringers instead of equivalent uniform loads, because maximum horizontal shearing stress may be significantly affected by the location of the point loads.

5. Shore design to support stringers is based on principles set forth on p. 107. Shore design (both spacing and size) may precede selection of stringers, or it may be made after other formwork components have been chosen. If available shores are not suitable to support stringers at the designed spacing, spacing must be changed, and this may necessitate other design changes.

6. Check bearing stresses as recommended on p. 89, wherever loads are transmitted perpendicular to the grain of a wood member.

7. Design lateral bracing for shores to carry minimum lateral force prescribed in Table 5-4. Design of bracing is explained on p. 113.

SLAB FORM EXAMPLE

Design forms to support flat slab floor 8 in. thick of conventional density concrete using 1-in. board sheathing, construction grade Douglas fir framing members and shoring. Ceiling height is 8 ft, and bays are 15 × 15 ft. Since the forms will be used only once, increase working stresses as provided for short term load in Table 4-2, p. 33.

Step 1. *Estimate loads:*

dead load of concrete + steel $\frac{8}{12} \times 150 = 100$ psf

minimum recommended live load on forms = 50 psf
(weight of forms neglected)

DESIGN LOADING = $\overline{150 \text{ psf}}$

Step 2. *Sheathing design:* Assuming that 1-in. nominal size board sheathing is to be used, determine its maximum allowable

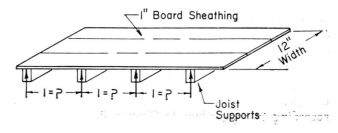

span, working with a 1 ft wide strip for convenience in design. Actual thickness of a finished 1-in. board is ¾ in.

$$I \text{ for a 12-in. strip} = \frac{bh^3}{12}$$
$$= \frac{12(¾)^3}{12} = 0.42 \text{ in.}^4$$

$$S \text{ for a 12-in. strip} = \frac{bh^2}{6}$$
$$= \frac{12(¾)^2}{6} = 1.13 \text{ in.}^3$$

Use working stresses of Table 4-2, adjusted for short term loading and because lumber will be used wet:

$f = 1050 \times 1.25 \times 0.86 = 1129$ psi
$H = 185 \times 1.25 \times 0.97 = 224$ psi
$E = 0.97 \times 1,500,000 = 1,455,000$ psi (no increase for
short term load)

CHECK BENDING for 12-in. width of sheathing loaded uniformly at 150 lb per ft. By Eq. (6-9), for a continuous beam, the maximum allowable span is

$$l = 10.95\sqrt{\frac{fS}{w}}$$
$$= 10.95\sqrt{\frac{1129 \times 1.13}{150}}$$
$$l = 31.9 \text{ in.}$$

This is the maximum allowable span based on bending strength of the wood; however, it will be necessary to check deflection, which frequently governs sheathing design. A shear check will also be shown, although it is not generally necessary for *sheathing* with light loads such as this.

CHECK DEFLECTION, again considering a 12-in. width of sheathing. Maximum allowable deflection Δ is assumed to be $\frac{1}{360}$ of span or $\frac{1}{16}$ in., whichever is ~~greater.~~ smaller. Substituting in Eq. (6-2) for $\Delta_{max} = l/360$:

$$l = 1.69\sqrt[3]{\frac{1,455,000 \times 0.42}{150}}$$
$$= 1.69\sqrt[3]{4074}$$
$$l = 27 \text{ in.}$$

and substituting in Eq. (6-15) for $\Delta_{max} = \frac{1}{16}$ in:

$$l = 3.23\sqrt[4]{4074}$$
$$= 3.23 (8.0)$$
$$l = 25.8 \text{ in.}$$

Maximum allowable span on the basis of deflection limit of $\frac{1}{16}$ in. would be 25.8 in.

CHECK SHEAR, using Eq. (6-10), substituting $0.6wL$ for V for a continuous beam:

$$H = \frac{0.9 \, wL}{bh}$$

The maximum allowable span is therefore:

$$L = \frac{Hbh}{0.9w}$$

Substituting values given above,

$$L = \frac{224 (12 \times ¾)}{0.9 (150)}$$
$$= 14.9 \text{ ft or } 179 \text{ in.}$$

This extremely long span based on shear strength shows that shear is far from being a governing consideration in this loading range.

Comparison of the above allowable spans shows that deflection governs design, and this 1-in. sheathing requires supports no farther than 25.8 in. apart. Choice of an actual span may depend on bay sizes, and the desire to divide bay dimensions into a number of equal or nearly equal formwork spans. With bays 15x15 ft, 26 in. would be a convenient span; $7 \times 26 = 182$, compared with 180 in. (15 ft). One end span could be made shorter by 2 in. This would give seven supporting joists per bay at 26 in. o.c. and one at 24 in.

Step 3. *Joist size* and *spacing of stringers* to support joists. Assume that 2x4 lumber is on hand to be used as joists, which will be continuous over several spans. For construction grade Douglas fir and Class I formwork, $H = 231$ psi, $E = 1,500,000$ psi, and $f = 1313$ psi.

The equivalent uniform load w on each joist is

$$\frac{\text{joist spacing, in.}}{12} \times \text{design load, psf}$$

or $\quad W_{joist} (lb/ft) = p \times \left(\frac{S_{joists}}{12}\right)$

$$\frac{26}{12} \times 150 = 325 \text{ lb per lineal ft}$$

For the 2x4's which are S4S, $bh = 5.25$ in.², $I = 5.36$ in.⁴, and $S = 3.06$ in.³ (values from Table 4-1, p. 32).

CHECK BENDING: For a continuous beam

$$l = 10.95\sqrt{\frac{fS}{w}} \quad\dots\dots\dots\dots\dots(6\text{-}9)$$

Substituting in Eq. (6-9)

$$l = 10.95\sqrt{\frac{1313 \times 3.06}{325}}$$
$$= 10.95\sqrt{12.4}$$
$$l = 38.5 \text{ in. maximum allowable span of joists}$$

CHECK DEFLECTION: For a continuous beam, with allowable $\Delta = \frac{1}{360}$ of the span

$$l = 1.69\sqrt[3]{\frac{EI}{w}} \quad\dots\dots\dots\dots\dots\dots(6\text{-}2)$$
$$= 1.69\sqrt[3]{\frac{1,500,000 \times 5.36}{325}}$$
$$= 1.69\sqrt[3]{24,740}$$
$$l = 49 \text{ in.}$$

CHECK SHEAR: Solving Eq. (6-12) (continuous beam) for L:

$$L = \frac{Hbh}{0.9w} + \frac{2h}{12}$$

h for a 2x4 S4S is 3½ in. Substituting this and other values given above:

$$L = \frac{231 (5.25)}{0.9 (325)} + \frac{2 (3½)}{12}$$
$$= 4.15 + 0.58$$
$$L = 4.73 \text{ ft or } 57 \text{ in.}$$

Comparison of the three spans calculated above shows that bending governs design and the longest allowable span of joists —that is the maximum spacing of stringers—is 38.5 in. Looking again at the 15-ft bays, we might decrease this by trial and error to some measurement which will give uniform spacing across each bay. In this case, 36 in. spacing of stringers would give 5 equal spaces per bay (5×36 in. $= 180$ in. or 15 ft).

$$w_{str} = P\left(\frac{S_{str}}{12}\right)$$

Step 4. *Stringer size* and *span.* The stringer span determines maximum *shore spacing.* First, find the equivalent uniform load w on the stringers:

$$w = \frac{\text{stringer spacing, in.}}{12} \times (\text{load on forms, psf})$$

$$w = \frac{36}{12}(150) = 450 \text{ lb per lineal ft}$$

This equivalent uniform loading is usually sufficiently accurate; however, if the stringer design selected is close to limiting stresses or deflection, a recheck on basis of point loading of joists on the stringers might be necessary. However, rounding off of values to get modular layout frequently adds extra safety and makes this recheck unnecessary.

Using construction grade Douglas fir stringers, working stresses will be the same as for joists above. Assuming that a surfaced 2x6 stringer is used, get cross-sectional properties as follows from Table 4-1, p. 32, before beginning calculations:

$h = 5\frac{1}{2}$ in., $bh = 8.25$ in.^{2}, $S = 7.56$ in.^{3}, $I = 20.80$ in.^{4}

CHECK BENDING: For a continuous beam, Eq. (6-9) is used, just as for checking joists.

$$l = 10.95\sqrt{\frac{fS}{w}}$$
$$= 10.95\sqrt{\frac{1313 \times 7.56}{450}}$$
$$l = 51.4 \text{ in.}$$

CHECK DEFLECTION: Working with a limiting deflection of $\frac{1}{360}$ of the span, Eq. (6-2) is used to find maximum allowable span:

$$l = 1.69\sqrt[3]{\frac{EI}{w}}$$
$$= 1.69\sqrt[3]{\frac{1,500,000(20.80)}{450}}$$
$$= 1.69\sqrt[3]{69,330}$$
$$= 1.69(41.1)$$
$$l = 69 \text{ in.}$$

CHECK SHEAR: For continuous beam, use Eq. (6-12) as in checking joists:

$$L = \frac{Hbh}{0.9w} + \frac{2h}{12}$$
$$= \frac{232(8.25)}{0.9(450)} + \frac{2(5\frac{1}{2})}{12}$$
$$L = 5.64 \text{ ft or } 67.7 \text{ in.}$$

Bending appears to govern the maximum allowable span for stringers. Considering the 15-ft building module, a span of 45 in. would probably be selected. This 45-in. span is the distance between shores, which will be checked in Step 5 below.

$$P_{shore} = w_{str}\left(\frac{S_{shores}}{12}\right)$$

Step 5. *Shore design:* Stringers are now spaced 36 in. on centers and supported by shores at 45-in. intervals. This gives an area of $\frac{45}{12} \times \frac{36}{12}$ or 11.25 sq ft of forms to be carried by each shore. Total load per shore will be

$$11.25 \text{ sq ft} \times 150 \text{ psf} = 1688 \text{ lb}$$

Adjustable patented shores which carry 3000 lb safe working load are available and satisfactory for this job since ceiling height is only 8 ft. Length of shores should always be carefully checked to see that they will fit in. Depth of slab forming (in this case $9\frac{3}{4}$ in.) plus thickness of any sills used must

be subtracted from the ceiling height to determine the actual space available for shore extension.

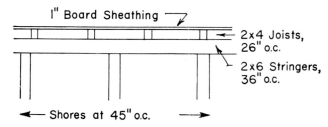

See Table 6-3, p. 109, for wood shoring material that might also be satisfactory. Since 3x4 shores can carry this load for an unbraced length of 8 ft, solving this same problem in the opposite sequence of calculations using a 5-ft module and heavier framing members might be indicated, depending on local job conditions.

Step 6. *Check bearing stresses:* Where shores bear on stringers and where joists bear on stringer.

Stringer bearing on shore

Assume the head piece of adjustable shore is $11\frac{1}{2} \times 3\frac{5}{8}$ in. The 2x6 stringer is actually $1\frac{1}{2}$ in. wide. If the head piece is

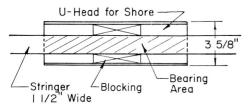

placed parallel to stringer, bearing area is $1\frac{1}{2} \times 11\frac{1}{2}$ or 17.25 sq in. Bearing stress will be

$$\frac{\text{total shore load}}{\text{bearing area}} = \frac{1688}{17.25}$$
$$= 98 \text{ psi}$$

which is well below the $c \perp$ of 480 psi.

Joist bearing on stringer: Both members are $1\frac{1}{2}$ in. (nominal 2 in.) wide. Bearing area $= 1\frac{1}{2} \times 1\frac{1}{2} = 2.25$ sq in.

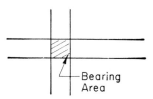

Average load transmitted by joist to stringer is

joist spacing $\times$ joist span $\times$ form load
$$\frac{26}{12} \times \frac{36}{12} \times 150 = 975 \text{ lb}$$

$$\frac{975 \text{ lb}}{2.25 \text{ sq in.}} = 433 \text{ psi}$$

Bearing at this point is also within the 480 psi allowable. Since all bearing stresses are within the allowable, no check is needed on adjusted allowable $c \perp$ because of short length of bearing.

Step 7. Lateral bracing for this type of form is discussed on p. 113.

Beam Forms

Beam forms, like slab forms, carry a vertical load, and they are also subject to lateral pressure of the fresh concrete just as wall forms are. In addition, where slabs frame into beams a part of the load from the slab forms may be carried by the beam form to the supporting shores. Since there are several ways of forming beam and slab intersections, a review of the beam form construction methods beginning on p. 169 will be helpful in understanding and apply-

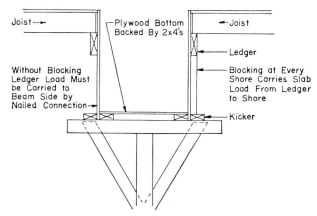

ing the principles of design. It is important to note how and how much of the slab load (if any) is to be carried to the beam form, and judging by the details of the form construction, how that load is transmitted to the supporting shores.

1. *Beam Bottom:* Determine the load on the beam bottom, following principles outlined in Chapter 5. Dead and live load are estimated much the same as for slabs, but where the beam is heavily reinforced, some allowance must be made for extra weight of steel. If the beam side is supported directly on the beam bottom, then any additional load transmitted from the slab through the beam side is also included.

After the loading on the beam bottom has been estimated, design as other formwork components, checking for bending, deflection, and shear. The allowable span of the beam bottom material generally determines the required shore spacing under the beam.

2. *Beam Sides:* The beam side is subject to lateral pressure from the freshly placed concrete, and may also carry some vertical load from the slab forms framing into it. A careful inspection of the forming method to see how the loads are transmitted is necessary for working out a rational design. Portions of these members are often selected on the basis of experience, and local or intra-company habit may be reflected in the final design.

Considering *vertical loads* for example first, one designer is careful always to put blocking under the

ledger at each shore, thus safely transmitting slab load via beam action of the ledger to the supporting shores, as discussed in the example which follows. Although these ledgers are nailed to the beam sides, the strength of the nailed connections is neglected in this design approach. Another designer, however, might design the nailed connections of the ledger to safely transmit slab load to the beam side, assuming the beam side strong enough to distribute such load to the shores. Only where slab load proves too heavy for nails in the ledger is some blocking added.

In considering the *lateral loads* on beam sides, the general principles used in wall design are applicable, but again experience and local practices are important in selections made. For shallow beams, a nominal size of sheathing or plywood is frequently chosen on the basis of experience, rather than calculated design. One designer for example reports using ¾-in. plywood with ledger attached, then adding vertical 2x4 "stiffeners" for these beam sides whenever beam depth is greater than 20 in. For beams up to about 2 ft deep, a single tie across the top, and/or knee bracing to the shore heads is considered satisfactory. Slab sheathing may sometimes be framed in to con-

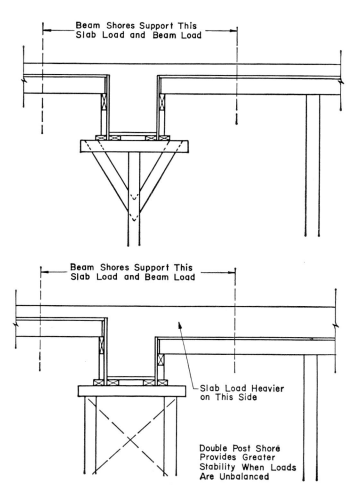

99

tribute to this lateral support. For heavier deep beams, ties designed for the head of fresh concrete are a must. Because of the comparatively heavy reinforcement in beams, interference with the ties is more likely to occur than in walls, and more careful tie location is required.

3. Shores: Supports for beam forms are generally spaced on the basis of support requirements of the beam bottom. However, they carry dead and live load not only from the beam, but usually from adjoining slab forms whose joists bear on the ledger fixed to the beam side. Determine the total load to be supported and design these shores according to suggestions on p. 107.

Where a single post shore is used under the beams, a T-head carries the beam and slab loading to the shore. If the slab on one side of the beam is concreted ahead of the beam form and opposite slab, or if the slab loading on one side is considerably heavier, there is a rotational effect on the shore head that may endanger alignment and stability of the formwork. Concreting the beam first, placing a considerable part of the shore loading concentrically in advance of slab concreting, is one way to overcome this problem. If this cannot be done, then double post shores should be considered.

4. Bearing stresses: Where heavy loads are involved, bearing stresses may require investigation as explained on p. 89. Ties may be required for deep beams, and their design follows suggestions on p. 101.

BEAM FORM EXAMPLE

The beam form shown in the accompanying sketch is to be used twice. Assume that no extra weight allowance for beam reinforcement is necessary; *i.e.*, steel + concrete weighs 150 lb per cu ft.

Step 1. *Beam bottom design:* First estimate the loading.

$$\text{dead load of concrete + steel} = \frac{12 \times 20}{144}(150) = 250 \text{ lb/ft}$$

$$\text{live load @ 50 psf} = \frac{12}{12} \times 50 = 50 \text{ lb/ft}$$

TOTAL UNIFORMLY DISTRIBUTED LOAD $= \overline{300 \text{ lb/ft}}$
(neglecting weight of forms)

Design the beam bottom form for this load, just as other beam components of formwork are designed, checking for bending, deflection, and shear. Assuming that 1½-in. (nominal) sheathing of construction grade Douglas fir is used, find the maximum distance it can span between supports.

From Table 4-2, working stresses adjusted for short term load and wet usage, as for sheathing shown on p. 97, are: $f = 1129$ psi, $H = 224$ psi, and $E = 1,455,000$. For the 12-in. width of sheathing,

$$bh = 12(1\tfrac{1}{4}) = 15.00 \text{ sq in.}$$

$$I = \frac{bh^3}{12} = \frac{12(1\tfrac{1}{4})^3}{12} = 1.95 \text{ in.}^4$$

$$S = \frac{bh^2}{6} = \frac{12(1\tfrac{1}{4})^2}{6} = 3.12 \text{ in.}^3$$

The beam bottom will be continuous over several supports and its maximum deflection between supports will be held to ⅟₁₆ in.

CHECK BENDING: Maximum unsupported length will be, by Eq. (6-9):

$$l = 10.95\sqrt{\frac{fS}{w}}$$
$$= 10.95\sqrt{\frac{1129 \times 3.12}{300}}$$
$$l = 37.5 \text{ in.}$$

CHECK DEFLECTION: Use Eq. (6-14) to determine the maximum unsupported length allowable for a deflection of ⅟₁₆ in.

$$l = 3.23\sqrt[4]{\frac{EI}{w}}$$
$$= 3.23\sqrt[4]{\frac{1,455,000 \times 1.95}{300}}$$
$$= 3.23\sqrt[4]{9,460}$$
$$l = 3.23 \times 9.86 = 31.9 \text{ in.}$$

CHECK SHEAR: Solving Eq. (6-12) for L, the maximum unsupported length is

$$L = \frac{Hbh}{0.9w} + \frac{2h}{12}$$
$$= \frac{224 \times 15.00}{0.9(300)} + \frac{2(1\tfrac{1}{4})}{12}$$
$$= 12.44 + 0.21$$
$$L = 12.65 \text{ ft or } 152 \text{ in.}$$

Deflection clearly governs the need for support spacing under this beam bottom, and shores should not be more than 32 in. apart. For convenience in layout, assume that a 2½ ft or 30-in. spacing is used.

An alternate approach to design of this beam bottom form would be to select a convenient shore spacing first, then check to see what cross section (in terms of I, S, and bh) would be needed to span the chosen distance.

Step 2. *Beam side design:* Assume that ¾-in. plywood sheathing and the 2x4 kicker have been selected on the basis of experience. Shore spacing determined in Step 1 is 30 in., and the construction plan as indicated in the sketch is to place blocking at each shore to support the ledger. Thus the ledger will be continuous over several spans of 30 in., neglecting strength of nailed connection to the sheathing. What size

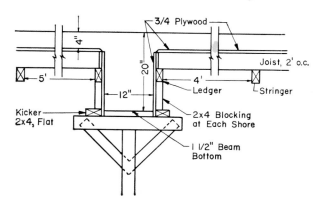

ledger will be required? Working stresses will be adjusted from Table 4-2, for short term load (no reduction for wet usage): $f = 1313$ psi and $H = 231$ psi.

Loading must first be estimated. Although the joist loads represent a series of concentrated loads, they may be simplified to get an equivalent uniform loading, w. If w were quite heavy, or if the ledger section selected were loaded at or near its capacity, then a more precise check using point loads might be advisable.

Ledger loading: On the right side of the beam the ledger carries a 2-ft width of 4-in. slab plus assumed live load on that 2-ft width. Therefore for the right ledger:

$$\text{slab load} = 2 \times \tfrac{4}{12} \times 150 = 100 \text{ lb/ft}$$
$$\text{live load} = 2 \times 50 \qquad = 100 \text{ lb/ft}$$
$$w \text{ (total on ledger)} \qquad = 200 \text{ lb/ft}$$

On the left side, the ledger carries a 2½-ft slab width, so total loading on left ledger is:

$$\text{slab load} = 2\tfrac{1}{2} \times \tfrac{4}{12} \times 150 = 125 \text{ lb/ft}$$
$$\text{live load} = 2\tfrac{1}{2} \times 50 \qquad = 125 \text{ lb/ft}$$
$$w \text{ (total on ledger)} \qquad = 250 \text{ lb/ft}$$

Using the larger value of w, 250 lb per ft, determine the required section of the ledger.

BENDING REQUIREMENT will be determined by solving Eq. (6-18) for S, required section modulus.

$$S = \frac{wl^2}{120f}$$
$$= \frac{250(30^2)}{120(1313)}$$
$$S = 1.43 \text{ in.}^3$$

DEFLECTION REQUIREMENT: Assuming that $\frac{1}{360}$ of the span is the allowable deflection, solve Eq. (6-1) for I, required moment of inertia:

$$\frac{l}{360} = \frac{w}{12} \times \frac{l^4}{145EI}$$
$$I = \frac{wl^3 \times 360}{12(145E)}$$
$$= \frac{0.207 \, wl^3}{E}$$
$$= \frac{0.207(250)(30)^3}{1,500,000}$$
$$I = 0.93 \text{ in.}^4$$

SHEAR REQUIREMENT: Solving Eq. (6-10) for bh, and substituting $V = 0.6wL$ for a continuous beam:

$$bh = \frac{0.9 \, wL}{H}$$
$$= \frac{0.9(250)\frac{30}{12}}{231}$$
$$bh = 2.44 \text{ in.}^2$$

Comparing the calculated required S, I, and bh with cross-section properties in Table 4-1, p. 32, it is evident that a 2x4, the smallest conventional framing member, exceeds all these requirements and would be the member selected to serve as ledger.

Step 3. Shore design requires a determination of the total load per shore. In Step 1, shore spacing was planned as 30 in. Shore load, including live load is:

from beam	300 lb/ft × 2½ ft =	750 lb
from left slab	200 lb/ft × 2½ ft =	500 lb
(see Step 2)		
from right slab	250 lb/ft × 2½ ft =	625 lb
(see Step 2)		
total load per shore		1875 lb

Using this total load, and assuming an unsupported length of 8 ft, an adequate shore may be selected from Table 6-3, or from a manufacturer's rating of patented shoring devices.

Step 4. Bearing check should be made following same principles as for the slab form example presented on p. 98.

Ties, Anchors, and Hangers

In general the strength of form-accessory units should usefully balance the strength and spans of the framing members. The most economical tie is one that will fully develop the strength of the form lumber, when the tie is loaded to its recommended capacity. Normally, the fewer units used to provide safety needed and to take the required maximum working loads from the framing provide the best balance. Light formwork uses lighter form tying accessories and more of them than heavy work. Required safety factors vary with the type of work and an appraisal of any unusual hazards which may be involved. The recommendations of ACI Committee 347 in this regard are listed on p. 86.

Ties

When preliminary spacing of the ties has been determined on the basis of requirements of the framing members, this spacing will have to be checked against the load capacity of the ties. Use the manufacturer's load rating, adjusted if necessary to give the desired safety factor. To get the total load on each tie, determine the contributing area of form (equal to distance between ties horizontally times the vertical distance between ties) and multiply by the average unit pressure of concrete on that area. If the equivalent uniform load on wales has already been computed,

6-3 "Contributing area" of form for tie design covers half the distance from tie to tie in both directions.

then merely multiply this load times the distance between ties to get total load per tie. If total load computed in either of these ways exceeds the capacity of the selected size of tie, then the spacing must be reduced or the size of tie rods increased, or rate of placement decreased, whichever may be more economical for a given job.

If plain rods or band iron, or unrated ties are to be used, the necessary size is easily computed as:

$$A_{tie} = \frac{p_{av} \times A_{form}}{f_s} \dots\dots\dots\dots (6\text{-}19)$$

where

A_{tie} = cross-sectional area of the tie, sq in.
p_{av} = average lateral pressure on the form area being considered, psf
A_{form} = contributing form area, sq ft
f_s = allowable working stress for tie material. (25,000 psi may be used for structural steel, temporarily loaded; for other tie materials get manufacturer's stress rating.)

Bearing Plates or Washers

The form load is transmitted to the tie through an external holding device (variously called tie holder, wedge, form clamp, hairpin, button, etc.) bearing on the stud or waler. The area of this plate or wedge should be large enough, that the allowable stress in compression perpendicular to the grain of lumber will not be exceeded. Otherwise there will be crushing of the wood and "give" in the forms. (Refer to p. 89 for discussion of allowable bearing stresses for timber.) This is not a problem if metal form members are used.

It is advisable to check bearing area at the end of

all ties loaded to over 3000 lb. However, it is not always possible for the designer to check this bearing stress since many of the holding devices are of irregular shape with no published information on area; some are so shaped that maximum bearing area is developed only after initial crushing of the wood fibers takes place.

The manufacturer should design external holding devices in balance with the rated load of the tie rod, so that bearing stresses in form lumber are not excessive. Since there is presently no industry-wide standard, the manufacturer may use bearing stresses considerably higher than those recommended for species of wood likely to be used in formwork. The designer should be aware of this and be prepared for some crushing to take place if he uses these tying devices at or near their maximum load capacity. Experience will indicate whether this will seriously affect the proposed form assembly.

Hangers

Hangers which support the weight of forms and wet concrete plus construction load from the already-in-place steel or concrete structural frame may be checked in much the same way that ties are checked. Preliminary spacing will have been arrived at on the basis of formwork requirements for support.

Determine the area of formwork to be supported by each hanger (usually the distance of beams center to center times the spacing of hangers along the beam) and multiply by the total unit design load for the formwork. Be sure to allow for the weight of concrete encasing the beam or forming any irregular haunches or overhangs. For non-fireproofed structures, the load on the hanger may be determined by permissible spacing of formwork joists, rather than having hangers carry their maximum load.

If this load exceeds the capacity of the hanger tentatively chosen, then a heavier one must be found, or spacing adjusted accordingly. Some suppliers give load capacity of their hangers on a per leg basis;

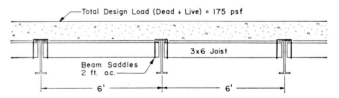

6-4 Beam saddles used to support formwork from steel frame, when steel beams are not fireproofed. Load per hanger in this case is 175 psf × 6 ft × 2 ft = 2100 lb. Typical safe working loads for such hardware range upward from 2500 lb.

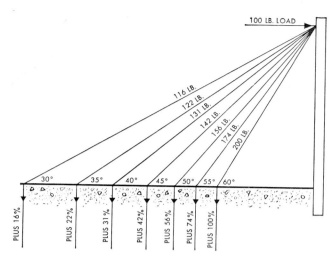

6-5 Increase of pressure load when ties are inclined

check carefully to be sure of the *total load* rating of the hanger. If a different safety factor than that indicated by the hanger manufacturer is desired, adjust the load rating.

Care is required in design to equalize the loading on the two legs of the hanger to avoid twisting of the steel supporting beams due to unbalanced loading. For example, in Figure 6-4, if the slab span from A to B were substantially longer than the span from B to C, the load on the left side of the hanger would be heavier than the load on the right, and there would be a tendency for the beam to twist. When one-sided hangers are used, they should be alternated from one side to the other along the length of the supporting beam to counteract the rotational effect. Forms for fireproofing steel beams often have to be braced to prevent shifting sideways until concrete is placed on both sides of the web.

Anchors

Form anchors secure formwork to rock or previously placed concrete of adequate strength. They must have not only sufficient tensile strength to carry the load imposed upon them, but they must also have enough embedment in the concrete or rock to develop that holding strength. Sufficient length of embedment is particularly important because anchors are often placed in the low-strength concrete used for massive structures, or in concrete that will have only part of its strength developed when the anchor is acting. Calculation of the loads to be supported by these anchors depends on the details of the form under consideration; they are usually used for cantilever forms, and for sloping surfaces more than one row of anchorages may be necessary. "Tied" cantilever forms

are supported by a row of anchorages at the face of the concrete, plus additional ties from the top of the form inclined down to anchors embedded in the top of the previous lift. This is discussed more fully in the chapter on mass concrete, p. 260. When the anchorage unit supports a cantilever form at the face of a previous lift, the bolt portion of the unit carries the weight of the forms as well as a tension or pull-out load.

Although the load on the tie or anchor may be calculated in a horizontal direction, the embedded anchor is often inclined. In such a case it is necessary to increase the load on the anchor as shown in Figure 6-5. For example, if the anchor rod is inclined 55° from the horizontal, 174 pounds of load for every 100 pounds of calculated horizontal pull must be used in design of anchor rod.

Column Form Design

The method selected for forming columns on a given job will be based on cost, previous experience, available labor and materials, column size, number of possible reuses of the forms, and other factors which are discussed under form planning (p. 17) and construction of column forms (p. 162).

If proprietary column forms or column clamps are used, the manufacturer's recommendations, based on load tests or a successful experience record, should be followed. It is important to note the manufacturer's suggestions carefully; for example, if there is a suggested rate of filling the forms, it should be strictly followed. Faster filling will produce greater pressures that may cause unsightly deformation of the finished columns.

There are several kinds of shop-built or job-built forms made by the contractor, for which the following design suggestions are applicable. Since the amount of interaction between sheathing and yokes or clamps varies considerably from one kind of construction to another, and because the degree of rigidity of connections in clamps and yokes is also variable, a simplified approach to design is necessary.

General Procedure

1. Determine the pressure on the form, based on formulas presented in Chapter 5. The design pressure may vary uniformly from a maximum at the base of the column to zero at the top, or it may be a con-

stant maximum throughout part of the form height and then vary linearly to zero at the top of the form.

2. Check the column form sheathing for deflection, bending, and shear. A deflection of $\frac{1}{16}$ inch in the sheathing span between clamps or yokes is about as much as can be allowed in exposed columns, and calculations for this are shown in the example below. The design tables for sheathing, p. 121, could be applied instead of making detailed calculations.

Column sheathing design is similar to wall sheathing, but decreasing pressure toward the top of the forms is considered in determining an increased spacing of yokes or clamps at the higher levels. Conditions of span and support vary with the kind of framing used, and for plywood it is important to note whether it is used the strong or weak way.

Design can be safely simplified by working up from the base of the column, assuming that pressure is uniform between clamps (yokes) and of an intensity equal to that at the lower clamp. Using this simplification, determine support spacing required for the sheathing selected. Note that bending may govern for part of the distance, and then as loads decrease and spans lengthen, deflection may govern. This spacing is the tentative clamp spacing, subject to checking in Step 3.

3. Investigate strength and deflection of proposed yokes or clamps, if spaced to meet the support requirements of the sheathing. This means a check of shear and bending moment (possibly combined bending and axial load) as well as deflection (deflection seldom governs yoke design). Certain variations in this step will be caused by different types of construction; e.g., tension in tie bolts may be involved.

If yoke stresses are below the allowable limit, then spacing can be based on sheathing calculation. However, if the yokes are decidedly underloaded, it may be advantageous to use a stronger sheathing material that will permit spacing the yokes farther apart.

If the yokes are overstressed at spacings based on sheathing requirements, then calculate spacing throughout the column height on the basis of strength of yokes. For columns of large cross section, ties may be introduced to increase the yoke strength and rigidity.

4. Compare spacing requirements of both sheathing and yokes, and determine a yoke spacing that will meet both requirements, and at the same time add up to total column height in increments convenient for the form builder. The uppermost clamp is usually a fixed distance below the top of the column, depending on the type of construction. The bottom clamp is also spaced an arbitrary distance above the column base, from 6 or 8 in. up to about 12 in. Thickness of

the template at the bottom may affect the distance, and if a cleanout door is used, the first clamp should be spaced to hold it.

Types of Column Forms

Several methods of column forming are shown below, and the general method of analysis is indicated for each. Other methods of column forming are shown in the chapter on form building, but it is impossible to develop design procedures in detail for all of these. Basic steps necessary for design are indicated, and may be applied to other similar types of forms.

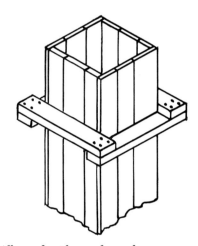

CASE 1. All wood with wooden yokes
  A. Check support requirements of sheathing.
  B. Investigate combined bending and axial load in each component of yoke.

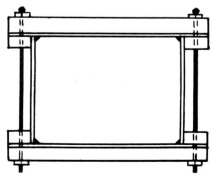

CASE 2. Plywood with combination wood and tie bolt yoke
  A. Check support requirements of sheathing.
  B. Investigate combined bending and axial load in wood yokes; investigate tension in rod or chain member.

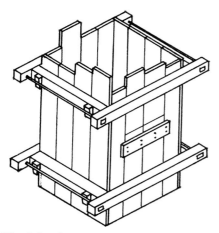

CASE 3. Wood sheathing with wood and tie bolt yoke, wedged
A. Check support requirements of sheathing.
B. Investigate combined bending and axial load in wood yokes; check tension in tie member and bending stress in cleat or batten.

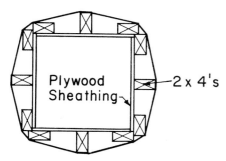

CASE 4. Trussed sheathing, tied with steel strapping
A. Check support requirements of sheathing.
B. Check hoop tension in steel strap.

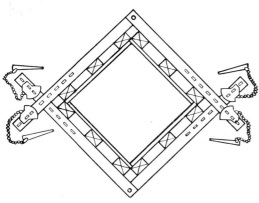

CASE 5. Braced plywood sheathing and steel column clamps
A. Check support requirements of sheathing.
B. Follow manufacturer's recommendations for clamp spacing, so long as requirements for support of sheathing are met.

COLUMN FORM EXAMPLE

Assume that an 18-in. square column 12 ft high is to be concreted in 1 hr at a temperature of 60F (concrete). (Note: Where beams or girders frame into column, figure height to bottom surface of lowest intersecting beam.) Design the form for ten or more uses, with construction grade or equal Plyform Class I sheathing braced by 2x4's used flat and clamped with patented metal "self-squaring" clamps.

Step 1. *Lateral pressure* should be determined for $R = 12$, and $T = 60$, using the ACI formula, Eq. (5-3) or Table 5-3, p. 79. By Eq. (5-3), maximum lateral pressure

$$p = 150 + \frac{9000R}{T}$$
$$= 150 + \frac{9000(12)}{60}$$
$$= 150 + 1800$$
$$p = 1950 \text{ psf}$$

However this p value exceeds the limit of 150 h, so $150 \times 12 = 1800$ psf will be used as the maximum lateral pressure for design, varying uniformly from zero at the top of the column to 1800 psf at the base.

Step 2. *Column form sides* will be assembled as shown in Case 5 (opposite).

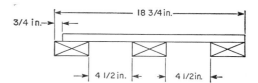

Support requirements of plywood must be met. A check by same methods as for wall sheathing (p. 92) indicates that for the maximum pressure anticipated, ¾ in. sheathing may be safely used on 6 in. spans with face grain horizontal, or 4-in. spans with grain vertical. With 2x4's flat, the spacing between them will be 4½ in. Use plywood face grain vertical. The center flat 2x4 is the most heavily loaded. Assume pressure on a 9-in. width of sheathing is transmitted to the 2x4, and compute clamp spacing to support this load.

Design will be based on working stresses * for "normal" duration of load from Table 4-2: $H = 185$ psi, $f = 1050$ psi, and $E = 1,500,000$ psi. Allowable deflection will be held to $\frac{1}{16}$ in. For the 2x4 used flat, $I = 0.98$ in.^{4}, $S = 1.31$ in.^{3}, $bh = 5.25$ sq in., and $h = 1\frac{1}{2}$ in.

Working up from the column base, assume that the pressure is uniform between clamps and of an intensity equal to that at the lower clamp. Assuming that first clamp will be 6 in. above the base, compute allowable span to second clamp using $p = 1800 - \frac{6}{12} (150) = 1725$ psf. $w = 0.75p = 1300$ lb/ft.

Investigate as a continuous beam, using the three checks—bending, deflection, and shear as in other formwork components.

CHECK BENDING, using Eq. (6-9) for maximum allowable span:

$$l = 10.95 \sqrt{\frac{fS}{w}}$$
$$= 10.95 \sqrt{\frac{1050 \times 1.33}{1300}}$$
$$l = 11.3 \text{ in.}$$

* Although it was not elected to use the increase here, the National Design Specification permits a 10 percent increase in bending stress when 2x4's are used flat. Consult Reference 1 for details.

CHECK DEFLECTION, using Eq. (6-14) for maximum Δ of $\frac{1}{16}$ in.

$$l = 3.23 \sqrt[4]{\frac{EI}{w}}$$
$$= 3.23 \sqrt[4]{\frac{1,500,000 \times 0.98}{1300}}$$
$$= 3.23 \sqrt[4]{1131} = 18.7 \text{ in.}$$

CHECK SHEAR using Eq. (6-12) solved for l (inches):

$$l = \frac{13.33Hbh}{w} + 2h$$
$$= \frac{13.33(185)\,5.25}{1300} + 2(1.5)$$
$$= 13 \text{ in.}$$

Bending strength governs at this point, so Clamp 2 would be spaced tentatively at 11 in. above Clamp 1 or $6 + 11 = 17$ in. above base of column.

To check spacing of (next) Clamp 3, determine w (equal to 0.75 times lateral pressure) at the level of Clamp 2 and assume that is the uniform load for locating Clamp 3.

At 17 in. above base $p = 1800 - \frac{17}{12}(150) = 1588$ psf. $w = 0.75(1588) = 1191$ lb/ft. Since shear was not governing in spacing Clamp 2, and loads decrease as spans increase, going up the column, the shear check may be dropped.

CHECK BENDING, with w now $= 1191$ lb/ft

$$l = 10.95 \sqrt{\frac{fS}{w}}$$
$$= 10.95 \sqrt{\frac{1050 \times 1.31}{1191}}$$
$$l = 11.8 \text{ in.}$$

CHECK DEFLECTION

$$l = 3.23 \sqrt[4]{\frac{EI}{w}}$$
$$= 3.23 \sqrt[4]{\frac{1,500,000 \times 0.98}{1191}}$$
$$l = 19.1 \text{ in.}$$

Bending strength governs location of Clamp 3, since this calculated span is the shorter. Set Clamp 3 tentatively 12 in. above Clamp 2 or $17 + 12 = 29$ in. above the base of column. Recompute p at 29 in. from base to get load w for spacing Clamp 4.

$$p \text{ at } 29 \text{ in.} = 1800 - \frac{29}{12}(150) = 1438 \text{ psf.}$$
$$w = 0.75p = 1080 \text{ lb/ft}$$

To find the allowable span between Clamp 3 and Clamp 4: *CHECK BENDING*, substituting in Eq. (6-9) as before:

$$l = 10.95 \sqrt{\frac{1050 \times 1.31}{1080}}$$
$$l = 12.4 \text{ in.}$$

CHECK DEFLECTION

$$l = 3.23 \sqrt[4]{\frac{EI}{w}}$$
$$= 3.23 \sqrt[4]{\frac{1,500,000 \times 0.98}{1080}}$$
$$l = 19.6 \text{ in.}$$

Bending again governs span, and Clamp 4 will be tentatively spaced 12 in. above Clamp 3 or $29 + 12 = 41$ in. above base. Recompute p at Clamp 4 as a basis for determining load for spacing Clamp 5.

$$p \text{ at Clamp 4} = 1800 - \frac{41}{12}(150) = 1288 \text{ psf.}$$
$$w = 0.75p = 966 \text{ lb/ft}$$

To find the allowable span between Clamp 4 and Clamp 5: *CHECK BENDING*, as before:

$$l = 10.95 \sqrt{\frac{fS}{w}}$$
$$= 10.95 \sqrt{\frac{1050 \times 1.31}{966}}$$
$$l = 13 \text{ in.}$$

CHECK DEFLECTION

$$l = 3.23 \sqrt[4]{\frac{EI}{w}} = 3.23 \sqrt[4]{\frac{1,500,000 \times 0.98}{966}}$$
$$= 3.23 \sqrt[4]{1522}$$
$$l = 20.2 \text{ in.}$$

Bending again governs and Clamp 5 would be tentatively spaced 13 in. above Clamp 4 or $41 + 13 = 54$ in. from base of column.

Recompute pressure at Clamp 5 and continue calculations in this fashion until last clamp elevation is equal or greater than column height.

Step 3. *Strength of yokes or clamps* should be investigated. In this case, a patented device is being used and the manufacturer's suggested clamp spacing will be taken as evidence of clamp strength, since this column is of relatively small cross section. The recommendations of reputable manufacturers are generally satisfactory in this regard, but it is well to find out if possible what deflection values and what lateral pressure values are used in arriving at the manufacturer's recommended spacings. This is particularly important if the longer span clamps (4-7 ft) are to be used without intermediate ties.

If bowing of column sides due to deflection of the column clamp would be objectionable, it would be well to check the beam action of the clamp member to estimate deflection under load. In the absence of detailed data on properties of steels used, etc., this would necessarily be an approximation. For job-built yokes, steel strapping, and other methods of clamping, a general design approach is suggested on p. 103.

One manufacturer's suggested spacing for a 12-ft column is presented below.

Step 4. Compare spacing requirements of the clamp manufacturer with the tentative spacing calculated on basis of sheathing strength and deflection.

Calculated on basis of sheathing strength and stiffness (allowable $\Delta = \frac{1}{16}$ in.)				Based on clamp manufacturer's recommendation for this type of column construction		
Clamp No.	Spacing between clamps, in.	Distance of clamp above base, in.	p at clamp level	Clamp No.	Spacing between clamps	Distance of clamp above base
10		147	0±			
	27					
9		120	300	9		136
	20				24	
8		100	550	8		112
	17				24	
7		83	763	7		88
	15				16	
6		68	950	6		72
	14				16	
5		54	1125	5		56
	13				16	
4		41	1288	4		40
	12				16	
3		29	1438	3		24
	12				12	
2		17	1588	2		12
	11				12	
1		6	1725	1		0

Assuming that construction requirements place the top clamp 6 in. below top of column, convenient spacing of clamps should be chosen to meet requirements of the sheathing for support. The calculated and manufacturer's recommendations agree reasonably well. Since the column in question is relatively small and clamps will not be used at maximum span, it should be possible to modify the manufacturer's recommended spacing. Just at this stage, knowing the exact basis of calculation of his recommended spacing would be helpful in adjusting dimensions to meet both sheathing and clamp requirements.

CLAMP NO.	10	6"
		20"
CLAMP NO.	9	
		20"
" "	8	
		16"
" "	7	
		16"
" "	6	
		14"
" "	5	
		12"
" "	4	
		12"
" "	3	
		12"
CLAMP NO.	2	
		10"
CLAMP NO.	1	
		6"

12' or 144"

The spacing indicated, arrived at by trial and error to total *h* of 144 in., covers support requirements of sheathing and is conservative by comparison with clamp manufacturer's suggestions.

Shoring and Scaffolding

It is sufficiently accurate to assume that each shore or scaffolding leg supports a formwork area extending halfway to the adjacent shore or leg on all sides. Both dead load and construction live load must be figured for this area to determine the total load on the shore or scaffold leg.

Simple Wood Shores

Common wood shores, either rectangular or round in cross section, are designed as simple solid columns. As in the design of columns of all types, the load capacity depends on the slenderness ratio.

Slenderness Ratio

The slenderness ratio is the relationship of unsupported length of shore to the cross-sectional dimension in the face under consideration, usually the narrower of the two faces. This ratio is expressed as l/d, where l = unsupported length in inches and d = net dimension in inches of the face under consideration. For wood shores, l/d must not exceed 50.

When shores are braced laterally on one or more faces, or at different points along their length, the slenderness ratio in each plane of lateral support must be determined and the greater ratio used in computing allowable loads. Figure 6-6 illustrates the determination of l/d ratio for a 3x4 shore with different bracing plans. To be effective such bracing must be anchored to or bear against some positive stop such as permanent construction or firmly placed stakes.

Allowable Load

The maximum unit load in psi for rectangular wood shores is determined by the following modification of the Euler formula. P/A must not exceed the value of c, allowable stress in compression parallel to the grain for the species and grade of lumber being used.

$$P/A = \frac{0.30\,E}{(l/d)^2} \quad\quad\quad (6\text{-}20)$$

where

P = total load on shore, lb
A = net cross-sectional area, sq in.
E = modulus of elasticity of wood, psi

This formula provides a safety factor of 3 against buckling for axially loaded pin-ended columns. Where there is some partial restraint or square ends, as in the case of wood shores, the actual safety is greater, tending to compensate for eccentricities of load that are likely to occur in formwork.

Other conditions being equal, round and square columns of equal cross-sectional area will carry the same loads and have equal stiffness. Therefore the design of a round wood shore can also be based on Eq. (6-20) by assuming a square column for analytical purposes and then using a round shore of the same cross-sectional area.

Example: Allowable load on 4x4 shore
What load will a 4x4 S4S construction grade Douglas fir shore carry if its unsupported length is 9 ft? From suggested working stresses, p. 33, compression parallel to grain for this shore will be 1150 psi and $E = 1,500,000$. With dimensions (actual) of 3½x3½ in. the area of cross section is 12.25 sq in., $l/d = (9 \times 12)/3½$ or 30.9, well within the 50 limitation.
Substituting in Eq. (6-20)

$$P/A = \frac{0.30 \times 1,500,000}{(30.9)^2} = 471 \text{ psi}$$

Since this is less than the allowable compressive stress, c, the P/A value governs and the total allowable load on the shore will be

$$P = 471A = 471 \times 12.25 = 5770 \text{ lb}$$

$$P_{shores}(\text{lb}) = W_{Str}\left(\frac{S_{shores}}{12}\right)$$

$$= P\left(\frac{S_{Str}}{12}\right)\left(\frac{S_{shore}}{12}\right)$$

107

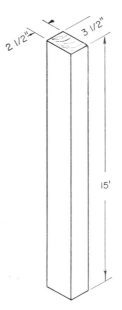

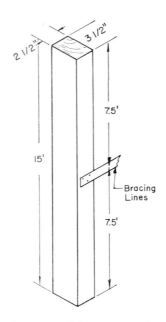

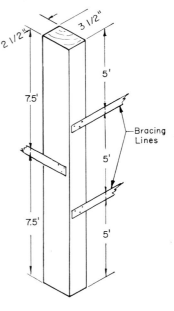

When neither face is braced use smaller *d*.

$$l/d = \frac{15 \times 12}{2\frac{1}{2}}$$
$$= 72.0$$

This exceeds limit of 50 so this shore could not be used without added bracing.

In plane parallel to narrow face
$$l/d = \frac{7.5(12)}{2\frac{1}{2}}$$
$$= 36.0$$

In plane parallel to wider face
$$l/d = \frac{15(12)}{3\frac{1}{2}} = 51.4$$

This exceeds limit of 50 so bracing is needed in this plane.

In plane parallel to narrow face
$$l/d = \frac{5 \times 12}{2\frac{1}{2}}$$
$$= 24.0$$

In plane parallel to wider face
$$l/d = \frac{7.5 \times 12}{3\frac{1}{2}}$$
$$= 25.7$$

The larger ratio governs.

6-6 Determination of *l/d* ratio for a 3x4 S4S with different bracing plans

End Bearing of Shores

If the wood shore bears directly against a joist, stringer, or other horizontal wooden member it supports, the load will often be limited by bearing stress in the member being supported, as explained on p. 89. This bearing stress is frequently the governing design consideration. The total allowable load depends on the area of contact between shore and member being supported. The bearing area may be the full area of the shore, or it may be considerably less as shown if a narrow member rests on the shore.

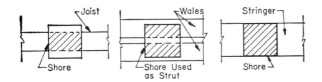

Shaded area indicates bearing of supported member on shore.

Consider the 4x4 shore of the preceding example. Suppose this shore is used directly beneath a 2x6

joist; the area of contact will be $1\frac{1}{2} \times 3\frac{1}{2}$ or 5.25 sq in. The allowable stress of 385 psi perpendicular to the grain of the joist is increased to 426 because of the short length of bearing (see p. 89). This shore used in this location would have a load limited to 426×5.25 or 2237 lb, not 5770 lb shown in the preceding example. If the full area ($3\frac{1}{2} \times 3\frac{1}{2}$) of the shore is in contact with the form member being supported, the allowable load would be $3\frac{1}{2} \times 3\frac{1}{2} \times 426$ or 5219 lb, also less than the load based on strength of shore.

Metal or hardwood plates or fittings attached to the top of the shores may be used to increase the load above these bearing limits.

Splicing of Shores

Shore splices must be designed against buckling and bending as for any other structural compression member. Only one splice point per shore is advisable unless diagonal and two-way lateral bracing in both directions is provided at every splice point. ACI

TABLE 6-3: ALLOWABLE LOAD IN POUNDS ON SIMPLE WOOD SHORES,* FOR LUMBER OF THE INDICATED STRENGTH, BASED ON UNSUPPORTED LENGTH

$c\parallel$ to grain = 750 psi $\quad$ E = 1,100,000 psi $\quad$ l/d_{max} = 50 $\quad$ $P/A_{max} = \dfrac{0.30E}{(l/d)^2}$

BRACING NEEDED †

Nominal lumber size, in. Unsupported length, ft	2x4 R**	2x4 S4S**	3x4 R	3x4 S4S	4x4 R	4x4 S4S	4x2 R	4x2 S4S	4x3 R	4x3 S4S	4x6 R	4x6 S4S	6x6 R	6x6 S4S
4	2200	1700	7100	6600	9900	9200	4400	3900	7100	6600	15300	14400	23700	22700
5	1400	1100	6000	5000	9900	9200	4400	3900	7100	6600	15300	14400	23700	22700
6	1000	800	4200	3500	9900	9200	4400	3900	7100	6600	15300	14400	23700	22700
7	–	–	3100	2600	8100	7000	3600	3000	5800	5000	12500	11000	23700	22700
8			2300	2000	6200	5400	2800	2300	4500	3800	9600	8400	23700	22700
9			1900	1500	4900	4200	2200	1800	3500	3000	7600	6700	23700	22700
10			1500	1200	4000	3400	1800	1500	2900	2500	6100	5400	23000	21000
11			–	–	3300	2800	1500	1200	2400	2000	5100	4500	19000	17300
12					2700	2400	1200	1000	2000	1700	4300	3700	16000	14600
13					2300	2000	1000	900	1700	1400	3600	3200	13600	12400
14					2000	1700	900	700	1500	1200	3100	2800	11700	10700
15					1800	–	800	–	1300	–	2700	–	10200	9300
16					–		–		–		–		9000	8200
17													7900	7300
18													7100	6500
19													6400	5800
20													5700	5200

$c\parallel$ to grain = 900 psi $\quad$ E = 1,100,000 psi $\quad$ l/d_{max} = 50 $\quad$ $P/A_{max} = \dfrac{0.30E}{(l/d)^2}$

BRACING NEEDED †

Nominal lumber size, in. Unsupported length, ft	2x4 R**	2x4 S4S**	3x4 R	3x4 S4S	4x4 R	4x4 S4S	4x2 R	4x2 S4S	4x3 R	4x3 S4S	4x6 R	4x6 S4S	6x6 R	6x6 S4S
4	2200	1700	8600	7800	11800	11000	5300	4700	8600	7900	18300	17300	28500	27200
5	1400	1100	6000	5000	11800	11000	5300	4700	8600	7900	18300	17300	28500	27200
6	1000	800	4200	3500	11000	9500	4900	4100	8000	6800	17100	15000	28500	27200
7	–	–	3100	2600	8100	7000	3600	3000	5800	5000	12500	11000	28500	27200
8			2300	2000	6200	5400	2800	2300	4500	3800	9600	8400	28500	27200
9			1900	1500	4900	4200	2200	1800	3500	3000	7600	6700	28300	25800
10			1500	1200	4000	3400	1800	1500	2900	2500	6100	5400	22900	21000
11			–	–	3300	2800	1500	1200	2400	2000	5100	4500	19000	17300
12					2700	2400	1200	1000	2000	1700	4300	3700	15900	14600
13					2300	2000	1000	900	1700	1400	3600	3200	13600	12400
14					2000	1700	900	700	1500	1200	3100	2800	11700	10700
15					1800	–	800	–	1300	–	2700	–	10200	9300
16					–		–		–		–		9000	8200
17													7900	7300
18													7100	6500
19													6400	5800
20													5700	5200

$c\parallel$ to grain = 700 psi $\quad$ for E = 1,400,000 psi $\quad$ l/d_{max} = 50 $\quad$ $P/A_{max} = \dfrac{0.30E}{(l/d)^2}$

BRACING NEEDED †

Nominal lumber size, in. Unsupported length, ft	2x4 R**	2x4 S4S**	3x4 R	3x4 S4S	4x4 R	4x4 S4S	4x2 R	4x2 S4S	4x3 R	4x3 S4S	4x6 R	4x6 S4S	6x6 R	6x6 S4S
4	2800	2200	6700	6100	9200	8600	4100	3700	6700	6100	14300	13500	22100	21200
5	1800	1400	6700	6100	9200	8600	4100	3700	6700	6100	14300	13500	22100	21200
6	1300	1000	5300	4400	9200	8600	4100	3700	6700	6100	14300	13500	22100	21200
7	—	—	3900	3300	9200	8600	4100	3700	6700	6100	14300	13500	22100	21200
8			3000	2500	7870	6800	3500	2900	5700	4900	12200	10700	22100	21200
9			2400	2000	6200	5400	2800	2300	4500	3900	9700	8500	22100	21200
10			1900	1600	5000	4400	2300	1900	3600	3100	7800	6900	22100	21200
11			—	—	4200	3600	1900	1500	3000	2600	6500	5700	22100	21200
12					3500	3000	1600	1300	2500	2200	5400	4800	20300	18500
13					3000	2600	1300	1100	2200	1800	4600	4100	17300	15800
14					2600	2200	1200	1000	1900	1600	4000	3500	14900	13600
15					2200	—	1000	—	1600	—	3500	—	13000	11900
16					—		—		—		—		11400	10400
17													10100	9200
18													9000	8200
19													8100	7100
20													7300	6700

* Calculated to nearest 100 lb. ** R indicates rough lumber; S4S indicates lumber finished on all four sides.
† The dimension used in determining l/d is that shown first in the size column. Where this is the larger dimension, the column must be braced in the other direction so that l/d is equal to or less than that used in arriving at the loads shown. For 4x2's bracing in the plane of the 2-in. dimension must be at intervals not greater than 0.4 times the unsupported length. For 4x3's bracing in the plane of the 3-in. dimension must be at intervals not more than 0.7 times the unsupported length.

TABLE 6-3 (Continued): ALLOWABLE LOAD IN POUNDS ON SIMPLE WOOD SHORES,* FOR LUMBER OF THE INDICATED STRENGTH, BASED ON UNSUPPORTED LENGTH

c‖ to grain = 1150 psi   E = 1,400,000 psi $l/d_{max} = 50$ $P/A_{max} = \dfrac{0.30E}{(l/d)^2}$

Nominal lumber size, in. / Unsupported length, ft	2x4 R**	2x4 S4S**	3x4 R	3x4 S4S	4x4 R	4x4 S4S	4x2 R	4x2 S4S	4x3 R	4x3 S4S	4x6 R	4x6 S4S	6x6 R	6x6 S4S
							BRACING	NEEDED †						
4	2800	2200	10900	10000	15100	15000	6800	6000	10900	10100	23400	22100	36400	34800
5	1800	1400	7700	6400	15100	15000	6800	6000	10900	10100	23400	22100	36400	34800
6	1300	1000	5300	4400	14000	12200	6300	5200	10100	8700	21700	19100	36400	34800
7			3900	3300	10300	8900	4600	3800	7400	6400	15900	14000	36400	34800
8			3000	2500	7870	6800	3500	2900	5700	4900	12200	10700	36200	32900
9			2400	2000	6200	5400	2800	2300	4500	3900	9700	8500	29200	26700
10			1900	1600	5000	4400	2300	1900	3600	3100	7800	6900	24100	22100
11			—	—	4200	3600	1900	1500	3000	2600	6500	5700	20300	18500
12					3500	3000	1600	1300	2500	2200	5400	4800	17300	15800
13					3000	2600	1300	1100	2200	1800	4600	4100	14900	13600
14					2600	2200	1200	1000	1900	1600	4000	3500	13000	11900
15					2200	—	1000	—	1600	—	3500	—	11400	10400
16					—		—		—		—		10100	9200
17													9000	8200
18													8100	7100
19													7300	6700
20													—	

c‖ to grain = 1000 psi   E = 1,600,000 psi $l/d_{max} = 50$ $P/A_{max} = \dfrac{0.30E}{(l/d)^2}$

Nominal lumber size, in. / Unsupported length, ft	2x4 R**	2x4 S4S**	3x4 R	3x4 S4S	4x4 R	4x4 S4S	4x2 R	4x2 S4S	4x3 R	4x3 S4S	4x6 R	4x6 S4S	6x6 R	6x6 S4S
							BRACING	NEEDED †						
4	3200	2500	9500	8700	13100	12200	5900	5200	9500	8700	20400	19200	31600	30200
5	2100	1600	8700	7300	13100	12200	5900	5200	9500	8700	20400	19200	31600	30200
6	1400	1100	6100	5100	13100	12200	5900	5200	9500	8700	20400	19200	31600	30200
7	—	—	4500	3700	11700	10200	5300	4400	8500	7300	18200	16000	31600	30200
8			3400	2800	9000	7800	4000	3300	6500	5600	13900	12300	31600	30200
9			2700	2200	7100	6200	3200	2600	5100	4400	11000	9700	31600	30200
10			2200	1800	5800	5000	2600	2100	4200	3600	8900	7900	27600	25200
11			—	—	4800	4100	2100	1800	3400	2900	7400	6500	23200	21200
12					4000	3500	1800	1500	2900	2500	6200	5500	19700	18000
13					3100	3000	1500	1300	2500	2100	5300	4600	17000	15600
14					2900	2500	1300	1100	2100	1800	4600	4000	14800	13600
15					2600	—	1100	—	1800	—	4000	—	13000	11900
16					—		—		—		—		11500	10500
17													10300	9400
18													9200	8400
19													8300	7600
20														

c‖ to grain = 1000 psi   E = 1,700,000 psi $l/d_{max} = 50$ $P/A_{max} = \dfrac{0.30E}{(l/d)^2}$

Nominal lumber size, in. / Unsupported length, ft	2x4 R**	2x4 S4S**	3x4 R	3x4 S4S	4x4 R	4x4 S4S	4x2 R	4x2 S4S	4x3 R	4x3 S4S	4x6 R	4x6 S4S	6x6 R	6x6 S4S
							BRACING	NEEDED †						
4	3400	2600	9500	8800	13100	12300	5900	5300	9500	8800	20400	19200	31600	30200
5	2200	1700	9300	7700	13100	12300	5900	5300	9500	8800	20400	19200	31600	30200
6	1500	1200	6500	5400	13100	12300	5900	5300	9500	8800	20400	19200	31600	30200
7	—	—	4700	4000	12500	10800	5600	4600	9000	7700	19400	17000	31600	30200
8			3600	3000	9600	8300	4300	3600	6900	5900	14800	13100	31600	30200
9			2900	2400	7600	6600	3400	2800	5500	4700	11700	10300	31600	30200
10			2300	1900	6100	5300	2700	2300	4400	3800	9500	8400	31600	30200
11			—	—	5100	4400	2300	1900	3700	3100	7900	6900	29300	28000
12					4200	3700	1900	1600	3100	2600	6600	5800	24600	22500
13					3600	3100	1600	1300	2600	2200	5600	4900	21000	19200
14					3100	2700	1400	1200	2300	1900	4800	4300	18100	16500
15					2700	—	1200	—	2000	—	4200	—	15800	14400
16					—		—		—		—		13800	12600
17													12300	11200
18													10900	10000
19													9800	9000
20													8900	8100

* Calculated to nearest 100 lb. ** R indicates rough lumber; S4S indicates lumber finished on all four sides.
† The dimension used in determining l/d is that shown first in the size column. Where this is the larger dimension, the column must be braced in the other direction so that l/d is equal to or less than that used in arriving at the loads shown. For 4x2's bracing in the plane of the 2-in. dimension must be at intervals not greater than 0.4 times the unsupported length. For 4x3's bracing in the plane of the 3-in. dimension must be at intervals not more than 0.7 times the unsupported length.

TABLE 6-3A: ALLOWABLE LOAD BASED ON MAXIMUM SHORE AREA IN DIRECT CONTACT WITH WOOD MEMBER BEING SUPPORTED

Nominal lumber size	2x4		3x4		4x4		4x2		4x3		4x6		6x6	
Area of cross sec., sq in.	R ** 5.89	S4S ** 5.25	R 9.52	S4S 8.75	R 13.14	S4S 12.25	R 5.89	S4S 5.25	R 9.52	S4S 8.75	R 20.39	S4S 19.25	R 31.64	S4S 30.25
c ⊥ of member supported														
250	1500	1300	2400	2200	3300	3100	1500	1300	2400	2200	5100	4800	7900	7600
350	2100	1800	3300	3100	4600	4300	2100	1800	3300	3100	7100	6700	11100	10600
385	2300	2000	3700	3400	5100	4700	2300	2000	3700	3400	7800	7400	12200	11600
400	2400	2100	3800	3500	5300	4900	2400	2100	3800	3500	8200	7700	12700	12100

* Calculated to nearest 100 lb. ** R indicates rough lumber; S4S indicates lumber finished on all four sides.

Committee 347 recommends a minimum splice length of 2 ft for timber shores, with four such pieces at each splice for square timbers and three splice pieces for round timbers.* Splicing material should be not less than 2-in. (nominal) lumber or ⅝-in. plywood and no less than the width of the material being spliced. To avoid buckling, splices should not be placed near midheight of unbraced shores or midway between points of lateral support.

Design Table for Wood Shores

Table 6-3 of allowable loads on wood shores has been developed for some of the more commonly used timber sizes. It shows loads for wood shores with c, allowable compression parallel to the grain, ranging from 700 to 1150 psi, with modulus of elasticity values from 1,100,000 to 1,700,000 psi. These loads can be used for several grades of forming lumber, as the allowable stress ranges in Table 4-2 indicate. Note that for compression parallel to the grain green lumber is permitted only 70 percent of the stress allowed for lumber seasoned to 19 percent moisture content. No loads are shown in Table 6-3 where l/d exceeds 50.

Where the shore is in direct contact with the wood member being supported, the allowable load based on unsupported length l must not exceed total permissible load based on bearing stress in the member be-

ing supported. Values of Table 6-3A indicate total allowable load based on bearing stress when the full shore area directly contacts the wood member it supports.

Tubular Steel Shores

Formulas provided below for concentrically loaded steel columns may be used for the design of simple tubular steel shores or for investigation of single parts of tubular scaffolding frames.* For adjustable shores, combinations of steel and wood, or other patented shores and shoring methods, manufacturer's recommendations based on load tests should be used because varied connection, assembly, and jacking details make a precise theoretical analysis complicated, if not impossible.

Slenderness Ratio

As in the case of wood shores, the slenderness ratio is a governing design consideration. For tubular members, the slenderness ratio is expressed as Kl/r, where l = unsupported length in inches, r = radius of gyration, and K = effective length factor ($K = 1$ is used for steel shores, which are conservatively assumed to be pin ended). For steel shores, l/r should not exceed 200.

The radius of gyration is easily calculated when inside and outside diameters of the tubular section are known.

$$r = \frac{\sqrt{\text{I.D.}^2 + \text{O.D.}^2}}{4}$$

* This does not apply to proved patented splicing devices which are used to make an adjustable wooden shore by forming a lap joint of two wooden members with a special clamp. See "Other Patented Shoring Devices," p. 111.

* These formulas apply to cold formed steel compression members with a yield point of 33,000 psi; for other metals or for special alloy steels, manufacturer's special design recommendations should be followed.

$$A = \frac{\pi}{4}(\text{O.D.}^2 - \text{I.D.}^2)$$

Both longitudinal and transverse planes of support should be considered when checking for l, the unsupported length used for design. For example, the maximum unbraced length of member ABCD is 4 ft in the longitudinal plane, while the unbraced length is 8 ft in the transverse plane. The larger l value of course would be used in checking allowable stress.

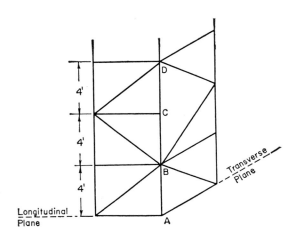

In a tubular structure where bracing does not provide complete triangular rigidity, l cannot be so readily determined by inspection. This case is discussed in more detail in the section on scaffold-type shoring.

Allowable Stress

For axially loaded, undamaged * shores of structural steel, the following formula for allowable stress applies when l/r is less than C_c:

$$P/A = \frac{\left[1 - \frac{(l/r)^2}{2C_c^2}\right]F_y}{\text{F.S.}} \qquad (6\text{-}21)$$

where

$$\text{F.S.} = \text{factor of safety} = \frac{5}{3} + \frac{3(l/r)}{8C_c} - \frac{(l/r)^3}{8C_c^3}$$

and

$$C_c = \sqrt{\frac{2\pi^2 E}{F_y}} = 126 \text{ for } 36,000 \text{ psi yield strength steel.}$$

For l/r greater than C_c:

$$P/A = \frac{149,000,000}{(l/r)^2} \qquad (6\text{-}22)$$

* Damaged sections must not be used because their remaining strength cannot be estimated.

110

*Example: Allowable load on tubular steel shore ***

What total load will an A36 steel pipe shore carry if its outside diameter is 1⅝ in., inside diameter is 1⁷⁄₁₆ in., and unsupported length is 7 ft?

First find the radius of gyration:

$$r = \frac{\sqrt{\text{I.D.}^2 + \text{O.D.}^2}}{4}$$

$$= \frac{\sqrt{1.625^2 + 1.437^2}}{4}$$

$$r = 0.54 \text{ in.}$$

l is 12×7 or 84 in.; thus

$$\frac{l}{r} = \frac{84}{0.54} = 156$$

Since this is larger than C_c for 36,000 psi steel, Eq. (6-22) for allowable stress applies:

$$P/A = \frac{149,000,000}{(l/r)^2} = \frac{149,000,000}{(156)^2} = 6123 \text{ psi}$$

$$A = \frac{\pi}{4}(\text{O.D.}^2 - \text{I.D.}^2)$$

$$= \frac{\pi}{4}(1.625^2 - 1.437^2)$$

$$= 0.45 \text{ sq in.}$$

and allowable load P is $6123 \times A$ or 2755 lb.

Tubular Steel Scaffold-Type Shoring

The design of tubular steel scaffold-type shoring is complicated by the fact that much of it is assembled with bracing that does not afford complete triangular rigidity in the structure, as shown in Figure 6-7. Connections of the bracing are of varying degrees of fixity, and with some bending possible at the joints, the unsupported length l cannot be accurately estimated. Assembly of the scaffold frames in tower structures of varying heights further complicates attempts at mathematical analysis.

For structures of this sort, safe load capacities can be determined by load tests, and most reputable manufacturers are now conducting such tests and recommending allowable loads on that basis. Load tests should be made under conditions approximating

** Design information in the *Manual of Steel Construction* (Reference 10) includes tabulated P/A values for l/r from 1 to 200.

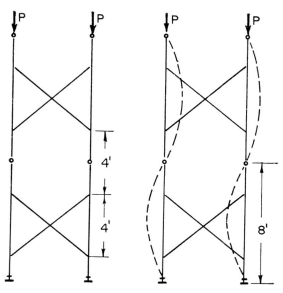

A. Longitudinal Bracing   B. Deflected Structure

6-7 Typical longitudinal bracing for scaffold-type shoring tower is shown in A. Cursory examination would indicate an unbraced length in this longitudinal plane of 4 ft. However, because of the lack of complete triangular rigidity and because the degree of fixity of connections varies, deflection may be as shown in B where the actual unbraced length is 8 ft instead of 4 ft (including jacks). Other deflection configurations are possible for this same type of structure, making it impossible to accurately assign l/r values before use.

those of actual use as nearly as possible. The Scaffolding and Shoring Institute has developed a recommended load test procedure, outlining duration, speed, and other loading conditions, in an effort to help manufacturers to develop uniform recommendations for allowable loads on sectional steel scaffolding and shoring components. The SSI has also recommended a minimum safety factor of 2.5 for these members based on the ultimate load capacity as established by test.

The best practice, then, in designing scaffold type shoring is to use the load capacity recommended by the manufacturer, *on the basis of load tests* conducted under standardized conditions. Manufacturer's recommendations for bracing, assembly, and erection conditions should be carefully followed. In many cases engineering assistance is offered by the suppliers or producers of these proprietary scaffold shoring devices.

Scaffold shoring example for beam and slab construction:

For a typical scaffold frame available for concrete shoring the manufacturer recommends a maximum working load of 10,000 lb per frame, or 5000 lb on each leg under good job conditions (firm support under legs and height of assembly less than 14 ft). The frames are ordinarily assembled in "towers"

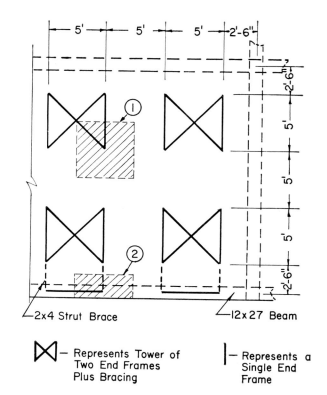

⋈ — Represents Tower of Two End Frames Plus Bracing

| — Represents a Single End Frame

consisting of two end frames plus diagonal bracing between them.

Note that crossed lines in drawing do not represent bracing location. The bracing is in planes at right angles to plane of the frame. This particular scaffold frame is 5 ft wide, and adjustable bracing is available to allow frame spacing of 3 to 7 ft in 6-in. increments.

Assume that each leg supports the formwork area extending halfway to the adjacent leg on each side.

Shaded Area (1)

10 in. slab area = 5 × 5 = 25 sq ft × 125 psf	= 3125 lb	
construction live load 25 sq ft × 50	= 1250	
Load per leg	4375 lb	

Shaded Area (2)

10 in. slab area = 5 × 1 = 5 sq ft × 125 psf	= 625 lb	
12×27 beam = 5 ft × 337 lb per lineal ft	= 1705	
construction live load, 2 × 5 = 10 sq ft × 50 psf	= 500	
Load per leg	2830 lb	

Other Patented Shoring Devices

In addition to the increasingly common scaffold-type shoring, single post adjustable steel shores are available with varied design of jacking and adjustment features. Also there are adjustable shores made of wood and metal combinations, as well as clamping devices which in effect create an adjustable shore from two pieces of lumber. So-called horizontal shoring—single span metal members which support forms over relatively long spans, and thereby reduce the

6-8 Typical scaffold shoring tower load-tested to failure. Note that buckling occurred in the plane of the longitudinal bracing, and effective length is considerably greater than the distance between points at which the braces are connected.

number of vertical shores required—may also be considered in this category. The more common of these devices are described in the chapter on formwork materials and accessories (p. 69).

When these patented shores or methods of shoring are used, manufacturers' recommendations as to load carrying capacities may be followed if they are based on load tests conducted under standard conditions, with a safety factor of 2 to 3 used to determine working loads. It is preferable that load tests be made by a qualified and recognized testing laboratory. The designer must carefully follow the manufacturer's recommendations as to bracing and working loads for given length of unsupported shore.

Bracing for Lateral Loads

Adequate lateral bracing is extremely important to stability and safety in formwork construction, but all too often it is treated carelessly or even omitted entirely. Lateral bracing should be provided to resist wind and the various lateral forces that may occur during construction due to starting and stopping of equipment, dumping of concrete, and the like. The formwork system must be designed to safely transfer all lateral loads to the ground or to completed construction. Since it is generally not possible to predict the exact amount and nature of such loads, ACI Committee 347 has set up recommended minimum design values to use for these lateral loads (Tables 5-4 and 5-5, p. 81).

Much of the diagonal bracing in use for formwork today is erected on the basis of experience and judgment of the superintendent or foremen on the job. While this may be generally satisfactory where capable and conscientious workmen are available, it is possible to make a more exact approach to design of the lateral bracing using the minimum lateral loads established by Committee 347. Some possible bracing layouts and design suggestions are shown in the examples that follow. Any laterally braced system should be anchored adequately to insure stability of the total system (note provisions for stability in Figures 6-9, 6-10, and 6-11).

The federal Occupational Safety and Health Act adopted by the United States in 1970 embodies indirectly many of the recommendations of Committee 347 for lateral bracing, since it incorporates by reference ANSI A10.9-1970 Safety Requirements for Concrete Construction and Masonry Work, which in turn draws heavily from provisions of ACI 347-68. There are also some explicit provisions for forms and shoring in Sec. 1926.701 [11] which must be considered by the designer. At the present writing, because some of these appear to need clarification and may be subject to revision, this text is limited to implementing the ACI 347-68 recommendations, which we believe offer the best means at present of accomplishing the OSHA objectives.

Wall Forms

Consider the necessary bracing for a wall form 14 ft high, above grade, in an area where the local building code specifies a minimum 20 psf wind loading. Table 5-5 indicates that 140 lb per lineal ft should be used for design of bracing, since the wind force prescribed by local code gives a value larger than the 100 lb/ft minimum established by Committee 347.

Guy Wire Bracing

This 140 lb per ft is applied at the top of the wall and may act in either direction. If guy wires, which act only in tension are used, bracing must be placed on both sides of the wall. Tension in the wire depends on the angle it makes with the wall; this tension in the wire can be calculated easily using the relationship between sides of a right triangle. For example, if stakes to which guys are attached are set 10 ft away from the base of the wall:

H = 140 lb./ft.

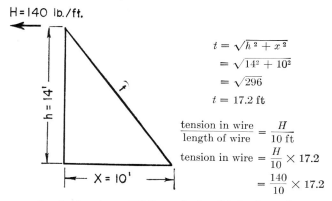

$$t = \sqrt{h^2 + x^2}$$
$$= \sqrt{14^2 + 10^2}$$
$$= \sqrt{296}$$
$$t = 17.2 \text{ ft}$$

$$\frac{\text{tension in wire}}{\text{length of wire}} = \frac{H}{10 \text{ ft}}$$

$$\text{tension in wire} = \frac{H}{10} \times 17.2$$
$$= \frac{140}{10} \times 17.2$$

tension in wire = 240 lb per ft of wall being braced

This indicates a 240-lb tension load for every ft of wall braced; if guys are 8 ft apart, the total tension would be 8 × 240 or 1920 lb. With working strength of guy material known, guys can be spaced to use their maximum safe load capacity. Stakes must be securely placed to resist this load, and top wales must be able to carry horizontal forces accumulated to each point where guys are attached.

This same approach would apply to 1-in. lumber bracing since it is good only for tension loads, except in short spans of about 4 ft or less.

Strut Bracing

If wooden strut bracing is provided, strong enough to take either a tension or compression load, then single side bracing may be used. Nailed connections at either end must be strong enough to transmit the tension load, and wales or other form members must be strong enough to transmit accumulated horizontal forces to the strut bracing.

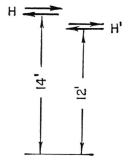

If wooden bracing is attached 1 or 2 ft below the top of the wall, the bracing must carry more than the 140 lb per ft load applied at the top.

H' the horizontal resisting force 2 ft below the top of the wall would have to be $^{14}/_{12}$ (140) or 163 lb per ft in order to balance the 140 lb per ft design load applied at the top of the wall.

If end of brace is placed 8 ft from the wall, use the relationship between sides of a right triangle to find the length of brace and load it must carry.

H' = 163 lb./ft.

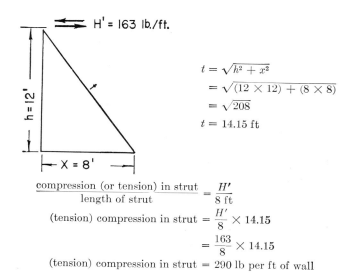

$$t = \sqrt{h^2 + x^2}$$
$$= \sqrt{(12 \times 12) + (8 \times 8)}$$
$$= \sqrt{208}$$
$$t = 14.15 \text{ ft}$$

$$\frac{\text{compression (or tension) in strut}}{\text{length of strut}} = \frac{H'}{8 \text{ ft}}$$

$$\text{(tension) compression in strut} = \frac{H'}{8} \times 14.15$$
$$= \frac{163}{8} \times 14.15$$

(tension) compression in strut = 290 lb per ft of wall

If struts are spaced every 8 ft along the wall, then 8 × 290 or 2320 lb must be carried by each brace. Design the same as for simple wood shores (p. 107). Any wood member strong enough to carry this load in compression will also be adequate in tension. However the strength of connections (nails, etc.) must be made adequate for the tension load.

Slab Forms Supported by Individual Shores

As discussed in the design information on shores, lateral supporting braces are often necessary to increase the carrying capacity of the shores. However, regardless of the l/d ratios of shores, some bracing is desirable for all shoring systems, and certain minimum lateral loads to be provided for have been suggested by Committee 347. The bracing system must be tied to solid ground or permanent construction, unless it is multidirectional (Figure 6-9) with sufficient X-bracing to give it internal rigidity.

If shores are spliced more than once, diagonal bracing and two-way lateral bracing should be provided at every splice point; for shores with a single splice point, diagonal bracing is desirable. For one-piece shores, horizontal strut bracing may be adequate. Figures 6-9, 6-10, and 6-11 show three alternate schemes for bracing slab shoring, using (1) braced bays, (2) braced lines, and (3) tying to completed columns or walls.

Minimum loads used in designing components of this bracing are given in Table 5-4. Design must provide for the force acting at the edge of the slab in either direction, and the intensity of lateral force depends on the slab width in the direction of the force. In applying Table 5-4, consider as the "slab" only that part which will be concreted at one time.

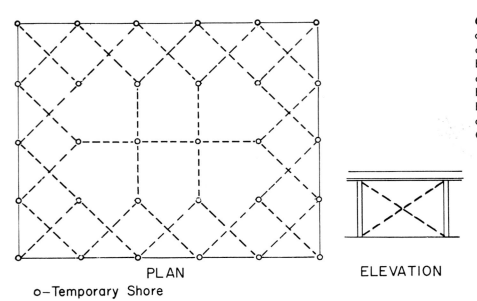

PLAN   ELEVATION

o—Temporary Shore

6-9 Braced bays; no exterior guys or anchors needed. Bays marked with dashed X-lines have complete X-bracing system on vertical lines in both directions as well as horizontal X-bracing. Distance between braced bays depends on size of bay, weight on form, height of form, live load, etc. Center shores tied in with strut bracing.

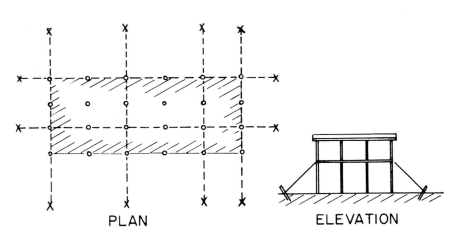

PLAN   ELEVATION

▨—Slab Area   o—Temporary Shore

6-10 Braced lines. Distance between braced lines depends on height of form, size of bay, etc. X's mark either dead men or existing concrete for anchorage. Bracing lines may be struts only for short heights; X-brace for spliced shores.

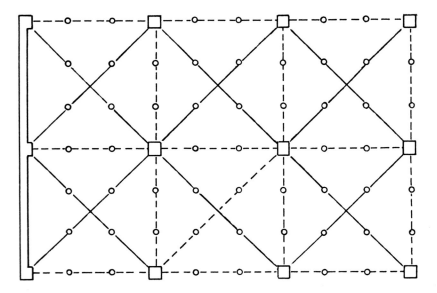

□ Concrete Column
o Temporary Shore

6-11 Use of completed columns or walls for bracing. Dashed lines indicate one line of strut braces to columns cast earlier. Solid lines represent X-bracing also tied into existing columns. Intermediate lines are needed if shores are spliced.

For example, a 60x90-ft slab, 8 in. thick, is shored at 4-ft intervals in both directions. According to Table 5-4, H in lb per lineal ft is 207 lb per ft along the 60 ft edge (because width of slab in direction of force is 90 ft) and 138 lb per ft along the 90-ft edge (width of slab in direction of force is 60 ft).

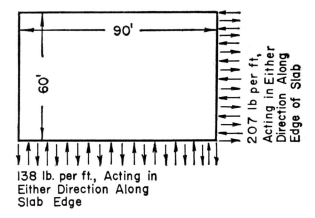

If bracing is placed on alternate lines of shores (8 ft apart), design load along the 90-ft side would be 8 × 138 or 1104 lb per line of bracing. By spacing bracing at every line along the 60 ft side, design load per line would be 4 × 207 or 828 lb.

For shoring systems made up of tubular scaffold-type components, the recommendations of reputable manufacturers as to strength of their bracing systems should be followed in designing for the specified lateral loads.

Camber and Adjustment for Settlement

It is frequently necessary to set formwork elevations before concreting to compensate for the following:

(a) Anticipated deflection or settlement of the forms and their supports.

(b) Anticipated deflection of the completed structure under load, from the time it begins to carry its own weight. This may involve both instantaneous and long-term (or creep) deflections.

(c) Optical sag (the illusion of sagging in long members that are perfectly horizontal).

Anticipated Deflection or Settlement of Formwork

Formwork deflection or settlement may be due to such factors as closure of form joints, settlement of mudsills, shrinkage of lumber, dead load deflections, elastic shortening of the form members, and the like. A frequently applied rule of thumb has been to camber ¼ in. per 10 ft of span to take care of these deflections and movements. However, it is possible to estimate required camber or adjustment more closely in terms of individual job conditions.

Deflection of individual form members under load has already been explained in this chapter (p. 86); with good form design, this deflection is kept quite small. Where beam bottoms, stringers, and other form components are supported at a number of points along their length, camber for this small form deflection is generally not required. If relatively long span form members—such as the so-called horizontal shoring—are used, camber to correct for form deflection is necessary. These patented members usually have a built-in camber, and they must be fully loaded to their design capacity to remove the camber and obtain a level completed slab.

Adjustment for settlement of forms and mudsills is not camber, strictly speaking, since it is a uniform amount at each support point, resulting merely in a level form slightly higher than indicated on the plans. Probable settlement of wood formwork can be approximated as the total of columnar shortening of shores plus "taking up" and "biting" at joints. Shortening of wood shores may be computed by the formula $c = 12\,SL/E$ where c = columnar shortening, in.; S = compressive stress, psi, in timber column, parallel to grain; L = unsupported length of column, ft; and E = modulus of elasticity, psi.

Assume a value of settlement for each horizontal joint for "taking up" and an additional value at each joint where end grain bears upon side grain for "biting" of end grain into side grain. For normal carpentry work, each assumed value may be taken as ¹⁄₁₆ in.; where particular care is taken, each may be taken as ¹⁄₃₂ in. The total estimated settlement should be the combined total of these plus columnar shortening, c.

It is preferable to plan falsework so that settlements under full load will be a minimum consistent with economy. Where wood timbers are used, the number of horizontal joints and particularly the number of joints where end grain bears on side grain should be kept at a practical minimum. The unit compressive stress perpendicular to the grain should not exceed the allowable for the kind of lumber being used.

With good construction practices, soil under mudsills should be stable enough that no appreciable settlement occurs.* If this is not the case, an additional allowance for settlement of the sills should be made.

---

* Frozen soil may be softened by concrete drip and heating under the forms, resulting in settlement of sills that were apparently secure when placed. For discussion of this and other problems of support for shoring, see p. 183.

Camber or adjustment in elevation to compensate for anticipated deflection or settlement of formwork would then be based on the following:

(a) Estimated columnar shortening
(b) Allowance for take up or biting of wood
(c) Estimated settlement of mudsills, if any
(d) Calculated deflection of long span form members between supports
(e) Anticipated shape change of supporting members before taking load, especially at the ends of such members.

Deflection of the Finished Structure

When supporting formwork is removed and the concrete structure begins to carry its own weight, some deflection takes place. In the past, for structures of customary dimensions, excessive deflections were rarely a problem. Today with increasing use of flat plates and special shapes such as thin shells and folded plates, and with increasing acceptance of ultimate strength design methods that lead to members with larger span-depth ratios, deflection of finished structures will be a more common problem—one, however, that can be met by proper cambering.

The composite character of reinforced concrete, complicated by partial cracking of the tensile zone and by creep, makes accurate deflection calculations difficult. Not only is it difficult to predict deflection of reinforced concrete structures; there is the problem of deciding what net amount of deflection can be permitted. This is largely a matter of judgment, and *it is clearly the responsibility of the architect-engineer to specify the amount and shape of camber desired to compensate for deflection of the finished structure,* but an alert form designer will request such instructions if they have been inadvertently omitted. The architect-engineer may also require additional camber for exposed long-span horizontal members to overcome the effect of "optical sag."

Where camber requirements may become cumulative, such as in cases where beams frame into other beams or girders at right angles, and at midspan of the latter, the engineer-architect should specify exactly the manner in which this condition is to be handled.

Cast-in-place structures that are to be prestressed present special problems with respect to camber, because tightening of the cables will produce an upward deflection in the member being prestressed.

Total Allowance for Camber and Adjustments

Forms should always be built to provide necessary compensations for both (a) anticipated deflection or settlement of the formwork and (b) anticipated dead load and creep deflection of the finished structure. During and after concreting the contractor or builder should continue to check form elevations to be sure that desired camber is being maintained. Appropriate adjustments should be made by promptly jacking and wedging before initial set of the concrete takes place.

The contractor is expected to set and maintain forms so as to insure completed work to the camber specified by the engineer-architect, within the tolerance limits specified. Satisfactory performance is generally judged on the basis of elevation after settlement or deflection of the formwork and before forms and supports are removed. The contractor is *not* responsible for immediate or creep deflection of the structure after shoring has been removed.

Some attention must be given to the upper screeded surface when forms have been cambered to compensate for deflection of the finished structure. Such a slab or beam should not be screeded level; its top surface should be curved upward as nearly parallel as possible to the cambered form surface. Thus a uniform thickness of beam or slab is attained, and when the structure deflects as it becomes self-supporting, the top surface is level, not dished. This cambered upper surface can be reasonably well achieved by using screed chairs of uniform height set on the cambered sheathing.

REFERENCES

1. "National Design Specification for Stress Grade Lumber and Its Fastenings," National Forest Products Association, Washington, D. C., 1971.
2. *Wood Structural Design Data*, National Forest Products Association, Washington, D. C., 1970 edition, 236 pp.
3. American Institute of Timber Construction, *Timber Construction Manual*, John Wiley and Sons, New York, First Edition, 1966.
4. "Plywood Design Specification," American Plywood Association, Tacoma, Wash., 1966.
5. "Plywood for Concrete Forming," American Plywood Association, Tacoma, Wash., 1971, 32 pp.
6. Pilling, Alan H., and Boll, Martin W., "How to Plan Forms in Detail," reprinted by Richmond Screw Anchor Co., Inc., Brooklyn, N. Y., from a series appearing in *Construction Methods and Equipment*, Oct., Nov., and Dec. 1954.
7. "Forms for Architectural Concrete," Portland Cement Association, Chicago, Ill., 1952, 54 pp.
8. "Design of Wood Formwork for Concrete Structures," Wood Construction Data No. 3, National Forest Products Association, Washington, D. C., 1971 edition.
9. Wynn, A. E., *Design and Construction of Formwork for Concrete Structures*, Concrete Publications Ltd., London, 4th revised edition, 1956, 314 pp.
10. *Manual of Steel Construction*, American Institute of Steel Construction, New York, 7th Edition, 1970.
11. Federal Occupational Safety and Health Act, *Federal Register*, Part II, V. 37, No. 243, December 16, 1972.

7:DESIGN TABLES

FOLLOWING THE PRINCIPLES outlined in Chapter 6, safe spans for many timber and plywood formwork components have been calculated and arranged in tables for use by the form designer. Calculations cover single span beams, two-span beams, and beams continuous over three or more spans carrying a uniformly distributed load. The spans are applicable for any uniformly loaded form member and wherever the design simplification of using equivalent uniform loadings in place of point loads is regarded as sufficiently accurate. The tables may also be used to develop a preliminary design for cases where a rigorous structural analysis is required before the formwork design can be finalized.

Four sets of working stresses have been included in preparing the tables, roughly corresponding to Class II (multiple use or heavy construction) stresses for formwork made of construction grade Eastern spruce, Southern pine and Douglas fir-larch; and Class I (single use) and Class II stresses for No. 2 Douglas fir-larch. Working stress values are indicated on each table, and the spans therein are applicable for other lumber whose working stresses approximate or exceed the indicated values. Expressions used to calculate the safe support spacings are tabulated on p. 122.

The tables are in three groups: Tables 7-1–7-4 for sheathing, both wood and plywood; Tables 7-5–7-7 for joists, studs, stringers or any other beam components of the formwork where framing members are used singly; and Tables 7-8–7-10 for wales or other beam components of formwork where the members are used double. Nominal lumber sizes are shown in the tables but all calculations are based on lumber finished on all four surfaces (S4S); actual thicknesses are shown for plywood. In each table, it is shown whether the safe span is controlled by bending, deflection, or shear. Design examples demonstrating the use of the tables are presented following a brief description of allowable deflection, working stresses and loading conditions for each group of tables.

Sheathing Design: Tables 7-1–7-4

Tables 7-1, and 7-2 and 7-2A for board sheathing give safe spans for 1, 1¼, 1½, and 2-in. (nominal size) boards supported as simple one-span beams, as two span beams, or continuous over three or more spans. Two sets of working stresses are used, in an effort to make tables applicable to different grades of lumber, or to different classes of formwork if the Committee 347 recommendation is followed:

$$f = 1000 \text{ psi}, H = 200 \text{ psi}, \text{ and } E = 1,300,000 \text{ psi}$$

applying to construction grade Douglas fir or Southern pine loaded for a short time, as in formwork for only one or two uses, and

$$f = 800 \text{ psi}, H = 160 \text{ psi}, \text{ and } E = 1,300,000 \text{ psi}$$

applying to the same grades and species of wood for formwork subject to continuing or repeated usage. The above values of E, f, and H have been reduced as recommended by the 1971 specifications of the National Forest Products Association to allow for moisture from concrete penetrating the wood.

These tables are applicable to sheathing for columns, slabs, and walls. Theoretical deflection of spans based on these tables will not exceed ¹⁄₁₆ in. For spans less than 22½ in., $l/360$ governs and deflection will be less than ¹⁄₁₆ in. If deflection must be limited to $l/400$, use 0.96 times the span shown where deflection is the criterion governing span length.

Tables 7-3 and 7-4 for plywood sheathing are set up on the same basis as Tables 7-1 and 7-2 with respect to allowable deflection, and with working stresses for Class I concrete form plywood as given in Table 4-2. However, plywood acting as a beam is stronger when used with its face grain parallel to the span of the beam than if the face grain is perpendicular to the beam span. Therefore two divisions are necessary, one for spans with the face grain parallel and the other for face grain perpendicular to direction of span.

Calculated span lengths for face grain parallel to span may be used with Plyform Class I, Structural I, Exterior A-B, Exterior B-B, and Exterior B-C grades of plywood or their equivalent. The span lengths indicated in Tables 7-3 and 7-4 for plywood with face grain perpendicular to the span are applicable to Plyform Class I or Structural I grades or their equivalent.*

Plywood is checked for rolling shear according to the manufacturers' recommendations.

*See *Plywood Design Specification*, issued November 1966 by the American Plywood Association.

Joists, Studs, Beams: Tables 7-5–7-7

These tables are applicable to joists, studs, or any other formwork members which are loaded uniformly as a beam. They may also be used to approximate spans for members which carry a series of point loads by converting those point loads to an "equivalent uniform loading." (In formwork design, where loads are heavy and spans are short in relation to spacing between the point loads, this approximation may not be sufficiently accurate. Refer to discussion of this matter in Chapter 6.)

Theoretical deflection for spans given in these tables is limited to $\frac{1}{360}$ of the beam span, but not to exceed $\frac{1}{4}$ in. As this works out, for spans less than 45 in. deflection is less than $\frac{1}{8}$ in.; for spans between 45 and 90 in. deflection will be from $\frac{1}{8}$ to $\frac{1}{4}$ in. depending on the span. For spans over 90 in. theoretical deflection is $\frac{1}{4}$ in. Thus in the range of the more commonly used spans, deflection is held to about $\frac{1}{8}$ in. or less. To obtain spans with deflection limited to $\frac{1}{400}$, take 0.96 times the tabulated spans governed by deflection.

Note that the uniform load value shown in these tables is not the same as form pressure or load in psf, but is an *equivalent uniform loading*, generally computed as uniform load on forms (psf) times the spacing (ft) between members being considered.

Tables 7-5.1 through 7-5.4 are for beams continuous over three or more spans with the following working stresses:

$f = 775$ psi	$H = 140$ psi	$E = 1,100,000$ psi
$f = 1000$ psi	$H = 180$ psi	$E = 1,400,000$ psi
$f = 1500$ psi	$H = 180$ psi	$E = 1,700,000$ psi
$f = 1875$ psi	$H = 225$ psi	$E = 1,700,000$ psi

The first set of stresses can be used for construction grade Eastern spruce, and the second is applicable for construction grade Southern pine and Douglas fir-larch, both for forms subject to continuing reuse. The third and fourth sets of stresses apply to No. 2 Douglas fir for continuing- and single-use forms, respectively. The design tables can be applied to other lumber with strength characteristics approximating or exceeding those used. Check Table 4-2 in this text for suggested working stresses, or use Table 1a of the National Design Specification for Stress Grade Lumber.

Tables 7-6 and 7-7 are like 7-5, except that span lengths are calculated for simply supported and two-span rather than continuous beams.

Notice that beam sizes are given in the conventional fashion with b or width of beam face to which load is applied given first and the second number indicating h or depth of beam. Thus a 2x4 is used in this position:

and a 4x2 is the same member used flat, thus:

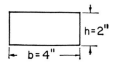

Double Wales or Other Double Members: Tables 7-8–7-10

Tables 7-8, 7-9 and 7-10 are similar to Tables 7-5, 7-6, and 7-7 in terms of working stresses and general layout, but they cover double members which are commonly used for wales and frequently for stringers. Spans are calculated on the basis of using these members side by side, with their longer dimension as the depth of the beam.

Form Design Using the Tables

Flat Slabs

Determine a stringer, joist, and sheathing combination suitable for flat slab form with dead plus live load of 200 psf, supported on shores spaced 4 ft on centers in both directions. Assuming that construction grade Southern pine is used to build multiple-use forms, the values of $f = 1000$ psi, $H = 180$ psi, and $E = 1,400,000$ psi will be used.

Stringers

With shores spaced 4 ft on centers both ways, the stringers will be 4 ft apart and have a span of 4 ft between supports. They will be designed as continuous beams with an equivalent uniform load equal to the distance between the stringers (ft) times the uniform load on the formwork (psf):

$$4 \text{ ft} \times 200 \text{ psf} = 800 \text{ lb per lineal ft}$$

Referring to Table 7-5.2, enter the table at the left on the 800 lb per ft load line and note which members can be used for stringers at 48-in. span. Among the smaller members that are suitable are the 2x10 with an allowable span of 57 in. and the 3x8 with an allowable span of 57 in. The 4x6 with an allowable span of 51 in. is also satisfactory. The 2x10 provides the necessary span with the least lumber, but local supply conditions or construction problems may make another member more practical.

Sheathing

Shore spacing places the stringers 4 ft apart, and this 4 ft then is the *span* of the joists. How the joists are spaced depends on requirements of the sheathing. Assume ¾-in. Plyform Class I or equal quality plywood is used with its face grain parallel to the span. Since sheathing will be continuous over several spans, refer to Table 7-3. The right side of the table, with $f = 1600$ psi, applies since this is a multiple-use form. From the column for ¾-in. thickness with face grain parallel to the span, read the allowable span of 20 in. opposite the load of 200 psf. In order to use 4x8 sheets of plywood efficiently, a span of ⁹⁶⁄₅ or 19⅕ in. probably would be used, dividing each 8-ft. piece of plywood into five equal spans.

Joists

This 19⅕ in. becomes the required joist spacing, and joist span has already been fixed at 4 ft. What is the required joist size? Joist loading = joist spacing × load on forms (neglecting weight of joist):

$$\frac{19.2}{12} \times 200 = 320 \text{ lb per ft}$$

Again using Table 7-5.2 since joists will be continuous over several spans, note that a 2x6 loaded at 300 lb per ft has an allowable span of 55 in. and at 400 lb per ft has an allowable span of 48 in. By inspection it can be seen that the 2x6 would be satisfactory on a 48-in. span.

In some cases, approximation of the span would be required for loads not given exactly in the tables. For example, to work out this case:

1. The span difference for the 400 lb per ft and 300 lb per ft loads is $55 - 48$ or 7 in.
2. Actual load of 320 lb per ft exceeds 300 by 20 lb per ft which is 20/100 or 2/10 of the difference between 300 and 400 lb per ft.
3. Take 2/10 of the span difference: $2/10 \times 7 \text{ in.} = 1.4$ in.
4. Subtract this from the allowable span at 300 lb per ft: $55 \text{ in.} - 1.4 \text{ in.} = 53.6$ in. allowable span. (Span will be shorter than span for 300 lb per ft because actual load is greater.) $\ell = 55 - \left[(320 - 300)/(400 - 300) \right]$

The 2x6 selected is less than 1 percent of applied load. Where joist is heavy relative to applied load, its weight should be included as part of the design loading.

Bearing

A check of bearing stresses where joists rest on stringers and where stringers rest on shores would be advisable. This is explained on p. 89.

Column Sheathing

Wood

Find a trial spacing of column clamps (yokes) where maximum lateral pressure is expected to be 1800 psf at the base of the column, decreasing uniformly to zero at the top (see p. 78 for procedure to estimate lateral pressure). Assuming that sheathing is 1¼-in. boards of quality comparable to construction grade Douglas fir, Table 7-1 will apply since boards are continuous over several supports. If forms are intended for multiple usage, follow the right side of Table 7-1 where $f = 800$ psi and $H = 160$ psi.

As explained on p. 101, column sheathing can be checked simply by working up from the base of the column, assuming that pressure is uniform between clamps or yokes and of an intensity equal to that at the lower clamp. If the first clamp is placed 4 in. above the base $p = 1800 - \frac{4}{12}(150) = 1750$ psf. Entering Table 7-1 at the 1800-psf line, the allowable span of $1\frac{1}{4}$-in. sheathing is 10 in., so Clamp 2 is tentatively placed 10 in. above Clamp 1.

Lateral pressure at Clamp $2 = 1750 - \frac{10}{12}(150) = 1625$ psf. This is the value of p used to determine spacing of Clamp 3. Enter table at 1600 psf and find a permissible span of 11 in. at this loading. Set Clamp 3 tentatively 11 in. above Clamp 2.

Pressure at Clamp $3 = 1625 - \frac{11}{12}(150) = 1487$. Use this pressure to find an allowable span of 11 in. This is the spacing of Clamp 4 above Clamp 3.

Pressure at Clamp $4 = 1487 - \frac{11}{12}(150) = 1349$. Use this value to find the distance to Clamp 5, and so on up the column until the clamp spacings equal or exceed the desired column height of 12 ft.

The tentative clamp spacing based on sheathing strength and stiffness should then be checked to see that column clamp strength is not exceeded.

Plywood

Suppose a column is sheathed with Plyform Class I $\frac{3}{4}$-in. plywood backed by vertical 2x4's used flat, with face grain of plywood running vertically. If the maximum lateral pressure is 1800 psf, what clear distance is permissible between the supporting 2x4's for a multi-use form? If plywood is used with face grain vertical, the grain is then perpendicular to the span being considered, and $f = 1600$ (Class II formwork according to Committee 347 recommendation).

If the column cross section is small enough that there are likely to be only one or two spans, use Table 7-4 for simple beams; otherwise follow Table 7-3 for continuous beams. Reading at the 1800 psf level, we find a span of 4 in. for a simple beam, and less than 4 in. for a continuous beam. This is in a load-span range where rolling shear governs and a span calculation for rolling shear (see p. 89) is required if the column is large enough to require three or more spans (continuous beam conditions). Use the applicable span or less as the clear distance between supporting 2x4's for this plywood sheathing.

Beam Bottom

Suppose 2-in. (nominal) boards of construction grade Southern pine or equal are to be laid longitudinally for a beam bottom that is expected to have a number of reuses. What spacing of shores is required

if the beam bottom is 18 in. wide and carries a total load of 500 lb per lineal ft of beam?

The load per lineal ft of beam must be converted to a load per square ft of sheathing:

$$\frac{\text{total load per lineal ft}}{\text{width of beam, in ft}} = \text{load on sheathing, psf}$$

$$\frac{500 \text{ lb/ft}}{1.5 \text{ ft}} = 333 \text{ psf}$$

Since the beam bottom will be continuous over several spans Table 7-1 applies; use the right side ($f = 1500$) since beam bottom is subject to continuing use.

Allowable span of sheathing (which determines shore spacing) is 36 in. for 300 psf load and 33 in. for 400 psf load. A 35 in. spacing for shores would be theoretically correct. Practical considerations would probably make a 3-ft spacing the one used.

Wall Forms

Use the tables to determine spacing of wall form members, assuming continuing reuse of the forms and No. 2 grade Douglas fir or equal lumber, with sheathing of Plyform Class I or equal plywood. Design a 10 ft high wall form for a maximum lateral pressure of 600 psf, assuming no reduction of pressure near the top of the form.

Sheathing

Assuming that $\frac{3}{4}$-in. plywood is used with face grain horizontal, the grain will be parallel to span between studs and plywood panel will be continuous across several spans. Table 7-3 right side ($f = 1600$), applies. Entering the table from the left at the 600 psf level, the span is found to be 12 in. and this determines spacing of studs.

Studs

With studs 12 in. apart, the load per lineal ft is $\frac{12}{12}(600)$ or 600 lb per ft. Assuming that studs are continuous over three or more spans, refer to Table 7-5.3 for choice of span and member. Entering table at left on the 600 lb per ft load line, the 2x4 stud has an allowable span of 28 in. Support for studs (wales or ties) would be needed at about 2-ft intervals. Placing top and bottom wales 1 ft above bottom of form and 1 ft below top of form would permit use of five wales spaced 2 ft apart. A heavier stud selection of course could be made to reduce the number of wales required.

Wales

If wales are spaced 2 ft apart, the equivalent uniform load per lineal ft is $^{24}/_{12}$ (600) or 1200 lb per ft. Assuming continuity of wales, Table 7-8.2 would be used to determine spacing of wale supports.

Entering the table from left on the 1200 lb per ft load line, a convenient span and double member combination may be chosen from the upper part of the table where $f = 1500$ psi; for example, if double 2x6 wales are used the spacing between the supporting ties can be a maximum of 44 in. A check of the load capacity of ties available might be helpful in selecting the wale.

If the double 2x6 were used at 44 in., the average tie load would be $^{44}/_{12} \times ^{24}/_{12} \times 600 = 4400$ lb. A 3000-lb tie would be overloaded, and a heavier one is needed.

If double 2x4 wales were used with a tie spacing of 24 in. (28 in. support spacing allowed by Table 7-8.3), average tie load would be $^{24}/_{12} \times ^{24}/_{12} \times 600 = 2400$ lb, and a 3000-lb tie would be satisfactory. This solution is preferable since the 24-in. spacing is a multiple of stud spacing *and* divides 8-ft plywood sheets into four equal parts, as well as permitting use of 3000-lb ties.

TABLE 7-1: SAFE SPACING IN INCHES OF SUPPORTS FOR BOARD SHEATHING CONTINUOUS OVER FOUR * OR MORE SUPPORTS

Maximum deflection is $^1/_{360}$ of support spacing, but not more than $^1/_{16}$ in.

Pressure or load from concrete, psf	$f = 1000$ psi $H = 200$ psi $E = 1,300,000$ psi				$f = 800$ psi $H = 160$ psi $E = 1,300,000$ psi			
	Nominal thickness of S4S boards, in.				Nominal thickness of S4S boards, in.			
	1	1¼	1½	2	1	1¼	1½	2
75	30	37	44	50	30	37	44	50
100	28	34	41	47	28	34	41	47
125	26	33	39	44	26	33	39	44
150	25	31	37	42	25	31	37	42
175	24	30	35	41	24	30	35	41
200	23	29	34	39	23	29	34	39
300	21	26	31	35	19	25	31	36
400	18	24	29	33	16	22	27	33
500	16	22	27	31	15	20	24	29
600	15	20	25	30	13	18	22	27
700	14	18	23	28	12	17	21	25
800	13	17	22	26	12	15	19	23
900	12	16	20	24	11	15	18	22
1000	12	15	19	23	10	14	17	21
1100	11	15	18	22	10	13	16	20
1200	11	14	18	21	9	13	16	19
1400	10	13	16	20	9	12	15	18
1600	9	12	15	18	8	11	14	16
1800	9	12	14	17	8	10	13	15
2000	8	11	14	16	7	10	12	15
2200	8	10	13	16	7	9	12	14
2400	7	10	12	15	7	9	11	13
2600	7	10	12	14	6	9	11	13
2800	7	9	12	14	6	8	10	12
3000	7	9	11	13	6	8	10	12

NOTE: Calculations are based on span distances center to center of supports where supports are relatively narrow. Where supports may be wide in relation to the distance between them, such as 2x4's used flat where the spacing is 8 in., use the tabulated spacing as the clear distance between supports.
* Above dashed line span length is controlled by deflection; below dashed line bending governs.

TABLE 7-2: SAFE SPACING IN INCHES OF SUPPORTS FOR BOARD SHEATHING ON SIMPLE SPAN SUPPORTED AT TWO POINTS *

Maximum deflection is $\frac{1}{360}$ of support spacing, but not more than $\frac{1}{16}$ in.

Spacing

Pressure or load from concrete, psf	$f = 1000$ psi $\quad H = 200$ psi $E = 1{,}300{,}000$ psi				$f = 800$ psi $\quad H = 160$ psi $E = 1{,}300{,}000$ psi			
	Nominal thickness of S4S boards, in.				Nominal thickness of S4S boards, in.			
	1	1¼	1½	2	1	1¼	1½	2
75	25	32	37	43	25	32	37	43
100	24	29	35	40	24	29	35	40
125	22	28	33	38	22	28	33	38
150	21	26	31	36	21	26	31	36
175	20	25	30	35	20	25	30	35
200	19	25	29	33	19	25	29	33
300	17	22	26	30	17	22	26	30
400	15	20	24	28	15	20	24	28
500	14	19	23	27	13	17	22	26
600	13	18	22	25	12	16	20	24
700	12	17	21	24	11	15	18	22
800	12	15	19	23	10	14	17	21
900	11	15	18	22	10	13	16	20
1000	10	14	17	21	9	12	15	19
1100	10	13	16	20	9	12	15	18
1200	9	13	16	19	8	11	14	17
1400	9	12	15	18	8	10	13	16
1600	8	11	14	16	7	10	12	15
1800	8	10	13	15	7	9	12	14
2000	7	10	12	15	7	9	11	13
2200	7	9	12	14	6	8	10	12
2400	7	9	11	13	6	8	10	12
2600	6	9	11	13	6	8	10	11
2800	6	8	10	12	6	7	9	11
3000	6	8	10	12	5	7	9	11

NOTE: Calculations based on span distances center to center of supports, where supports are relatively narrow. Where supports are wide in relation to the distance between them, as a 3 in. wide support where the spacing is 8 or 9 in., use the tabulated spacing as the clear distance between supports.
* Above dashed line span length is controlled by deflection; below dashed line bending governs.

EXPRESSIONS USED TO CALCULATE SAFE SUPPORT SPACINGS OF CHAPTER 7 DESIGN TABLES

CRITERION	SINGLE SPAN BEAM	TWO-SPAN BEAM	THREE OR MORE SPANS
$\Delta_{max} = l/400$	$l = 1.32\sqrt[3]{\dfrac{EI}{w}}$	$l = 1.77\sqrt[3]{\dfrac{EI}{w}}$	$l = 1.63\sqrt[3]{\dfrac{EI}{w}}$
$\Delta_{max} = l/360$	$l = 1.37\sqrt[3]{\dfrac{EI}{w}}$	$l = 1.83\sqrt[3]{\dfrac{EI}{w}}$	$l = 1.69\sqrt[3]{\dfrac{EI}{w}}$
$\Delta_{max} = \frac{1}{16}$ in.	$l = 2.75\sqrt[4]{\dfrac{EI}{w}}$	$l = 3.43\sqrt[4]{\dfrac{EI}{w}}$	$l = 3.23\sqrt[4]{\dfrac{EI}{w}}$
$\Delta_{max} = \frac{1}{8}$ in.	$l = 3.27\sqrt[4]{\dfrac{EI}{w}}$	$l = 4.08\sqrt[4]{\dfrac{EI}{w}}$	$l = 3.84\sqrt[4]{\dfrac{EI}{w}}$
$\Delta_{max} = \frac{1}{4}$ in.	$l = 3.90\sqrt[4]{\dfrac{EI}{w}}$	$l = 4.85\sqrt[4]{\dfrac{EI}{w}}$	$l = 4.57\sqrt[4]{\dfrac{EI}{w}}$
BENDING	$l = 9.80\sqrt{\dfrac{fS}{w}}$	$l = 9.80\sqrt{\dfrac{fS}{w}}$	$l = 10.95\sqrt{\dfrac{fS}{w}}$
HORIZONTAL SHEAR	$l = \dfrac{16Hbh}{w} + 2h$	$l = \dfrac{192Hbh}{15w} + 2h$	$l = \dfrac{40}{3}\dfrac{Hbh}{w} + 2h$

l = spacing of supports, in.
h = depth of section, in.
I = moment of inertia, in.⁴

w = load, lb per lineal ft
E = modulus of elasticity, psi
b = width of section, in.

S = section modulus, in.³
f = extreme fiber stress, psi
H = horizontal shear stress, psi

TABLE 7-2A: SAFE SPACING IN INCHES OF SUPPORTS FOR BOARD SHEATHING CONTINUOUS OVER TWO SPANS (THREE SUPPORTS) *

Maximum deflection is $\frac{1}{360}$ of support spacing, but not more than $\frac{1}{16}$ in.

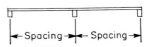
←Spacing→←Spacing→

Pressure or load from concrete, psf	$f = 1000$ psi $\quad H = 200$ psi $E = 1,300,000$ psi				$f = 800$ psi $\quad H = 160$ psi $E = 1,300,000$ psi			
	Nominal thickness of S4S boards, in.				Nominal thickness of S4S boards, in.			
	1	1¼	1½	2	1	1¼	1½	2
75	32	39	47	53	32	39	47	53
100	30	37	43	50	29	37	43	50
125	28	35	41	47	26	35	41	47
150	27	33	39	45	24	32	39	45
175	25	32	38	43	22	30	37	43
200	23	31	36	42	21	28	35	41
300	19	25	32	38	17	23	28	34
400	16	22	27	33	15	20	24	29
500	15	20	24	29	13	17	22	26
600	13	18	22	27	12	16	20	24
700	12	17	21	25	11	15	18	22
800	12	15	19	23	10	14	17	21
900	11	15	18	22	10	13	16	20
1000	10	14	17	21	9	12	15	19
1100	10	13	16	20	9	12	15	19
1200	9	13	16	19	8	11	14	17
1400	9	12	15	18	8	10	13	16
1600	8	11	14	16	7	10	12	15
1800	8	10	13	15	7	9	12	14
2000	7	10	12	15	7	9	11	13
2200	7	9	12	14	6	8	10	12
2400	7	9	11	13	6	8	10	12
2600	6	9	11	13	6	8	10	11
2800	6	8	10	12	6	7	9	11
3000	6	8	10	12	5	7	9	11

NOTE: Calculations based on span distances center to center of supports, where supports are relatively narrow. Where supports are wide in relation to the distance between them, as a 3 in. wide support where the spacing is 8 or 9 in., use the tabulated spacing as the clear distance between supports.
* Above dashed line span length is controlled by deflection; below dashed line bending governs.

TABLE 7-3: SAFE SPACING IN INCHES OF SUPPORTS FOR PLYWOOD SHEATHING, CONTINUOUS OVER FOUR * OR MORE SUPPORTS

Data prepared by the American Plywood Association. For plywood used with face grain parallel to span, the tabulated span lengths may be used with Plyform Class I, Structural I, Exterior A-B, Exterior B-B, and Exterior B-C or equivalent grades of plywood. For face grain perpendicular to span, tabulated span lengths are suitable only for use with Plyform Class I or Structural I grades or their equivalent.

Maximum deflection is $\frac{1}{360}$ of support spacing, but not more than $\frac{1}{16}$ in.

Pressure or load of concrete, pounds per square foot	$f = 2000$ psi; rolling shear = 75 psi; $E = 1{,}600{,}000$ psi								$f = 1600$ psi; rolling shear = 60 psi; $E = 1{,}600{,}000$ psi							
	5-ply sanded, face grain parallel to span				5-ply sanded, face grain perpendicular to span				5-ply sanded, face grain parallel to span				5-ply sanded, face grain perpendicular to span			
	½ in.	⅝ in.	¾ in.	1 in. (7 ply)	½ in.	⅝ in.	¾ in.	1 in. (7 ply)	½ in.	⅝ in.	¾ in.	1 in. (7 ply)	½ in.	⅝ in.	¾ in.	1 in. (7 ply)
75	20	24	26	31	13	18	23	30	20	24	26	31	13	18	23	30
100	18	22	24	29	12	17	22	28	18	22	24	29	12	17	22	28
125	17	20	23	28	11	15	20	27	17	20	23	28	11	15	20	27
150	16	19	22	27	11	15	19	25	16	19	22	27	11	15	19	25
175	15	18	21	26	10	14	18	24	15	18	21	26	10	14	18	24
200	15	17	20	25	10	13	17	24	15	17	20	25	10	13	17	24
300	13	15	17	22	8	12	15	21	13	15	17	22	8	12	15	21
400	12	14	16	20	8	11	14	19	11	13	15	19	8	11	14	19
500	11	13	15	19	7	10	13	18	10	12	13	17	6	9	11	18
600	10	12	14	17	6	9	12	17	9	11	12	15	5	8	9	15
700	10	11	13	16	6	9	11	16	9	10	11	14	4	6	8	13
800	9	10	12	15	5	8	11	15	8	9	10	13	4	6	7	11
900	9	10	11	14	4	8	9	15	7	9	10	13	–	5	6	10
1000	8	9	10	13	4	7	9	14	6	8	9	12	–	5	6	9
1100	7	9	10	12	4	6	8	12	6	7	9	10	–	4	5	8
1200	7	8	10	11	–	6	7	11	5	7	8	9	–	4	5	8
1300	6	8	9	11	–	5	7	11	5	6	8	8	–	–	4	7
1400	6	7	9	10	–	5	6	10	4	6	7	8	–	–	4	7
1500	5	7	9	9	–	5	6	9	4	5	7	7	–	–	4	6
1600	5	6	8	9	–	4	5	9	4	5	6	7	–	–	4	6
1700	5	6	8	8	–	4	5	8	4	5	6	6	–	–	–	5
1800	4	6	8	8	–	4	5	8	–	4	5	6	–	–	–	5
1900	4	5	8	7	–	4	4	7	–	4	5	6	–	–	–	5
2000	4	5	7	7	–	–	4	7	–	4	5	5	–	–	–	5
2200	4	5	6	6	–	–	4	6	–	4	4	5	–	–	–	4
2400	–	4	5	6	–	–	4	6	–	–	4	5	–	–	–	4
2600	–	4	5	5	–	–	–	5	–	–	4	4	–	–	–	4
2800	–	4	4	5	–	–	–	5	–	–	4	4	–	–	–	–
3000	–	–	4	5	–	–	–	5	–	–	–	4	–	–	–	–

NOTE: Spans shorter than 4 in. are not shown. Calculations give distances center to center of supports where supports are relatively narrow. In the case of column or other forms where supports may be wide in relation to the distance between them, such as 2x4's used flat 7 or 8 in. apart, take the tabulated spacing as the clear distance between supports.

* For plywood continuous over three supports (two spans) support spacing for simple span shown in Table 7-4 may be safely used.

TABLE 7-4: SAFE SPACING IN INCHES OF SUPPORTS FOR PLYWOOD SHEATHING WITH ONLY TWO POINTS OF SUPPORT *

Data prepared by the American Plywood Association. For plywood used with face grain parallel to span, the tabulated span lengths may be used with Plyform Class I, Structural I, Exterior A-B, Exterior B-B, and Exterior B-C or equivalent grades of plywood. For face grain perpendicular to span, tabulated span lengths are suitable only for use with Plyform Class I or Structural I grades or their equivalent.

Maximum deflection is $\frac{1}{360}$ of support spacing, but not more than $\frac{1}{16}$ in.

Pressure or load of concrete, pounds per square foot	f = 2000 psi; rolling shear = 75 psi; E = 1,600,000 psi								f = 1600 psi; rolling shear = 60 psi; E = 1,600,000 psi							
	5-ply sanded, face grain parallel to span				5-ply sanded, face grain perpendicular to span				5-ply sanded, face grain parallel to span				5-ply sanded, face grain perpendicular to span			
	½ in.	⅝ in.	¾ in.	1 in. (7 ply)	½ in.	⅝ in.	¾ in.	1 in. (7 ply)	½ in.	⅝ in.	¾ in.	1 in. (7 ply)	½ in.	⅝ in.	¾ in.	1 in. (7 ply)
75	16	19	22	27	11	15	19	26	16	19	22	27	11	15	19	26
100	15	18	20	25	10	13	18	24	15	18	20	25	10	13	18	24
125	14	16	19	24	9	13	16	23	14	16	19	24	9	13	16	23
150	13	15	18	23	9	12	15	21	13	15	18	23	9	12	15	21
175	12	15	17	22	8	11	15	20	12	15	17	22	8	11	15	20
200	12	14	16	21	8	11	14	19	12	14	16	21	8	11	14	19
300	10	12	14	18	7	9	12	17	10	12	14	18	7	9	12	17
400	9	11	13	16	6	9	11	15	9	11	13	16	6	9	11	15
500	9	10	12	15	6	8	10	14	9	10	12	15	6	8	10	14
600	8	10	11	14	5	7	10	13	8	10	11	14	5	7	10	13
700	8	9	11	14	5	7	9	13	8	9	10	13	5	7	9	13
800	7	9	10	13	5	7	9	12	7	8	9	12	5	7	9	12
900	7	8	10	13	5	6	8	12	7	8	9	11	4	6	8	12
1000	7	8	9	12	5	6	7	11	6	7	8	11	4	5	7	11
1100	7	8	9	11	4	5	6	10	6	7	8	10	–	5	6	10
1200	6	8	9	11	4	5	6	10	6	7	8	10	–	5	6	9
1300	6	7	8	10	4	4	5	9	6	7	7	9	–	4	5	8
1400	6	7	8	10	–	4	5	8	5	6	7	9	–	4	5	8
1500	6	7	8	10	–	4	5	8	5	6	7	9	–	4	5	7
1600	6	7	7	9	–	4	4	7	5	6	7	8	–	–	4	7
1700	6	6	7	9	–	–	4	7	4	6	6	8	–	–	4	6
1800	5	6	7	9	–	–	4	6	4	5	6	7	–	–	4	6
1900	5	6	7	9	–	–	4	6	4	5	6	7	–	–	4	6
2000	5	6	7	8	–	–	4	6	4	5	6	7	–	–	–	5
2200	4	5	6	7	–	–	–	5	–	4	5	6	–	–	–	5
2400	4	5	6	7	–	–	–	5	–	4	5	5	–	–	–	5
2600	4	5	6	6	–	–	–	4	–	4	5	5	–	–	–	4
2800	–	4	5	6	–	–	–	4	–	–	4	5	–	–	–	4
3000	–	4	5	5	–	–	–	4	–	–	4	4	–	–	–	4

NOTE: Spans shorter than 4 in. are not shown. Calculations give distances center to center of supports where supports are relatively narrow. In the case of column or other forms where supports may be wide in relation to distance between them, such as 2x4's used flat 6 or 7 in. apart, take the tabulated spacing as the clear distance between supports.

* May also be used for sheathing continuous over three points of support.

TABLE 7-5.1: SAFE SPACING, IN., OF SUPPORTS FOR JOISTS, STUDS (OR OTHER BEAM COMPONENTS OF FORMWORK), CONTINUOUS OVER THREE OR MORE SPANS

$\Delta_{max} = l/360$, but not to exceed ¼ in.

$f = 775$ psi $E = 1,100,000$ psi $H = 140$ psi

Nominal size of S4S lumber

Uniform load, lb per lineal ft (equals uniform load on forms times spacing between joists or studs, ft)	2x4	2x6	2x8	2x10	2x12	3x4	3x6	3x8	3x10	4x2	4x4	4x6	4x8	6x2	6x4	6x6	6x8	8x2	8x8	10x2
100	53	84	110	141	171	69	108	140	168	35	81	123	152	43	98	138	174	48	189	52
200	38	59	78	100	121	49	76	101	129	25	58	90	119	31	72	113	147	35	159	40
300	31	48	64	81	99	40	62	82	105	20	47	74	97	25	59	93	126	29	143	33
400	27	42	55	70	86	34	54	71	91	17	41	64	84	22	51	80	109	25	128	28
500	24	37	49	63	77	31	48	64	81	16	36	57	75	20	46	72	98	22	114	25
600	22	34	45	58	70	28	44	58	74	14	33	52	69	18	42	65	89	20	104	23
700	20	32	42	53	65	26	41	54	69	13	31	48	64	16	39	61	83	19	97	21
800	19	30	39	50	61	24	38	50	64	12	29	45	60	15	36	57	77	18	90	20
900	18	28	37	47	57	23	36	48	61	12	27	43	56	15	34	53	73	17	85	19
1000	17	26	35	44	54	22	34	45	58	11	26	40	53	14	32	51	69	16	81	18
1100	16	25	33	42	51	21	33	43	55	10	25	39	51	13	31	48	66	15	77	17
1200	15	24	31	40	49	20	31	41	52	10	23	37	49	13	29	46	63	14	74	16
1300	14	23	30	38	47	19	30	40	50	10	23	35	47	12	28	44	61	14	71	16
1400	14	22	29	37	45	18	29	38	49	9	22	34	45	12	27	43	58	13	68	15
1500	13	21	28	36	43	18	28	37	47	9	21	33	44	11	26	41	56	13	66	15
1600	13	21	27	35	42	17	27	36	45	9	20	32	42	11	25	40	55	13	64	14
1700	13	20	26	34	41	17	26	34	44	8	20	31	41	11	25	39	53	12	62	14
1800	12	20	26	33	40	16	25	33	42	8	19	30	40	10	24	38	52	12	60	13
1900	12	19	25	32	39	16	24	32	41	8	19	29	39	10	23	37	50	11	59	13
2000	12	19	25	31	38	15	24	31	40	8	18	29	38	10	23	36	49	11	57	13
2100	12	18	24	31	37	15	23	31	39	8	18	28	37	10	22	35	48	11	56	12
2200	11	18	24	30	37	14	23	30	38	7	17	27	36	9	22	34	47	11	54	12
2300	11	17	23	29	36	14	22	29	37	7	17	27	35	9	21	33	46	10	53	12
2400	11	17	23	29	35	14	22	29	36	7	16	26	34	9	21	33	45	10	52	12
2500	11	17	22	28	34	13	21	28	36	7	16	25	33	9	20	32	44	10	51	11
2600	10	16	22	28	34	13	21	27	35	7	16	25	33	9	20	31	43	10	50	11
2700	10	16	21	27	33	13	20	27	34	7	15	24	32	8	20	31	42	10	49	11
2800	10	16	21	27	32	13	20	27	34	6	15	24	31	8	19	30	41	9	48	11
2900	10	16	20	26	32	13	20	26	33	6	15	23	31	8	19	30	41	9	47	10
3000	10	15	20	26	31	12	20	26	33	6	15	23	30	8	19	29	40	9	47	10
3200	9	15	19	25	30	12	19	25	32	6	14	22	29	8	18	28	39	9	45	10
3400	9	14	19	24	29	12	18	24	31	6	14	22	28	7	17	27	37	9	44	10
3600	9	14	18	23	29	11	18	24	30	6	13	21	28	7	17	27	36	8	43	9
3800	8	14	18	23	28	11	18	23	29	5	13	20	27	7	16	26	35	8	41	9
4000	8	13	17	22	27	11	17	23	29	5	13	20	26	6	16	25	34	7	40	9
4500	8	12	16	21	26	10	16	20	27	5	12	19	25	6	15	23	32	7	38	9
5000	7	12	16	20	24	10	15	20	26	5	11	18	24	6	14	22	30	7	36	8

NOTE: Span values above the solid line are governed by deflection. Values within dashed line box are spans governed by shear.

TABLE 7-5.2: SAFE SPACING, IN., OF SUPPORTS FOR JOISTS, STUDS (OR OTHER BEAM COMPONENTS OF FORM-WORK), CONTINUOUS OVER THREE OR MORE SPANS

$\Delta_{max} = l/360$, but not to exceed $\frac{1}{4}$ in.

$f = 1000$ psi $E = 1,400,000$ psi $H = 180$ psi

Uniform load, lb per lineal ft (equals uniform load on forms times spacing between joists or studs, ft)	Nominal size of S4S lumber																			
	2x4	2x6	2x8	2x10	2x12	3x4	3x6	3x8	3x10	4x2	4x4	4x6	4x8	6x2	6x4	6x6	6x8	8x2	8x8	10x2
100	61	95	125	157	182	78	121	148	178	40	93	131	161	47	—	147	185	52	200	56
200	43	67	89	113	138	55	87	115	146	28	65	103	136	35	82	123	156	40	168	44
300	35	55	72	92	112	45	71	94	119	23	53	84	111	29	67	105	141	33	152	37
400	30	48	63	80	97	39	61	81	103	20	46	73	96	25	58	91	124	28	142	32
500	27	43	56	72	87	35	55	72	92	18	41	65	86	22	52	81	111	25	130	29
600	25	39	51	65	79	32	50	66	84	16	38	59	78	20	47	74	101	23	118	26
700	23	36	47	60	74	30	46	61	78	15	35	55	72	19	44	69	94	22	110	24
800	21	34	44	57	69	28	43	57	73	14	33	51	68	18	41	64	88	20	103	23
900	20	32	42	53	65	26	41	54	69	13	31	48	64	17	39	61	83	19	97	21
1000	19	30	40	51	62	25	39	51	65	12	29	46	61	16	37	58	79	18	92	20
1100	18	29	38	48	59	24	37	49	62	12	28	44	58	15	35	55	75	17	87	19
1200	17	27	36	46	56	23	35	47	60	11	27	42	55	14	33	53	72	16	84	19
1300	17	26	35	44	54	22	34	45	57	11	26	40	53	14	32	51	69	16	80	18
1400	16	25	33	42	51	21	33	43	55	11	25	39	51	13	31	49	66	15	78	17
1500	15	24	32	41	49	20	32	42	53	10	24	38	49	13	30	47	64	15	75	17
1600	15	23	31	39	48	20	31	40	52	10	23	36	48	12	29	46	62	14	73	16
1700	14	23	30	38	46	19	30	39	50	10	22	35	46	12	28	44	60	14	70	16
1800	14	22	29	37	45	18	29	38	49	9	22	34	45	12	27	43	59	13	68	15
1900	14	21	28	36	44	18	28	37	47	9	21	33	44	11	27	42	57	13	67	15
2000	13	21	27	35	43	17	27	36	46	9	21	32	43	11	26	41	56	13	65	14
2100	13	20	27	34	42	17	27	35	45	9	20	32	42	11	25	40	54	12	63	14
2200	13	20	26	34	41	16	26	34	44	8	20	31	41	11	25	39	53	12	62	14
2300	12	20	26	33	40	16	25	33	43	8	19	30	40	10	24	38	52	12	60	13
2400	12	19	25	32	39	16	25	33	42	8	19	30	39	10	24	37	51	11	59	13
2500	12	19	25	32	39	15	24	32	41	8	18	29	38	10	23	36	50	11	58	13
2600	12	19	24	31	38	15	24	31	40	8	18	28	38	10	23	36	49	11	57	13
2700	12	18	24	31	37	15	23	31	39	8	18	28	37	10	22	35	48	11	56	12
2800	11	18	24	30	37	14	23	30	38	7	17	27	36	9	22	34	47	11	55	12
2900	11	18	23	30	36	14	22	29	38	7	17	27	35	9	21	34	46	11	54	12
3000	11	17	23	29	36	14	22	29	37	7	17	26	35	9	21	33	45	10	53	12
3200	11	17	22	28	34	14	21	28	36	7	16	25	33	9	20	32	44	10	51	11
3400	10	16	21	27	33	13	21	27	35	7	16	25	32	8	20	31	43	10	50	11
3600	10	16	21	27	32	13	20	27	34	6	15	24	31	8	19	30	41	9	48	11
3800	10	15	20	26	32	12	20	26	33	6	15	23	30	8	19	30	40	9	47	10
4000	10	15	20	25	31	12	19	25	32	6	14	22	30	8	18	29	39	9	46	10
4500	9	14	19	24	29	12	18	24	31	6	13	21	28	7	17	27	37	8	43	10
5000	9	13	18	23	27	11	17	23	29	5	13	20	27	7	16	25	35	8	41	9

NOTE: Span values above the solid line are governed by deflection. Values within dashed line box are spans governed by shear.

TABLE 7-5.3: SAFE SPACING, IN., OF SUPPORTS FOR JOISTS, STUDS (OR OTHER BEAM COMPONENTS OF FORMWORK), CONTINUOUS OVER THREE OR MORE SPANS

$\Delta_{max} = 1/360$, but not to exceed $\frac{1}{4}$ in.

$f = 1500$ psi $E = 1,700,000$ psi $H = 180$ psi

Uniform load, lb per lineal ft (equals uniform load on forms times spacing between joists or studs, ft)	2x4	2x6	2x8	2x10	2x12	3x4	3x6	3x8	3x10	4x2	4x4	4x6	4x8	6x2	6x4	6x6	6x8	8x2	8x8	10x2
									Nominal size of S4S lumber											
100	74	111	137	164	190	90	126	156	187	43	98	138	170	50	110	154	195	55	210	60
200	52	82	109	138	160	68	106	131	157	34	80	116	142	40	92	130	164	44	177	47
300	43	67	89	113	138	55	87	115	142	28	65	103	129	35	81	117	148	38	160	41
400	37	58	77	98	119	48	75	99	127	24	57	89	117	30	71	109	138	35	149	38
500	32	51	67	85	103	43	67	89	113	22	51	80	105	27	64	100	130	31	141	35
600	28	44	58	74	90	39	61	81	103	20	46	73	96	25	58	91	124	28	134	32
700	25	39	52	66	80	36	57	75	96	18	43	67	89	23	54	84	115	26	129	30
800	23	36	47	60	73	33	52	69	88	17	40	63	83	21	50	79	108	25	125	28
900	21	33	43	55	67	30	48	62	80	16	38	59	78	20	47	74	101	23	119	26
1000	20	31	41	52	63	28	44	58	74	15	36	56	74	19	45	71	96	22	112	25
1100	18	29	38	49	59	26	41	54	69	14	34	53	70	18	43	67	92	21	107	24
1200	17	27	36	46	56	24	38	51	65	13	31	49	65	18	41	64	88	20	102	23
1300	17	26	35	44	54	23	36	48	61	13	30	46	61	17	40	62	84	19	99	22
1400	16	25	33	42	51	22	35	46	58	12	28	44	58	16	38	60	81	19	95	21
1500	15	24	32	41	49	21	33	43	55	11	27	42	55	16	37	58	78	18	92	20
1600	15	23	31	39	48	20	32	42	53	11	25	40	53	15	35	56	76	17	89	20
1700	14	23	30	38	46	19	30	40	51	10	24	38	50	15	34	54	73	17	86	19
1800	14	22	29	37	45	19	29	38	49	10	23	37	48	14	33	51	70	16	84	19
1900	14	21	28	36	44	18	28	37	48	9	22	35	47	13	31	49	67	16	82	18
2000	13	21	27	35	43	17	27	36	46	9	22	34	45	13	30	47	64	16	80	18
2100	13	20	27	34	42	17	26	35	45	9	21	33	43	12	29	46	62	15	78	17
2200	13	20	26	33	41	16	26	34	44	8	20	32	42	12	28	44	60	15	76	17
2300	12	20	26	33	40	16	25	33	43	8	20	31	41	12	27	42	58	14	74	16
2400	12	19	25	32	39	16	25	33	42	8	19	30	40	11	26	41	56	14	71	16
2500	12	19	25	32	39	15	24	32	41	8	19	29	39	11	25	40	54	13	69	16
2600	12	19	24	31	38	15	24	31	40	8	18	29	38	11	25	39	53	13	67	15
2700	12	18	24	30	37	14	23	30	39	7	18	28	37	10	24	38	52	13	65	15
2800	11	18	24	30	37	14	23	30	38	7	17	27	36	10	23	37	50	12	63	15
2900	11	18	23	30	36	14	22	30	38	7	17	27	35	10	23	36	49	12	61	14
3000	11	18	23	30	36	14	22	29	37	7	17	26	35	10	22	35	48	12	60	14
3200	11	17	23	29	35	13	21	28	36	7	16	25	33	9	21	34	46	11	57	13
3400	11	17	22	28	34	13	21	27	35	7	16	25	32	9	20	32	44	11	55	13
3600	10	16	22	28	34	13	20	27	34	6	15	24	31	8	20	31	42	10	52	12
3800	10	16	21	27	33	12	19	26	33	6	15	23	30	8	19	30	41	9	50	12
4000	10	16	21	27	33	12	19	25	32	6	14	22	30	8	18	29	40	9	49	11
4500	10	15	20	26	31	12	18	24	31	6	13	21	28	7	17	27	37	9	45	10
5000	10	15	20	25	31	11	18	23	30	5	13	21	27	7	16	26	35	8	42	10

NOTE: Span values above the solid line are governed by deflection. Values within the dashed line box are spans governed by shear.

TABLE 7-5.4: SAFE SPACING, IN., OF SUPPORTS FOR JOISTS, STUDS (OR OTHER BEAM COMPONENTS OF FORM-WORK), CONTINUOUS OVER THREE OR MORE SPANS

$\Delta_{max} = 1/360$, but not to exceed $1/4$ in.

$f = 1875$ psi $E = 1,700,000$ psi $H = 225$ psi

Spacing → | ← Spacing → | ← Spacing → | ← Spacing

Uniform load, lb per lineal ft (equals uniform load on forms times spacing between joists or studs, ft)	2x4	2x6	2x8	2x10	2x12	3x4	3x6	3x8	3x10	4x2	4x4	4x6	4x8	6x2	6x4	6x6	6x8	8x2	8x8	10x2
									Nominal size of S4S lumber											
100	76	111	137	164	190	90	126	156	187	43	98	138	169	50	110	154	195	55	210	60
200	59	92	115	138	160	72	106	131	157	34	80	116	142	40	92	130	164	44	177	47
300	48	75	99	125	145	62	96	118	142	30	70	105	129	35	81	117	148	38	160	41
400	41	65	86	110	133	54	84	110	132	27	63	97	120	32	74	109	138	35	149	38
500	37	58	77	98	119	48	75	99	125	24	57	89	113	29	69	103	130	32	141	35
600	33	52	69	88	107	44	69	91	116	22	52	81	107	28	65	98	124	30	134	33
700	29	46	61	78	95	40	64	84	107	20	48	75	99	26	60	94	120	29	129	31
800	27	42	55	70	86	38	59	78	100	19	45	70	93	24	56	88	116	28	125	30
900	24	38	51	65	79	36	56	74	94	18	42	66	87	23	53	83	112	26	121	29
1000	23	36	47	60	73	33	52	69	88	17	40	63	83	21	50	79	109	25	118	28
1100	21	33	44	56	68	31	48	64	82	16	38	60	79	20	48	75	103	24	115	27
1200	20	32	42	53	65	29	45	60	76	16	37	57	76	20	46	72	99	23	113	25
1300	19	30	40	50	61	27	43	56	72	15	35	55	73	19	44	69	94	22	110	24
1400	18	29	38	48	59	26	40	53	68	14	33	52	69	18	42	67	91	21	106	24
1500	17	27	36	46	56	24	38	51	65	13	31	49	65	18	41	64	88	20	103	23
1600	17	26	35	44	54	23	37	48	62	13	30	47	62	17	40	62	85	19	100	22
1700	16	26	34	43	52	22	35	46	59	12	29	45	59	16	38	61	83	19	97	21
1800	16	25	33	42	51	22	34	45	57	12	27	43	57	16	37	59	80	18	94	21
1900	15	24	32	40	49	21	33	43	55	11	26	41	55	16	36	57	78	18	91	20
2000	15	23	31	39	48	20	32	42	53	11	25	40	53	15	35	56	76	17	89	20
2100	14	23	30	38	47	19	31	40	51	10	24	38	51	15	34	54	74	17	87	19
2200	14	22	29	37	45	19	30	39	50	10	24	37	49	14	33	52	71	17	85	19
2300	14	22	29	37	44	18	29	38	49	10	23	36	48	14	32	50	69	16	83	18
2400	14	21	28	36	44	18	28	37	47	10	22	35	46	13	31	49	66	16	81	18
2500	13	21	27	35	43	17	27	36	46	9	22	34	45	13	30	47	63	16	80	18
2600	13	20	27	34	42	17	27	35	45	9	21	33	44	12	29	46	61	15	78	17
2700	13	20	27	34	41	17	26	35	44	9	20	32	43	12	28	45	60	15	77	17
2800	13	20	26	33	41	16	26	34	43	9	20	32	42	12	28	43	59	15	75	17
2900	12	19	26	32	40	16	25	33	42	8	20	31	41	11	27	42	58	14	73	16
3000	12	19	25	32	39	16	25	32	41	8	19	30	40	11	26	41	56	14	71	16
3200	12	19	25	31	38	15	24	31	40	8	18	29	38	11	25	39	54	13	68	16
3400	12	18	24	31	37	15	23	30	39	8	18	28	37	10	24	38	51	13	65	15
3600	11	18	24	30	37	14	22	30	38	7	17	27	36	10	23	36	49	12	62	15
3800	11	17	23	30	36	14	22	29	37	7	17	26	34	9	23	35	48	12	59	14
4000	11	17	23	29	35	14	21	28	36	7	16	25	33	9	22	34	46	11	57	13
4500	10	16	22	28	34	13	20	27	34	6	15	24	31	8	20	31	43	10	53	12
5000	10	16	21	27	33	12	19	25	32	6	14	22	30	8	18	29	40	9	49	11

NOTE: Span values above the solid line are governed by deflection. Values within dashed line box are spans governed by shear.

TABLE 7-6.1: SAFE SPACING, IN., OF SUPPORTS FOR JOISTS, STUDS (OR OTHER BEAM COMPONENTS OF FORMWORK), SINGLE SPAN OR CONTINUOUS OVER TWO SPANS

$\Delta_{max} = l/360$, but not to exceed ¼ in.

$f = 775\,psi$ $E = 1,100,000\,psi$ $H = 140\,psi$

Nominal size of S4S lumber

Uniform load, lb per lineal ft (equals uniform load on forms times spacing between joists or studs, ft)	2x4	2x6	2x8	2x10	2x12	3x4	3x6	3x8	3x10	4x2	4x4	4x6	4x8	6x2	6x4	6x6	6x8	8x2	8x8	10x2
100	48	75	99	126	146	62	97	119	143	30	71	105	130	35	82	118	149	39	161	42
200	34	53	70	89	108	44	68	90	115	22	52	81	107	28	65	99	125	31	135	33
300	28	43	57	73	89	36	56	74	94	18	42	66	87	23	53	83	113	26	122	29
400	24	37	49	63	77	31	48	64	81	16	36	57	75	20	46	72	98	22	114	25
500	21	34	44	56	69	28	43	57	73	14	33	51	68	17	41	64	88	20	102	23
600	19	31	40	51	63	25	39	52	66	13	30	47	62	16	37	59	80	18	93	21
700	18	28	37	48	58	23	37	48	62	12	28	43	57	15	35	54	74	17	86	19
800	17	26	35	45	54	22	34	45	58	11	26	40	53	14	32	51	69	16	81	18
900	16	25	33	42	51	20	32	43	54	10	24	38	50	13	30	48	65	15	76	17
1000	15	24	31	40	48	19	31	40	51	10	23	36	48	12	29	45	62	14	72	16
1100	14	23	30	38	46	19	29	38	49	9	22	35	45	12	28	43	59	14	69	15
1200	14	22	28	36	44	18	28	37	47	9	21	33	44	11	26	41	57	13	66	15
1300	13	21	27	35	43	17	27	35	45	9	20	32	42	11	25	40	54	12	63	14
1400	13	20	26	34	41	16	26	34	43	8	19	31	40	10	24	38	52	12	61	14
1500	12	19	25	33	40	16	25	33	42	8	19	30	39	10	24	37	51	12	59	13
1600	12	19	25	31	38	15	24	32	41	8	18	29	38	10	23	36	49	11	57	13
1700	12	18	24	31	37	15	23	31	39	8	18	28	37	9	22	35	47	11	55	12
1800	11	18	23	30	36	14	23	30	38	7	17	27	36	9	21	34	46	11	54	12
1900	11	17	23	29	35	14	22	29	37	7	17	26	35	9	21	33	45	10	52	12
2000	11	17	22	28	34	14	22	28	36	7	16	26	34	9	20	32	44	10	51	11
2100	10	16	22	27	33	13	21	28	35	7	16	25	33	8	20	31	43	10	50	11
2200	10	16	21	27	33	13	21	27	35	7	15	24	32	8	19	31	42	10	49	11
2300	10	16	21	26	32	13	20	27	34	6	15	24	31	8	19	30	41	9	48	11
2400	10	15	20	26	31	13	20	26	33	6	15	23	31	8	19	29	40	9	47	10
2500	9	15	20	25	31	12	19	25	33	6	15	23	30	8	18	29	39	9	46	10
2600	9	15	19	25	30	12	19	25	32	6	14	22	30	8	18	28	38	9	45	10
2700	9	14	19	24	29	12	19	25	31	6	14	22	29	7	18	28	38	8	44	10
2800	9	14	19	24	29	11	18	24	31	6	14	22	28	7	17	27	37	8	43	10
2900	9	14	18	23	28	11	18	24	30	6	13	21	28	7	17	27	36	8	42	9
3000	9	14	18	23	28	11	18	23	30	6	13	21	28	7	17	26	36	8	42	9
3200	8	13	17	22	27	11	17	23	29	5	13	20	27	7	16	25	35	8	40	9
3400	8	13	17	22	26	11	17	22	28	5	12	20	26	7	16	25	34	8	39	9
3600	8	12	16	21	26	10	16	21	27	5	12	19	25	6	15	24	33	7	38	8
3800	8	12	16	20	25	10	16	21	26	5	12	19	24	6	15	23	32	7	37	8
4000	7	12	16	20	24	10	15	20	26	5	11	18	24	6	14	23	31	7	36	8
4500	7	11	15	19	23	9	14	19	24	5	11	17	22	6	14	21	29	6	34	8
5000	7	11	14	18	22	9	14	18	23	4	10	16	21	5	13	20	28	6	32	7

NOTE: Values above solid line are spans governed by deflection and are therefore conservative for two-span beams. All other values are governed by bending.

TABLE 7-6.2: SAFE SPACING, IN., OF SUPPORTS FOR JOISTS, STUDS (OR OTHER BEAM COMPONENTS OF FORMWORK), SINGLE SPAN OR CONTINUOUS OVER TWO SPANS

$\Delta_{max} = l/360$, but not to exceed ¼ in.

$f = 1000$ psi $E = 1,400,000$ psi $H = 180$ psi

Uniform load, lb per lineal ft (equals uniform load on forms times spacing between joists or studs, ft)	2x4	2x6	2x8	2x10	2x12	3x4	3x6	3x8	3x10	4x2	4x4	4x6	4x8	6x2	6x4	6x6	6x8	8x2	8x8	10x2
100	54	85	111	134	155	68	103	127	152	33	77	112	138	38	89	125	158	42	171	45
200	38	60	79	101	123	49	78	103	128	25	59	92	116	30	71	105	133	33	144	36
300	31	49	65	83	101	40	63	84	107	20	48	75	99	26	60	94	120	29	130	31
400	27	43	56	72	87	35	55	72	92	18	41	65	86	22	52	82	111	25	121	29
500	24	38	50	64	78	31	49	65	83	16	37	58	77	20	46	73	99	23	114	26
600	22	35	46	58	71	29	45	59	75	14	34	53	70	18	42	67	91	21	106	24
700	20	32	42	54	66	26	42	55	70	13	31	49	65	17	39	62	84	19	98	22
800	19	30	40	51	62	25	39	51	65	13	29	46	61	16	37	58	79	18	92	20
900	18	28	37	48	58	23	37	48	62	12	28	43	57	15	35	54	74	17	87	19
1000	17	27	35	45	55	22	35	46	58	11	26	41	54	14	33	52	70	16	82	18
1100	16	26	34	43	53	21	33	44	56	11	25	39	52	13	31	49	67	15	78	17
1200	16	25	32	41	50	20	32	42	53	10	24	38	49	13	30	47	64	15	75	17
1300	15	24	31	40	48	19	30	40	51	10	23	36	48	12	29	45	62	14	72	16
1400	14	23	30	38	47	19	29	39	49	9	22	35	46	12	28	44	59	14	69	15
1500	14	22	29	37	45	18	28	37	48	9	21	34	44	11	27	42	57	13	67	15
1600	14	21	28	36	44	17	27	36	46	9	21	32	43	11	26	41	56	13	65	14
1700	13	21	27	35	42	17	27	35	45	9	20	32	42	11	25	40	54	12	63	14
1800	13	20	26	34	41	16	26	34	44	8	19	31	40	10	24	38	52	12	61	14
1900	12	20	26	33	40	16	25	33	42	8	19	30	39	10	24	37	51	12	60	13
2000	12	19	25	32	39	16	25	32	41	8	18	29	38	10	23	36	50	11	58	13
2100	12	19	24	31	38	15	24	32	40	8	18	28	37	10	23	36	49	11	57	13
2200	12	18	24	31	37	15	23	31	39	8	18	28	37	9	22	35	47	11	55	12
2300	11	18	23	30	36	15	23	30	39	7	17	27	36	9	22	34	46	11	54	12
2400	11	17	23	29	36	14	22	30	38	7	17	27	35	9	21	33	45	10	53	12
2500	11	17	22	29	35	14	22	29	37	7	17	26	34	9	21	33	44	10	52	11
2600	11	17	22	28	34	14	22	28	36	7	16	25	34	9	20	32	44	10	51	11
2700	10	16	22	28	33	13	21	28	36	7	16	25	33	9	20	31	43	10	50	11
2800	10	16	21	27	33	13	21	27	35	7	16	25	32	8	20	31	42	10	49	11
2900	10	16	21	27	32	13	20	27	34	7	15	24	32	8	19	30	41	9	48	11
3000	10	16	20	26	32	13	20	26	34	6	15	24	31	8	19	30	41	9	47	10
3200	10	15	20	25	31	12	19	26	33	6	15	23	30	8	18	29	39	9	46	10
3400	9	15	19	25	30	12	19	25	32	6	14	22	29	8	18	28	38	9	45	10
3600	9	14	19	24	29	12	18	24	31	6	14	22	29	7	17	27	37	8	43	10
3800	9	14	18	23	28	11	18	23	30	6	13	21	28	7	17	26	36	8	42	9
4000	9	13	18	23	28	11	17	23	29	6	13	21	27	7	16	26	35	8	41	9
4500	8	13	17	21	26	10	16	22	28	5	12	19	26	7	15	24	33	8	39	9
5000	8	12	16	20	25	10	16	20	26	5	12	18	24	6	15	23	31	7	37	8

Nominal size of S4S lumber

NOTE: Values above solid line are spans governed by deflection and are therefore conservative for two-span beams. All other values are governed by bending.

TABLE 7-6.3: SAFE SPACING, IN., OF SUPPORTS FOR JOISTS, STUDS (OR OTHER BEAM COMPONENTS OF FORM-WORK), SINGLE SPAN

$\Delta_{max} = l/360$, but not to exceed $\frac{1}{4}$ in.

$f = 1500$ psi $E = 1,700,000$ psi $H = 180$ psi

Uniform load, lb per lineal ft (equals uniform load on forms times spacing between joists or studs, ft)	2x4	2x6	2x8	2x10	2x12	3x4	3x6	3x8	3x10	4x2	4x4	4x6	4x8	6x2	6x4	6x6	6x8	8x2	8x8	10x2
100	62	95	116	140	162	73	108	133	159	35	82	117	144	41	94	131	166	45	179	48
200	47	74	97	118	137	58	91	112	134	28	65	99	121	32	75	110	140	35	151	38
300	38	60	79	101	123	49	78	101	121	24	57	89	110	28	66	100	126	31	136	33
400	33	52	69	88	107	43	67	89	113	22	51	80	102	26	60	93	117	28	127	30
500	30	47	61	78	95	38	60	79	101	19	45	71	94	24	55	87	111	26	120	28
600	27	43	56	72	87	35	55	72	92	18	41	65	86	22	52	82	106	24	115	27
700	25	40	52	66	81	32	51	67	86	16	38	60	79	21	48	75	102	23	110	25
800	23	37	49	62	75	30	48	63	80	15	36	56	74	19	45	71	99	22	107	24
900	22	35	46	58	71	29	45	59	75	14	34	53	70	18	42	67	91	21	103	23
1000	21	33	43	55	67	27	43	56	72	14	32	50	66	17	40	63	86	20	101	22
1100	20	31	41	53	64	26	41	54	68	13	31	48	63	16	38	60	82	19	96	21
1200	19	30	40	51	62	25	39	51	65	12	29	46	61	16	37	58	79	18	92	20
1300	18	29	38	49	59	24	37	49	63	12	28	44	58	15	35	55	76	17	88	20
1400	18	28	37	47	57	23	36	47	61	12	27	43	56	15	34	53	73	17	85	19
1500	17	27	35	45	55	22	35	46	58	11	26	41	54	14	33	52	71	16	82	18
1600	16	26	34	43	53	21	34	44	57	11	25	40	52	14	32	50	68	16	80	18
1700	16	25	33	42	51	21	33	43	55	10	25	39	51	13	31	48	66	15	77	17
1800	15	24	32	41	49	20	32	42	53	10	24	38	49	13	30	47	64	15	75	17
1900	15	23	31	39	48	20	31	41	52	10	23	37	48	12	29	46	63	14	73	16
2000	14	23	30	38	47	19	30	40	51	10	23	36	47	12	28	45	61	14	71	16
2100	14	22	29	37	46	19	29	39	49	9	22	35	46	12	28	44	59	14	70	15
2200	14	22	29	37	45	18	29	38	48	9	22	34	45	12	27	43	58	13	68	15
2300	14	21	28	36	44	18	28	37	47	9	21	33	44	11	26	42	57	13	66	15
2400	13	21	27	35	43	17	27	36	46	9	21	32	43	11	26	41	56	13	65	14
2500	13	20	27	34	42	17	27	35	45	9	20	32	42	11	25	40	55	12	64	14
2600	13	20	26	34	41	17	26	34	44	8	20	31	41	11	25	39	53	12	63	14
2700	13	20	26	33	40	16	26	34	43	8	19	31	40	10	24	38	52	12	61	14
2800	12	19	26	33	40	16	25	33	42	8	19	30	40	10	24	38	52	12	60	13
2900	12	19	25	32	39	16	25	32	41	8	19	30	39	10	24	37	51	12	59	13
3000	12	19	25	32	39	15	24	32	41	8	18	29	38	10	23	36	50	11	58	13
3200	12	18	24	31	38	15	23	31	39	8	18	28	37	10	22	35	48	11	56	12
3400	11	18	24	30	37	14	23	30	38	7	17	27	36	9	22	34	47	11	55	12
3600	11	17	23	29	36	14	22	29	37	7	17	26	35	9	21	33	45	10	53	12
3800	11	17	22	28	35	14	21	28	36	7	16	26	34	9	21	32	44	10	52	11
4000	10	16	22	28	34	13	21	27	35	7	16	25	33	9	20	32	43	10	50	11
4500	10	16	20	26	32	13	20	26	33	6	15	23	31	8	19	30	40	9	47	10
5000	9	15	19	25	30	12	19	25	32	6	14	22	29	8	18	28	39	9	45	10

Nominal size of S4S lumber

NOTE: Span values above the solid line are governed by deflection. Values within dashed line box are spans governed by shear.

TABLE 7-6.4: SAFE SPACING, IN., OF SUPPORTS FOR JOISTS, STUDS (OR OTHER BEAM COMPONENTS OF FORM-WORK), SINGLE SPAN

$\Delta_{max} = l/360$, but not to exceed $1/4$ in.

$f = 1875$ psi $E = 1,700,000$ psi $H = 225$ psi

Spacing

Nominal size of S4S lumber

Uniform load, lb per lineal ft (equals uniform load on forms times spacing between joists or studs, ft)	2x4	2x6	2x8	2x10	2x12	3x4	3x6	3x8	3x10	4x2	4x4	4x6	4x8	6x2	6x4	6x6	6x8	8x2	8x8	10x2
100	62	95	117	140	162	73	108	133	159	35	82	117	144	41	94	131	166	45	179	48
200	49	77	98	118	137	58	91	112	134	28	65	99	121	32	75	110	140	35	151	38
300	43	67	88	107	123	51	79	101	121	24	57	89	110	28	66	100	126	31	136	33
400	37	58	77	98	115	46	72	94	113	22	51	81	102	26	60	93	117	28	127	30
500	33	52	69	88	107	43	67	88	107	20	48	75	97	24	55	87	111	26	120	28
600	30	48	63	80	97	39	61	81	102	19	45	71	92	22	52	82	106	24	115	27
700	28	44	58	74	90	36	57	75	96	18	43	67	88	21	50	78	102	23	110	25
800	26	41	54	69	84	34	53	70	90	17	40	63	83	20	47	75	99	22	107	24
900	25	39	51	65	80	32	50	66	84	16	38	59	78	20	46	72	96	21	103	23
1000	23	37	49	62	75	30	48	63	80	15	36	56	74	19	44	69	93	21	101	22
1100	22	35	46	59	72	29	45	60	76	15	34	54	71	18	43	67	92	20	98	22
1200	21	34	44	57	69	28	43	57	73	14	33	51	68	18	41	64	88	19	96	21
1300	21	32	43	54	66	27	42	55	70	13	31	49	65	17	39	62	85	19	95	21
1400	20	31	41	52	64	26	40	53	68	13	30	48	63	16	38	60	82	18	93	20
1500	19	30	40	51	62	25	39	51	65	13	29	46	61	16	37	58	79	18	91	20
1600	19	29	38	49	60	24	38	50	63	12	28	45	59	15	36	56	76	17	89	19
1700	18	28	37	48	58	23	36	48	61	12	27	43	57	15	34	54	74	17	86	19
1800	17	27	36	46	56	23	35	47	60	11	27	42	55	14	33	53	72	16	84	18
1900	17	27	35	45	54	22	35	46	58	11	26	41	54	14	33	51	70	16	82	18
2000	16	26	34	43	53	21	34	44	57	11	25	40	52	14	32	50	68	16	80	18
2100	16	25	33	42	51	21	33	43	55	11	25	39	51	13	31	49	66	15	78	17
2200	16	24	32	41	50	20	32	42	54	10	24	38	50	13	30	48	65	15	76	17
2300	15	24	31	40	49	20	31	41	53	10	24	37	49	13	30	47	64	15	74	16
2400	15	23	31	39	48	20	31	40	52	10	23	36	48	12	29	46	62	14	73	16
2500	15	23	30	38	47	19	30	40	51	10	23	36	47	12	28	45	61	14	71	16
2600	14	22	30	38	46	19	29	39	50	9	22	35	46	12	28	44	60	14	70	15
2700	14	22	29	37	45	18	29	38	49	9	22	34	45	12	27	43	59	13	69	15
2800	14	22	28	36	44	18	28	37	48	9	21	34	44	11	27	42	58	13	67	15
2900	13	21	28	36	43	18	28	37	47	9	21	33	44	11	26	41	57	13	66	15
3000	13	21	27	35	43	17	27	36	46	9	21	32	43	11	26	41	56	13	65	14
3200	13	20	27	34	41	17	26	35	44	9	20	31	41	11	25	39	54	12	63	14
3400	13	20	26	33	40	16	26	34	43	8	19	31	40	10	24	38	52	12	61	14
3600	12	19	25	32	39	16	25	33	42	8	19	30	39	10	24	37	51	12	59	13
3800	12	19	25	32	38	15	24	32	40	8	18	29	38	10	23	36	49	11	58	13
4000	12	18	24	31	38	15	23	31	39	8	18	28	37	10	22	35	48	11	56	12
4500	11	17	23	29	35	14	22	29	37	7	17	26	35	9	21	33	45	10	53	12
5000	10	16	22	28	34	13	21	27	35	7	16	25	33	9	20	32	43	10	50	11

NOTE: Span values above the solid line are governed by deflection. Values within dashed line box are spans governed by shear.

TABLE 7-7.3: SAFE SPACING IN INCHES OF SUPPORTS FOR JOISTS, STUDS (OR OTHER BEAM COMPONENTS OF FORMWORK), CONTINUOUS OVER TWO SPANS

Δ_{max} is $\frac{1}{360}$ of spacing, but not more than $\frac{1}{4}$ in.

f = 1500 psi   E = 1,700,000 psi   H = 180 psi

Uniform load, lb per lineal ft (equals uniform load on forms times spacing between joists or studs, ft)	2x4	2x6	2x8	2x10	2x12	3x4	3x6	3x8	3x10	4x2	4x4	4x6	4x8	6x2	6x4	6x6	6x8	8x2	8x8	10x2
100	66	104	138	175	202	86	134	165	199	43	101	146	180	54	117	164	207	60	223	65
200	47	74	97	124	151	61	95	126	160	31	72	113	149	38	90	138	174	44	188	50
300	38	60	79	101	123	49	78	103	131	25	59	92	121	31	73	115	157	36	170	41
400	33	52	69	88	107	43	67	89	113	22	51	80	105	27	64	100	137	31	158	35
500	30	47	61	78	95	38	60	79	101	19	45	71	94	24	57	89	121	28	143	32
600	27	43	56	72	87	35	55	72	92	18	41	65	86	22	52	82	111	25	130	29
700	24	38	50	64	78	32	51	67	86	16	38	60	79	21	48	75	103	24	120	27
800	22	35	46	58	71	30	48	63	80	15	36	56	74	19	45	71	97	22	113	25
900	20	32	42	54	66	29	45	59	75	14	34	53	70	18	42	67	91	21	106	24
1000	19	30	40	50	61	27	43	56	72	14	32	50	66	17	40	63	86	20	101	22
1100	18	28	37	48	58	25	40	52	67	13	31	48	63	16	38	60	82	19	96	21
1200	17	27	35	45	55	24	37	49	63	13	29	46	61	16	37	58	79	18	92	20
1300	16	26	34	43	52	22	35	47	59	12	28	44	58	15	35	55	76	17	88	20
1400	16	25	32	41	50	21	34	44	57	12	27	43	56	15	34	53	73	17	85	19
1500	15	24	31	40	48	20	32	42	54	11	26	41	53	14	33	52	71	16	82	18
1600	15	23	30	38	47	20	31	41	52	11	25	39	51	14	32	50	68	16	80	18
1700	14	22	29	37	45	19	30	39	50	10	24	37	49	13	31	48	66	15	77	17
1800	14	22	28	36	44	18	29	38	48	10	23	36	47	13	30	47	64	14	75	17
1900	13	21	28	35	43	18	28	36	46	9	22	34	45	12	29	46	63	14	73	16
2000	13	20	27	34	42	17	27	35	45	9	21	33	44	12	28	45	61	14	71	16
2100	13	20	26	34	41	17	26	34	44	9	20	32	42	12	28	44	59	14	70	15
2200	12	20	26	33	40	16	25	33	43	8	20	31	41	12	27	43	58	13	69	15
2300	12	19	25	32	39	16	25	33	42	8	19	30	40	11	26	41	57	13	66	15
2400	12	19	25	32	39	15	24	32	41	8	19	29	39	11	25	40	55	12	65	14
2500	12	19	24	31	38	15	24	31	40	8	18	29	38	11	25	39	53	12	64	14
2600	12	18	24	31	37	15	23	31	39	8	18	28	37	10	24	38	51	12	62	14
2700	11	18	24	30	37	14	23	30	38	7	17	27	36	10	23	37	50	12	61	14
2800	11	18	23	30	36	14	22	29	37	7	17	27	35	10	23	36	49	12	60	13
2900	11	18	23	29	36	14	22	29	37	7	17	26	35	10	22	35	48	12	59	13
3000	11	17	23	29	35	14	22	28	36	7	16	26	34	9	22	34	47	11	58	13
3200	11	17	22	28	35	13	21	27	35	7	16	25	33	9	21	33	44	11	55	12
3400	11	17	22	28	34	13	20	27	34	7	15	24	32	9	20	31	43	10	53	12
3600	10	16	21	27	33	13	20	26	33	6	15	23	31	8	19	30	41	10	51	12
3800	10	16	21	27	33	12	19	25	32	6	14	23	30	8	18	29	40	10	49	11
4000	10	16	21	26	32	12	19	25	32	6	14	22	29	8	17	28	39	9	47	11
4500	10	15	20	26	31	11	18	24	30	6	14	21	27	7	17	26	36	8	44	11
5000	9	15	19	25	30	11	17	23	29	5	13	20	26	7	16	25	34	8	41	9

Nominal size of S4S lumber

NOTE: Tables 7-7.1 and 7-7.2 for two-span beams have been omitted because safe spans are covered in Tables 7-6.1 and 7-6.2, respectively.

NOTE: Span values above the solid line are governed by deflection. Values within the dashed line box are spans governed by shear.

DESIGN TABLES

TABLE 7-7.4: SAFE SPACING IN INCHES OF SUPPORTS FOR JOISTS, STUDS (OR OTHER BEAM COMPONENTS OF FORMWORK), CONTINUOUS OVER TWO SPANS

Δ_{max} is $1/360$ of spacing, but not more than $1/4$ in.

$f = 1875$ psi $E = 1,700,000$ psi $H = 225$ psi

Uniform load, lb per lineal ft (equals uniform load on forms times spacing between joists or studs, ft)	2x4	2x6	2x8	2x10	2x12	3x4	3x6	3x8	3x10	4x2	4x4	4x6	4x8	6x2	6x4	6x6	6x8	8x2	8x8	10x2
100	74	117	146	175	202	96	134	165	199	47	104	146	180	54	117	164	207	60	223	65
200	52	82	109	139	169	68	106	139	167	34	80	123	151	43	98	138	174	47	188	51
300	43	67	89	113	138	55	87	115	146	28	65	103	136	35	82	124	157	40	170	45
400	37	58	77	98	119	48	75	99	127	24	57	89	117	30	71	112	146	35	158	39
500	33	52	69	88	107	43	67	89	113	22	51	80	105	27	64	100	136	31	149	35
600	30	48	63	80	97	39	61	81	103	20	46	73	96	25	58	91	124	29	142	32
700	28	44	58	74	90	36	57	75	96	18	43	67	89	23	54	84	115	26	134	30
800	26	41	54	68	83	34	53	70	90	17	40	63	83	21	50	79	108	25	126	28
900	23	37	49	63	76	32	50	66	84	16	38	59	78	20	47	74	102	23	119	26
1000	22	35	46	58	71	30	48	63	80	15	36	56	74	19	45	71	96	22	113	25
1100	21	33	43	55	67	29	45	60	76	15	34	54	71	18	43	67	92	21	107	24
1200	20	31	41	52	63	28	43	57	73	14	33	51	68	18	41	64	88	20	103	23
1300	19	29	39	49	60	26	41	55	70	13	31	49	65	17	39	62	85	19	99	22
1400	18	28	37	47	57	25	39	52	66	13	30	48	63	16	38	60	82	19	95	21
1500	17	27	35	45	55	24	37	49	63	13	29	46	61	16	37	58	79	18	92	20
1600	16	26	34	43	53	23	36	47	60	12	28	45	59	15	36	56	76	17	89	20
1700	16	25	33	42	51	22	34	45	58	12	27	43	57	15	34	54	74	17	86	19
1800	15	24	32	41	49	21	33	43	55	11	27	42	55	14	33	53	72	16	84	19
1900	15	23	31	39	48	20	32	42	54	11	26	40	53	14	33	51	70	16	82	18
2000	15	23	30	38	47	20	31	41	52	11	25	39	51	14	32	50	68	16	80	18
2100	14	22	29	37	46	19	30	39	50	10	24	37	49	13	31	49	66	15	78	17
2200	14	22	29	37	45	18	29	38	49	10	23	36	48	13	30	48	65	15	76	17
2300	14	21	28	36	44	18	28	37	47	10	22	35	46	13	30	47	64	15	74	16
2400	13	21	27	35	43	17	27	36	46	9	22	34	45	12	29	46	62	14	73	16
2500	13	20	27	34	42	17	27	35	45	9	21	33	44	12	28	45	61	14	71	16
2600	13	20	26	34	41	17	26	35	44	9	21	32	43	12	28	44	60	14	70	15
2700	13	20	26	33	40	16	26	34	43	9	20	31	42	12	27	43	59	13	69	15
2800	12	19	26	33	40	16	25	33	42	8	20	31	41	11	27	42	57	13	67	15
2900	12	19	25	32	39	16	25	32	41	8	19	30	40	11	26	41	56	13	66	15
3000	12	19	25	32	39	15	24	32	41	8	19	29	39	11	25	40	55	13	65	14
3200	12	18	24	31	38	15	23	31	39	8	18	28	37	10	24	38	52	12	63	14
3400	11	18	24	30	37	14	23	30	38	7	17	27	36	10	23	37	50	12	61	14
3600	11	18	23	30	36	14	22	29	37	7	17	26	35	10	22	35	48	12	59	13
3800	11	17	23	29	35	14	21	28	36	7	16	26	34	9	22	34	47	11	58	13
4000	11	17	22	28	35	13	21	27	35	7	16	25	33	9	21	33	45	11	55	12
4500	10	16	21	27	33	13	20	26	33	6	15	23	31	8	19	30	41	10	50	11
5000	10	16	21	26	32	12	19	25	32	6	14	22	29	8	18	28	39	9	47	11

Nominal size of S4S lumber

NOTE: Span values above the solid line are governed by deflection. Values within dashed line box are spans governed by shear.

TABLE 7-8.1: SAFE SPACING, IN., OF SUPPORTS FOR DOUBLE WALES CONTINUOUS OVER THREE OR MORE SPANS

Maximum deflection is $\frac{1}{360}$ of spacing, but not more than $\frac{1}{4}$ in.

← Spacing → Spacing → Spacing →

Equivalent uniform load, lb per lineal ft (equals uniform load, psf, on forms times spacing of wales in ft)	$f = 775$ psi				$E = 1,100,000$ psi			$H = 140$ psi	
	Nominal size of S4S lumber used double								
	2x4	2x6	2x8	3x4	3x6	3x8	4x4	4x6	4x8
1000	24	37	49	31	48	64	36	57	75
1100	23	36	47	29	46	61	35	55	72
1200	22	34	45	28	44	58	33	52	69
1300	21	33	43	27	42	56	32	50	66
1400	20	32	42	26	41	54	31	48	64
1500	20	31	40	25	40	52	30	47	62
1600	19	30	39	24	38	50	29	45	60
1700	18	29	38	24	37	49	28	44	58
1800	18	28	37	23	36	48	27	43	56
1900	17	27	36	22	35	46	26	42	55
2000	17	26	35	22	34	45	26	40	53
2200	16	25	33	21	33	43	25	39	51
2400	15	24	31	20	31	41	23	37	49
2600	14	23	30	19	30	40	23	35	47
2800	14	22	29	18	29	38	22	34	45
3000	13	21	28	18	28	37	21	33	44
3200	13	21	27	17	27	36	20	32	42
3400	13	20	26	17	26	34	20	31	41
3600	12	20	26	16	25	33	19	30	40
3800	12	19	25	16	24	32	19	29	39
4000	12	19	25	15	24	31	18	29	38
4200	12	18	24	15	23	31	18	28	37
4400	11	18	24	14	23	30	17	27	36
4600	11	18	23	14	22	29	17	27	35
4800	11	17	23	14	22	29	16	26	34
5000	11	17	23	13	21	28	16	25	33

Equivalent uniform load, lb per lineal ft (equals uniform load, psf, on forms times spacing of wales in ft)	$f = 1000$ psi				$E = 1,400,000$ psi			$H = 180$ psi	
	Nominal size of S4S lumber used double								
	2x4	2x6	2x8	3x4	3x6	3x8	4x4	4x6	4x8
1000	27	43	56	35	55	72	41	65	86
1100	26	41	53	33	52	69	39	62	82
1200	25	39	51	32	50	66	38	59	78
1300	24	37	49	31	48	64	36	57	75
1400	23	36	47	30	46	61	35	55	72
1500	22	35	46	29	45	59	34	53	70
1600	21	34	44	28	43	57	33	51	69
1700	21	33	43	27	42	56	32	50	66
1800	20	32	42	26	41	54	31	48	64
1900	20	31	41	25	40	53	30	47	62
2000	19	30	40	25	39	51	29	46	61
2200	18	29	38	24	37	49	28	44	58
2400	17	27	36	23	36	47	27	42	55
2600	17	26	35	22	34	45	26	40	53
2800	16	25	33	21	33	43	25	39	51
3000	15	24	32	20	32	42	24	38	49
3200	15	23	31	20	31	40	23	36	48
3400	14	23	30	19	30	39	22	35	46
3600	14	22	29	18	29	38	22	34	45
3800	14	21	28	18	28	37	21	33	44
4000	13	21	27	17	27	36	21	32	43
4200	13	20	27	17	27	35	20	32	42
4400	13	20	26	16	26	34	20	31	41
4600	12	20	26	16	25	33	19	30	40
4800	12	19	25	16	25	33	19	30	39
5000	12	19	25	15	24	32	18	29	38

NOTE: Within the dashed lines shear is the governing design criterion. Elsewhere bending strength governs the span. Load within distance h from supports neglected in computing shear.

TABLE 7-8.2: SAFE SPACING, IN., OF SUPPORTS FOR DOUBLE WALES CONTINUOUS OVER THREE OR MORE SPANS

Maximum deflection is $\frac{1}{360}$ of spacing, but not more than $\frac{1}{4}$ in.

Spacing | Spacing | Spacing

Equivalent uniform load, lb per lineal ft (equals uniform load, psf, on forms times spacing of wales in ft)	f = 1500 psi				E = 1,700,000 psi			H = 180 psi	
	Nominal size of S4S lumber used double								
	2x4	2x6	2x8	3x4	3x6	3x8	4x4	4x6	4x8
1000	32	51	67	43	67	89	51	80	105
1100	30	47	62	41	64	85	48	76	100
1200	28	44	58	39	61	81	46	73	96
1300	26	41	55	38	59	78	44	70	92
1400	25	39	52	36	57	75	43	67	89
1500	24	37	49	35	55	72	41	65	86
1600	23	36	47	33	52	69	40	63	83
1700	22	34	45	32	50	66	39	61	80
1800	21	33	43	30	48	63	38	59	78
1900	20	32	42	29	46	60	37	58	76
2000	20	31	41	28	44	58	36	56	74
2200	18	29	38	26	41	54	34	53	70
2400	17	27	36	24	38	51	32	48	65
2600	17	26	35	23	36	48	31	46	61
2800	16	25	33	22	35	46	28	44	58
3000	15	24	32	21	33	43	27	42	55
3200	15	23	31	20	32	42	25	40	53
3400	14	23	30	19	30	40	24	38	50
3600	14	22	29	19	29	39	23	37	48
3800	14	21	28	18	28	37	22	35	47
4000	13	21	27	17	27	36	22	34	45
4200	13	20	27	17	27	35	21	33	43
4400	13	20	26	16	26	34	20	32	42
4600	12	20	26	16	25	33	20	31	41
4800	12	19	25	16	25	33	19	30	40
5000	12	19	25	15	24	32	19	29	39

Equivalent uniform load, lb per lineal ft (equals uniform load, psf, on forms times spacing of wales in ft)	f = 1875 psi				E = 1,700,000 psi			H = 225 psi	
	Nominal size of S4S lumber used double								
	2x4	2x6	2x8	3x4	3x6	3x8	4x4	4x6	4x8
1000	37	58	77	48	75	99	57	89	113
1100	35	56	73	46	72	95	54	85	111
1200	33	52	69	44	69	91	52	81	107
1300	31	49	65	42	66	87	50	78	103
1400	29	46	61	40	64	84	48	75	99
1500	28	44	58	39	61	81	46	73	96
1600	27	42	55	38	59	78	45	70	93
1700	25	40	53	37	58	76	43	68	90
1800	24	38	51	36	56	74	42	66	87
1900	24	37	49	35	54	72	41	65	85
2000	23	36	47	33	52	69	40	63	83
2200	21	33	44	31	48	64	38	60	79
2400	20	32	42	29	45	60	37	57	76
2600	19	30	40	27	43	56	35	55	73
2800	18	29	38	26	40	53	33	52	69
3000	17	27	36	24	38	51	31	49	65
3200	17	26	35	23	37	48	30	47	62
3400	16	26	34	22	35	46	29	45	59
3600	16	25	33	22	34	45	27	43	57
3800	15	24	32	21	33	43	26	41	55
4000	15	23	31	20	32	42	25	40	53
4200	14	23	30	19	30	40	24	38	51
4400	14	22	29	19	30	39	24	37	49
4600	14	22	29	18	29	38	23	36	48
4800	14	21	28	18	28	37	22	35	46
5000	13	21	27	17	27	36	22	34	45

NOTE: Within the dashed lines shear is the governing design criterion. Within the solid line deflection governs; elsewhere bending strength governs the span. Load within distance h from supports neglected in computing shear.

TABLE 7-9.1: SAFE SPACING, IN., OF SUPPORTS FOR DOUBLE WALES, SINGLE SPAN OR CONTINUOUS OVER TWO SPANS

Maximum deflection is $\frac{1}{360}$ of spacing, but not more than $\frac{1}{4}$ in.

Equivalent uniform load, lb per lineal ft (equals uniform load, psf, on forms times spacing of wales in ft)	$f = 775$ psi			$E = 1,100,000$ psi			$H = 140$ psi		
	Nominal size of S4S lumber used double								
	2x4	2x6	2x8	3x4	3x6	3x8	4x4	4x6	4x8
1000	21	34	44	28	43	57	33	51	68
1100	20	32	42	26	41	55	31	49	65
1200	19	31	40	25	39	52	30	47	62
1300	19	29	39	24	38	50	29	45	59
1400	18	28	37	23	37	48	28	43	57
1500	17	27	36	22	35	47	27	42	55
1600	17	26	35	22	34	45	26	40	53
1700	16	26	34	21	33	44	25	39	52
1800	16	25	33	20	32	43	24	38	50
1900	16	24	32	20	31	41	24	37	49
2000	15	24	31	19	31	40	23	36	48
2200	14	23	30	19	29	38	22	35	45
2400	14	22	28	18	28	37	21	33	44
2600	13	21	27	17	27	35	20	32	42
2800	13	20	26	16	26	34	19	31	40
3000	12	19	25	16	25	33	19	30	39
3200	12	19	25	15	24	32	18	29	38
3400	12	18	24	15	23	31	17	28	37
3600	11	18	23	14	23	30	17	27	36
3800	11	17	23	14	22	29	17	26	35
4000	11	17	22	14	22	29	16	26	34
4200	10	16	22	13	21	28	16	25	33
4400	10	16	21	13	21	27	16	24	32
4600	10	16	21	13	20	27	15	24	31
4800	10	15	20	13	20	26	15	23	31
5000	9	15	20	12	19	26	15	23	30

Equivalent uniform load, lb per lineal ft (equals uniform load, psf, on forms times spacing of wales in ft)	$f = 1000$ psi			$E = 1,400,000$ psi			$H = 180$ psi		
	Nominal size of S4S lumber used double								
	2x4	2x6	2x8	3x4	3x6	3x8	4x4	4x6	4x8
1000	24	38	50	31	49	65	37	58	77
1100	23	36	48	30	47	62	35	55	73
1200	22	35	46	29	45	59	34	53	70
1300	21	33	44	27	43	57	32	51	67
1400	20	32	42	26	42	55	31	49	65
1500	20	31	41	26	40	53	30	47	63
1600	19	30	40	25	39	51	29	46	61
1700	19	29	39	24	38	50	28	45	59
1800	18	28	37	23	37	48	28	43	57
1900	18	28	36	23	36	47	27	42	56
2000	17	27	36	22	35	46	26	41	54
2200	16	26	34	21	33	44	25	39	52
2400	16	25	32	20	32	42	24	38	49
2600	15	24	31	19	30	40	23	36	48
2800	14	23	30	19	29	39	22	35	46
3000	14	22	29	18	28	37	21	34	44
3200	14	21	28	17	27	36	21	32	43
3400	13	21	27	17	27	35	20	32	42
3600	13	20	26	16	26	34	19	31	40
3800	12	20	26	16	25	33	19	30	39
4000	12	19	25	16	25	32	18	29	38
4200	12	19	24	15	24	32	18	28	37
4400	12	18	24	15	23	31	18	28	37
4600	11	18	23	15	23	30	17	27	36
4800	11	17	23	14	22	30	17	27	35
5000	11	17	22	14	22	29	17	26	34

NOTE: All spans governed by bending.

130H

TABLE 7-9.2: SAFE SPACING, IN., OF SUPPORTS FOR DOUBLE WALES, SINGLE SPAN

Maximum deflection is $1/360$ of spacing, but not more than $1/4$ in.

Spacing

Equivalent uniform load, lb per lineal ft (equals uniform load, psf, on forms times spacing of wales in ft)	$f = 1500$ psi	$E = 1,700,000$ psi				$H = 180$ psi			
	Nominal size of S4S lumber used double								
	2x4	2x6	2x8	3x4	3x6	3x8	4x4	4x6	4x8
1000	28	47	61	38	60	79	45	71	94
1100	28	44	59	37	57	76	43	68	90
1200	27	43	56	35	55	72	41	65	86
1300	26	41	54	34	53	70	40	62	82
1400	25	39	52	32	51	67	38	60	79
1500	24	38	50	31	49	65	37	58	77
1600	23	37	49	30	48	63	36	56	74
1700	23	36	47	29	46	61	35	55	72
1800	22	35	46	29	45	59	34	53	70
1900	22	34	45	28	44	58	33	52	68
2000	21	33	43	27	43	56	32	50	66
2200	20	31	41	26	41	54	31	48	63
2400	19	30	40	25	39	51	29	46	61
2600	18	29	38	24	37	49	28	44	58
2800	18	28	37	23	36	47	27	43	56
3000	17	27	35	22	35	46	26	41	54
3200	16	26	34	21	34	44	25	40	52
3400	16	25	33	21	33	43	25	39	51
3600	15	24	32	20	32	42	24	38	49
3800	15	23	31	20	31	41	23	37	48
4000	15	23	30	19	30	40	23	36	47
4200	14	22	29	19	29	39	22	35	46
4400	14	22	29	18	29	38	22	34	45
4600	14	21	28	18	28	37	21	33	44
4800	13	21	27	17	27	36	21	32	43
5000	13	20	27	17	27	35	20	32	42

Equivalent uniform load, lb per lineal ft (equals uniform load, psf, on forms times spacing of wales in ft)	$f = 1875$ psi	$E = 1,700,000$ psi				$H = 225$ psi			
	Nominal size of S4S lumber used double								
	2x4	2x6	2x8	3x4	3x6	3x8	4x4	4x6	4x8
1000	33	52	69	43	67	88	48	75	97
1100	32	50	66	41	64	85	46	73	94
1200	30	48	63	39	61	81	45	71	92
1300	29	46	60	38	59	78	44	69	90
1400	28	44	58	36	57	75	43	67	88
1500	27	43	56	35	55	72	41	65	86
1600	26	41	54	34	53	70	40	63	83
1700	25	40	53	33	52	68	39	61	81
1800	25	39	51	32	50	66	38	59	78
1900	24	38	50	31	49	64	37	58	76
2000	23	37	49	30	48	63	36	56	74
2200	22	35	46	29	45	60	34	54	71
2400	21	34	44	28	43	57	33	51	68
2600	21	32	43	27	42	55	31	49	65
2800	20	31	41	26	40	53	30	48	63
3000	19	30	40	25	39	51	29	46	61
3200	19	29	38	24	38	50	28	45	59
3400	18	28	37	23	36	48	27	43	57
3600	17	27	36	23	35	47	27	42	55
3800	17	27	35	22	35	46	26	41	54
4000	16	26	34	21	34	44	25	40	52
4200	16	25	33	21	33	43	25	39	51
4400	16	24	32	20	32	42	24	38	50
4600	15	24	31	20	31	41	24	37	49
4800	15	23	31	20	31	40	23	36	48
5000	15	23	30	19	30	40	23	36	47

NOTE: Within the dashed lines shear is the governing design criterion. Within the solid line deflection governs; elsewhere bending strength governs the span. Load within distance h from supports neglected in computing shear.

TABLE 7-10: SAFE SPACING, IN., OF SUPPORTS FOR DOUBLE WALES CONTINUOUS OVER TWO SPANS

Maximum deflection is $\frac{1}{360}$ of spacing, but not more than $\frac{1}{4}$ in.

← Spacing → ← Spacing →

Equivalent uniform load, lb per lineal ft (equals uniform load, psf, on forms times spacing of wales in ft)	$f = 1500$ psi			$E = 1,700,000$ psi			$H = 180$ psi		
	Nominal size of S4S lumber used double								
	2x4	2x6	2x8	3x4	3x6	3x8	4x4	4x6	4x8
1000	30	47	61	38	60	79	45	71	94
1100	28	44	59	37	57	76	43	68	90
1200	27	43	56	35	55	72	41	65	86
1300	26	40	53	34	53	70	40	62	82
1400	24	38	50	32	51	67	38	60	79
1500	23	36	48	31	49	65	37	58	77
1600	22	35	46	30	48	63	36	56	74
1700	21	33	44	29	46	61	35	55	72
1800	20	32	42	29	45	59	34	53	70
1900	20	31	41	28	44	58	33	52	68
2000	19	30	40	27	43	56	32	50	66
2200	18	28	37	25	40	52	31	48	63
2400	17	27	35	24	37	49	29	46	61
2600	16	26	34	22	35	47	28	44	58
2800	16	25	32	21	34	44	27	43	56
3000	15	24	31	20	32	42	26	41	53
3200	15	23	30	20	31	41	25	39	51
3400	14	22	29	19	30	39	24	37	49
3600	14	22	28	18	29	38	23	36	47
3800	13	21	28	18	28	36	22	34	45
4000	13	20	27	17	27	35	21	33	44
4200	13	20	26	17	26	34	20	32	42
4400	12	20	26	16	25	33	20	31	41
4600	12	19	25	16	25	33	19	30	40
4800	12	19	25	15	24	32	19	29	39
5000	12	19	24	15	24	31	18	29	38

Equivalent uniform load, lb per lineal ft (equals uniform load, psf, on forms times spacing of wales in ft)	$f = 1875$ psi			$E = 1,700,000$ psi			$H = 225$ psi		
	Nominal size of S4S lumber used double								
	2x4	2x6	2x8	3x4	3x6	3x8	4x4	4x6	4x8
1000	33	52	69	43	67	89	51	80	105
1100	32	50	66	41	64	85	48	76	100
1200	30	48	63	39	61	81	46	73	96
1300	29	46	60	38	59	78	44	70	92
1400	28	44	58	36	57	75	43	67	89
1500	27	43	56	35	55	72	41	65	86
1600	26	41	54	34	53	70	40	63	83
1700	25	39	51	33	52	68	39	61	81
1800	24	37	49	32	50	66	38	59	78
1900	23	36	47	31	49	64	37	58	76
2000	22	35	46	30	48	63	36	56	74
2200	21	33	43	29	45	60	34	54	71
2400	20	31	41	28	43	57	33	52	68
2600	19	29	39	26	41	55	31	49	65
2800	18	28	37	25	39	52	30	48	63
3000	17	27	35	24	37	49	29	46	61
3200	16	26	34	23	36	47	28	45	59
3400	16	25	33	22	34	45	27	43	57
3600	15	24	32	21	33	43	27	42	55
3800	15	23	31	20	32	42	26	40	53
4000	15	23	30	20	31	41	25	39	51
4200	14	22	29	19	30	39	24	37	49
4400	14	22	29	18	29	38	23	36	48
4600	14	21	28	18	28	37	23	35	46
4800	13	21	27	17	27	36	22	34	45
5000	13	20	27	17	27	35	21	33	44

NOTE: Within the dashed lines shear is the governing design criterion. Elsewhere bending strength governs the span. Load within distance h from supports neglected in computing shear. For two-span beams with lower E values, and with $f = 775$ and 1000 psi, where bending governs, safe spans are the same as for single span beams given in Table 7-9.1.

8:FORMWORK DRAWINGS

AFTER THE FORM DESIGN has been prepared on the basis of the contract drawings and specifications, formwork design information must be given to the men at the job site or mill so that they can build the forms. Much time and expense can be saved in the office, shop, and on the job if simple, clear, and complete drawings are prepared. The ideal drawings contain essential notes and instructions for constructing the forms, but they are not cluttered with unnecessary lines, marks, symbols, or dimensions.

Items that are standard practice with the contractor are sometimes omitted to simplify the drawings, but this requires draftsmen, designers, and a field force thoroughly familiar with the contractor's established procedures. With frequent changes of personnel the rule rather than the exception in today's construction industry, it is much safer to provide a stamp, or pre-printed paste in, which will repeat the standard practice items on each applicable drawing, or at least refer back to a standard drawing.

A formwork drawing is more than a picture of the proposed formwork; it is a definite order to workmen to perform certain operations in a specified manner and should be complete. With this thought in mind, the draftsman can materially improve the presentation by following these simple rules:

1. Issue orders as commands—"chamfer column corners with 1-in. skewback," rather than "this column is to be chamfered at the corners."

2. Make all notes brief, clear, and explicit, leaving no chance for misunderstanding.

3. Make all drawings large and bright—a scale of ⅜ in. = 1 ft, or larger is desirable—and letter them clearly enough so they will still be legible to the user in the field after repeated handling, folding, and fading of prints. Dimensions must be carefully checked and legibly written.

4. Use easily recognized standard symbols and abbreviations for all projects; symbols may be tabulated on one of the drawing sheets.

5. Standardize layout of drawings.

6. Use a standardized, large, clear title block with plenty of space for full identification of the part of the structure for which formwork is to be used. If possible number formwork drawing sheets in order of their use on the job.

General Layout and Detail Drawings

If panel forms or other pre-built form components are to be used for an entire job, or for a major part of it, an assembly or layout drawing showing location of panels is essential. Such a drawing can be a mere skeleton or outline, showing only major dimensions needed for locating formwork components. Each panel should be given an appropriate identifying mark to aid in positioning it when the forms are erected. Panels of the same size and shape will all bear the same mark. By means of subscripts or other identifying numbers the order in which panels are to be used can also be indicated if desired.

To supplement the layout drawing, a detail or "make-up" drawing of each panel or form component must be prepared, showing all essential dimensions so that bench carpenters or mill men need not refer to the architect's drawings. The detail drawing should indicate the mark number corresponding to the basic layout drawing, and indicate how many of any given unit are required. Various additional details are needed to show how to handle intersections, corners, bulkheads, inserts, and other special items. Details frequently are shown on the same drawing with the layout and other components, but it simplifies shop work if a single sheet is prepared for each panel or other component to be built.

When non-standard, complex items are required, the designer or detailer can often help speed the work by giving the carpenter a simple pictorial sketch to supplement the conventional plan and elevation.

For such standard elements as rectangular beams and columns, some contractors have found mimeographed or printed sheets with prepared outlines of beam and column parts (Figure 8-3) helpful in giving the men in the shop or field instructions on the fabrication and placing of form parts. The designer simply pencils in dimensions, details, and necessary notes on the printed outline drawing. The shop foreman or job superintendent can then use these sketches in directing his workmen. These sheets may also be made up to include a bill of materials required.

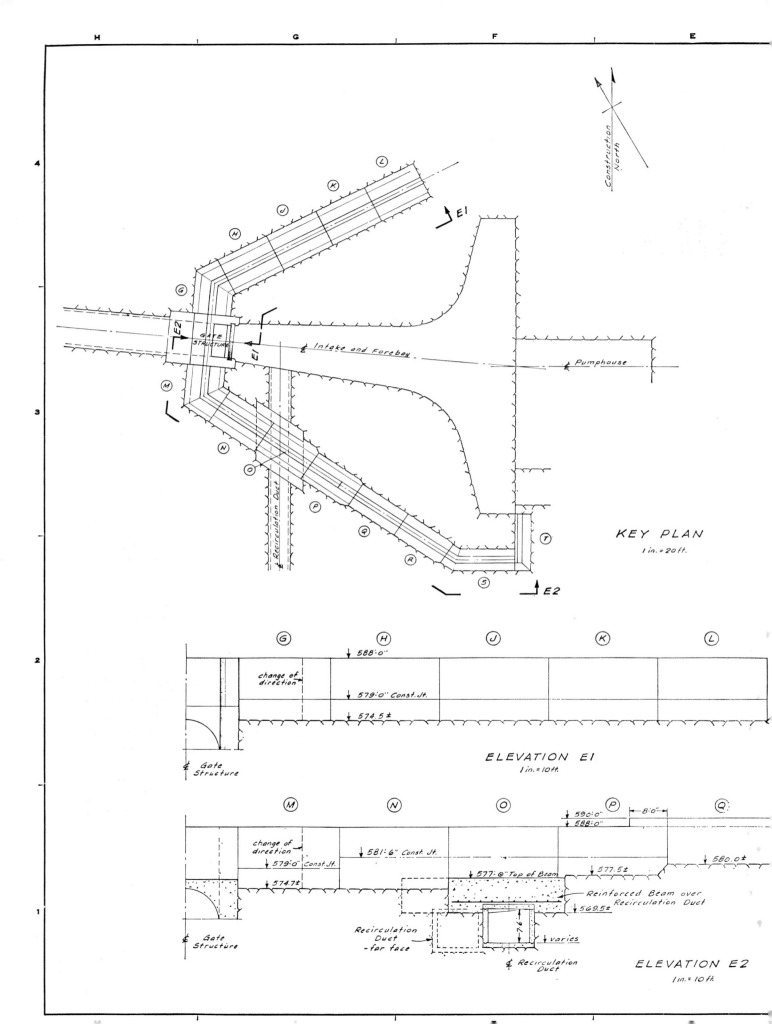

KEY PLAN
1 in. = 20 ft.

ELEVATION E1
1 in. = 10 ft.

ELEVATION E2
1 in. = 10 ft.

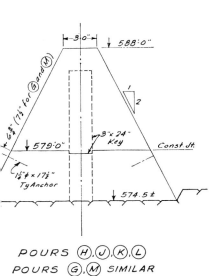

POURS (H)(J)(K)(L)
POURS (G)(M) SIMILAR
¼"= 1'-0"

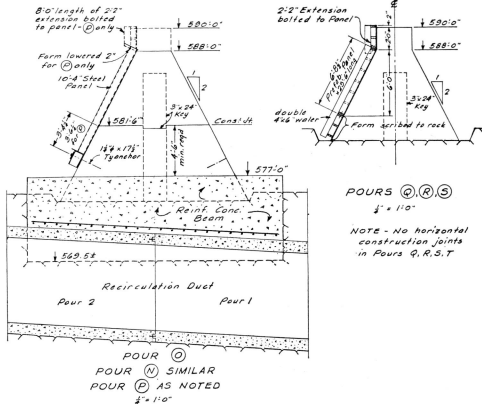

8'-0" length of 2'-2" extension bolted to panel-(P) only

Form lowered 2" for (P) only

10'-4" Steel Panel

2'-2" Extension bolted to Panel

POURS (Q)(R)(S)
¼"= 1'-0"

NOTE - No horizontal construction joints in Pours Q,R,S,T

590'-0"
588'-0"

3"x 24" Key
Const. Jt.

double 4"x6" waler

Form scribed to rock

Reinf. Conc. Beam

Recirculation Duct

Pour 2   Pour 1

POUR (O)
POUR (N) SIMILAR
POUR (P) AS NOTED
¼"= 1'-0"

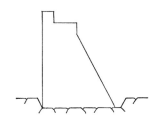

POUR (T)
¼"= 1'-0"

FORMING ARRANGEMENT

POUR	CONST. JT. ELEV.	PANEL TYPE	DWG. NO.	REMARKS
G	579.0	Wood	DCF-25212-155	Panels reused from Pour M
H	"	Steel	DCF-25212-153	
J	"	"	"	
K	"	"	"	
L	"	"	"	
M	"	Wood	DCF-25212-155	Panels 13'-9"; 18'-0"; 6'-6"; 12'-0" x 10'-6", and fillers
N	581.5	Steel	This Dwg.	
O	"	"	" "	
P	"	"	" "	Panel lowered 2" for 2' extension (8' long)
Q	No Joint	Wood	" "	Panels 23'-6" x 6'-8½" (2 req'd) with 2' extension
R	" "	"	" "	Reused from Pour S
S	" "	"	" "	Reused from Pour Q, with fillers from G
T	" "	"	" "	Hold - for Pumphouse Dwg.

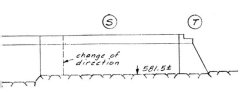

(S)   (T)

change of direction

581.5±

REFERENCE DWGS.
Concrete Details   FG-25212-1

ISSUE	DATE	REVISION	DRWN.	CHKD.	APPD.

C.W. INTAKE - FIRST STAGE
FOREBAY GRAVITY WALLS
CONCRETE FORMING
GENERAL ARRANGEMENT

CONSTRUCTION DIVISION

WORK ORDER	DATE Sep.—,—	SCALE As Shown

DRWN. J.E.S.   DESIGN A.E.F.
CHKD.

CHIEF DRAFTSMAN   PROJECT ENGINEER   SR. DESIGN ENGINEER

CONSTRUCTION (GEN.) ENGINEER

DWG. No. DCF-25212-159R   O

8-1 Example of formwork layout drawing, indicating planned use of prefabricated panels

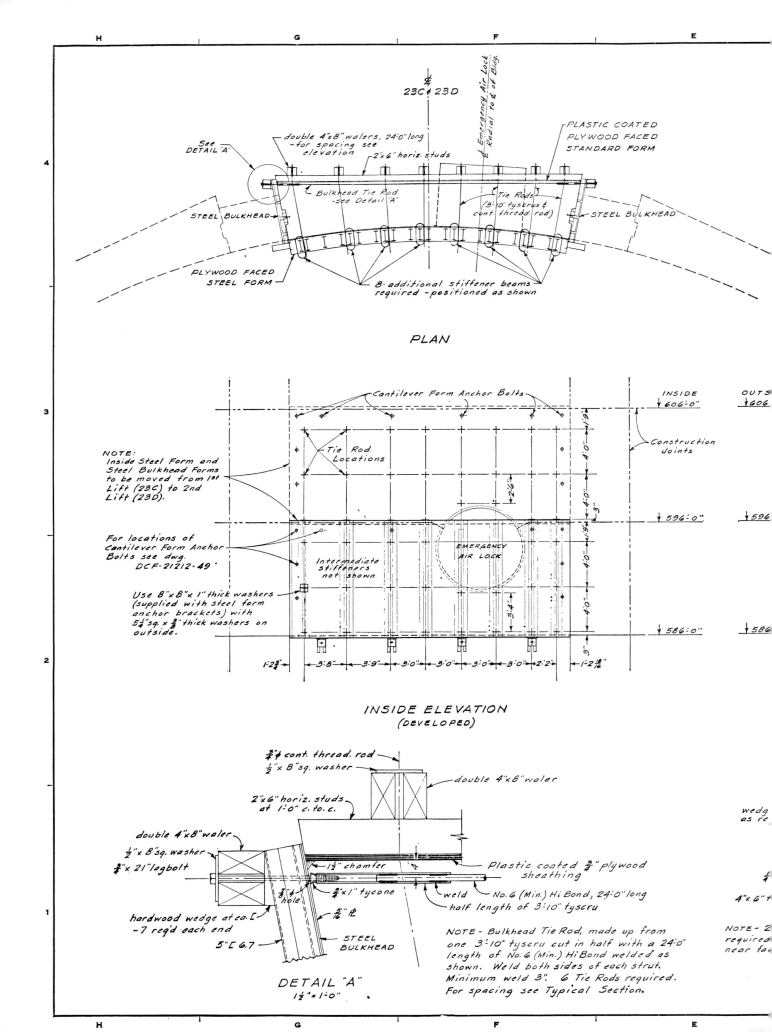

PLAN

INSIDE ELEVATION
(DEVELOPED)

DETAIL "A"
1½" = 1'-0"

NOTE:
Inside Steel Form and
Steel Bulkhead Forms
to be moved from 1st
Lift (23C) to 2nd
Lift (23D).

For locations of
Cantilever Form Anchor
Bolts see dwg.
DCF-21212-49'

Use 8"x8"x1" thick washers
(supplied with steel form
anchor brackets) with
5¼"sq. x ⅜"thick washers on
outside.

NOTE - Bulkhead Tie Rod, made up from
one 3'-10" tyscru cut in half with a 24'-0"
length of No.6 (Min.) Hi Bond welded as
shown. Weld both sides of each strut.
Minimum weld 3". 6 Tie Rods required.
For spacing see Typical Section.

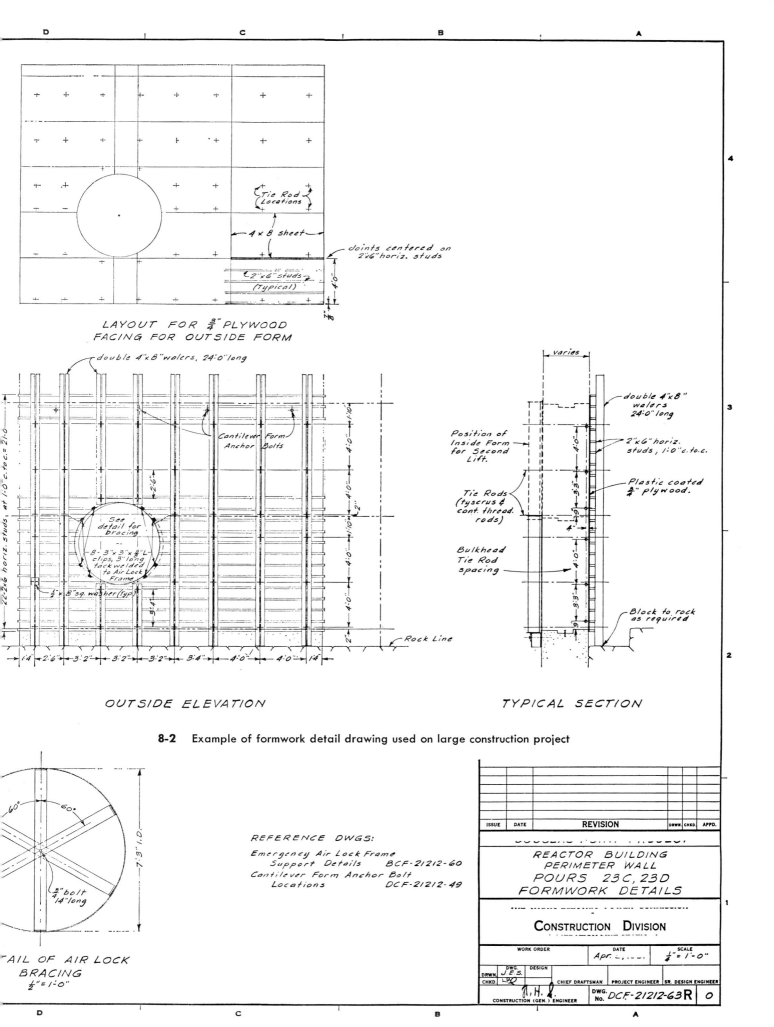

LAYOUT FOR ¾" PLYWOOD
FACING FOR OUTSIDE FORM

Tie Rod (Locations)

4 x 8 sheet

Joints centered on 2"x6" horiz. studs

2"x6" studs (Typical)

double 4"x8" walers, 24'0" long

Cantilever Form Anchor Bolts

See detail for bracing

8 - 3"x 3"x ½" L-clips, 3" long tack welded to Air Lock Frame

½"x 8" sq. washer (typ)

2"x6" horiz. studs at 1'-0" c. to c. = 21'-0

Rock Line

1'4" 2'6" 3'2" 3'2" 3'2" 3'4" 4'0" 4'0" 1'4"

OUTSIDE ELEVATION

varies

Position of Inside Form for Second Lift.

Tie Rods (tyscrus & cont. thread. rods)

Bulkhead Tie Rod spacing

double 4"x8" walers 24'0" long

2"x6" horiz. studs, 1'-0" c. to c.

Plastic coated ¾" plywood.

Block to rock as required

TYPICAL SECTION

8-2 Example of formwork detail drawing used on large construction project

60° 60°

7'3" I.D.

½" bolt 14" long

AIL OF AIR LOCK
BRACING
½"=1'-0"

REFERENCE DWGS:

Emergency Air Lock Frame
    Support Details   BCF-21212-60
Cantilever Form Anchor Bolt
    Locations   DCF-21212-49

ISSUE	DATE	REVISION	DRWN.	CHKD.	APPD.

REACTOR BUILDING
PERIMETER WALL
POURS 23C, 23D
FORMWORK DETAILS

CONSTRUCTION DIVISION

WORK ORDER	DATE Apr. 2, ----	SCALE ¼"=1'-0"

DRWN. J.E.S.
CHKD. L.P.Q.

DWG. DESIGN

CHIEF DRAFTSMAN | PROJECT ENGINEER | SR. DESIGN ENGINEER

CONSTRUCTION (GEN.) ENGINEER

DWG. No. DCF-21212-63 R   0

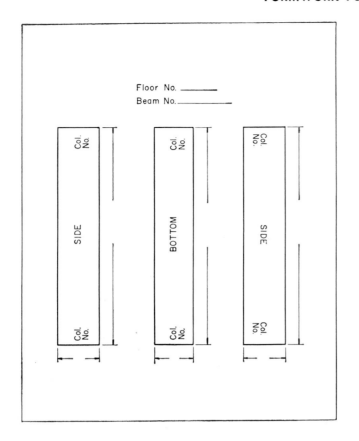

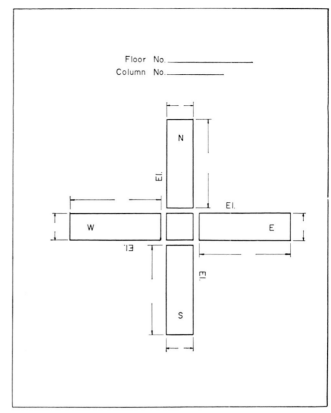

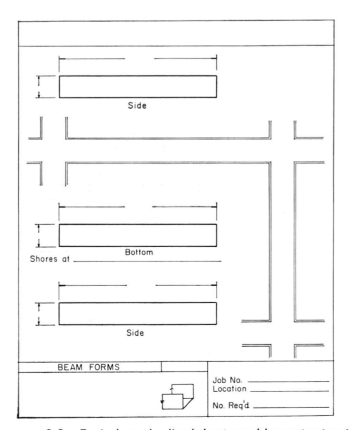

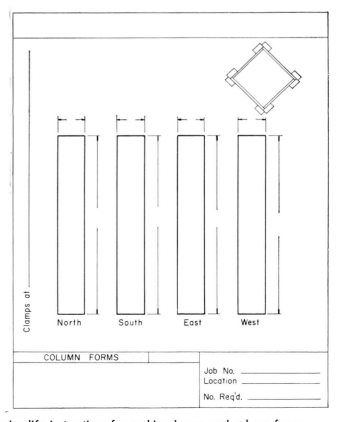

8-3 Typical standardized sheets used by contractors to simplify instructions for making beam and column forms

Major design values, loading conditions, and pertinent tolerances, should be shown on formwork layout or erection drawings or accompanying notes. These include assumed values of live load, maximum rate and order of placement, temperature of concrete, height of drop, weight of moving equipment which may be operated on formwork, foundation pressures, design stresses, grade and type of form materials, camber diagrams, and other pertinent information. A list of required ties and other accessories, showing the manufacturer's name, load capacity, etc. may also be shown on the drawings. Figure 8-4 illustrates the type of information that is frequently included in these notes. Such information is not required on the detailed make-up drawings or sketches used by workmen in building individual form parts.

Check List of Details

In addition to specifying method of construction, types of materials, sizes, lengths, and connection details, formwork drawings should provide for numerous other details. The following items may be useful as a check list, although not all will apply to every job.

1. Sequence of concrete placement and minimum elapsed time between adjacent placements if required for proper action of the formwork design.
2. Field adjustment of the form during placing of concrete.
3. Sequence of removal of forms and shores, including a layout for complex projects.
4. Details on shoring, reshoring, or leaving original shores in place as forms are stripped.
5. Design allowance for construction loads on new slabs when such allowance will affect the development of shoring and/or reshoring schemes.
6. Anchors, form ties, shores, and braces, including spacing and fastenings for diagonal bracing.
7. Waterstops and keyways; inserts required for later attachment of other construction materials; curb angles.
8. Working scaffolds, ladders, and runways including safety features.
9. Weepholes or vibrator holes where required.
10. Drilling, if required, for prefabricated panels to take necessary ties.
11. Screeds and grade strips and their supports.
12. Crush plates or wrecking plates where stripping may damage concrete.
13. Details of all ties and spreaders, including removal of spreaders or temporary blocking.
14. Cleanout holes and temporary openings for placing concrete up to height of opening.
15. Construction joints, control joints, and expansion joints to conform to design drawings.

8-4 Actual specimens, reduced in size, of notes used on formwork drawings. These were taken from several different jobs and show variation in current practice.

DESIGN DATA

LOADING
LIVE LOAD = 30 PSF
DEAD LOAD = 70 PSF

ALLOWABLE STRESSES
GLULAM - DF 204. WET CONDITION
OF USE (BASIC + 15% INCREASE)
$S = 1840$ psi $t = 2070$
$C = 1610$ psi $CL = 300$ psi
$H = 167$ psi $E = 1.6 \times 10^6$ psi

SAWN - DF 204 (BASIC + 15% INCREASE)
$S = t = 1670$ psi
$C = 1380$ psi
$CL = 300$ psi (33% decrease for wet cond.)
$H = 138$ psi
$E = 1.6 \times 10^6$ psi

CONNECTORS
BASIC CONNECTOR VALUES PER
TECO DESIGN MANUAL + 15% FOR
SHORT TIME LOADING - 33% FOR
WET CONDITION OF USE.
MAX. ALLOWABLE LOADS
4" SH R = 4060#   2⅝ SH R = 2420#
4" S.R. = 4360#   2½ S.R. = 1610#
SEE TECO DESIGN MANUAL FOR VALUES
@ ANGLE TO GRAIN.
ALL STRESSES PER NATIONAL DESIGN
SPECIFICATIONS, 1952 ED. REV.
ALL GLULAM & SAWN MEMBERS DF 204
PER WCLA RULES EXCEPT AS NOTED.

NOTES: CAMBER OF BEAM TO BE ACCOMPLISHED
BY STEEL & BETWEEN TOP FLANGE OF 33 WF 130
AND LOWER FLANGE OF 6 WF 15.5'S
POURING SEQUENCE - THE TWO HAUNCHES OVER THE PIER
SHAFTS SHALL BE CONCRETED LEVEL WITH BOTTOM OF CENTER
PORTION OF BEAM. THE BALANCE OF BEAM SHALL BE
CONCRETED IN LAYERS NOT OVER 12" THICK EACH LAYER
TO BE POURED STARTING AT CENTER OF MAIN SPAN AND
POURING CONTINUOUSLY TOWARDS END OF BEAM.

GENERAL NOTES
- All panels 2x3 except as noted.
- Horizontal and Vertical Liners are required on outside form only.
- Bulkheads are standard forming.
- Door openings are prefabricated.

NOTES :

I   LUMBER DESIGN VALUES :
THESE VALUES GOVERN ALL SHORING
FORMS, DESIGN VALUES ARE FOR DOUGLAS
FIR COAST REGION #1 COMMON OR EQUIVALENT.
ALL FIBER STRESS 1500 PSI
ALL HORIZONTAL SHEAR 150 PSI
COMPRESSION PERP. TO GRAIN 390 PSI
MODULUS OF ELASTICITY 1,600,000 PSI

II   ALL DESIGN ASSUMES A LIVE LOAD AND
FORM ALLOWANCE OF 41#/SQ.FT. UNLESS
OTHERWISE SPECIFIED.

III   ALL SHORING DESIGN MUST BE CHECKED
BY CONTRACTOR TO INSURE A DESIGN
WHICH MEETS HIS OWN SAFETY REQUIREMENTS.

4431	NAILING PLATE	84
SP-1	COUPLING PIN	184
SJ-6	SCREW JACK	400
255-0	4' x 10' CROSSBRACES	112
255	4' x 7' CROSSBRACES	104
S-145-2A	5' FRAME	24
S-146-2B	6' FRAME	168
PART N⁰.	DESCRIPTION	N⁰. REQ'D.
EQUIPMENT LIST		

16. Dimensioned chamfer strips for exposed corners if not standard practice; if chamfers are standard practice, show only locations where they are prohibited.

17. Camber or adjusted elevations to compensate for settlement or deflection of forms, as well as any camber specified by structural designer.

18. Mudsills or other formwork foundation.

19. Special provisions such as protection from ice and debris at stream crossings; fire protection; and safety program for the entire formwork operation.

20. Formwork coatings, and how often to apply them.

21. Notes to formwork erectors for conduits and pipes embedded in concrete.

Recheck of Structural Drawings

Structural and contract drawings and specifications are the formwork designer's major source of information concerning the job being formed. A number of items in the foregoing check list are derived directly from the contract drawings, and when the formwork plans have been completed, a final recheck for agreement with the contract documents is advisable. The following are important items to cover:

1. Number, location, and details of all construction joints, contraction joints, and expansion joints that are *required or permitted*.

2. Locations of and details for architectural concrete; any special architectural patterns specified.

3. Intermediate supports under permanent forms (such as forms of metal decking, insulation board, etc.), supports required by the structural engineer's design for composite action, and any other supports.

4. Specified location and order of erection and removal of shores for composite construction. The same type of specification may apply to shell structures where proper deflection sequence is necessary for the structure to assume its proper stress pattern and loaded shape.

5. Essential provisions for specialized construction techniques.

6. Location and amount of camber specified to compensate for deflections in the completed structure.

7. Requirements for inserts, built-in frames for openings, holes through concrete, and the work of other trades to be attached to or supported by formwork.

Drawing Approval

Although the safety and adequacy of formwork is the responsibility of the contractor, the engineer or architect may, in certain cases, wish to approve the formwork design. If so, provisions for such approval should be included in the job specifications, and formal approval of each drawing should be obtained.

Drawing approval may be required for unusually complicated structural shapes; for designs which are based upon a particular method of construction; for structures in which the forms impart a desired architectural finish; for folded plates, thin shells, and long span roof structures. Well organized notes on form design values and assumptions simplify checking and generally speed approval of the formwork plans.

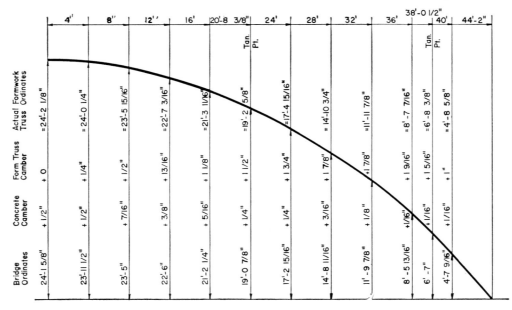

8-5 One method of indicating camber on formwork drawings. The timber truss, for which ordinates are shown, supported forms for part of a concrete arch bridge.

9: BUILDING AND ERECTING THE FORMWORK

HOW FORMWORK IS BUILT and erected depends on many factors—the materials available or required, the type and cost of local labor supply, and demands of the job for accuracy and perfection of finish. For most formwork jobs there is no single correct building procedure; rather there are several workable alternatives, and a choice among them depends on cost comparisons as well as local preferences or customs. At times it may be preferable to handle the work in a way familiar to the available crews rather than try to train them for a new system.

The techniques presented in this chapter are not the only way to do a given job, but they do represent ideas that have wide current acceptance, or some that have proved particularly valuable to experienced form builders. Following a description of the necessary carpentry shop, mill, or yard facilities for form building, discussion centers on various formwork components in the following divisions:

1. Footings
2. Slab on grade and paving
3. Walls
4. Columns
5. Slabs
6. Beam and girder forms
7. Shoring and scaffolding

A concluding section of the chapter describes some of the methods common in bridge formwork construction. Major emphasis is given to conventional construction with standard concreting techniques, since special structures and special techniques are treated separately in Chapters 11 through 17.

Sizes and spacings of form members shown in many of the examples are typical of good forming practices, but they cannot be "copied" without making a careful analysis for conditions peculiar to the individual job. The formwork designer is in no way relieved of the responsibility of checking his particular job and choosing framing members on the basis of design theory explained in Chapter 6.

Carpentry Shop and Job Mill

For all but very small jobs it is customary to set up a carpenter shop or mill where form parts or entire forms may be efficiently fabricated and moved to the site for assembly and erection. Where to put the shop, how large to make it, what equipment is needed—all these depend on the size and conditions of the individual job. How much of the formwork can be prefabricated and how much must be built in place help determine the size of shop required.

A contractor whose operations are limited to a relatively small geographical area may locate the mill or shop in his main yard and haul fabricated forms to nearby job sites. This gives him the advantage of having on hand short pieces for cleats as well as other stock that will save using new lumber. Where distances are great, or where hauling is excessive, he will probably set up the mill on the job site. Obviously a small job will not require a pretentious mill; a radial arm saw and a bench roofed over but not enclosed may be all that is needed. However, for the larger jobs, the mill requires careful planning. Adequate working space should be organized for an efficient flow of materials and parts in process to take advantage of the benefits of assembly line techniques. Careful consideration should be given to achieving the best possible in safety and comfort of the workers as an aid to maintaining high productivity.

Although each job has its own special requirements determined by local conditions, consideration of some

9-1 Roofed work area with open sides containing bench for saws and lumber handling is all that is needed for the small carpenter shop. For the layout of a much larger mill, see Figure 9-2.

of the general requirements which apply to most all larger jobs will aid in planning the mill for a specific project.

Location of Mill at Job Site

Generally the mill should be placed as close as possible to the work under construction, but space must also be allowed for storage of finished forms. Availability of power supply and consideration of lumber flow to job will also be factors in locating the mill. If a large percentage of form lumber passes through the mill, it should be located near the material receiving point or storage point. If very little passes through the mill, the mill can be located closer to the construction work. The space available and location of the building site in relation to adjoining streets will influence mill layout. If at all possible, the mill should be so located that the operation is progressive from the point where lumber is received to the place where finished forms are delivered to the erection crew. Similar considerations affect the interior layout of the mill.

If the building occupies an entire site, and there is no adjoining vacant land, the mill must often be strung out along the building site on the sidewalk. A space 10 to 12 ft wide, long enough to accommodate all equipment, is required. The mill should be placed next to the street to allow delivery of materials without interfering with pedestrians. A covered walkway for pedestrians is then placed between the mill and the building, and a light fence is erected on the street side to protect workers from traffic. For multistory building work, it is often desirable to place the mill inside the building, particularly if exterior space is limited.

Storage of Materials and Finished Parts

The storage space required for incoming lumber depends on job size and whether materials can be had on short notice in small lots, or whether carload lots will have to be stored. The receiving yard should be convenient to saws to reduce handling of material. It should also be convenient to assembly benches, because much of the material will not require sawing.

Material should be stockpiled according to sizes as soon as it is received so that no time will be lost in finding a desired size. On very large jobs it may be desirable to label piles to help carpenters find the desired stock quickly with a minimum of cutting. Lumber and other materials should be palletized for mass handling whenever conditions warrant.

Next to the mill and as close as possible to the lifting equipment, space should be provided for storage of completed panels or partially assembled forms ready for erection. This space should be convenient to the benches within the mill or just outside the mill where the panels are built.

Lockers should be available for special tools or for the personal tools belonging to workmen. Neat, tidy nail storage and rod storage houses or containers are desirable, as well as storage bins for wedges or other parts that are made up in quantity. Form oil storage rack and steel storage rack to hold rods, bars, and angles should also be kept on the job. Within the shop there should be storage bins for scrap pieces which may be used for cleats, shims, and the like, as well as a rack for long items such as rustication, chamfer, or grade strips that are made up in volume.

The typical carpenter shop layout for a large job in Figure 9-2 shows how these storage areas may be arranged together with the components of the mill itself.

Equipment and Layout

The well equipped mill for an average job will require all or part of the following:

    1 cut-off saw
    1 rip saw
    1 portable electric saw
    1 planer
    1 sander
    1 band saw
    1 boring machine
    Equipment for saw filing and tool sharpening

One saw may be available that will perform both ripping and cut-off operations; usually a swing type cut-off saw is best if separate saws are used. The saws should be capable of handling at least 4-in. material, and adjustable to cut or rip at any angle. If there is to be considerable ornament, a band saw will reduce the amount of handwork. Roller conveyors to facilitate handling long or heavy pieces to the power tools may be desirable.

The mill should have a roof to protect the equipment and men, but the sides should be as open as climatic conditions will permit. Good lighting, either artificial or through skylights, and adequate ventilation are essential. A clear space of 4 or 5 ft around the table saws with their haul-off tables is sufficient; more than this is undesirable. There should be 3- or 4-ft aisles between benches so carpenters do not interfere with each other.

A smooth, flat, level platform for form assembly is frequently placed just outside the mill; for some large formwork components outdoor assembly is absolutely necessary because of their size (Figure 9-3). Ad-justable assembly benches made by laying planks on sawhorses are better than permanent benches, because of difficulty in working around panels of varying sizes when the bench is made large enough for the largest form panels. Outdoor assembly areas allow more room for working around the benches, but inclement weather may halt work. If the assembly area is under cover, work can proceed on panels in preparation for the erection crew when outside work is resumed. If this is done, a few extra men in the erection crew can often make up for time lost in bad weather.

The shop or storage areas should include facilities for wetting down prefabricated parts to prevent drying and shrinkage before use.

Good Housekeeping

The mill area should be kept free of rippings, sawdust, and shavings. A dust collector may be desirable to carry dust and chips from the shop. An outdoor collecting point for scraps to be hauled away may be

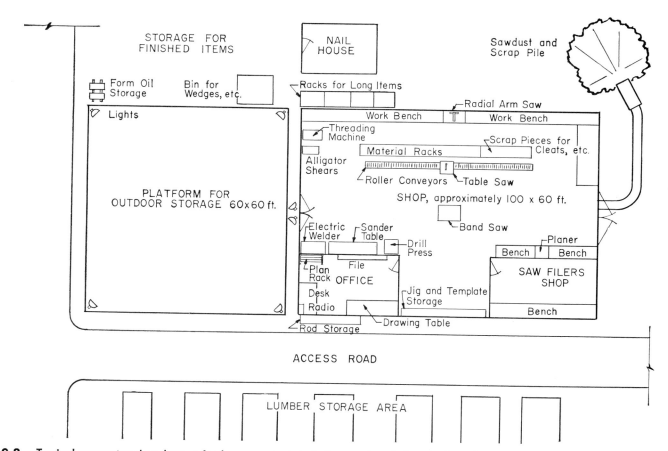

9-2 Typical carpenter shop layout for large project, including enclosed shop and outdoor assembly platform, and showing access road and storage areas for materials and equipment.

9-3 Outdoor assembly platform is a necessity when large formwork parts like these for draft tubes are being built.

required on a large job. A neat, clean mill and shop area improve production and reduce fire danger, but adequate fire extinguishers or other fire protection are advisable.

Footings

The principal construction requirements for footings are sound concrete and correct position to match column and wall plans. Tolerances for footing construction suggested by ACI Committee 347 are given in Table 9-1. Since appearance is rarely important because the footing is below grade, any old or used material that is sound may be used to build the forms. Sometimes fabricated forms are omitted entirely and concrete is cast directly against the excavation. When casting concrete against earth, it is frequently desirable to form the top 4 in. of the footing. In case of rain or water buildup, this makes it easier to keep water and slime out of the bottom of a completed or partially completed earth form.

TABLE 9-1: RECOMMENDED TOLERANCES FOR FOOTINGS

Variation in plan dimensions	Minus ½ in., plus 2 in.*
Misplacement or eccentricity	2 percent of the footing width in the direction of misplacement, but not more than 2 in.*
Reduction in thickness	Minus 5 percent of specified thickness

* Applies to concrete only, not to reinforcing bars or dowels.

To set the building line from the surveyor's stakes, batter boards are set up outside the limits of the excavation at a convenient location. A string or wire supported by the batter boards is then put up in the plane of the building line as shown in Figure 9-4.

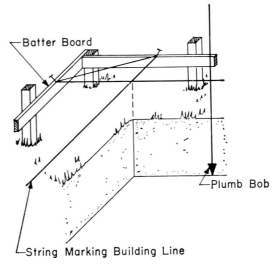

9-4 String or wire supported by batter boards is set in the plane of the building line.

Points below the string are located with a plumb bob. A convenient height should be selected for the batter boards (an even number of feet above or below some horizontal feature of the proposed structure such as the finished footing elevation) so they can be used for temporary bench marks.

Wall Footings

In good, cohesive soils that stand up well, all possible excavation down to the top of the footing is done with trencher, backhoe, or other digger, and the footing outline is cut by hand or by specialized mechanical equipment to the exact size. If the soil is porous or non-cohesive, the rough excavation proceeds to the bottom of the footing, and used planks, built up panels, prefabricated metal forms, or other available material can be used to form the sides of the footing. Since footings are generally shallow, lateral pressure from the fresh concrete is relatively small, and the required bracing is simple (Figure 9-6).

The panels or planks for one side of the form are adjusted to line and grade and staked into position. After one side is set, the other side is aligned by spreaders and held in position by stakes placed about every 6 ft. If the holding power of the stakes is poor because of ground conditions, the forms can be braced as shown in Figure 9-7. Sometimes earth can

9-5 Carefully excavated trench will serve as form for concrete grade beams to be placed without wood forms.

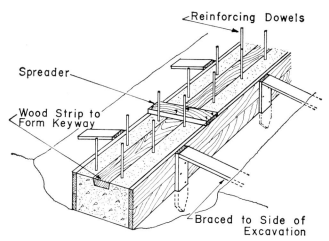

9-6 Low footing form for wall can be stake braced. No ties are required, and wood spreaders across the top hold sides at correct spacing.

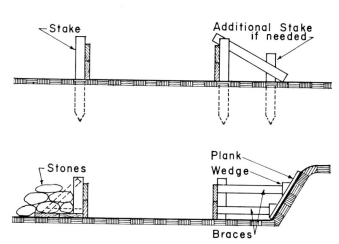

9-7 Alternate bracing systems for flat footings. Footings of greater depth may require ties.

be used as a brace by simply backfilling around the forms although this is a disadvantage when forms are stripped. No ties are needed for shallow forms.

Deeper wall footings or grade beams (in non-cohesive soil) require more bracing or ties to withstand concrete pressure, and are constructed much like wall forms (p. 149). Figures 9-8 and 9-9 show construction of these deeper forms.

If the supporting ground for a wall footing slopes, the footing may be stepped longitudinally with formwork as shown in Figures 9-10 and 9-11.

Column Footings

The forms for simple, rectangular column footings are bottomless boxes. They are constructed in four pieces, two end sections and two side sections. The end sections are built to the exact dimensions of the footing and the sides somewhat longer with vertical cleats to hold the ends as shown in Figure 9-12. Ties prevent the sides of the box from bulging under concrete pressure, and no external bracing is needed. Since the correct concrete elevation can be marked with a nail, available planks should be used and no time wasted in ripping them to exact height. Stakes should be set to maintain the correct position of the form. A template for positioning dowels can be attached to the form box (Figure 9-12).

For small shallow column footings, the ties are sometimes omitted and diagonal wood braces are

9-8 Thick boards used in this grade beam form are braced on outside against the excavation; inside form is tied to outside one and wood spreaders maintain proper spacing.

9-9 Concreting in progress on this heavy form for a tie-beam; formwork consisting of sheathing, studs, and wales is tied to resist concrete pressure, resembles wall forms, but is braced against excavation on both sides.

9-11 Formwork in place for longitudinally stepped wall footing: similarly stepped footings are visible in the background after form removal.

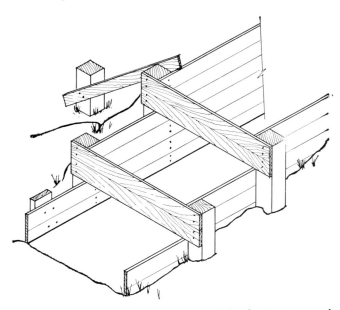

9-10 Construction of simple formwork for footing stepped down longitudinally because of sloping subgrade

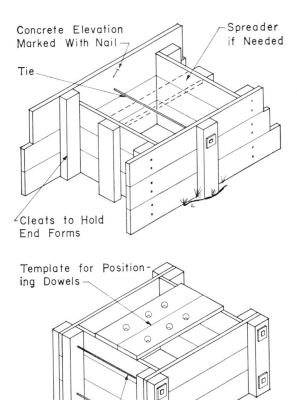

Concrete Elevation Marked With Nail

Spreader if Needed

Tie

Cleats to Hold End Forms

Template for Positioning Dowels

External Ties

9-12 Two methods of forming column footings, one with internal ties, one with tie bolts outside the form box, similar to simple column forms

144

nailed across the top of the form box. Round footings may be formed with short lengths of the fiber tubing used to form round colums.

Stepped Column Footings

Stepped column footing forms are similar to flat footing forms but they are made in decreasing sizes and stacked one on top of the other to form a series of two or three pedestals or steps. If a stiff concrete of proper slump (about 2 in) is used, or there is a short time between placing successive steps, the only difference from flat footing forms is the method of support of the forms for the upper steps (Figure 9-13).

If the entire footing is to be cast at one time with higher slump concrete, top forms for the space between the steps will be needed to keep the concrete from pushing out. When this area between the steps is covered, there is an upward pressure on the top forms and the whole assembly must be weighted or tied down to resist this uplift from the freshly placed concrete. The form may be anchored as for sloped footings shown in Figure 9-14, but the entire anchoring procedure is better avoided by use of stiffer concrete and timing the placement sequence of the several steps to suit the mix.

Sloped Footing Forms

The sloped footing is shaped like a cut-off pyramid resting on a pedestal of the same size as its base. Many sloped footings which are accessible for proper placing and finishing can be cast without top forms up to about 40° slope. If top forms are required, the reduction in concrete permitted by sloped footing design is more than offset by increased forming costs.

The base of the sloped footing forms is built from boards or panels in the same way as the flat footing. The sloped portion of the forms is supported by the flat pedestal forms and is built in four parts: two edge panels and two end panels. Both parts are trapezoidal in shape. The end panels are built to the exact shape of the concrete face, just as was done for the flat footing. The sides may be made rectangular or irregular in shape so long as they overlap the ends a few inches. The sides may be tied to prevent spreading (depending on depth of footing), and the entire form must be tied down to resist uplift. Figure 9-14 shows one type of sloped footing form.

Usually only the height and the top and bottom plan of the sloped footing are given, so the proper height of the side and end panels must be calculated. This can be done by laying out the cross section of the proposed footing and measuring the sloping sides

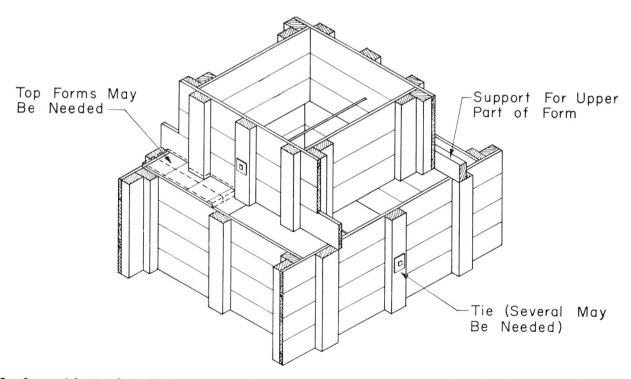

Top Forms May Be Needed

Support For Upper Part of Form

Tie (Several May Be Needed)

9-13 Stepped footing form showing two methods of supporting the upper box; on the left side, an extended sheathing board supports the box while drawing shows an added supporting member at the right.

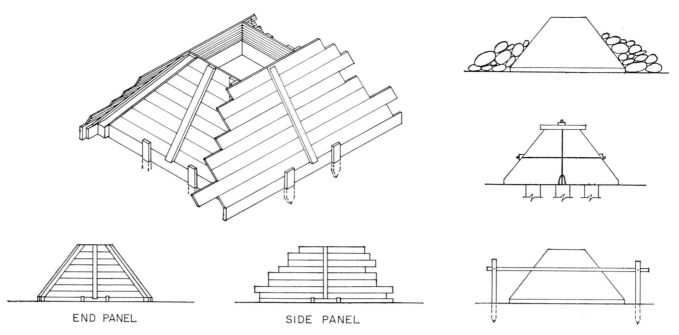

END PANEL   SIDE PANEL

9-14   One method of construction of a sloped footing form.   Small sketches indicate some alternate tying and hold-down methods.

to obtain the proper height of the panels.   The end panels are built to the exact shape of the concrete face.   The side panels need not be made to a precise shape because they overlap the end panels.   After the side panels have been built, sloping cleats are nailed to their inside face to hold the end panels in place as shown in Figure 9-14.   Full size boards may be used and the top of the concrete marked with a nail rather than ripping one of the boards to make the form the exact height of the proposed footing.

Sloped footing forms must be weighted or tied down to resist uplift caused by freshly placed concrete.   Stones, sand bags, earth, or various tie downs can be used as shown in Figure 9-14.   If the base is

cast before the sloping portion of the footing, the forms may be tied to hairpins or anchors cast in the previously placed concrete, or wired to reinforcing rods in the mat at the bottom of the footing.

Forms for large footings are described in the section on bridge work (p. 189).

Combined Footing Forms

Combined or strap footings are used to transfer part of the load of one footing to another or to support two columns on a single footing.   If two columns bear on one footing, the combined footing form is built in the same way as for flat or stepped footings. If the load of one footing is to be partly transferred to another, a strap or beam must be constructed between the two footings or pads.

If the beam or strap is to be cast after the pads, the beam forms are supported by the previous place-

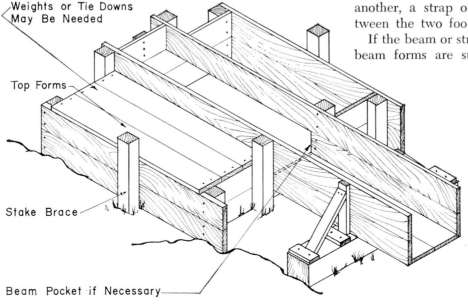

Weights or Tie Downs May Be Needed

Top Forms

Stake Brace

Beam Pocket if Necessary

9-15   One type of strap footing form, where entire footing is to be cast monolithically

146

ment. If the footing is to be cast monolithically, its construction is much like that of the stepped footing. The boxes for the pad forms are built with a cutout for the beam if necessary. The beam forms are supported on timbers or blocks and the flat footing portions are covered and tied down like forms for stepped footings. The beam forms can be braced to the supporting timbers. A suggested method of forming a strap footing is shown in Figure 9-15.

Slab on Grade and Paving Work

Concrete forming on grade is relatively simple. The carefully compacted earth or other base material serves as the bottom form, and only simple edge forms are required. Thorough compaction of the base is essential, particularly so in paving work or where heavy loads are to be carried. Frequently in building construction a plastic film or sheet is laid over the compacted base as a moisture barrier.

Plywood, boards, or metal panel paving forms are common materials for edge forms. They are held in position by stakes, much the same as simple footing forms. Occasionally other materials such as concrete block units may serve as edge forms, or the already cast walls of the building may become the edge forms. ACI Committee 302 * has made recommendations for construction joints (Figure 9-18) and for floor slab joints to isolate floors structurally from other building elements and thus accommodate differential vertical and horizontal movements as well as plastic deformations.

* "Recommended Practice for Concrete Floor and Slab Construction (ACI 302-69)," American Concrete Institute, Detroit, 1969, 34 pp.; reprinted in ACI Manual of Concrete Practice, Part I.

9-16   Placing concrete for floor slab. Small pieces of concrete beneath reinforcement hold it at the desired elevation in the slab.

9-17   Alternate strip paving of parking lot with wood edge forms staked to the desired position.

Highway and Airport Paving

Although it is possible to erect wood edge forms for highway and airport paving slabs, almost all of this paving work is now done with prefabricated metal paving forms except for non-standard curved fill-in pieces to form fillets, etc. at intersections.

9-18   One method of forming floor slab construction joints suggested by ACI Committee 302. These keyed joints may also be formed with premolded compressible material or with prefabricated permanent or reusable metal forms.

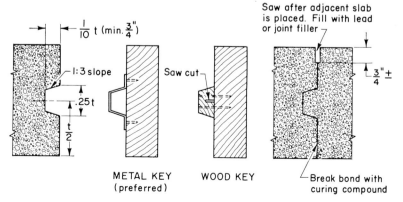

$\frac{1}{10}$ t (min. $\frac{3}{4}$")

1:3 slope

.25 t

$\frac{t}{2}$

METAL KEY (preferred)   WOOD KEY

Saw cut

Saw after adjacent slab is placed. Fill with lead or joint filler

$\frac{3}{4}$" ±

Break bond with curing compound

NOTE: Beveled 1x2 wood strip provides an adequate key for 5 to 8 in. thick slabs.

147

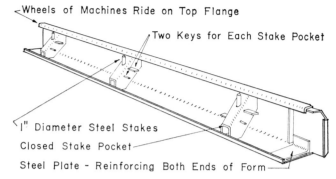

Wheels of Machines Ride on Top Flange

Two Keys for Each Stake Pocket

1" Diameter Steel Stakes

Closed Stake Pocket

Steel Plate - Reinforcing Both Ends of Form

These standard metal forms are simple in principle, but have been developed with considerable care because they serve not only as an edge form but as a running rail for heavy automatic spreading, screeding, and finishing equipment. A number of firms specialize in the manufacture of many variations of these forms and numerous accessories.

The metal side forms for highway (road) paving are usually L-shaped, stiffened by diagonal channel braces which are welded or riveted at about 3-ft intervals. The braces are punched with holes to serve as guides for steel stakes which pin the form to the subgrade; wedges are used to lock the forms at desired elevation. In contrast to street curb and gutter forms, the base is broad (Figure 9-19) to provide necessary bearing for the weight of equipment as well as stability. Although special sizes are available, forms are generally made in 10-ft lengths, and are joined with a sliding lock wedge joint. This joint should be free of play or movement in any direction in order to maintain correct alignment of succeeding sections. It should be easily disconnected for stripping.

ACI Standard 617-58 * indicates a number of requirements for materials, dimensions, setting, and removal of forms for concrete highway and airport pavements. Among these are the following provisions for *materials and dimensions:*

Side forms shall be made of metal having a thickness of not less than $7/32$ in. and shall have a depth equal to the specified edge thickness of the concrete. Building up of forms shall not be permitted. Flexible or curved forms of proper radius shall be used for curves of 100 ft radius or less. Forms shall not deflect more than $1/4$ in. when tested as a simple beam with a span of 10 ft and a load equal to that which the finishing machine or other construction equipment will exert upon them. Forms 8 in. or more in height shall be at least 8 in. wide at the base; forms less than 8 in. in height shall have a base width at least equal to the height of the forms. The flange braces must extend outward on the base not less than two-thirds the height of the form. The forms shall

* "ACI Standard Specifications for Concrete Pavements and Concrete Bases (ACI 617-58)," reprinted in *ACI Manual of Practice—Part 1,* originally published in the ACI JOURNAL, *Proceedings* V. 55, No. 1, July 1958, pp. 53-81. Provisions for forming joints of various kinds in paving are also covered in this ACI Standard.

9-19 Typical prefabricated edge form for highway paving. Boxed end construction (small detail) is also available for forms 13 in. or more in height. Wedges or keys in stake pockets permit vertical adjustment.

be free from warp, bends, or kinks. The top of the form shall not vary from a 10-ft straightedge by more than $1/8$ in. at any point and the side of the form by more than $1/4$ in.

Support and grade alignment of the forms are covered in these paragraphs:

The soil foundation under the forms shall be compacted and cut to grade so that the forms, when set, shall be uniformly supported for their entire length and at the specified elevations. Such soil foundation found to be below established grade at the form line shall be filled to grade in lifts of $1/2$ in. or less for 18 in. on each side of the base of the form and thoroughly re-rolled or tamped. Imperfections and variations above grade shall be corrected by tamping or by cutting, as necessary.

The alignment and grade elevations of the forms shall be checked and the necessary corrections made by the contractor immediately before placing the concrete. When any form has been disturbed or any subgrade thereunder has become unstable, the form shall be reset and rechecked.

ACI 617-58 also requires that forms be staked with at least three pins in every 10-ft section, and that they should be cleaned and oiled before placing con-

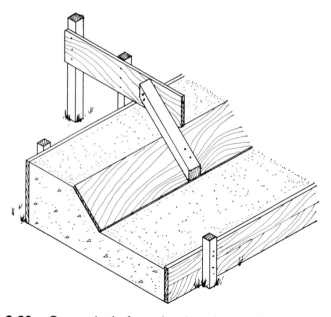

9-20 One method of wood curb and gutter forming

crete. It is desirable to set the forms at least 300 ft in advance of the point where concrete is being placed to permit proper progress and adequate time for inspection of the forms before the concrete is placed.

Curb and Gutter Forms

The curb and gutter common in city street paving are of various sizes and shapes, which may be formed in wood (Figure 9-20), but like highway paving are much more commonly built with ready-made steel forms. The curb and gutter forms are lighter than the forms used for highway paving. Typical combined curb and gutter forms are shown in Figure 9-21, and similar assemblies are available for casting curbs only in roll, batter, vertical and other shapes. Form manufacturers can also supply a full line of comparable fixed radius and adjustable radius forms for curved curb and street work.

One common construction sequence is to place the curb and gutter as a unit using metal forms, then pave the roadway between with the already cast curb or curb and gutter serving as the edge form. In such a case, after the grade line has been set for the outside (back) curb form, the forms are set in position on the ground and a stake placed in each pocket. Stakes are driven when the form is precisely located; then the form can be raised on the stakes to correct elevation and wedges driven to lock the stakes. Then a second form member is loosely connected to the first, staked, raised to line, and locked.

When all the back forms are in, or after each form is locked up, the division plates are hooked into slots along the curb form at desired intervals, and then front forms (either gutter form or curb face form if only a simple curb is being cast) may be set. The

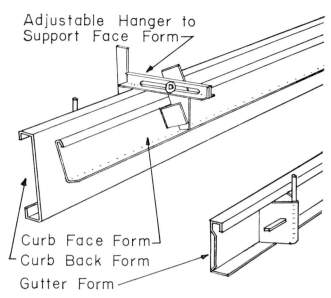

9-21-B   Another type of prefabricated curb and gutter forming where curb face form is supported by hanger from the back, and division plates are eliminated

free ends of division plates are hooked into the opposite front form, the forms squared up, and the stakes driven. The front form can then be raised to grade line and locked with the wedging device. This completes the sequence if only a curb is being cast.

If a combined curb and gutter is to be cast, curb face forms are next mounted on the division plates and locked into position with wedge-shaped keys. Division plates are made in a number of shapes to accommodate various curb designs.

If division plates are not used, the curb face form may be supported by skeleton division plates (also called auxiliary support plates) or adjustable hangers mounted on the back of the outside curb forms (Figure 9-21). For installations without division plates, large curb forms may require diagonal braces, or support at their midpoint with adjustable spreaders to prevent bulging.

Curb face forms are removed about 2 hr after casting, and the division plates can then be lifted out, and finishing completed. Side forms are usually removed 12 hr or more after placing concrete.

Wall Forms

Built-in-Place Forms

Wall forms are constructed from five basic parts: (1) sheathing to retain the concrete until it hardens; (2) studs which support the sheathing; (3) wales to support the studs and align the forms; (4) braces to

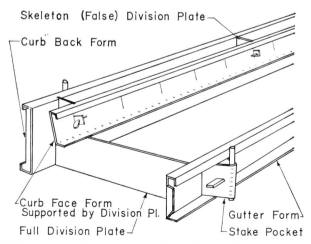

9-21-A   Prefabricated metal form for combined curb and gutter where division plates are used

hold the forms against construction and wind loads; and (5) separate spreaders and ties or tie-spreader units to hold the forms at the correct spacing under the pressure of the fresh concrete.

The first step in building a wall form is to attach a sill or ledger to the footing as a base for studs. The sill may be attached to preset anchors or stub-nailed to the concrete with specially hardened nails. Special care must be taken in aligning this strip because it will determine the line of the wall. It is set out from the proposed line of the wall a distance equal to the thickness of the sheathing.

After the starting plate or sill is in place, the studs are erected (Figure 9-23). The bottom of each stud is toenailed to the sill and held vertical by temporary braces of 1x6 or other suitable stock. The stud spacing at the top of the form is held by temporary ribbons until the sheathing is placed. To save time and material, studs may be left extending above the top of the form rather than cutting them off evenly.

The next step is to attach sheathing to the studs. The bottom edge of the first sheathing board or plywood panel is set on the highest point on the foundation and leveled accurately to establish alignment for succeeding boards or panels. If the footing is uneven or stepped, the space between the first sheathing unit placed and the footing may be filled out with specially cut pieces to make a tight joint if appearance is important.

The sheathing for the remainder of the wall is nailed to the inside of the studs after the first unit has been aligned and attached. When nominal 1-in. sheathing lumber is used, it is usually nailed from the inside face with two 6d or 8d nails at each stud. Plywood sheets ⅝ in. and thicker are nailed with 6d nails at 12- to 16-in. intervals. When thin plywood and hardboard liners are nailed over the sheathing, small nails with thin flat heads such as 3d blue shingle nails are desirable.

Contractors who install ties as the sheathing is being placed, can notch the edge of a sheathing board that is at the required height so that holes through the sheathing are formed at the joint between sheathing boards. Otherwise, holes must be drilled in the sheathing after it is in place. Tie holes must be located at the proper elevation so that the ties will thread through the wales when they are installed.

Wales may be installed as soon as the sheathing is in place or after the other face of the form has been built. Wales are attached to the outside of the studs and held in place by nails, clips, or brackets or patented devices. Wales are generally constructed of two members, which saves drilling for ties. In long wales, the joints between members should be staggered. If double wales are used, there need be no transverse joint completely through the wale.

Permanent bracing can be installed after the wales are in place or as the form is plumbed. These braces

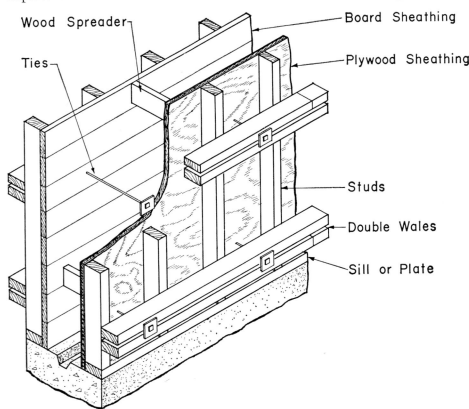

Wood Spreader — Board Sheathing
Ties — Plywood Sheathing
Studs
Double Wales
Sill or Plate

9-22 Typical wall form with components identified. Alternate sheathing materials are indicated. Wood spreaders are shown, but frequently the spreader device is part of the prefabricated tie.

9-23 Starting a wall form. In this case, a rustication strip located at the water table served also as the plate on which studs for the outside form were erected. One row of sheathing boards placed at the bottom served as a ribbon to hold the studs in line. Frame was temporarily braced to the ground and brought to final alignment after all sheathing was applied.

extend from the wale to the ground or other solid support. If the brace is designed to act in compression only, wedges may be used at the end to help in plumbing the forms.

If the braces are designed to act in tension only, they must be securely attached to the forms and tightly anchored at the other end. A cable is well adapted to this type of bracing. The cable length can be adjusted during the plumbing of the forms by a turnbuckle or other device.

When the forms are braced on only one side, the braces must take both compression and tension. Therefore, special attention should be given to fastenings at each end of the brace. Proprietary devices are available for attaching the brace and adjusting its length after it has been installed.

Plumbing is the final operation in building a wall form. Ties are usually installed and all permanent bracing placed before plumbing begins so that the form will not need to be disturbed after it has been plumbed. Most bracing systems have devices for adjusting the braces to facilitate the plumbing operation. If the braces are non-adjustable, the form must be plumbed as the braces are installed. No time should be spent in plumbing both sides of wall forms because the second form to be built will be automatically plumbed from the first by the spreaders.

After the form for one side of the wall has been built and braced, work is begun on the second form. In many operations, steel is placed before the second form is built. If a man can work inside the forms, the

second form is constructed as the first. If the wall is too thin for men to work inside the forms but is wide enough to swing a hammer, the carpenters can work from the outside over the top of the sheathing as it is placed. For thin walls, the second form can be constructed in an inclined position (or flat if there is enough space) and then tilted into position.

When both forms have been erected, and reinforcement has been placed, the ties are tightened. If ties with spreading devices are not used, the forms must be held apart at the correct spacing with spreaders which can be removed as the concrete rises in the

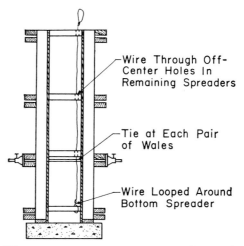

9-24 Wire attached to bottom spreader and passing through upper ones is used to withdraw spreaders as concrete rises in the form. This system prevents loss of spreaders in the concrete.

forms. A wire attached to the bottom spreader, running through all spreaders above, and anchored to the top of the forms will aid in their removal and avoid leaving any spreaders in as the concrete rises in the forms (Figure 9-24). Ties and spreading devices are discussed in more detail on p. 54.

Where through-the-wall tying is impossible, or prohibited by specifications, as is the case for some water retaining structures, external bracing must be provided to resist the lateral pressure of the fresh concrete (Figure 9-25).

Low Walls

In building low wall forms, wales are sometimes omitted and the forms are braced by members attached to the studs. The general sequence of the wall form construction just described applies to this light construction, except for the attachment of the wales. Another consideration in this type of construction is the anchorage of the form ties. Since wales are not used, the ties must be anchored to the studs.

9-25 Heavy external bracing of wall forms resists lateral pressure of freshly placed concrete when ties through the wall cannot be used.

9-26 Forms for low wall. Ties pass through studs and braces are also attached to studs; no wales required for this simple construction.

High Walls

When high walls are formed full height, greater form rigidity is obtained by using stronger members and adding vertical wales or strongbacks (Figure 9-27). These vertical wales are designed to support and align the horizontal wales. The method of construction for high wall forms is similar to that for normal one-story walls, but the design may specify more elaborate bracing or other details. High walls are more frequently built by raising the forms vertically in panel units (see p. 155).

Prefabricated Panel Systems

Use of ready-made or contractor-built prefabricated panels for wall forming has been on the increase in recent years. Such panels are durable enough for many reuses and simplify and reduce the labor required at the job site. Studs and sheathing are, in effect, preassembled in units small enough to be conveniently handled; the panels are set into position and tied together. Braces, wales, ties, are then attached or inserted as needed to complete the wall assembly. For light construction wales are sometimes omitted.

There are a number of ways to build the panels, and various materials are used—wood, metal, plywood with metal bracing, plywood with wood bracing, or glass fiber and plastic over wood or plywood A number of ready-made systems described in Chapter 4 (p. 60) are available usually on either a purchase or rental basis.

Building the Panels

Some contractors find that they can build their own panel systems for less than they can buy or rent the ready-made ones. Accessories manufacturers sell

9-27 For walls of great height or where precise alignment is extremely important, vertical wales (strongbacks) are added outside of the regular system of horizontal wales.

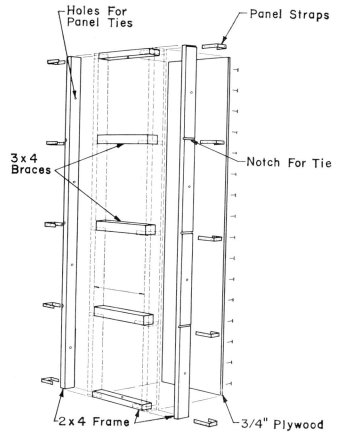

9-28 Framing and assembly of typical contractor-built panel for wall forming. Metal panel straps are shown, but similar panels can be built without such ready-made hardware.

hardware designed specially for this purpose. The frame is first assembled, often in a jig designed to speed up production. Special care is required to get accurate layout of frame members to assure square corners and straight edges. If any panel is not square and true to dimensions, it will throw other panels out of alignment when the forms are assembled.

The sheathing for panels, whether plywood or metal must conform to the outside line of the frame. Otherwise, shallow fins will be formed in the concrete at the joints between the panels. Since this type of form is usually designed for much reuse, the sheathing should be attached to the frame much more securely than for normal wall form sheathing. Typical construction of such panels is shown in Figure 9-28.

Provision must be made for attaching panels to one another. A variety of clamps and ties are available for this purpose. If they require holes through the frame, the holes must be accurately located so they will match up when the panels are erected.

Many kinds of hardware and ties suitable for form panel systems are available to the contractor who builds his own panels. Each proprietary panel system usually has its own special ties and other accessories.

Erecting the Panels

Panels—either contractor-made or ready-made—are erected in basically the same way as built-in-place wall forms except that the separate erection of studs and sheathing is eliminated. Some systems with rigid panel frames and connections eliminate the use of wales. An accurate line must be marked

9-29 Metal framed 2x8 prefabricated panels assembled as a wall form with horizontal and vertical wales, diagonal braces. Note panels at top placed horizontally to obtain desired wall height.

9-30 Square all-metal panels, erected, braced, and aligned to form wall

9-31 Large wall form built for crane handling is 12x45 ft, built of 2x4 studs and wales, ¾-in. plywood, with double steel scaffolding and form lift bars for raising the entire section at once. Note lifting beam with four pick-up points.

154

9-32 Steel-faced giant form for curved wall being positioned by crane. Benefits of building forms in large panels for mechanical hoisting are particularly evident on high walls like this one. Such panels are frequently used as "climbing" forms, being raised vertically for successive lifts.

9-33 Steel and plywood prefabricated panels assembled in 20-ft-high units with heavy strongbacks and wales. Crane sets panel into place.

on the footing for the alignment of the panels. They are then set into position, and adjacent panels are joined and braced. Other details such as setting the wales, permanent braces, ties, and plumbing the form are similar to those for built-in-place forms.

When proprietary panel systems are purchased or rented, the supplier frequently prepares layout drawings and provides erection instructions; sometimes trained supervisors familiar with a given system are sent out to aid the contractor in proper erection.

"Giant" Forms and Ganged Panel Forms

With greater demand for massive placements, and with the progress in development of cranes and other mechanical methods of transporting forms (see travelers, p. 293) the use of giant panels and ganged prefabricated forms for high walls is becoming more common. Ranging up to 30x50 ft, their size is limited only by the mechanics of handling. Large panels can be assembled flat on the ground where it is easier to work. Tools and materials are ready at hand and do not have to be hoisted to the workman. The same kind of delay and lost motion are avoided in stripping because the giant forms are stripped as a unit.

Materials for the large form units are much the same as for conventional built-in-place walls, except for extra bracing required to withstand the handling stresses (Figure 9-31). In some cases, a prefabricated cage of reinforcing steel is attached to the large form to be lifted with the unit. These large form units are frequently used as "climbing" forms in high wall construction, being raised vertically for one lift after another.

The same benefits of the large forms can be obtained by ganging or grouping small panels together to form larger units. They are joined with special hardware and braced with strongbacks (Figure 9-33) or special steel frames which maintain the stability of the unit during handling. After the small panels have been joined and attached to the frame, they are lifted into place as a unit. Such a unit may have a number of reuses and then be dismantled for use as individual panels on other jobs. The ganged panels are also frequently used as climbing forms, moving up for successive lifts of a high wall.

Square Corners

Handling of wall forms at corners is a critical operation. Continuity of sheathing and wales is

9-34 Typical formwork corner using overlapping wales held by a vertical kick strip. Stripping has begun at the lower level revealing a sharp, accurate corner line in the board-marked concrete.

broken, making this a potential weak point in the formwork. Corners must be drawn tight to prevent concrete leakage. Leakage here is particularly objectionable as patching to a square edge is most difficult, and chipped, weathered, poorly patched corners are particularly noticeable. Lateral pressure of the concrete, which tends to open the corner joint must be resisted by ties or suitable connections between the wales of the wall forms on either side of the corner.

One method of making a tight corner is shown in Figure 9-34. The wales overlap and two vertical kick strips are provided at the intersection, against which the wales are wedged to tighten the corner. Another method of securing corners in formwork (Figure 9-35) uses a diagonal tie across the corner. Special corner clamps and ties are available from formwork hardware suppliers.

"Log cabin" corners are sometimes used. Alternate sheathing boards are brought beyond the corner, and vertical kick strips behind the interlaced sheathing boards prevent movement. This type of corner is much more difficult to build and strip than those shown.

Curved Walls and Round Corners

Rounded corners or curved walls of radius greater than 4 ft can be formed with plywood attached directly to studs. Horizontal sheathing boards can be used for curves with a radius of 18 to 20 ft or larger, and vertical board sheathing is sometimes used for smaller radius curves. Rectangular prefabricated panels, with narrow or flexible fillers added, are often

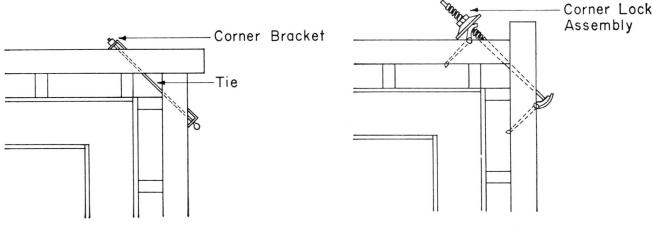

9-35 Two of the various corner tying devices. Hardware fits between double-member wales so that cutting or drilling is not required.

9-36 Unusual technique used to form second lift of reactor walls which slope inward as well as curve. Studs were 2x4's laid flat, close together against plywood sheathing but not nailed. Pairs of #6 reinforcing bars were bent to desired curvature to serve as wales.

9-37 These 2x8-ft panels were set vertically to form a long curved wall. A bracket at the top made it possible to attach plywood extension to get desired 9-ft height. Note bracing.

9-38 Circular wall above existing caisson, formed with 2x4-ft steel panels. Inside radius of wall is 32 ft 6 in.

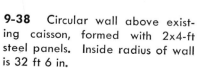

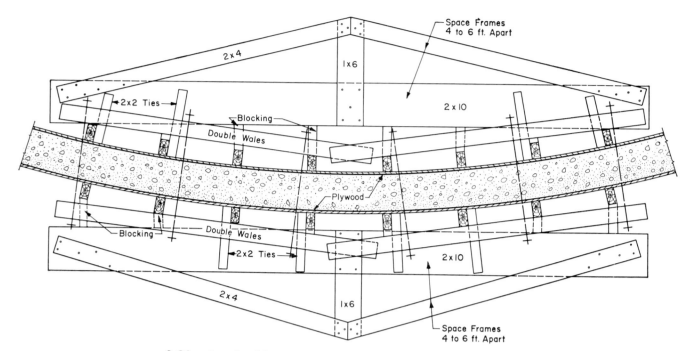

9-39 Details of long radius curve formed with plywood sheathing

used on long radius curves. Short radius curves frequently require a smooth lining material backed up by narrow vertical members. Thickness of sheathing and details of construction vary with the radius of the curve. Several of the many forming methods are described in the following paragraphs, and information on the radius of bend for several common materials is given in Chapter 4.

Long Radius Curves

Long radius curves are easily formed with prefabricated panels (Figures 9-37 and 9-38), and special filler panels and accessories, as well as suggestions for erection, are available from panel manufacturers.

A typical detail of a form for a long radius curve, not less than 20 ft, using plywood sheathing, is shown in Figure 9-39. The studs are vertical and are blocked out from yokes or frames which are spaced 4 to 6 ft apart vertically. By staggering the frames to break joints, a full circle or any part can be held rigid. For the outside form it is necessary at the center of

the frames and for a distance of two or three studs each way to tie the studs to the frames to prevent the spring of the sheathing from pulling it away from the frames. For the inside form it is necessary to tie the studs at the outer ends of the frame instead of those at the center.

Long radius curves may be formed with horizontal board sheathing in much the same way straight wall forms are erected. After the wall line has been marked on the footing, a sill is nailed down to set the line for the studs. Since wales cannot be bent to the curvature of the wall, short sections are used to span four to six studs according to the curvature of the wall as shown in Figure 9-39, or curved wales may be constructed from standard lumber as shown in Figure 9-40. With the former method, care must be taken to assure the correct amount of blocking so a smooth curve will be formed after the ties are tightened. The installation of ties, external bracing, and plumbing of the form is similar to that for straight wall forms. More external bracing is required for this type of form than for normal straight walls because of

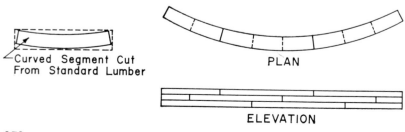

9-40 Arc segments cut from standard lumber sizes may be laminated to form a rigid curved piece. The built-up curved member may be placed next to the sheathing, with straight vertical wales or strongbacks on the outside, or it may serve as a curved horizontal wale outside of straight vertical studs.

the short wales. Where pressures are not excessive, a simpler construction (Figure 9-41) may be used.

Curved wall forms with vertical sheathing require curved horizontal ribs fabricated to support the sheathing. These ribs are usually cut from 8-in. or wider stock; they can be made of single or double segments.

Building curved wall forms in place with vertical sheathing is somewhat more difficult than the method of horizontal sheathing using vertical studs. The ribs must be set in place and held by vertical members and braces until the sheathing has been applied. After the sheathing has been applied, ties are inserted and vertical wales placed. Vertical sheathing is more frequently used to support the lining for short radius curves.

Short Radius Curves

Figure 9-43 shows a short radius corner formed with hardboard or plywood lining. Yokes are cut to the required curvature from 2-in. stock and spaced about 30 in. apart. The yokes are sheathed with vertical 2x2 dressed strips. The lining is then nailed securely to the 2x2 backing. Since the lining material will tend to spring back to its original flat shape, it must be nailed at 6-in. intervals in both directions.

Two thin sheets of form material may be used rather than one thick one because they can be bent to a smaller radius. Figure 9-45 shows one way of using double plywood for corner forming. The corner sheathing is brought out beyond the spring line in order to form tighter joints where it abuts the wall sheathing. The sheathing is supported by horizontal members cut to the curvature of the corner.

Wall Openings

The forms for window and door openings must be made rigid so they will not distort under the pressure of the fresh concrete. If metal sash or door frames are to have concrete cast around them, they may be braced and aligned to serve as a part of the formwork for the opening. The box forming the opening should be made of at least 2-in. material, well braced, to give adequate strength and prevent deflection so that the sash will fit properly.

Any strips required to form the recess to receive the sash are securely nailed to the 2-in. plank forming the frame. Cross braces should be located at each cleat horizontally and vertically unless there is an inner frame of 2x4's. The cleats should be not more than 24 in. apart. If less than 2-in. material is used, a closer spacing will be necessary. Extra cross

9-41 Simplified method of forming curved wall with horizontal sheathing boards. Ties bear on double stud members and no horizontal wales are used.

9-42 Completed curved wall form using vertical sheathing boards

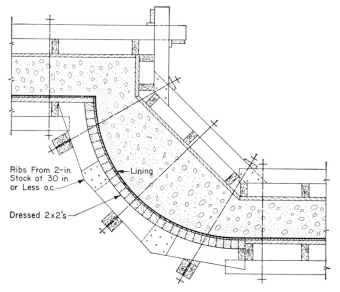

Ribs From 2-in. Stock at 30 in. or Less o.c.

Lining

Dressed 2x2's

9-43 Typical detail for small radius corner form using hardboard or plywood liner

9-44 Workmen bending two thicknesses of ¼-in. plywood to form curve of intermediate radius. This same technique is applicable for curves as small as 15-in. radius without wetting or steaming. Spacing of backing members depends on form strength requirements as well as radius of curvature.

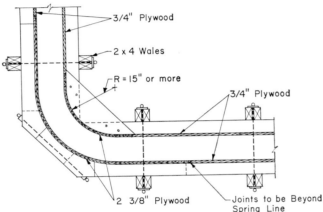

9-45 Small radius corner formed with two thin sheets of plywood supported on curved horizontal members

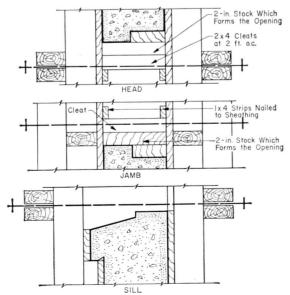

9-46 Form details for sill, jamb, and head of window

bracing should be provided in large window forms. The frame for the opening is supported by nailing to the form sheathing.

Except for windows with very steep sills, it is necessary to be able to get at the sill to finish it and to work the concrete into place properly. For these reasons, the sill of the form may be omitted altogether, as indicated in Figure 9-46, or the sill piece made in two sections for easy removal.

Door opening forms require special attention since they are larger and distortion can occur easily without proper bracing. The opening is made in much the same way as the forms for window openings. Wales running across the opening will help prevent twisting of the frame.

Small openings in walls can be formed by attaching a box frame to the forms to block out the concrete. The box should be rigid or braced so that it will not deform from the pressure of the concrete. It should be lightly tied to the face of the form so the form can be stripped leaving the box in place in the hardened concrete. Kickers to resist the uplift action of the fresh concrete may be required.

Joints

Vertical Construction Joints

Vertical construction joints are formed with a bulkhead placed in the forms at the end of the proposed concrete placement. Since the reinforcing steel continues past the joint, some provision must be made to allow it to pass through the bulkhead. The bulkheads may be built up from short pieces, placed horizontally, cut so they will fit evenly between the two faces of the wall form. Vertical boards may also be used (Figure 9-49). Reinforcement is passed through the bulkhead by notching the bulkhead boards at the desired steel location.

The bulkhead resists the pressure of the fresh concrete by cleats nailed to the inside face of the forms,

9-47 Cross bracing for large window forms. Note that full sheathing is used on one side of the formed opening to give added stability.

outside of the bulkhead sheathing. The short pieces forming the bulkhead are lightly attached to these cleats to hold them in place until the concrete is placed. The pressure of the concrete will hold them against the cleats. Keyways or waterstop materials are frequently attached to bulkhead forms as required by design specifications.

Horizontal Construction Joints

The technique of forming high walls with lift forms (or climbing forms) is used where it is impractical to place them full height. When the first concrete lift is placed, ties or bolts are placed in the concrete near the top of the lift. After the concrete has hardened sufficiently, the forms are stripped and raised to the elevation of the next lift and supported on the previously placed bolts below.

A row of ties should be placed about 6 in. above the joint between the concrete lifts to prevent leakage. The bolts or ties in the previous lift support the weight of the form, but cannot be relied on to prevent a slight spreading of the forms at the joint. The form members connected to the bolts must be an integral part of the form panel. If the wales are securely attached to the form, they may be used to support the panel. Sometimes a timber ledger is attached to bolts cast in the previous lift, and the studs of the form rest on it. Specially constructed strongbacks can also be used. Special brackets, attached to the previous lift by bolts, may also be used to support the forms.

Horizontal joint forming details for architectural concrete shown on p. 241 indicate a preferred method of obtaining clean, sharp lines where appearance of these joints is important.

9-48 Box attached to wall form to produce irregular shape of recess in concrete

9-49 Bulkhead at the left made with short horizontal boards. On the right, bulkhead still in place after wall forms were stripped is made of vertical boards.

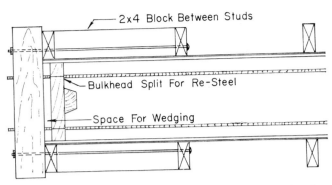

9-50 One method of bulkheading a wall form, showing strip for keyway attached to bulkhead

Control Joints

Control joints must be placed in concrete walls as shown on the plans. Such joints are formed by a beveled insert of wood, metal, or other material which is tacked to the form (picture, p. 242). This insert produces a groove in the concrete which will control surface cracking. It is frequently designed to be left in the concrete for some time after the forms have been stripped, and in such a case it must be only lightly attached to the form. If this insert or strip is removed too soon, the area around the joint may be damaged. Special care is required if control joint strips are removed along with the main form panel. If wood strips are used, they should be kerfed to prevent swelling that might crack the concrete.

Suggested Tolerances for Walls

The following tolerances suggested by ACI Committee 347 apply to the finished wall. The forms should be constructed to give a finished wall within these limits, unless otherwise specified.

1. *Variation from the plumb* should not be more than ¼ in. per 10 ft, but in no case should it exceed 1 in. High-rise structures (above 100 ft high) or other special types of structures may require special tolerances as noted in ACI 347-68.

2. *Variation from the plumb of conspicuous lines* such as control joints should not be more than ±¼ in. in any bay or 20 ft maximum. In 40 ft or more the variation should be less than ±½ in.

3. *Variation from the level or from specified grades* should be less than ±¼ in. in any bay or 20 ft maximum. Not more than ±½ in. variation in 40 ft or more is allowed.

4. *Variation of the linear building lines* from the established position in plan and the related position of walls and partitions should be less than ±½ in. in any bay or 20 ft maximum. In 40 ft or more the variation must be less than ±1 in.

5. *Variation in the sizes and locations* of wall openings should not be more than ±¼ in.

6. *Variation in thickness* is limited to −¼ in. or +½ in.

Column Forms

Because of their comparatively small cross section and relatively high rates of placement, column forms * are frequently subject to much higher lateral pressures than walls, as explained in Chapter 5. Tight joints and adequate anchorage at the base are required. A frame of 2x4's nailed to the completed slab is commonly used to position and anchor the column form. Because of the confined space in which concrete is placed, tall columns frequently have pockets or windows at midheight or other intervals to make placing and consolidating the concrete easier. A cleanout opening must be made at the column base for removal of waste or debris before concreting begins.

Columns may be round, rectangular, L-shaped, or of various irregular cross sections. Irregular shapes are frequently formed by attaching special inserts inside square or rectangular forms, and L-shaped columns may be formed like wall corners. Round col-

* See also bridge piers.

L – Shaped

Octagon

Cut Out Corners

9-51 Irregular shapes of column cross section are frequently formed by using inserts within standard square or rectangular forms.

umns may be built in wood, but ready-made forms of metal, fiber, or other materials are more commonly used. Prefabricated panel system parts are also used at times to form square or rectangular colums (Figure 9-52), and special techniques and materials are used for custom fabrication of special column shapes (Figure 9-53). Columns of irregular or decorative cross section may also be built in place from wood and plywood.

Detailed descriptions are limited to some of the more common column forms built by the contractor. Typical framing and sheathing members and yoke or clamp spacings shown in the drawings are representative of actual practice, but should not be used without first checking the proposed application on the basis of design principles discussed earlier. Temperature and rate of placing as well as column size influence the design, and a full investigation should be made to see that sizes and spacings are adequate for actual job conditions.

9-52 The 16 in. wide filler panels of a prefabricated panel system were clamped together to make a 24-ft column form which was erected by crane. Shorter panels (4 ft) at the 12-ft level were removed for placing and vibrating concrete at the bottom of the column, then replaced as concreting reached that level.

Erection Practices

Square or rectangular column forms are generally built in four panels, round ones in two or three circular segments. Clamp spacing and code numbers should be marked on the panels as they are built. The sequence and method of erection vary somewhat depending on the total job schedule, lifting equipment available, and plans for organizing work of the reinforcing bar setters. The column form may be erected in place panel by panel, or the forms may be assembled into a complete column box and set in place as a complete unit. Reinforcing bars may be assembled in place or prefabricated in cages and set in place either before or after the forms are in position, depending on individual conditions. For example if there are any ties that pass through the form, the cage may be set in place and wired to the column dowels, then forms set in place around steel and ties threaded through. For heavy bars and/or large columns (Figure 9-55), it is common practice to build the reinforcing cage in place.

If the panels are assembled in place, the first one is aligned and temporarily braced, then the others added and full bracing (like that in Figure 9-60) set up. The other method of assembling the entire column first is preferred if equipment is available to lift the assembled form because it saves some of the work of temporary bracing.

A template is generally set in place on the floor slab or footing to locate the column form accurately. Interior dimensions of the template should be slightly larger ($\frac{1}{8}$ in. or so) than the outside measurements of

9-53 Glass-fiber-reinforced plastic braced by plywood was used in the custom manufacture of forms for twisted column modules. Part of the recently removed form is near the column at the right.

9-54 Another technique for handling irregularly shaped columns. This flaring circular column form was built with dimension lumber lined in plywood.

9-55 Spirally reinforced columns commonly have steel assembled in place. Steel forms for these round columns will be set around the reinforcing cage.

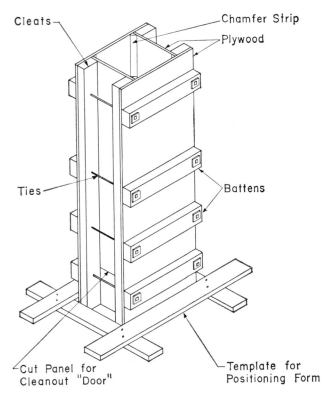

Cleats

Chamfer Strip

Plywood

Ties

Battens

Cut Panel for Cleanout "Door"

Template for Positioning Form

9-56 One method suitable for forming light columns, up to about 12x12 in. Plywood is backed by battens which are a part of the wood and bolt column yoke.

9-57 Bottom part of a light column form similar to the one detailed in 9-56. Note template nailed to slab for positioning the form. Cleanout door nailed to the side panel (left) to prevent loss.

the assembled form panel to make it easier to fit the form into proper position.

Careful erection of column forms is necessary to avoid "twisting" from the square or rectangular cross section. Alternating the direction of bolt members of yokes, or the direction of tensioning for certain types of clamps, helps to overcome this. Line and thickness tolerances will not control twist unless referenced to a *grid* on the floor such as column center lines. Column tolerances for width and thickness should not be checked from a reference point on the column form or from a single point on the floor unless twist is separately checked to about $-2°$ to $+5°$ separately.

True height of the column form is the story height less the slab thickness; if the slab is formed with the columns, the slab sheathing thickness must also be subtracted. Because of irregularities in the finished slab at column locations, the made-up panels are frequently cut ½ in. or more shorter than true height, and then shimmed up at the bottom or pieced at the top to exact height in the field. Exact amount of height reduction depends on local field practice and

164

job conditions. Sometimes grade is checked at the base and any necessary correction indicated by a mark on the template, or elevation may be checked at the top of the form to make final adjustments.

If columns are formed, cast, and stripped independently ahead of the forming of other structural members—a fairly common practice to permit columns to take initial shrinkage—the *adjusted form* should be slightly higher than the true height of column to allow for shrinkage and variations that may occur when other members are framed in. Some contractors allow about half an inch of extra concrete at this point to cover small shrinkage and any irregularities, but the exact amount depends on local conditions. Frequently specifications require the contractor to chisel or sandblast the top $\frac{1}{16}$ in. or more of concrete to remove laitance before casting the next lift.

Square or Rectangular Columns

The method of building form panels depends on the materials being used as well as the means of clamping or yoking the columns. Figure 9-56 shows construction suitable for light column forms up to 12x12 in., held together with a combination wood and bolt yoke. Battens attached to the plywood side panels are a part of the yoke, and ties or bolts with washers form the other two sides of the yoke. This same kind of construction may be used for columns

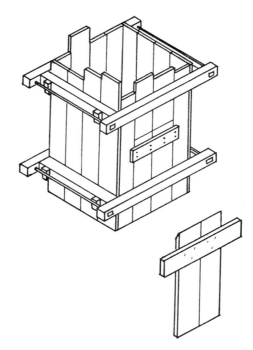

9-58 Column formed with board sheathing, using wood and bolt yoke: wedging between bolt and side panel batten to tighten form.

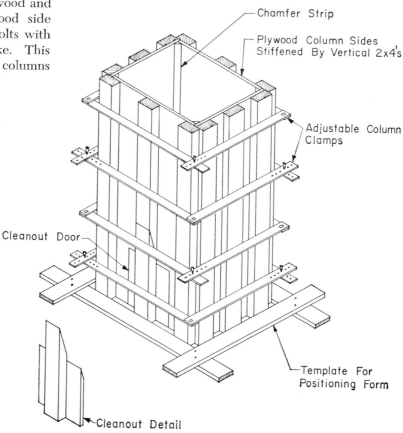

Chamfer Strip

Plywood Column Sides Stiffened By Vertical 2x4's

Adjustable Column Clamps

Cleanout Door

Template For Positioning Form

Cleanout Detail

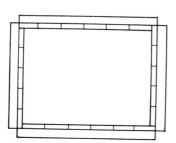

9-59 Typical construction of heavier column form using plywood sheathing backed by vertical stiffening members and clamped with adjustable metal clamps. Small section shows an alternate method using board sheathing with horizontal cleats.

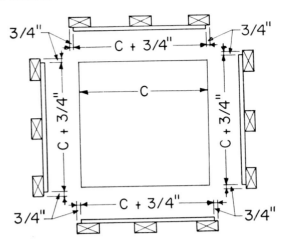

9-60 Rectangular column (bridge pier) form built with 1x4's backing the plywood, clamped with adjustable metal clamps. Note four-way bracing for alignment, template at base.

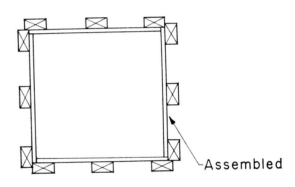

9-61 Square column form similar to the form of 9-59, but with all panels identical. Panels are interchangeable unless beam pockets are cut at the top. (Dimensions based on ¾-in. sheathing.)

up to 18x18 in. by adding battens to the end panels. Similar construction can be used with board sheathing as shown in Figure 9-58. Light column forms can also be built for tying with metal strapping by "trussing" the panels to eliminate right-angle bends in the strap tie.

Heavier column forms are commonly tied with adjustable ready-made column clamps which are available for column cross sections ranging from about 9-in. square to approximately 5x8 ft. Figure 9-59 shows a widely used method of forming columns using plywood backed by vertical 2x4 stiffening members. To build these panels, two ¾-in. plywood sheets are cut to exact column size and the 2x4 vertical backup strips are attached to extend 1⅜ in. over each side of the plywood. The plywood sheets for the other two sides are cut 1½ in. wider than that column dimension and the backing members are nailed flush along the plywood edges. Additional vertical strips

are used for wider columns to prevent excessive deflection of the plywood. The same type of assembly can be done with 1x4 vertical backing members if a design check indicates strength and stiffness are adequate. Such a column form is pictured in Figure 9-60.

The foregoing method of form building produces two matching sides and two matching ends. A useful variation of this scheme for square columns, shown in Figure 9-61, makes all panels identical and therefore completely interchangeable (if they are not cut at the top for beam pockets). If columns of this general type are to be tied with strap or band iron, trussing is required as shown in Figure 9-62.

Where column clamps are not available, or where heavy lateral pressures might cause overload or excessive deflection of clamps, columns may be formed using internal and external ties with heavy wales (Figure 9-63).

All square or rectangular column forms should have

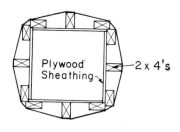

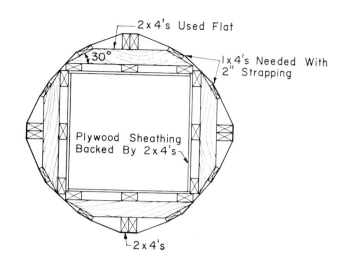

9-62 Typical arrangement of "trussing" when steel strapping is used to tie column form together. Smaller cross section shows arrangement suggested for columns up to 18x18 in. Method at right is suitable for larger columns, up to 32x32 in.

chamfer strips in the corners (unless architectural limitations prohibit them), because sharp edges are likely to be chipped or damaged while the concrete is green. Chamfer strips are usually nailed to two opposite panel units when the forms are being made up. Strips may be cut from wood for a sharp 45° flat fillet, or ready-made inserts of sheet metal or other materials may be used for a quarter-round fillet.

Round Columns

The ready-made single-use fiber tubes or multi-use steel forms for round columns (both pictured in Chapter 4) require only joining the parts, setting in place, and bracing to maintain alignment. No outside yokes are required, since lateral pressure is resisted by hoop tension in the forms. Figure 9-64 shows a round fiber form adapted for forming an obround column.

Round wood column forms are expensive to construct, and are rarely justified except where only a few are to be built, or where the surface finish attainable with other materials is not considered satisfactory. Figure 9-65 shows one method of constructing wood forms suitable for tying with steel strap. The round collars shown could be built out to rectangular shape to permit use of standard clamps.

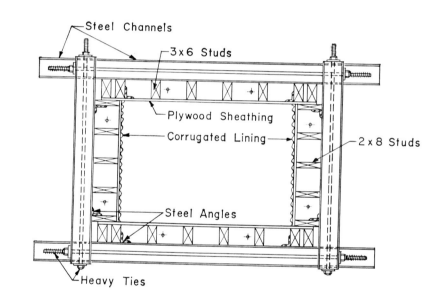

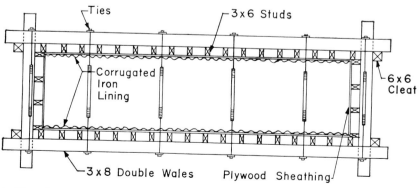

9-63 Cross-sections of forms for two heavy pier-type columns, one with internal ties, and the other with heavy-duty external tie bolts and heavy steel wales

9-64 Form for obround column assembled from plywood and cut sections of a standard fiber tube form. Part of the specially shaped yoke is visible.

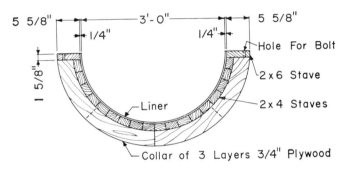

9-65 Round column form built in wood may be lined with plywood, hardboard, or steel. Two halves of such a column form are bolted together then tied or clamped externally. This design, suitable for tying with steel strapping, could be clamped with standard rectangular clamp if circular collar were extended to square shape.

9-66 Tapered round pier form of wood and plywood beside the pier formed with it

Column Heads

The top of the column form is sometimes made separate from the column proper to avoid remaking the form to fit varying sizes of beams and girders that frame in, or to facilitate the use of prefabricated capital forms of special shapes. The flaring "mushroom" capital common in flat slab work is commonly formed with ready-made steel units (p. 65). The drop panel that surrounds it is formed as a part of the slab.

For columns into which beams and girders frame, openings called beam pockets are cut in the top of the column form panels. The opening is generally made slightly larger than the actual size of beam to leave some room for adjustments as the final assembly is made in the field. The beam bottoms and sides may be placed within the pocket or merely brought up flush with it. In the former case, the opening must be cut to allow for thickness of beam side and bottom forms in addition to the $\frac{1}{4}$ to $\frac{1}{2}$ in. allowed for ease in assembly. The beam pocket may be reinforced around the edges with 1- or 2-in. material which also serves to support ends of beam form.

The beam forms are also cut a little short of true dimension to allow some leeway in assembly. These beam-column intersections are difficult to form, and it is easier to fit a small closure piece or bevel strip in the field than to have to make saw cuts to enlarge openings or shorten panels. One contractor reports success with a field-fitted metal closure tacked on at

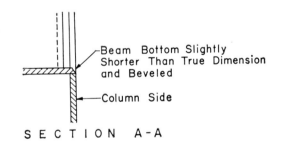

9-67 Details of one type of beam-column form intersection, showing a wedged vertical key as the closure piece. Removal of the key simplifies stripping the forms later.

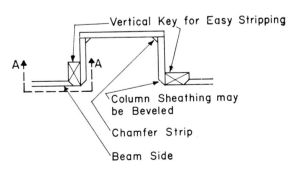

beam and column intersection lines to cover any gap left by approximate fitting of shop-built panels. Figure 9-67 shows another method of handling this closure, using a wedge-shaped key that also facilitates stripping.

Changing Sizes of Form Panels

If the plan for form reuse requires reducing column widths, it is better to build form panels of cleated boards which can simply be ripped along one or both edges to the desired new size. Plywood backed by vertical stiffeners would require considerably more refabrication to change panel widths. Reductions in column height may be made by cutting short at the

bottom if beam and girder pockets are to remain the same at the top. If column cross section remains constant but sizes of members framing in vary, several different head boxes can be devised to extend one common set of panels. Column boxes added to the top are also suitable for height changes where no in-framing members exist.

Beam or Girder Forms

Beam and girder formwork consists of a beam (or girder) bottom and two sides, plus necessary ties or braces. Usually the bottom is made to the exact width of the beam and supported directly on shore

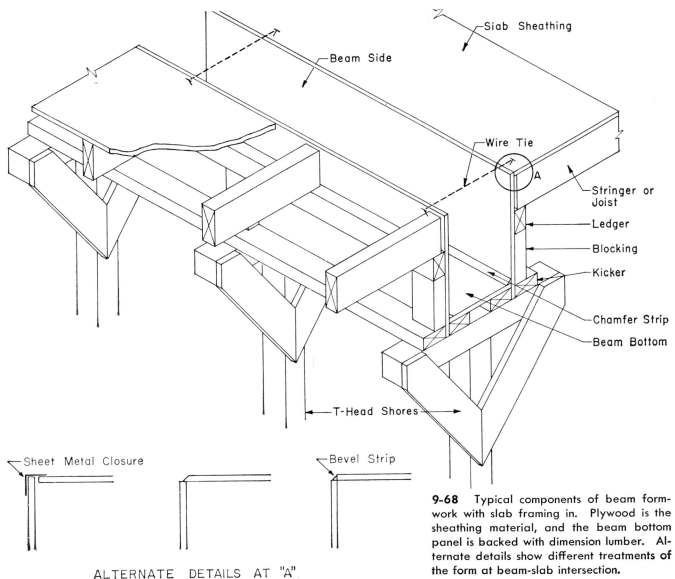

9-68 Typical components of beam formwork with slab framing in. Plywood is the sheathing material, and the beam bottom panel is backed with dimension lumber. Alternate details show different treatments of the form at beam-slab intersection.

ALTERNATE DETAILS AT "A".

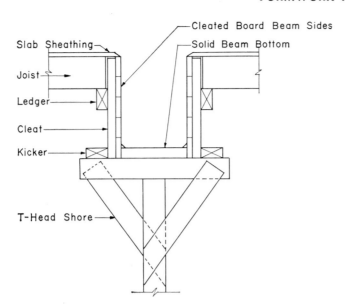

9-69 Beam form details when cleated boards serve as beam sides and beam bottom is a solid piece of dimension lumber

heads. Beam sides overlap the bottom form and also rest on the shore heads. For fireproofing structural steel and for some composite construction beam or girder forms may be supported from an existing structural frame.

Details of the formwork assembly vary, depending on plans for stripping as well as materials to be used, location of the member in the building, and the an-

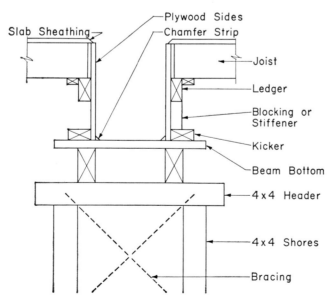

9-70 Another less common beam forming method. Beam sides rest on beam bottom, which is carried on stringers resting on double post shores. This design permits wider shore spacing and offers resistance to tipping when loading is unbalanced.

ticipated loads to be carried. Whether the beam forms are assembled in boxes prior to installation, or whether they are handled as separate bottom and sides, depends on the lifting equipment available as well as the planned sequence of form stripping. The following examples show some of the many ways the forms may be built. Size and spacing of members for an actual job should be checked according to the principles outlined in Chapter 6.

Figure 9-68 shows a typical interior beam form with slab forming supported on the beam sides. This drawing indicates plywood for beam sides and bottom, supported longitudinally on the beam bottom by 2x4's, and with blocking or stiffeners along the beam sides. The vertical side members are sometimes omitted if the beam is less than 20 in. deep and slab loads carried by the beam are not excessive. The ledger supports loads from adjoining slab forms, and the kicker holds beam sides in place at the bottom. Figure 9-69 shows the same type of framing using a different material—cleated boards for the side panels, and a plank for the beam bottom.

Figure 9-70 indicates another method, less commonly used, in which the beam bottom is carried on stringers resting on double post shores. Beam sides are carried on the beam bottom. This design permits wider spacing of the shores and offers more resistance to tipping when loads become unbalanced because of unsymmetrical placing of concrete. The double post shore may also be desirable when unusually heavy slab loads are carried on the beam sides. This might occur when horizontal shoring is used to support long slab spans (Figure 9-71).

Bottoms

Beam or girder bottoms are frequently made of ¾-in. or thicker plywood, with attached supporting members, usually 2x4's, running the length of the beam bottom. Spacing of 2x4's depends on form design standards and the load to be carried by the beam bottom. The bottom forms may also be made of board sheathing; nominal 2-in. stock is frequently used. If the beam is wider than the boards available, then several must be cleated together with 1x4 cleats on the underside at about 2-ft intervals.

The beam bottom is usually made the exact width of the exposed beam soffit, although at times it may be made wide enough to support the beam sides as well (Figure 9-70). Length of the beam bottom depends on how it is framed into the supporting column or girder. If it rests on column or girder sides, the bottom is made the exact clear distance, less a fraction of an inch for leeway in assembly. In such a case

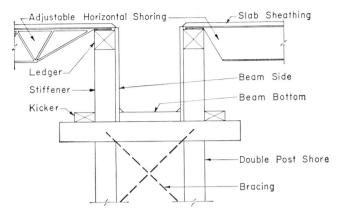

9-71 Heavy ledgers and stiffeners supported directly on head of double post shore carry the relatively heavier slab load transferred from long span horizontal shoring members.

the panel ends are usually beveled inward toward the supporting member, and keyed later on the outside.

If the beam bottom is to be butted against column or girder sheathing, its length is the clear span less total sheathing thickness of adjacent members at both ends (less a small allowance of about 2 in. for field fitting). The stiffening 2x4 members may be cut several inches shorter than the beam bottom sheathing if necessary to leave room for framing of intersecting members. More often, however, they rest on a column yoke or girder ledger which supports the beam form.

When beam bottom panels are assembled they are usually marked with identifying code number or letters to indicate their location in the structure. Shore spacing required should also be marked on the bottom to simplify accurate positioning in the field. A chamfer strip (unless prohibited by the specifications) can be lightly nailed to both edges of the beam bottom. At times it is preferable to insert these in the field.

Sides

If the beam side is made of boards, it will have vertical cleats or battens at 2 to 2½ ft intervals. Plywood beam sides eliminate the cleats, but may require vertical stiffeners * or vertical blocking to transfer deck load to the shores. For either wood or plywood sides the ledger is nailed to the beam side at a distance below the top to allow for the depth of slab forming joists that may be supported on the

---

* This is a problem for the form designer to settle. Uncleated plywood depth depends on slab load to be carried on beam sides as well as the plywood thickness.

beam sides. In some designs the distance also includes the slab sheathing thickness.

The kicker may be nailed flush with the bottom of the beam side, and will later be nailed to shore heads to prevent spreading of the beam sides when concrete is placed. Some prefer to keep the kicker separate for field installation, but putting it on as a part of the beam side gives added stiffness which is an advantage for members subject to repeated handling. Both ledgers and kickers are commonly cut a few inches shorter than the beam side so there is room for framing the intersections of members.

Vertical stiffeners may be nailed in place when the beam side is fabricated, and in the case of deep beams such as spandrels, some drilling for ties may be required. When the vertical members act primarily to transfer slab loads to the shores, some prefer to cut the required number of vertical pieces, and attach them loosely to beam side for final positioning in the field. In this way the blocking can be set directly over shore heads, in spite of any discrepancies in shore location that may occur. Completed beam sides should also be marked with identifying code numbers.

Exact length of the sides depends on the framing method chosen. They may be made equal to the clear span less the thickness of sheathing on both of the members which the beam intersects, less some fixed allowance, say 1½ in. at each end. This leaves a gap which is filled in the field with a beveled 2x4 (Figure 9-67) or other piece that can be fitted in if a larger opening is left. These small fillers can be easily removed before stripping the main form panel. Use of such short extender pieces lengthens the life of the form. When these pieces are damaged in stripping, they are simple and cheap to replace, compared with repairing or replacing the form panel. Their use also makes the beam form easier to strip.

Some use a piece of sheet metal to close such beam-girder or beam-column intersections neatly. Another method is to make the sides fit inside a beam pocket cut in column or girder sheathing. In this case, the sides are cut to the exact clear distance, less ½ to 1 in. and are beveled, sloping toward the supporting member.

The depth of beam sides depends on what slab form members frame in and how they are supported. It is usually the depth of beam, less depth of slab, less depth of slab sheathing, plus thickness of beam bottom framing when beam sides overlap the beam bottom. The slab sheathing generally rests on top of the beam side, is cut about ½ in. short of the full dimension, and is also beveled toward the beam side. If it is desired to have the slab sheathing butt up

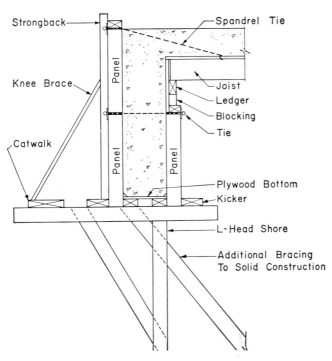

9-72 Forming of spandrel beam using prefabricated panels with ties. External strongbacks and knee bracing are shown. L-head shore is braced to solid, completed structure.

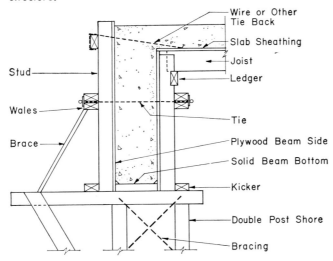

9-73 Stud and wale forming for spandrel beam, supported on braced double post shore

against the beam side, the depth of beam side is then figured as beam depth less slab thickness plus depth of beam bottom framing.

Beam Pockets in Girder Sides

As is evident from the foregoing discussion, there are two ways of framing the beam into the girder, much the same as framing a beam or girder into a column. The beam pocket may be made to exact size of inframing beam, plus a small allowance for give in the forms, and the beam form then butted up against it. Alternatively, the pocket may be made to beam dimension, plus allowances for thickness of beam bottom and sides, plus a small allowance for easy fitting. The beam form is then placed in the pocket with its ends beveled toward the supporting member. The beam pocket should be strengthened by framing with 1x2 or heavier stock around the opening, setting back the bracing as required by the contemplated framing in and support of sides or bottoms of beams.

Ties and Braces

A simple wire tie across the top of the beam is frequently used; for deep beams, ties like those in wall construction, are required. Their depth and spacing are determined according to design principles, depending on the rate and method of placing concrete, etc. Knee braces to the shore heads are more commonly used to hold beam sides against lateral pressure, and are particularly important for spandrel beams or interior beams that are formed independently of the slab.

Spandrel Beams

Spandrel beams require careful forming because of their critical location at the outer face of the building, where accurate alignment is the key to good appearance, even though they may be covered over with other materials. Spandrel beams are frequently deep enough to require ties through the beam forms, and the ties must be carefully located so as not to interfere with heavy reinforcement or the numerous inserts that are common in such beams.

Shore heads are commonly extended somewhat on the outside to accommodate knee braces required to maintain alignment. The extended shorehead frequently supports a catwalk (Figure 9-72) for work-

9-74 Snap tie hangers on structural steel frame support beam bottom ready for the setting of beam sides.

For Unfinished Work, Hanger Ends
Remain at Concrete Surface.

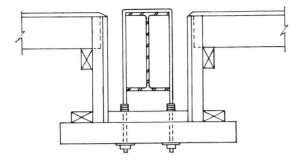

COIL-TYPE HANGERS

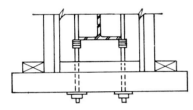

For Exposed Surfaces, Where Setback
is Specified, Recess to be Grouted
When Bolts are Removed.

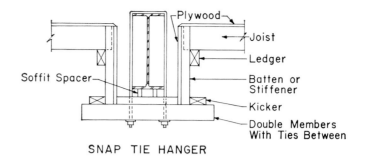

SNAP TIE HANGER

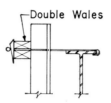

FASCIA HANGER

9-75 Typical beam encasement forms, showing both coil and snap type of hangers. Soffit spacers or spacing devices on the hangers hold beam soffit form at required distance from the beam to be encased.

men placing and vibrating concrete. In addition to the regular bracing of supporting shores, some form of tie back to permanent anchorage is desirable to prevent the entire spandrel beam assembly from being shoved out of line.

Suspended Forms for Fireproofing, Composite Construction

The various commercially available hangers that support beam forms for concrete encasement often required for structural steel frames make possible several different methods of forming such encasement. Frequently, as with other types of beam and girder forming, the beam form also supports deck forms. Where steel framing members are fairly closely spaced, this may be the only support required for the entire deck and beam concrete placement.

This same suspension system is adapted to placing concrete decks (see p. 181) on steel framing which is not encased. Similar methods are used for cast-in-place work supported on precast concrete members. Shoring may be required by the nature of the structural design for composite action, regardless of the ability of the structural frame to support the weight of forms and freshly placed concrete. This is a decision to be made by the structural designer, and he should clearly state in the contract documents the amount and kind of such shoring required. Otherwise, the contractor will be completely justified in supporting the formwork and its applied loads on the already placed structural frame.

Panel Assembly and Erection

Beam and girder forms are made up in the bottom and side panels previously described. If stripping of sides and bottom at the same time is planned, they may be assembled in a "beam box" for erection, if

173

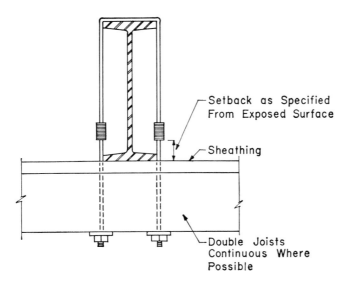

- Setback as Specified From Exposed Surface
- Sheathing
- Double Joists Continuous Where Possible

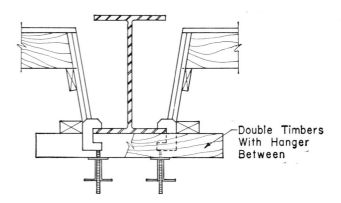

- Double Timbers With Hanger Between

9-76 Two methods of formwork assembly with hangers where bottom flange of steel beam does not require cover

9-77 One stage in the erection of beam forms. Shores are in place and the bottom panel rests on column forms and shores between columns.

9-78 Later stage in the beam form assembly, with beam sides in position, kickers and knee braces nailed. Note beam side built of cleated boards.

necessary hoisting equipment is available. Often, however, these forms are handled as separate panels; sides are stripped for early reuse and beam bottoms remain in place the longer time required.

For a typical structure where the beam and girder forms are preassembled in boxes, the erection sequence may be as follows: girder boxes are set in place spanning between column forms and supported on them at the ends; a few shore supports are set under them. Beam boxes are then set in place between girder forms with a few of their shores supporting them. Deck panels are placed, and shoring and bracing are completed as required under all members.

If the contractor has chosen to use separate side and bottom panels instead of boxes, girder bottoms are first set in place between column forms and shores placed under them (Figure 9-77). Then girder sides are set in place, lightly nailed to the bottom, and tied across the top or elsewhere as required. Any ties that are in a position to interfere with the setting of reinforcing bars may have to be added later. Beam bottoms between girders are then set on their shores, and beam sides set in place and lightly nailed. Then intersection details are taken care of, such as fitting in or attaching any filler pieces required for a neat closure.

After any slab forms that rest on beam or girder sides are placed, kickers are securely nailed to shore heads, and the entire form is brought to desired elevation by wedging or adjusting devices on the shores. When correct adjustment is obtained, cross bracing of the shore system may be completed.

If camber of beam or girder forms is required by structural design or formwork plan, it may be introduced by wedging, blocking, or other adjustment at the shore.

Beam and girder forms should be built to insure finished work within the specified tolerances for completed construction. In the absence of other stated tolerances, the recommendations of ACI Committee 347 for reinforced concrete buildings may be followed (see appendix, Section 2.4.1.).

Slab Forms

Forming for several common types of slab construction is discussed in this section:
Beam and slab construction
Flat slab or flat plate construction
Ribbed or waffle slabs (concrete joist construction)
Slabs supported on structural steel frame
Typical methods of construction are shown, but choice of individual members and determination of support spacing must be based on established design principles.

Beam and Slab Construction

Where the slab is cast monolithically with the beam and girder system, ledgers on the beam sides support joists on which the slab sheathing rests. If spans between beams are long enough to require additional support for the joists, stringers perpendicular to the joists are used. Additional shoring or scaffolding is provided to support the stringers.

The ledgers are generally a part of the beam side (p. 171) which is erected before the slab forming begins. The ledger is nailed to the beam side at a distance down equal to the exact depth of joists.* Beam sides must be carefully erected so that ledgers are at the proper elevation to give level support to slab joists. If this is not done, the ends of individual joists may have to be wedged up or cut down to make a level base for sheathing. If the beam form is cambered, slab forming follows the beam camber. Some contractors nail block supports to the beam sides at specified joist spacing instead of, or in addition to, the long ledger.

If stringer supports are needed for the joists, their shores must be set in place, and then stringers put in position. The stringer elevation should match that of the ledger top so that the slab form will be level. As soon as all joist supports are in position, the joists are

dropped into place at the required location.* To facilitate stripping, the joists are frequently not nailed to their supports. However, joists that are narrow in relation to their depth must be prevented from turning under load; nailing or bridging is often used. Some contractors prefer to use 4x4's which do not have the tendency to roll, and thus avoid the need of bridging or nailing.

Slab sheathing is next applied. Plywood sheets, individual boards, hardboard, or boards cleated into panels and laid loosely on the joists are used. A few nails at the corners keep the panels in place. To further facilitate slab forming, joists and sheathing can

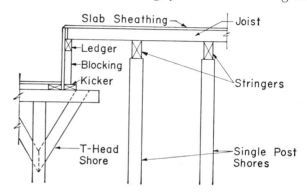

9-79 Slab form resting on beam ledger and stringers. For short spans between beams, intermediate stringer and shore support may not be required.

be prefabricated into large panels. The whole area between the beams can then be formed with a few large panels in a single operation without setting the joists separately.

Where a slab load is supported on one side of the beam only, edge beam forms should be carefully planned to prevent tipping of the beam due to unequal loading.

The details of the intersection of the slab decking and the beam side require special attention so that the panels will not become keyed into the concrete. Keying can be prevented by cutting the sheathing ¼ to ½ in. short of the inside face of the beam side form and beveling the sheathing panel edge. This and alternate methods are shown in Figure 9-68.

Flat Slabs, Flat Plates

Flat slabs and flat plates are supported directly by columns without the aid of beams and girders. In flat slab construction, columns flare out at the top to form capitals, and the slab may be thickened at the columns to make drop panels. In flat plate construc-

---

* Except in cases where slab sheathing is butted against beam side, in which case the distance down is equal to joist depth plus sheathing thickness.

* Since the deck panels between beams or girders are not loaded during erection, they are sometimes placed on the joists before the shoring and stringers are set. Stringer and/or shore supports can be placed and adjusted for elevation later on during the form erection work.

9-80 Forms are nearly finished for this beam and slab floor. Bar setters are at work in the background.

tion, capitals and drop panels are always omitted. Forming methods are generally the same for both flat slab and flat plate work, except for omission of drop panels in the latter.

The slab decking (sheathing) is usually formed of panels, but board sheathing can be used. Since there are no formed beam sides to support the joists, they are carried on stringers or ledgers resting on shores. In some designs, the joists may be carried directly by the shores.

The first step in construction of formwork for this type of structure is to erect and temporarily brace the shores. Stringers and joists are placed next and leveled by wedging or adjusting the length of the shores. Joists or stringers that are narrow in relation to their depth may require bridging or other lateral support to prevent their turning or tipping under load. Deck panels or sheathing are then placed over the joists. Deck panels adjoining the drop panel are beveled and extend over the top of the drop panel

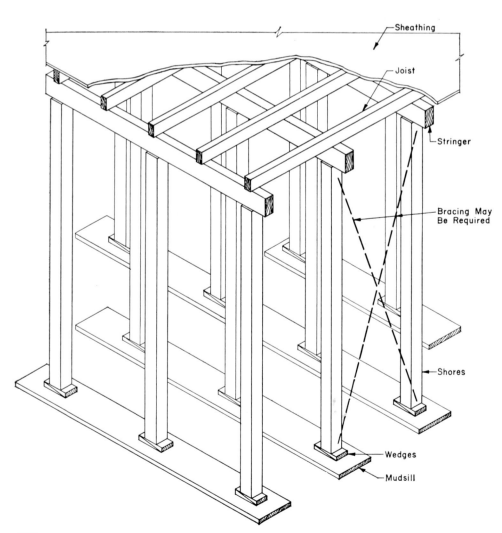

9-81 Typical flat slab formwork components

176

9-82 Drop panel supported on a pair of scaffold-type frames is built independently of slab forming, then framed in. Metal column form has flaring capital that joins drop panel.

9-84 Flat plate forming with prefabricated panels resting on steel stringers supported by adjustable metal shores. Slab sheathing is pieced around top of already cast column.

form just as slab sheathing extends over beam side forms.

Drop panels are built independently of the slab decking. They are usually supported on four shores or a pair of scaffold-type frames which are braced to form a rectangular supporting structure. Two ledgers may be attached to the top of this frame to support joists for the drop panel. Sheathing applied over the joists is cut out to fit the column cap, and the shallow panel side is attached. Drop panel units may also be shop fabricated and set in place on supporting shores.

Some flat slab and flat plate designs have voids in the slab. Materials for forming these voids are described on p. 64. Rubber or fiber tubes with the ends blocked to prevent concrete entering are commonly used. They are placed between upper and lower layers of reinforcement and tied to the bottom steel or formwork (Figure 9-83) to prevent them from floating.

"Permanent" shores are frequently needed in flat slab construction; that is, shores that remain in position while the rest of the formwork is stripped around them. This is accomplished by setting a small piece of formwork which can be detached from the rest, usually at the corner of four adjoining panels directly over a shore head. This method, however, leaves a conspicuous mark or indentation on the slab soffit and may be undesirable for exposed ceilings. Other methods of permanent shoring are described on p. 187.

Proprietary Forms

Special patented forming systems are available for flat slabs and flat plates, and a number of the standard panel systems can be adapted for this work. The same panels that are widely used for wall forms can be laid on the stringers to form the slab. One special system using metal panels and permanent shores is shown in Figure 9-85.

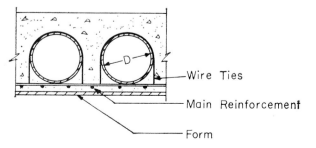

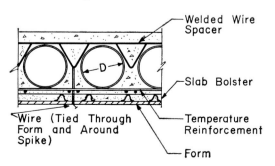

9-83 Two methods of tie-down for fiber tube void forms

9-85 Metal flat slab forming system using prefabricated panels. Detail shows how panels are stripped leaving shore in place. This method is suggested for concealed or non-architectural ceilings.

Concrete Joist Construction

Concrete joist construction is a monolithic combination of regularly spaced joists and thin slab cast in place to form an integral unit with concrete beams, girders, and columns. When the joists are all parallel, this is referred to as a ribbed slab or one-way joist construction. If the joists intersect each other at right angles, it is two-way joist construction, or the so-called waffle slab.

Proprietary forms made of a number of different materials for this type of forming are described on pp. 62-64, but this discussion of formwork erection will be limited to the widely used metal pans and domes. The forming system is basically the same, re-

gardless of the pan material. These forms are available on either a rental or purchase basis, and the supplier frequently provides engineering layouts for the forming. Installation and stripping of the forms, including the erection of necessary shores, stringers, and soffits or decking, may also be included as part of the service of a number of suppliers.

One-Way Joist System

Flange type pans nailed down to supporting soffit forms are used for this system, as well as the adjustable no-flange pans which are nailed to the side of the soffit form with double headed nails. Depth of joists can be varied with the latter by using nail holes at different levels on the sides of the pans. Use of adjustable pans nailed to the *sides* of soffit forms per-

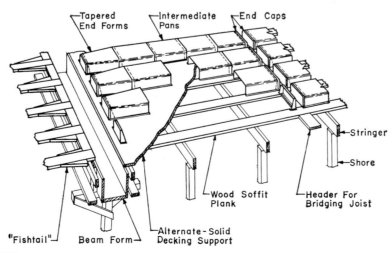

9-86 Nail-down pans for concrete joist construction may rest on either solid decking or an open system of soffit boards. If the latter are used, "fishtail" pieces (left) must be attached to soffit boards where tapered end pans are used.

9-87 One type of "long" pan form which has flange clamped to flange of adjoining pan. This longer pan reduces the number of seams, produces smoother exposed construction.

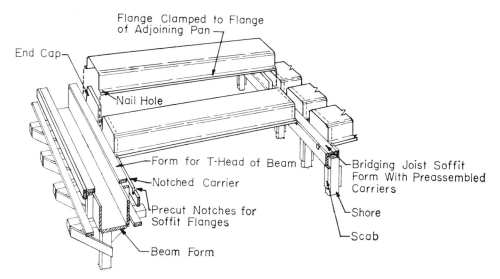

mits stripping of the pans while main soffit supports remain in place. Some flanged pans are also available with nail holes in the side which can be used for slip-in construction similar to the no-flange system. Long span steel pans (Figure 9-87) or wood forms for joist construction improve the appearance and reduce finishing where ceilings are to be exposed.

Nail-Down Pans

After beam, girder, and column forms are in place and braced, shoring and stringers are erected to approximate elevation. Wood soffit planks are then placed on top of the stringers, and are extended over to and on top of the beam side. (In some cases, the joist soffits are supported directly on shores.) Headers for bridging joists, beam tees, and "fishtail" wedges to accommodate tapered end forms are placed as needed. Shores are then adjusted to proper elevation in relation to supporting beams.

Flanged pans can then be nailed into position. A chalk line on the soffit form can be used to align the pans, so that precise alignment of the soffit boards is not required. End caps are placed first and work progresses toward the center of the member from both ends, overlapping the pans from 1 to 5 in. and setting a filler piece in the middle if required. After the pans are in place, they are oiled before reinforcing steel is set and mechanical trades make installations. A final check of elevation and alignment of the forms should be made before concrete is placed.

When concrete has obtained specified strength, shores and centering are removed. Stripping of the

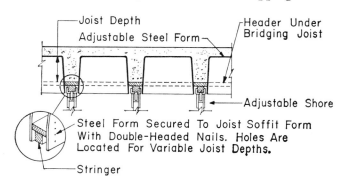

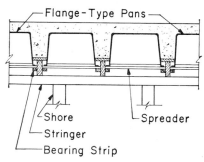

9-88 Workman setting nail-down type of pan on joist soffit form supported by heavy stringers

9-89 Cross section shows how adjustable pan forms are supported. Both flanged and unflanged types are shown.

pans is the final step, in contrast to the adjustable pans described below where pans may be removed for reuse ahead of supporting shores and joists.

Solid decking may be used to support nail-down pans if desired. It may offer some simplification of assembly, and provide a freer working area for laborers. It is particularly advantageous where all joists, beams, girders, etc. are designed at the same depth for a uniform floor thickness.

Adjustable Pans

Shores, stringers, and soffit forms for this type of forming are erected in the same way as for nail-down pans, except that the stringer (if one is required) is parallel to the soffit form and must be of a size to fit between the pan sides. Soffit boards must be cut to exact dimensions unless joist thickness has been designed to use standard lumber sizes. Soffit boards must also be cut to fit between tapered end pans. The pans are then adjusted to height and nailed to the side of the soffit form. A template (Figure 9-90) will aid in setting pans to proper height and will hold them temporarily in position at one end for nailing. This type of forming is frequently chosen for exposed joist ceilings, because joist soffits are formed without flange marks. The soffit forms must be very carefully positioned and aligned to give true, straight joists.

Two-Way Joist or Waffle Slab

These slabs are formed using dome-style pans. Shores and stringers are placed first, as was done for the one-way system. Soffit boards or solid deck forms are then set on the stringers. The design of a waffle slab usually requires some areas around the columns to be cast solid to the full depth of the joists. Domes

9-90 Template used to position adjustable form. One end of the pan is supported on template, the other rests on a form already nailed in place.

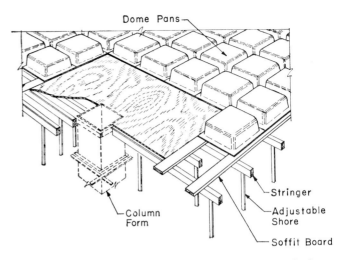

9-91 Two-way joist forming with prefabricated dome pans. Plywood deck form shown in area where solid slab is required may be extended to provide support for all the pans, replacing soffit boards.

are omitted, and solid deck forms are placed in these areas level with the joist soffit forms.

The steel pans or domes are placed next. They are nailed to the soffit form through holes in the flanges. If holes are not provided special hook-headed nails are used, or the pans can be anchored by driving a washer-headed nail at the intersection of four pans. Most designs require that the flanges be butted together on the soffit form, which facilitates alignment. If wider joists are required, a chalkline should mark the outside alignment of the pan flanges.

Filler Blocks

Lightweight concrete or clay tile filler blocks that remain in place are used in some designs. The formwork required is similar to that which supports the steel domes.

Slabs Supported on Steel Beams or Precast Concrete Beams

If structural steel framing is to be fireproofed, forms for encasing steel beams are required, as described on p. 173, and the slab forms usually are supported, at least in part, on the beam form sides. If additional intermediate supports are required conventional shoring is used. If the slab is simply on top of the steel or concrete, or has only the top flange of the beam embedded in it, slab formwork is frequently supported entirely from the already placed steel or concrete frame. If the structure is designed for composite action of slab with its beam or girder support, the design engineer should indicate whether special shoring is required.

Decking is laid on timber or steel cross pieces hung from the beams by conventional wire beam saddles or various other hanging devices. General system and materials are similar to other slab forming, except that support is from above rather than from shores below. Typical construction is shown in Figure 9-92. Further discussion is included under bridge decks, p. 198. The hangers are described on p. 57.

In some construction, timber supporting members for the deck forms are placed directly on the flange of the structural steel frame or precast concrete girder (Figure 9-94).

Metal Decking

Corrugated metal decking (described on p. 67) can also be used as formwork for slabs supported on previously placed steel or concrete members. It is laid across the existing structural members; joints may be left loose, welded, or clipped, according to details recommended by the manufacturer of the forming material. Longitudinal joints between decking panels are made by overlapping corrugations or interlocking flanges. The steel form remains in place after the concrete is cast.

Certain types of this decking material are designed to serve also as positive (bottom steel) slab reinforcement. If the decking form becomes part of the slab reinforcement, it should be galvanized and should not be subject to atmospheric corrosion.

Suggested Tolerances for Slab Work

In the absence of more rigid contract specifications, ACI Committee 347 suggests that formwork be constructed to produce slabs to the following tolerances. *Variation of slab soffit from the level or slope indicated on drawings* should not exceed ¼ in. in 10 ft, ⅜ in. in any bay or 20 ft maximum, or ¾ in. in 40 ft or more. *Variations in soffit level are to be measured before removal of supporting shores.* The contractor is not responsible for variations due to deflection, except when such deflections indicate inferior concrete quality or curing, in which case only the net variation due to deflection can be considered.

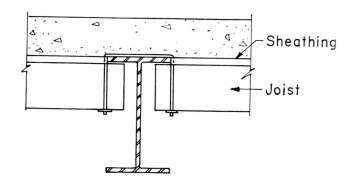

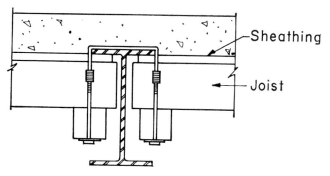

9-92 Two types of hanger devices used to support slab forms from existing steel structure

9-93 A simple method of slab forming when supporting steel joists are closely spaced and slab load is light. Clips attached to steel member support 2x8-ft panels of plywood.

9-94 Two methods of support from existing steel frame. At right, adjustable horizontal shoring members that carry slab forming are supported on timber ledger hung from top flange of steel beam. At left, timber supports for slab forms rest on lower flange of steel beam.

Variation in the sizes and locations of openings should be no more than ¼ in. *Variation in slab thickness* may be −¼ in. or +½ in. maximum.

Shoring and Scaffolding

Regardless of the type of shoring system—single post wood shores, adjustable shores, scaffold shoring towers, or horizontal shoring—the layout or plan should be worked out in advance by a qualified individual, with careful consideration of possible stress reversals in partially cured slabs when construction loads are applied later. This danger exists particularly when long span horizontal shoring is used on multistory work. A copy of the shoring layout should be kept on the job at all times, and it should be followed closely. If changes are necessary or desirable

9-95 Careful alignment of single post adjustable shores assembled in multi-tier form support. Note horizontal bracing and sill between tiers.

because of field conditions, approval of the shoring designer or engineer-architect should be secured. Permissible tower heights (for scaffold-type shoring) and necessary external lateral bracing should be shown on the layout.

Inspection before concreting should check actual layout against plans to see that shoring is correctly placed. Further inspection during and after concreting is also recommended.

Special attention should be given to beam and slab, or one-way and two-way joist construction to prevent local overloading when a heavily loaded shore rests on the thin slab. Shores resting on new construction which has not yet developed sufficient strength for full removal of shores should be placed as nearly as possible above the shores or reshores below to avoid excessive loading of the partially cured slab or beams. When vertical alignment of such shores and reshores is impractical, the shoring location should be approved in advance by the engineer.

Vertical shores for high multi-tier scaffolds must be set plumb and in alignment with lower tiers so that loads from upper tiers are transferred directly to the lower tiers (Figure 9-95). Particular care must be taken to transfer lateral loads to the ground or to completed construction of adequate strength. This may be done with guy wires, diagonal bracing, struts, or a combination of these, depending on the height and location within the structure. Committee 347 recommends two-way lateral bracing at each splice in the shore unless the entire assembly is designed as a structural framework or truss. Columns cast ahead of the deck are a further aid to lateral stability.

All shoring members should be straight and true without twists or bends. Shores or vertical posts must be erected so they cannot tilt, and must have firm bearing. Inclined shores must be braced against slipping or sliding. Shores supporting inclined formwork members should be firmly connected to the formwork after final adjustments of elevation have been made. Splices, couplings, or joints should be secure against bending and buckling. Connections of shore heads to other framing should be adequate to prevent the shores from falling out when reversed bending causes upward deflection of the forms.

The importance of adequate diagonal bracing to the safety and stability of the entire shoring system cannot be overemphasized (see also safety, p. 6). Diagonal bracing must be provided in both vertical and horizontal planes to provide stiffness and prevent buckling of individual members of the formwork. For multiple tier shoring, high scaffolding towers, or any other high shoring, increased attention is required to provide bracing that will prevent sway or lateral movement of shoring and buckling at splices. If the braces are required only to prevent buckling of individual members, struts may be used if anchored to masonry of adequate strength or to panel points of adjacent braced bays.

There may be a problem where two kinds of shoring are used in a single bay or section of formwork (combination of different types of shoring is not recommended). Tubular steel shoring does not show a gradual set or buckling as vertical load is applied; rather it fails abruptly when a certain maximum load is reached. On the other hand, wood shores (particularly adjustable wood shores) take an initial set when vertical loads are applied. When the two types are combined for shoring a single bay, if the wood shores are not raised enough to allow for this initial vertical set, part or all of the concrete load can be transferred to the rigid steel shores. Sudden shifting of load overloads these shores and may cause collapse. Where tubular metal shoring is used on top of wood shores, the two assemblies must be individually braced and individually stable, as complete structural connections between the two are not practical.

Mudsills or Shoring Foundations

Another consideration of critical importance to the stability of the shoring is the provision of adequate mudsills or other foundation support. A good foundation or sill distributes the shoring load over a suitable ground area. The footing must be firm, solid, or properly planked so that the load is evenly distributed to each leg. Unequal settlement of mudsills changes shore reactions and may cause serious overloading of some shores which do not settle as much as the others. Mudsills should not be placed on frozen ground, recently placed backfill, or where water will flow over them.

If the soil is of low bearing capacity, spread mudsills (Figure 9-98) are suggested. If the soil is, or is likely to become, incapable of supporting the superimposed loads without appreciable settlement, it may be stabilized with cement, lean concrete, or by other

9-96 X-bracing of shoring bents and inclined bracing to the ground at one end of this structure

9-97 X-bracing is needed for every tier of high wood shoring towers. Shoring for building construction is similar to that shown for bridges in Figures 9-133 and 9-137.

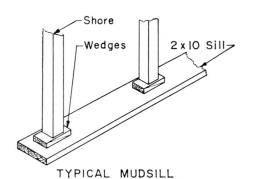

TYPICAL MUDSILL
GOOD SOIL BEARING

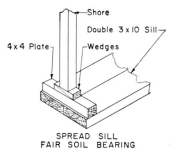

SPREAD SILL
FAIR SOIL BEARING

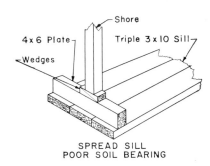

SPREAD SILL
POOR SOIL BEARING

9-98 Wood mudsills, showing spread types for fair and poor bearing

methods. Another alternative is to use piles or temporary concrete sills.

Shores supported on previously constructed floors may be assumed to have equal and uniform bearing. However sills may be required to distribute the shoring load on green concrete. Suitable sills are particularly important in concrete joist type of construction, or any other floor system involving voids, where a shore could concentrate an undesirable load on a thin concrete section.

Wood Shores

One-piece wood shores, cut slightly short of the desired elevation and adjusted by driving wooden wedges under the shore or at its top, are commonly used for slab and beam shoring where great heights are not involved. Braces can be readily nailed at any desired elevation.

Ends of all such shoring should be square cut and have a tight fit at splices. According to recommendations of ACI Committee 347, field constructed lap splices should not be used more often than for alternate shores under slabs or for every third shore under beams. Wood shores should not be spliced more than once, unless diagonal and two-way lateral bracing is provided at every splice point. Such spliced shores should be distributed as evenly as possible throughout the work. To avoid buckling, the splices should not be located near midheight of shores without lateral support, nor midway between points of lateral support. Splice pieces should be 2 ft or longer, no thinner than 2-in. nominal lumber or $\frac{5}{8}$-in. plywood, and as wide as the shore being spliced. Round shores should have three splice pieces, and rectangular shores should have one on each face.

Shores formed by overlapping wood members supported by patented splicing devices may be used when their load capacity has been established by tests and is guaranteed by a reputable manufacturer. However, when all shores are of this type, much more rigid lateral bracing is required. Field inspection of each splice is also necessary to insure that guaranteed capacity can, in fact, be developed.

For beam support, wood shores are usually assembled with T-heads (Figure 9-100) or L-heads for spandrel beams. Where loads are relatively heavy, a double post shore is frequently assembled with cross bracing. The double post shore gives greatly improved lateral stability and resistance to overturning when loads are unbalanced.

9-99 Long concrete sills constructed to support shoring bents, where the contractor elected to place grade slab after building was completed

9-100 Heavy T-head wood shores for beam support. Note bracing of heads, wedges at base.

Adjustable Shores

All-metal and wood-and-metal shores available with jack or screw type adjusting devices are used in much the same way as wood. They simplify the problem of fine adjustments of elevation made after the shores are in place. Manufacturers' load ratings are usually given for a certain extension of shore, and this should be carefully followed unless extra diagonal bracing is added to the system. Bracing may be nailed to the wood-and-metal shores anywhere on the wood members. All-metal single post shores usually have nailing brackets at fixed intervals or a movable device for attaching braces.

Adjustable shores have various fittings that can be interchanged at the top, providing extended height, flat bearing plate, U-head, or T-head. For support of stringers or other horizontal timbers in slab forming, the U-head is preferable because it permits nailing laterally into the stringer.

9-101 Double post shores with X-bracing

Scaffold-Type Shoring

Scaffold-type shoring * is generally assembled in tower structures consisting of a pair of prefabricated frames, plus the diagonal cross bracing required to make the tower. The manufacturer usually specifies or provides tower bracing, but additional bracing between towers is advisable for stability where large or high structures are involved, and bracing or guying to some solid construction is also needed.

Before assembling scaffold shoring, the parts should be checked and those that are heavily rusted, bent or bowed, or with damaged welds should be rejected. Locking devices, coupling pins, and any pivoted cross braces should also be examined to see that they are in good condition, and any that are not in good condition should be rejected.

Location of each tower, as shown in the shoring layout, should be marked on the floor by chalk line or other simple method. Sills are placed first, and then adjustment screws or base plates are distributed to each tower location. The adjustment screws should be set to their approximate final adjustment before tower assembly begins. The base unit should be leveled after assembly, regardless of how many upper frames are to be added.

Assembly should be planned so that the shoring load is carried on the legs of the frames, not on top horizontal members, unless the frames are specially designed for such a condition. It is important to avoid eccentric loading by centering stringers on the U-heads or top plates of the frame legs. Adjusting screw extensions should be kept to a minimum if the shores are being used at maximum rated load capacity.

The following check list of points to be covered in the final inspection of scaffold-type shoring was prepared by the Scaffolding and Shoring Institute. It is a good indication of approved erection practices.

1. Check to see that there is a sound footing, or sill, under every leg of every frame on the job. Check also for possible washout due to rain.

2. Check to make certain that all base plates or adjustment screws are in firm contact with the footing or sill. All adjustment screws should be snug against the legs of the frame.

3. Obtain a copy of the shoring layout that was prepared for the job. Make sure that the spacings between towers and the cross brace spacing of the towers do not exceed the spacings shown on the layout. If any deviation is necessary because of field condition consult with the engineer who prepared the layout for his approval of the actual field setup.

* Various types are described and illustrated on p. 70.

185

4. Frames should be checked for plumbness in both directions. The maximum allowable tolerance for a frame which is out of plumb is ⅛ in. in 3 ft. If the frames exceed this tolerance the base should be adjusted until the frames are within the tolerance.

5. If there is a gap between the lower end of one frame and the upper end of another frame it indicates that one adjustment screw must be adjusted to bring the frames in contact. If this does not help it indicates the frame is out of square and should be removed.

6. All frames must be connected to at least one adjacent frame to form a tower. Check to make sure that the towers have all the cross braces in place.

7. While checking the cross braces also check the locking devices to assure that they are all in their closed position or that they are all tight.

8. Check the upper adjustment screw or shore head to assure that it is in full contact with the formwork. If it is not in contact it should be adjusted or shimmed until it is.

9. Check to see that the obvious mistakes of omitting joists, using the wrong size ledger, or placing timber flat have not been made. Check the print to see that the lumber used is equal to that specified on the shoring layout. Check the general formwork scheme to make sure that it follows good standard practice for formwork.

10. If the shoring layout shows exterior bracing for lateral stability, check to see that this bracing is in place in the locations specified on the drawing. Check to make sure that the devices which attach this bracing to the equipment are securely fastened to the legs of the shoring equipment. If tubing clamps are used, make sure that they have been properly tightened. If devices for holding timber have been used, check to see that sufficient nails have been used to hold the bracing securely to the frame legs.

Horizontal Shoring

Adjustable metal members are used to support slab forms over comparatively long spans without intervening vertical shores. This reduction in the number of shores and leaving open spaces clear for work is a major advantage of horizontal shoring, but it frequently results in much heavier loads on the fewer vertical shores required. Consequently greater care must be taken in lacing and bracing the vertical shores that are used, and in providing solid footings or mudsills.

Because of the greater concentration of load at the vertical shore, more settlement due to compression of timbers will take place, and ledgers supporting the horizontal shoring should be set at an elevation to allow for this. About $\frac{1}{16}$ in. for each wood member concerned is suggested, or a total of $\frac{3}{16}$ in. for mudsill, shore, and ledger combined. The prongs of the shoring member should also have a minimum bearing of 1½ in. on the supporting vertical shore or ledger.

If beam sides are to carry the horizontal shoring, then they must be built heavier than common to carry

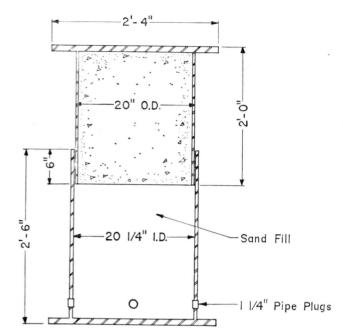

9-102 Sand jack consists of concrete-filled piston and sand-filled cylinder. Useful for slowly lowering heavy loads; motion can be stopped by replugging holes at the base.

the load (see Figure 9-71). A 4x4 ledger with stud support at each point where the horizontal shoring rests on the ledger is advisable. Extra bracing for stability must be provided, because the loading from the horizontal shoring on one side of the beam will occur before the beam is cast. This is even more critical for spandrel beams, and greater attention to diagonal bracing and tying is needed to keep spandrel beams in correct position.

Manufacturer's recommendations for adjusting length of the shoring members should be followed. Usually these members have a built-in camber of the correct amount to produce a *level slab as cast* when horizontal shores are loaded to the amount recommended by manufacturer. The designer must provide further camber if he wishes to offset deflection of the reinforced concrete member itself. If for some reason the full loading will not be carried—for example, horizontal shores are parallel to beam sides or walls, or a bulkhead occurs at midspan of the horizontal shore—compensating adjustments in camber must be made according to instructions of the manufacturer. Otherwise the finished slab may have an upward camber at that point.

This initial camber means that screed chairs set by instrument to desired elevation will be too low after concrete is placed in the forms and camber is removed. Screed chairs should be set from the deck sheathing to give correct slab thickness. It is preferable to place the screed bars perpendicular to the span of the horizontal shoring and to load the entire span before final strike off is made.

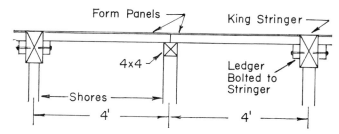

9-103 One method of leaving shoring in place when slab forms are stripped. Prefabricated panels 4 ft long used with king stringers 8 ft apart. Panels supported at one end on 2x4's bolted to king stringers and on 4x4 stringers at the other end. The 4x4's and their shores can be removed, freeing panels and leaving king stringers and their shores to support slab as long as desired.

Adjustment and Jacking

Jacks or wedges should be provided to permit alignment and facilitate stripping, and also as a positive means of adjustment and realignment if excessive settlement takes place at shores. Wedges may be used at the top or bottom of shores, but not at both ends. The best wedges are made of hardwood, driven in pairs to an even bearing. When final adjustment of shore elevation is complete, wedges are toenailed to the shore. Any wedges at the top of shores under sloping forms, which serve to establish bearing of form on shore, should be securely nailed to the shore head when adjustment is completed.

The various patented shoring devices have their own jack or screw adjustments for elevation. Screw jacks for pipe shores or scaffold-type shoring may be used at both top and bottom so long as they are secured by the shore or scaffold leg against loosening or falling out. A minimum of 8 in. embedment in the pipe leg or sleeve is recommended by Committee 347.

Where major movements of heavy loads are required, such as when a large section of shoring is to be lowered or raised as a unit, or where extremely careful control of decentering is required, hydraulic or pneumatic jacks are often used.

For decentering only, sand jacks lower heavy loads up to 300,000 lb, and offer the advantages of little deflection under load and no danger of failure during placing and curing. Their rate of travel is easily controlled by slight hand pressure over the plug hole to change flow of sand. Construction of such a jack is shown in Figure 9-102.

Permanent Shores

Since reshoring is such a costly and critical process, yet early reuse of form panels is so often desired, the installation of permanent shores frequently becomes important. A "permanent" shore is one that can remain undisturbed as form panels are stripped around it. Use of permanent shores avoids the special attention required to assure that reshores are placed uniformly tight under the slab. It also provides better assurance that shores are placed in the same pattern on each floor.

Two basic systems of permanent shoring are the *king stringer system* and the *king shore system*. The former uses ledgers on the sides of the stringer which may be released, permitting the removal of the joist and form contact surfaces between the stringers. Figure 9-103 shows how this may be done with panel slab forms, and Figure 9-104 shows its application with horizontal shoring members. In the *king shore system* the stringer is attached to the side of the shores so that the stringer may be removed, permitting the release of the joists and sections of the form contact surfaces. The shores and a trapped strip of contact surface are all that remain in place.

Shoring for Composite Construction

Shoring required by the structural design for composite action should be specified by the architect-engineer, and his instructions must be carefully followed. Such shoring must generally remain until concrete is fully cured, and so permanent shores are desirable.

Shoring of members which will act compositely with the concrete to be placed should be done with great care to assure sufficient bearing, rigidity, and tightness to prevent settlement or deflections beyond allowable limits. Wedges, shims, or jacks should be provided to make necessary adjustments before or

9-104 Horizontal shoring supported on braced wood bents. Filler pieces laid on top of bents allowed stripping slab decking and horizontal shores, while leaving wood bents in position as support for the partially cured slab.

during concreting as well as to permit removal without jarring or impact of the completed construction. Provision should be made for readily checking the accuracy of position and level during concrete placement.

Where camber is required, distinction should be made between that part which is an allowance for settlement or deflection of formwork or shoring and that which is provided for design loadings. The former is generally the responsibility of the contractor who designs the forms and supports unless such camber is stipulated by the engineer-architect. For acceptance purposes, measurement of camber provided for design loadings should be made after hardening of the concrete but before removal of the supports.

BRIDGE FORMWORK

Many of the problems and procedures in planning and building formwork for concrete bridges are the same as for other types of concrete construction. Forming bridge decks is similar in some respects to forming floor slabs in building construction, while bridge pier shafts are often adaptable to slip forming and climbing form techniques such as are used for silos and similar vertical structures. Smaller piers are formed like columns. Architectural appearance in

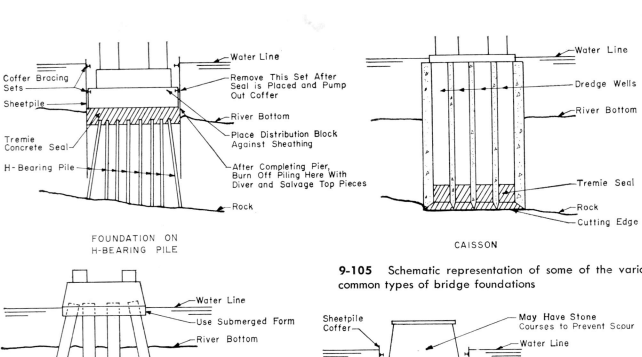

FOUNDATION ON
H-BEARING PILE

CAISSON

9-105 Schematic representation of some of the various common types of bridge foundations

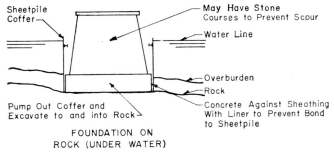

bridges is often as important as in buildings, and the same techniques for producing a desirable surface finish or texture, and pleasing effects are employed.

Site conditions are important in determining the most efficient way to build forms and plan a concrete bridge construction project. Both construction and removal of forms and their supports require careful advance planning. For a particular job, the contrac-

9-106 Interior wood form for the cutting edge and dredge well of caisson used for bridge support. Note 2x12's laid flat to support cutting edge until sinking begins. The timbers were later cut in a predetermined sequence to give caisson an even start.

tor may observe that savings can be made by using a different formwork technique or construction sequence than that envisaged by the designer. Permission from the owner or engineer to propose alternates will give the contractor greater freedom in exercising his ingenuity to achieve economy through better methods. It is wise to include in the specifications a provision for making such changes, particularly in the location of construction joints, with the approval of the engineer. Otherwise many bidders may feel that no changes whatever will be accepted.

Bridge forms are discussed in terms of substructure and superstructure; the typical bridge substructure has a foundation that supports two or more piers which are joined at the top by a pier cap. The superstructure, or deck, rests on the pier caps. Formwork is described here in the order that it would be used to build the bridge: that is, first the foundation or lower part of the substructure; then the upper substructure or piers; then the superstructure or deck. Arch bridges are treated separately.

Foundations

There are several different types of bridge foundations and many different designs depending on the location of the bridge, length of span between supports, whether over water or land, and the bearing material on which the foundation can be supported. Since each bridge presents its own problems in type of foundation and the conditions under which it must be constructed, the foundations usually offer the great-

est opportunity to explore alternate methods of construction and arrive at one that is most satisfactory and economical.

Caissons

Caissons are hollow structures sunk into position as excavation proceeds inside or under them. Built of steel or concrete, they offer an economical and practical method of constructing a foundation that must be located at great depth below ground or river bottom. Construction of the heavy caissons required for bridge support requires skilled supervision by those experienced in this type of work. Only a brief description of some of the formwork required for concrete caissons can be presented here.

Open caissons may be round, rectangular, or of any shape dictated by structural needs. They may be built as a shaft whose entire hollow center is a single dredge well, or the caisson shaft may be of large area requiring a number of dredge wells within. The bottom of the caisson is a sharp cutting edge, usually tipped with steel. If below the water line,

9-107 Later stage in work on the caisson shown in 9-106. Inside form for caisson wall is in place, and crane is setting outer form.

189

9-108 Rectangular wood forms for dredge wells in open caisson. Note sheet metal wrecking strips at corners to facilitate stripping.

dredge wells are open to the bottom so that muck may be removed as the caisson sinks. When the caisson reaches the desired elevation below the water line, tremie concrete is usually placed in the bottom of the dredge wells to seal and stabilize the structure (Figure 9-105). Some designs call for complete filling of the dredge wells.

Forms are required for caisson walls, cutting edges, dredge wells, working chamber, and man access tubes (the latter two for pneumatic caissons). Forms may be built of wood or steel, or a combination of the two. The caisson may be cast and sunk as a complete unit, but for the large depths generally involved, only the cutting edge portion and a small section above it are cast initially. Then the forms are raised, and as the lower part of the caisson sinks, the next section is cast, adding weight to assist in the sinking. With this method of climbing or lifting the forms, the wall forms for outer wall and dredge wells are generally reused many times. The cutting edge

is frequently cast in a steel fabricated unit which is left in place to produce a hard, sharp edge.

Dredge well forms, or internal forms, need not be as accurate and smooth as the forms for the external surfaces and cutting edges of the caisson. Their main requirement is that they be readily removable and replaceable if they are not left as a permanent part of the caisson. Stripping is usually more of a problem than with external forms. One method to ease stripping (Figure 9-108) makes use of sheet metal strips as closures forming the beveled corners of wood forms.

When a concrete caisson is to be started on soft ground it may be necessary to provide extra support until the first 10 or 15 ft are cast. The cutting shoe may be placed on closely spaced transverse timbers (Figure 9-106) and blocking used to support the beveled edge of the caisson, thus spreading the load and relieving some of the pressure on the cutting edge. When the caisson is ready for sinking, timbers must be carefully cut or removed to maintain even pressure of the cutting edge on the ground and prevent tipping. Sand islands are sometimes constructed in shallow water to permit starting a caisson in the dry.

The sinking must be carefully controlled to keep a level position while the caisson is being formed. Level can be checked by a water-tube level system with indicators located at four corners of the caisson. If the caisson becomes slightly out of plumb during sinking, it is important to cast the next lift out of plumb, parallel to the preceding one, so that an irregularity or "dog-leg" is not created in the plane of the concrete. It is usually possible to correct a slight tip in the caisson, and it is better to keep the walls a straight line since these "dog-legs" greatly increase the frictional drag on the sinking caisson.

In some cases a cofferdam is attached to the outside of the caisson to permit sinking below water before concreting. In this case, the cofferdam panels become a part of the permanent form. Concrete is placed against them and they are not stripped. If

9-109 Round steel dredge well forms being set in place on large open caisson for Throgs Neck Bridge

the upper part of the caisson is smaller than the lower, formwork may be built inside the cofferdam. After the upper part of the caisson is cast and the caisson has reached final elevation, this formwork and the upper section of the cofferdam are removed.

Piles

Solid support for a bridge foundation can be provided by H-bearing piles driven through the overburden into solid bearing material, as shown schematically in Figure 9-105. To avoid rusting, H-bearing piles must not be exposed to sea water, acid waters, or to certain types of overburden such as cinders or ash fill. One way to avoid continuous contact with water is to drive the piles below the river bottom and cover with a concrete cap.* When such a pile cap foundation is being built in water, a cofferdam is installed surrounding the piling, and a tremie seal is cast before dewatering to prevent "blow in." Tremie concrete cast against sheet piling requires no forming preparations other than cleaning the sheet pile underwater to assure a good bond.

After removing water and cleaning the tremie surface, forms are set for the distribution block and concrete is placed. The form may be simply a liner placed against the sheet piling of the cofferdam to

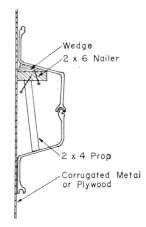

Wedge
2 x 6 Nailer
2 x 4 Prop
Corrugated Metal or Plywood

9-110 A method of attaching lining to sheet piling of cofferdam to prevent bonding of concrete to piling. This makes it possible to salvage piling.

prevent bonding of the concrete to the sheet so that the latter can be salvaged. This liner is usually a disposable type, either light corrugated metal or light plywood. It is nailed to 2x6 nailer blocks wedged into the recesses of the sheet pile, as shown in Figure 9-110.

The cofferdam remains in place until all operations below water level have been completed, including the setting of forms and concreting for the lower part

* Another technique is to encase part or all of each pile in concrete. This can be achieved by using watertight forms that are placed over the tops of the piles after they are driven. The forms are then filled with concrete and may subsequently be withdrawn or may be left in place. These forms are usually prefabricated of steel.

of the piers. Then, instead of removing the sheet-pile cofferdam completely, the sheets are burned off at the top of the tremie seal, thus salvaging the top of the sheeting while the lower part remains in place as a guard against scouring.

Concrete piling is usually used where the pier base is above the river bottom. A cap is cast encasing the heads of the piles at about water level (Figure 9-105) and serving as the foundation block for the piers. The form for this cap can be hung on the piling a few feet below the water surface. Another technique is to first drive some wooden piles on which the cap form is supported before the concrete piling is driven. Holes in the form serve as templates for setting and driving piles. After the piles are driven, the form is filled with concrete. The bottom or template is left in place, but side forms for the cap are stripped.

Forms used underwater present unusual problems of locating, aligning, and sealing. Elaborate methods of locating forms and piles from the surface must be developed, using sighting towers or preplaced guides, or divers must work underwater to relay instructions to guide the components into position. Sealing of openings to contain the concrete must be carefully carried out in advance since corrective measures after concreting commences are difficult and costly.

If underwater forms are to be salvaged for reuse, it is desirable that they be designed so that the stripping may be carried out from the surface. Thus, if possible, forms should have no undercuts or re-entrant angles that make it difficult or impossible to withdraw them from overhead. Hydraulic cylinders are sometimes used to jack the form open and break it from the concrete so it may be withdrawn. Special fittings on the form may be required to facilitate this operation.

Rock or Soil Offering Direct Support

If the ground level or river bottom is not too far above the rock bearing surface, a foundation can be built directly on the rock without resorting to piling or caissons. On land it is simply a matter of excavating to the rock, sloping the walls of the excavation to prevent cave-in as shown in Figure 9-105. Usually the excavation is continued a few feet into the rock to provide a key. Footing forms are built and anchored or braced to the rock, which serves as the bottom surface of the form. Then the foundation is concreted.

In water, a sheet-pile cofferdam is first driven through the overburden into the rock. After water is pumped out of the cofferdam, muck is excavated from the cofferdam until the rock bearing surface is exposed. The excavation may be continued into the rock for a few feet so that the foundation will key to the rock. The rock surface is cleaned, and a form liner of sheet metal or plywood is fastened to the sheet-pile. Concrete is placed directly on the rock, which serves as the bottom form surface. When the concrete has hardened sufficiently, the form for the pier base is erected on it and braced against the cofferdam. After pier construction rises above the water level, the cofferdam sheet piling may be withdrawn.

Whenever a cofferdam is used to back up a form liner or the bracing for form sides, the concrete pressure against the sheet piling is opposite to that which it is primarily designed to withstand. Normally this is of no consequence; however, if preplaced aggregate is being used, with high injection pressures, there could be an extremely high outward pressure on the cofferdam, and this must be taken into account in its design.

As in other types of construction, it is sometimes found that the soil beneath a land bridge or the land portion of an over-water bridge is firm and capable of supporting a pier or arch on a spread footing. Forms for such footings are relatively simple and can be constructed in the same manner as footing forms for buildings. The ground is leveled to serve as the form bottom, and the form sides are steel panels or built up of wood sheathing braced by stakes in the ground.

Piers

A pier shaft rests on the foundation or pier base and supports the bridge superstructure at the necessary height. Piers usually are rectangular or circular in cross section, but some may have more complex shapes for architectural effect. Pier sides may be vertical, battered, or stepped. The type of formwork depends on the shape and height of the piers and the number of similar piers.

When the bridge has many piers or the piers are quite high, careful study is justified to achieve maximum reuse of forms. Where considerable reuse is possible, pier forms are frequently custom made in steel by a supplier who specializes in this work. Wood forms as well as wood and metal forms may also be used. For smaller piers, forming materials are much the same as for building columns described on p. 162.

Forms Moved for Reuse

When there are few piers and they are of considerable height, it is desirable to have forms that can be reused vertically in successive lifts. If a pier has a constant cross section for all or a large part of its height, it is easy and economical to construct an efficient climbing form or slip form. Climbing forms should be designed to be easily loosened and raised for each successive lift.

However, a shaft that is battered or otherwise changes cross section is more of a problem. It requires a more expensive form that can be adjusted or modified as it is raised, or it may make the reuse of forms for successive lifts impractical.

In the case of a large number of piers of uniform shape, forms may be moved horizontally, using a different form for each lift, as in the form planning example, p. 24. Forms are designed to be removed from one pier and placed in position at another pier as simply as possible. Where pier shafts are relatively small in cross section, it may be possible to avoid the use of through tie rods. In this case, frequently the form may be merely loosened at the corners and lifted up and over the completed concrete instead of disassembling the panels, as in Figure 9-112.

9-111 Forms for pier of large, elongated cross section, tied internally. Barge mounted crane is placing concrete for the fourth lift. Form was lifted vertically for reuse.

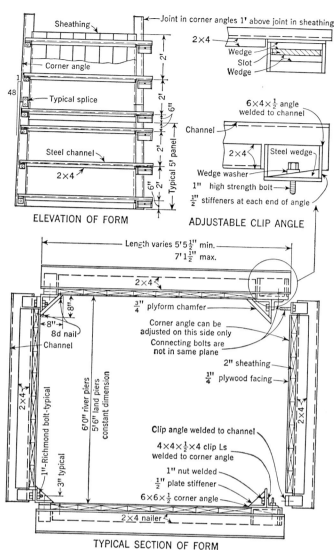

ELEVATION OF FORM

Sheathing

Corner angle

Typical splice

Steel channel

2×4

Joint in corner angles 1' above joint in sheathing

2×4

Wedge
Slot
Wedge

6×4×½ angle welded to channel

Channel

2×4

Steel wedge

Wedge washer

1" high strength bolt

½" stiffeners at each end of angle

ADJUSTABLE CLIP ANGLE

Length varies 5'5½" min.
7'1½" max.

2×4

¾" plyform chamfer

Corner angle can be adjusted on this side only

Connecting bolts are not in same plane

2" sheathing

¼" plywood facing

8d nail

Channel

2×4

1"—Richmond bolt-typical

6'0" river piers 5'6" land piers constant dimension

3" typical

Clip angle welded to channel

4×4×½×4 clip Ls welded to corner angle

1" nut welded

½" plate stiffener

6×6×½ corner angle

2×4 nailer

TYPICAL SECTION OF FORM

9-112 Details of adjustable lower lift forms built in 5-ft sections for horizontal movement from one pier to another. Piers varied in size at the bottom, and in height of lower lift, but all had two sloping faces of constant width and the same batter for the entire job. One adjustable side moves in or out by means of slotted clip angles while bolts remain in place. Clip angles are connected to corner angles, but connecting bolts are not in the same plane. To strip form, bolts in three corners are loosened, form is jacked to break bond, and lifted off as a unit by crane.

Various methods of breaking the bond of the form with the concrete are employed. In some cases, a positive corner releasing device is used to back the form away from the concrete in addition to loosening the corner. In other cases, a jack at the top of the lift working against a cross attachment connected to the form helps to break the bond. In some instances air nozzles may be installed in the form panel so that a shot of compressed air will break the seal.

9-113 Steel forms for large diameter columns with heavy cap tie struts for typical pier work. The top of the form indicates offset to a smaller column above this point. Access ladders are a part of the form. Temporary shores support strut form during assembly, but no external support will be required when assembly is complete and concreting begins.

Round Piers

Round bridge piers of relatively small cross section may be formed just as round columns with any of the several standard forming materials or techniques, including single use fiber tubes and ready-made metal forms. Heavy duty circular steel forms made of rolled sections bolted together are also available especially for bridge work. These may be of standard design or made to order for a particular job. The bolted flanges form stiffening rings that add to the rigidity of the form. Frequently the pier cap is a part of the assembly, as shown in Figure 9-113, and is supported on the side forms.

Stonework Facing

When the bridge design specifies that the pier shaft or base be enclosed by stonework, the stonework may serve as the outer form for the pier concrete. The stones are laid and mortared, and an open-face formwork is constructed on the outside of the stonework (Figure 9-114) to hold the stones in position. If the stone has a rough cut exterior surface, it may be necessary to use extensive wedging between the stones and the formwork to hold the stones in position, as shown in the picture. Tie rods pass through the spaces between stones, and tie rod size is limited by the maximum permissible joint spacing of the stones.

Massive Piers

Some piers or pier bases are low and wide so that their construction is more like that of mass concrete instead of tall shafts. Generally, such piers require a very large form or combination of form panels. Since panels or form sections are apt to be quite large, capacity of lifting equipment may be a critical factor. If it is possible to erect lifting beams and tackle of sufficient capacity to handle a complete form unit or the maximum practical size of form section, substantial savings in handling costs can be made.

Frequently special sections to form curved nose surfaces or other irregular shapes are made separately from the main slab form. Where galvanized steel or wrought iron plates are to be cast into the concrete at the waterline to prevent scour, the plate may be constructed as part of the form and left in place when the form is stripped. If the form is erected on top of the foundation inside a cofferdam, the walls of the form may be braced against the walls of the cofferdam, thus minimizing the need for ties.

Vertical Alignment

Guy lines connected from the upper part of the form to the ground provide one means of positive control of vertical alignment (Figure 9-116). Other methods may be more convenient and faster, or are used where it is not practical to connect guylines to the ground or to the foundation or base. The form may be aligned by adjustable jacks set on kickers attached

9-114 Concreting of pier structure with stone facing set in place and supported by vertical timbers held in place by ties. Wood wedging between rough stone face and back of timbers maintains alignment.

9-115 Massive supported formwork for coal unloader foundation similar to that sometimes required for massive bridge piers. Note 36WF beams embedded in previous lift for temporary support of formwork.

to the previous lift of concrete, or by cables with turn-buckles inside the form and connected to the previous lift.

Some free-standing circular steel forms have been made to produce straight vertical columns without the aid of formwork guying. A 2-ft lap ring at the top, held in place by the hardened concrete, supports and aligns form sections for the next lift.

Access for Workers

Pier shafts may be quite high and therefore present problems in getting workmen and equipment up to the point at which forms are being assembled or concrete placed. Working platforms, ladders, stair-ways and catwalks between shafts are usually necessary and often can be built as part of the formwork (Figure 9-113). A ladder can be bolted to inserts in the pier shaft, and scaffolding can be supported from the formwork as in Figure 9-116, or an access tower and stairway can be built as in Figure 9-115. Sometimes form reinforcing members can do double duty as ladders.

External Ties

Architectural appearance requirements may prevent the use of internal tie rods for pier shaft forms, and sometimes complex reinforcing steel within the shaft makes the use of internal tie rods impractical. External bracing or tying must be used in such cases, and various methods are readily adaptable to pier forms (see Figure 9-63).

Steel strapping is a simple method of tying together the sectors of a circular form, and it also may be adapted to piers with cross sections other than circular by using filler adapters or shaping the form studs or wales to fit the curve of the strap and develop its full hoop strength. Usually heavy steel structural angles or channels can double as stiffeners and ties. Drilled and bolted or nailed to wood sheathing, or welded to a sheet metal liner, the angles or channels may extend beyond the panel edges to be bolted to mating stiffen-ers on the adjacent panels to tie the form together.

Pier Caps and Tie Struts

Since a pier generally is designed to support a bridge deck that is much wider than the pier, a cap is cast at the top of the pier to distribute the load and support the full width of the deck. This may be a hammerhead- or T-cap at the top of a single shaft pier. More frequently, however, the cap connects two or more pier shafts at the top, thus serving as a tie

9-116 Circular heavy-duty shaft forms with strut beams being cast as one unit. Lower strut has been stripped and forms are in place for second lift and second strut. No shoring required for this type of formwork. Note guy wires for alignment, and workers' scaffold suspended from second level strut form.

9-117 Heavy-duty shoring frames support formwork for bridge superstructure between already cast piers. Steel beams supported on two rows of shoring frames kept rail-road clear for traffic.

9-118 Massive pier strut forms carried by steel beams which are supported on I-beam inserts cast in the pier shaft concrete

9-119 "Self-supporting" pier cap forms which are carried on a heavy yoke structure supported by center of the piers. This unusual structure was constructed with hinges so that the bottom can move outward on both sides and the entire form unit can be carried to the next concreting location.

strut. Where piers are especially high, one or more additional tie struts may connect the shafts at lower levels (Figure 9-116).

A pier cap is a beam, and forms for caps and struts may be constructed and supported in much the same manner as beam forms. To get maximum reuse of form parts, it should be possible to strip the strut sides separately from the bottom for early reuse.

Strut forms may be supported in various ways: as part of the shaft form; by shoring up from the ground with tubular scaffold-shoring or timber posts; on adjustable single post shores for low elevations; or

on steel I-beams or other inserts cast into a previous lift of concrete. For light beam caps on circular pier shafts, friction sleeves can be used to carry all or part of the cap formwork. Camber of the strut form may be required to assure desired final elevation of the strut.

Superstructures

Bridge superstructures include a deck or roadway, curbs, sidewalks, and railings or parapets. Concrete bridge decks may be simple slabs for short spans or slab and girder construction for longer spans. They may be entirely cast-in-place, entirely precast, or a combination of cast-in-place slab with steel or precast concrete supporting girders. Many of the forming problems and techniques are similar to those for other slab work, the major difference being the problem of support for formwork when spans are at great height, or over water, or unsatisfactory earth support.

Monolithic—Simple Slab, Beam and Girder

Bridge decks with short spans between supports (less than 25 ft) may be built as simple slabs. Since these simple slab bridges are often designed with the

9-120 Single post adjustable shores support pier caps at low elevation.

196

9-121 Movable steel formwork for simple, thick slab bridge deck. Steel form members supported from the pier structure give completely free area beneath. This form is built with sides that fold down, so that the entire unit can be stripped and moved forward between piers for concreting of the next span. Various kinds of scaffolding and shoring could also support forms for this type of slab.

9-122 Construction of slab and girder formwork for highway overpass; details of beam and girder forming are similar to those found in building construction, but heavier members and heavier supports may be required.

expectation that the curbs will supply part of the bending resistance, the curbs may be cast integrally with the deck slab. Formwork for a slab deck is like that for any other slab; sheathing of metal, wood, plywood, or other material is supported on joists and stringers. Edge forms are equal in height to the curbing and are braced externally from joists extending beyond the deck width. The form is supported from below by any one of the various types of shoring, or on heavy horizontal members supported on the piers.

On projects where there are many identical spans, large one-piece forms have frequently been used for an entire span, then lowered to barges and floated to the next position for casting. Figure 9-121 shows a similar single-unit form for casting an entire span with solid ground below.

A bridge deck of cast-in-place slab and girder design is similar in construction and forming problems to an integral slab and beam floor. In the design of the bridge, the curb is not usually considered a structural member and therefore may be cast after the centering for the main slab has been removed. This will prevent the curb from assuming any of the dead load. The forms should include bulkheads separating the curbs from the roadway, and the bulkheads are removed before the curbs are cast.

9-123 Typical installation of deck forming supported on steel structure. Main supporting form members are first hung between steel girders and adjusted for elevation.

9-124 Spacer blocks are set on main supporting members and joists are laid across the spacer blocks.

9-125 Decking material, plywood in this case, is then laid in place and lightly nailed to joists. Deck elevation is above the top flange, and sheathing is built down at an angle to provide a haunch for the girder.

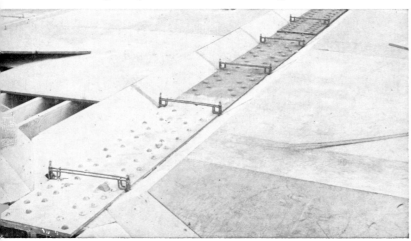

Cast-in-Place Deck Supported on Steel or Precast Girders

Formwork details may differ, but the general method of forming slabs supported on steel or precast concrete girders is the same. Formwork members either rest on the lower flange or haunch of the beam, or they are hung with various patented devices from the upper flange. (See also: shoring for composite action, p. 187.) A number of these hanging devices are illustrated on p. 57. Materials used may be any one or combination of those used for regular slab work. One major problem is that of access since work may be on long spans over canyons or waterways.

Another problem arises when there are excessive variations in the camber of steel or precast concrete girders. Adjustment of the slab thickness to give a smooth upper roadway may go beyond tolerances permitted in slab construction. A preferred design uses small haunches over the top flange. Changing the depth of haunch compensates for camber variations without changing slab thickness. Forming for such a haunch is shown in Figure 9-125.

Figures 9-123, 9-124, and 9-125 show sequence of operations in forming a bridge deck using adjustable hangers supported on the top flange of the steel beam. Main supporting form members are first hung between the steel girders and adjusted for elevation. Spacer blocks are set on these wood members and joists laid across the spacer blocks. Decking material is then laid on the joists and lightly nailed. Spacers and joists raise the level of the deck several inches above the top flange of the girders so the sheathing is built down at an angle to fit against the girder flanges

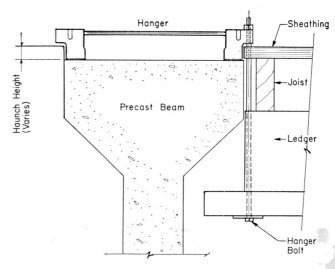

9-126 Typical forming method for deck slab supported on precast girder. This design provides for a small haunch.

and provide a haunch above each girder. It is important to avoid twisting of outer girders where there may be a hanger load on one side only. Bracing against interior girders should be used when this condition is critical.

A hanging device for a slab supported on precast concrete girders is shown in Figure 9-126. Forming hung from such a device may be used for slabs with or without adjustable haunches. Another method of formwork support using the bottom haunch of the precast girder is shown in Figure 9-127. Jacks like those pictured may also be used to support forms from the bottom flange of steel beams.

The structural design sometimes includes cast-in-place concrete diaphragms to give lateral support to the precast beams. Usually these are cast-in-place along with the deck, and the form construction (wood or metal) is similar to that for any other beam intersecting a slab. The diaphragm form may be hung from inserts cast in the beam or supported on a flange of the beam. Usually the diaphragm is concreted, then reinforcing steel is placed in the deck form and the deck is concreted.

To eliminate the problem of stripping forms high in the air, "permanent" metal forms are sometimes laid directly on steel or precast concrete bridge members. This form material is corrugated for strength so that no stiffening studs or joists are needed. It is usually used on short spans where intermediate supports are not required.

The corrugated metal may rest on top of or between the already placed bridge framing, and various methods of attaching it to bridge members are suggested by different suppliers. One method is shown in Figure 9-129.

Entirely Precast Deck

Site precasting of slab and beams for an entire bridge structure is similar to site precasting for any large structure, and forming problems are discussed in Chapter 16. After precasting, the construction problem is largely one of erection of the units and supplying any temporary support required until continuity of the members is established. The only forms required for the cast-in-place concrete may be those required for joints between the members (p. 310), and on some structures, not even these are required.

Expansion Joints

Where the design requires expansion joints in the slab, appearance and smoothness of the road surface can be improved if the expansion joint is narrow at the top and wider at the bottom. A method of achiev-

9-127 Double 2x4's spanning between lower flanges of precast girder. Screw jacks on these members support double 2x6's that carry joists and plywood decking.

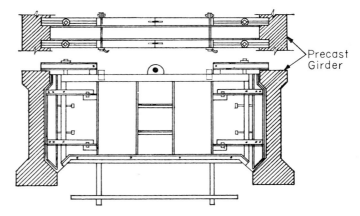

9-128 Plan and elevation of prefabricated steel form for diaphragm between precast girders

9-129 Close-up of stay-in-place forms. Steel angle supports are held in position along the upper edges of the beam by through bolts or by straps welded to shear keys projecting from the top surface of the beam. Corrugated sheet metal form panels are supported on the angles and usually welded to them. The angles serve as deck form corners to prevent leak-through of concrete during placing.

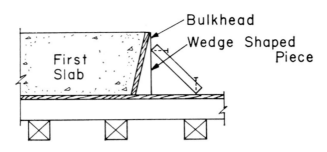

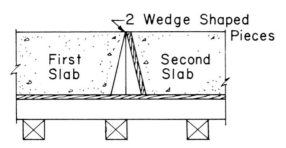

9-130 This method of forming expansion joints in bridge deck slab produces a joint wider at the bottom than at the top for improved appearance and smoothness of roadway.

ing this is illustrated in Figure 9-130. A light plywood bulkhead is laid against wedge-shaped vertical pieces braced by diagonal struts. After concrete for the first slab section is placed, the plywood bulkhead is removed, the wedge-shaped pieces are moved against the end of the slab and are backed up by a second set of wedges that slant in the opposite direction. The plywood bulkhead is laid against these, and concrete is placed in the second section of the slab. After

9-131 View from below shows form supports for canti-levered sidewalk where main bridge members are steel. Forms at left stripped, showing finished appearance of the overhang.

the concrete has hardened, the bulkhead and the wedges are slipped out of the expansion joint, leaving an opening that is narrow at the top and wide at the bottom.

Overhangs and Sidewalks

Overhangs including sidewalks are commonly cast along with the bridge deck, with horizontal construction joints on which the curbs or guard rails above deck level are cast separately later. If the overhangs are to be cast separately, inserts for supporting their formwork are sometimes cast in deck slabs, or girders, pier shafts, spandrel walls or arch rings, depending on the type of bridge being built.

In a bridge with steel girders or flanged concrete girders, sidewalk or overhanging deck formwork may be supported on the girders as shown in Figure 9-131. Braces for this formwork were pre-assembled in a field carpentry shop to speed erection. Another type of overhanging slab sidewalk formwork construction is illustrated in Figure 9-132.

Support for Superstructure Forms

The choice of shoring or falsework support for bridge deck forms depends in large measure on the height above ground and the nature of the terrain. Other site factors, such as need to keep a highway or railway open for traffic, will also influence the layout of deck supports. Since the decks for long span girder or rigid frame bridges usually are much deeper at the piers than at center-span, the falsework often must be built up to a specified curvature using the same techniques as in constructing arch forms.

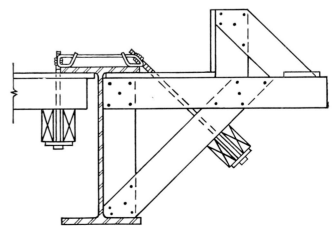

9-132 Hanger frame with inclined tie supports forms for simple overhang from steel girder.

9-133 High timber shoring for bridge superstructure has a network of horizontal and diagonal bracing in both directions to stabilize the towers at great height. Solid sills are used between tiers of poles and members are carefully aligned above one another. Note timber plates on which the falsework stands. Hydraulic jacks are being used to skid entire falsework into position for casting a similar adjacent structure.

9-134 Powered platform traveling on rails on the precast bridge girders moves beneath the deck for form stripping as well as concrete finishing. This view also shows clearly both deck and diaphragm forms.

9-135 Simple timber trusses support arch forms for low, short span bridge

Timber shoring, adjustable wood and metal as well as all-metal single post shores, and scaffold-type shoring are all adaptable where solid ground support is available. Erection procedures are much the same as for building construction described previously (p. 182), except where greater heights call for more diagonal bracing to stabilize the supporting structure (Figure 9-133). Where shoring is required by the design for composite action, the engineer should specify its nature and location. The recommendations of ACI Committee 347 * should also be consulted.

If shoring from the ground is impractical or impossible, various other means, some of them already shown in text illustrations, can be devised to support the deck formwork from piers or other parts of the substructure. In rigid frame structures where the deck is continuous over several spans, it may be necessary to build a complete falsework for all spans acting together.

Jacks or wedges under the shoring or other type of

* See ACI 347-68 (appendix) for rules regarding shoring for composite construction.

centering should permit adjustment during placement of concrete to maintain designed elevations and camber as the load is applied to the forms.

Where a large volume of concrete is placed over an extended period, it may be necessary to use additives to retard setting and prevent the inducement of unequal stresses throughout the deck structure. The falsework also must limit deflection as placement continues, to prevent unequal loadings.

Hollow girder bridges pose additional problems because of the great importance of the falsework remaining in place, without deflection, until the upper lift of deck is concreted, tying top tension reinforcing into the structure. Falsework or shoring for such bridges should be founded on driven piles if possible. If pile driving is not feasible, large concrete pads are preferred to conventional mudsills.

Stripping Deck Forms

ACI Committee 347 has made the following recommendations as to time of stripping bridge formwork and its supports:

Falsework or shoring: Falsework should not be released until the concrete has attained 70 percent of its design strength, and in no case until at least 5 days have elapsed after the concrete has been placed. In continuous structures, falsework should not be released in any span until the first and second adjoining spans on each side have reached the specified strength.
Form removal: Forms for ornamental work, railings, parapets, and vertical surfaces which require a surface finishing operation should be removed not less than 12 hr, nor more than 48 hr after casting the concrete, depending on weather conditions. Bulkheads at construction joints should not be removed for a period of 15 hr after casting adjacent concrete. Forms under slab spans, beams, girders, and brackets must not be removed until the concrete has attained at least 70 percent of its design strength.

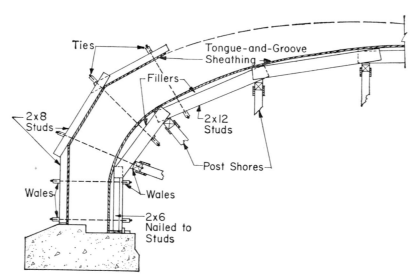

9-136 Typical detail of wood forming for arch bridge with span of about 80 ft. Tied outer or top forms used where curvature is steep.

9-137 Heavily braced timber falsework for support of arch forms

When cast-in-place post-tensioned bridges are constructed, falsework must remain in place during the curing period and until prestressing has been accomplished. Prestressing force usually lifts the member above the formwork at midspan. This type of construction requires advance planning and direction by the structural designer. In composite construction, also, the engineer-architect should include any special provisions that are required for form or shoring removal in the job specifications.

For bridge decks cast at great height or over water, the problem of stripping the forms from beneath the deck presents considerable challenge. Various methods are used to provide safe and convenient working conditions. Stripping scaffolds may be suspended from equipment riding on top of the deck. Similar scaffolds also may ride on rails beneath the deck (Figure 9-134), and towers or equipment are sometimes elevated from the ground. Sometimes holes are formed in deck slabs, through which the forms are lowered from above by a hand winch. A hole in the deck is also sometimes used to aid in breaking the bond between concrete and forms.

The gantry shown with the form travelers on p. 297 served both for setting and removing forms. Another type of stripping device shown in Figure 9-134 likewise does double duty in removing forms and transporting them forward for resetting. Barges frequently are required for stripping and transporting forms in open water. (See Figure 17-2.)

9-138 Arch bridge forms supported on steel scaffold towers. Six extra-heavy-duty towers at the lower level are 48 ft high, support steel I-beams that carry shoring towers at the upper level.

203

9-139 Wooden trusses for support of arch rib forms rest on bridge supports, require no intermediate support. Tower at right used only temporarily during truss erection. Similar truss supports for arch forms may be made in steel.

Arch Bridges

Problems of shoring or centering, together with the critical operation of decentering, are major areas in which arch bridge forming differs from other kinds of forming problems. Careful attention must also be given to the camber of arch forms in order to produce a finished arch at the desired elevation. Decentering operations require detailed advance planning, much the same as shell structures do, so that the structure can assume its load properly without being damaged.

These problems require the attention of a specialist, preferably a structural designer, because the falsework or centering itself is frequently a major structure, even though a temporary one. It is impossible to give any detailed discussion of these problems here, but a few illustrations suggesting the range of solutions possible in arch forming are included.

Low, short span arches may be supported on simple wood trusses, or shaped form members may rest directly on shores (Figures 9-135 and 9-136). For longer span, higher arches, either timber or metal shoring in heavily braced tower assemblies may be used (Figures 9-137 and 9-138).

Where high, long span arches cannot be suitably or economically supported on shoring, it is necessary to design self-supporting arches which serve as the form support. They are frequently fabricated in wood or metal truss components to simplify field erection.

Tolerances in Bridge Work

Where tolerances are not stated in the specifications or drawings ACI Committee 347 recommends the permissible deviations from line, grade, and dimensions suggested below. Formwork should be constructed to insure completed work within the tolerance limits.

Departure from established alignment	1 in.
Departure from established grades	1 in.
Variation from plumb or specified batter in lines and surfaces of columns, piers, walls, and in arrises	½ in. in 10 ft, if exposed 1 in. in 10 ft, if backfilled
Variation from level or indicated grade in slabs, beams, horizontal grooves, and railing offsets	½ in. in 10 ft, if exposed 1 in. in 10 ft, if backfilled
Variation in cross sectional dimensions of columns, piers, slabs, walls, beams, and similar parts	−¼ in., +½ in.
Variation in slab thickness	−⅛ in., +¼ in.
Footings: Plan dimensions	−½ in., +2 in.
Misplacement or eccentricity	2 percent of footing width in direction of misplacement, not exceeding 2 in.
Reduction in thickness	−5 percent of specified thickness
Variation in sizes and locations of slab, wall openings.	½ in.

10: USING THE FORMS

CONSTRUCTION PROCEDURES should be carefully planned in advance to achieve the proper balance between safety and economy in producing quality concrete work. This advance planning should be coordinated with the design and construction of the formwork. A knowledge of conditions for which the forms were intended and a common sense willingness to meet these limitations are absolutely necessary. For example, if forms are designed for a rise of concrete of 4 ft per hr, that rate should not be exceeded if forms are to function properly. If slab forms are designed for perhaps 125 to 150 psf total load, do not expect to land heavy bundles of reinforcing steel or other construction materials without damage or undue deflection of the formwork. By the same token, heavy construction loads should be kept off new, partially-cured concrete structures.

The purpose of this chapter is to point out the many factors to be considered in using the forms, such as the cleaning and coating of forms before concreting, care in placing the reinforcement and inserts, and operation of the placing equipment in such a way that forms are not damaged or misaligned. Inspection of the formwork before, during, and after concreting is important to both the contractor and the owner's representative, and some suggestions on how this should be handled are included. Stripping the forms and reshoring require considerable care to protect the concrete, and for this reason are often controlled directly by the engineer-architect. Some of the factors affecting his decisions on these points are enumerated and recommended techniques are included. Reconditioning and proper storage and handling of forms benefit the contractor who wants his forms to give maximum reuse, and suggestions for these practices are given. Insulation of formwork for use during cold weather is also discussed.

Placing Reinforcement and Inserts

Detailed recommendations for placing reinforcing bars have been published [1]* by the Concrete Reinforcing Steel Institute; comments made here cover only those aspects of bar setting that have a direct effect on the formwork. The place of bar setting in the construction sequence depends on the member as well as the system of form erection and other construction details including facilities for hoisting and placing reinforcing cages and forms. For walls, the

* Numbers refer to references listed at the end of the chapter.

10-1 Tying steel for the baffle walls of a filtration plant. One side of the wall form is in place with some lateral bracing at the top. All ties are in position, the bulkhead at the end of the wall panel is built, and bars project for the next wall section to be concreted later. Wooden box inserts for wall openings are in position and steel has been set around them.

external form is usually set in place, followed by the reinforcing mat, and then the interior wall form is erected and secured in place. For columns, the reinforcing bars may be preassembled and set in place, then the panels of the column form erected, aligned, and clamped around them; alternatively, the reinforcing cage may be dropped down inside the preassembled column form. Sometimes the entire preassembled column form may be set down over the erected reinforcement.

Beam and girder boxes are usually fully assembled to receive the reinforcing, and beam and girder reinforcement is assembled in place in the forms; less frequently the cage is preassembled and set in place as a unit. Spandrel beams having reglets, anchors, and the like usually have these placed by the form builder ahead of the steel setters. If beam sides are to be tied across the top to prevent spreading this must be done after the bar setters have finished, and such ties should not interfere with the bars.

Regardless of the exact sequence established, it is extremely important to have the work of bar setter correlated with that of other trades to see that inserts, sleeves, conduits, ducts, straps, and anchors which should be placed ahead of the bars are so placed, and any which should properly be placed later are not in place when the bar setter goes to work. Similar coordination with the form builders is necessary to get formwork in position, braced, and aligned ready to receive bars. Provision must also be made

for formwork parts that cannot be erected until after the bars are set.

Form oil or other coatings should be applied before steel is placed, so that the coating material does not get on the steel where it could reduce or destroy bond between the hardened concrete and its reinforcement. Most sleeves and inserts should be securely fastened in place before steel is set, and bar setters should take care not to remove or kick them out of place. Sheet metal pipe sleeves held in place by a dozen or more nails can have a very damaging effect on the forms. When the forms are stripped, these nails tear the surface, and many times the form material cannot be reused. A pipe sleeve of fiber material now available can be held in place by a metal cup and a single nail. This is cheaper for the mechanical trade to use and is a considerable saving to the form contractor.

Support for Reinforcing Bars

In footings, concrete bricks or precast concrete blocks are commonly used to support mats of bars. For top bars in heavy foundation mats, special heavy bar supports can be obtained with bearing plates to rest upon the earth subgrade. For other members such as joists, slabs, beams, and girders, a wide variety of ready-made wire, plastic, and even concrete bar supports are available. Any steel bar supports used at concrete surfaces which are to be exposed to the elements should be cadmium plated, galvanized, or plastic coated to prevent rusting. It is preferable that the entire bar support in such locations be made of plastic or other non-rusting material.

For horizontal members bar supports are commonly spaced 5 ft on centers, but because of possible effects on the formwork, this often requires reduction to 4 ft or less. Bar chairs or bolsters should be strong enough and spaced closely enough that they are not excessively loaded and bite into the form; this can be particularly troublesome in architectural concrete. Heavy reinforcing cages may cause beam bottoms to deflect objectionably at the point where bar chairs or other bar supports are located. This can be overcome by hanging the reinforcing cage from the top of the form, or by closer spacing of bar supports to distribute the load more evenly over the beam bottom.

Bar supports for cantilevered reinforced members should be made extra heavy to maintain reinforcement in proper design position. This requires particular attention because the major reinforcement is

10-2 Beam and slab deck form with network of conduits, pipes, circular inserts to form openings, mountings for anchor bolts, and reinforcing steel all in position. Complex installations such as this make it extremely important to coordinate the work of bar setter and form builder with electrical, mechanical, and other trades.

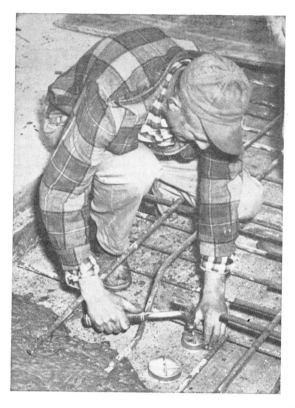

10-3 Installing fiber pipe sleeve. Metal cup (left) held by a single nail establishes location. Fiber tube (center) is set in place over the cup, and a metal closure is inserted (right).

near the *top* of the member where it is more vulnerable to accidental displacement by construction activities.

Vertical bars in wall mats are usually tied to dowels at the bottom, and attached to the forms in some way at the top. Nails driven into the formwork near the top of the bars, projecting the required amount of cover and matched to the vertical bars, with wire looped around the nail head, make good spacers. Sometimes the mat is wired to the form ties, or sometimes wire or stamped metal spacers are used and the mat is wired to the wall forms and pulled tight against these spacers. From the point of view of the form builder, the wall reinforcing should be attached to nails in the forms as little as possible. Nails make stripping difficult and may cause damage to form panels. They may also cause streaks later on the surface of exposed structures.

Another method of spacing vertical reinforcement mats is to rip long strips of 2-in. material to the required dimension, and insert them at intervals between the wall sheathing and the steel mat before concrete is placed. The strips are raised as the form is filled, and care should be taken to see that they are entirely removed before completing the concrete placement. If there is more than one layer of steel in a wall or other vertical member, the same procedure can be used in both faces, or spacing can be done from one face only, with the second mat of steel

spaced off the first by accurately pre-formed spacer rods.

For some exposed walls small concrete cubes with tie wire cast in them may be used as spacers to hold reinforcing bars at the proper distance from the forms. The short lengths of embedded tie wire are used to fasten the block to the reinforcing steel before the outside wall form is positioned. Such spacer blocks can be economically cast in large quantity on the job.

Steel in columns is spaced from the form and tied to it at least near the top. Wherever access permits, column reinforcing is braced away from the forms at three or four points as near top, bottom, and mid-height as possible. For such spacing, some erectors cast concrete doughnuts that are slid onto the appropriate column verticals during assembly. Others slide wire slab bolsters of suitable height down the erected column cage to bear against the formwork, and then wire them to the steel. Any practices that hinder stripping or damage forms should be avoided.

Positioning Bars; Tolerances in Placement

Tolerances in effective (structural) depth and in concrete cover for the placement of reinforcing bars will generally be according to ACI 318 Building Code

207

Requirements for Reinforced Concrete, unless the engineer architect specifies otherwise. ACI 318-71 presents the following tolerances * for bar placement:

Where d is	Tolerance on d and on clear cover
8 in. or less	$\pm\frac{1}{4}$ in.
more than 8 in., but less than 24 in.	$\pm\frac{3}{8}$ in.
24 in. or more	$\pm\frac{1}{2}$ in.

However, the reduction in clear cover is limited by ACI 318-71 to one-third of the specified cover.

Since the effective depth and the clear concrete cover are components of total depth, the tolerances on these dimensions are directly related to tolerances on over-all depth of member,* which must be considered by the form builder. Every precaution should be taken to prevent bar placing tolerances from becoming additive with tolerances for formwork to leave steel with insufficient cover or depth. Where combinations of bar placement and formwork tolerances may present problems, the engineer-architect should indicate which dimension is more critical or select special tolerances to take care of the individual situation.

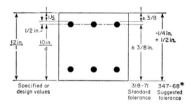

STANDARD TOLERANCES FOR ORDINARY 12-IN. SQUARE INTERIOR COLUMN, WITH #8 BARS

By 318-71 tolerances: cover may vary from $1\frac{1}{8}$ to $1\frac{7}{8}$ in.
               d may vary from $9\frac{5}{8}$ to $10\frac{3}{8}$ in.

For this 12-in. square interior column, it is possible to meet 318 tolerances on both cover and d with over-all dimension ranging from $11\frac{1}{4}$ to $12\frac{3}{4}$ in. If it were desired to follow Committee 347's suggested tolerance for the completed column —which permits the size to range from $11\frac{3}{4}$ to $12\frac{1}{2}$ in.—it would not be possible to permit the full 318 bar placement tolerances, and the designer should indicate which dimension is more critical.

In architectural concrete exposed to the weather, cover on the exposed face is usually more critical than structural depth. One important exception is in heavily loaded exposed columns designed for minimum size. For such cases, a special tolerance (-0 and $+\frac{1}{2}$ in.) on form dimensions and on effective depth (-0 and $+\frac{1}{4}$ in.) is a wise precaution. The same special tolerance of -0 in. and $+\frac{1}{2}$ in. is also advisable for thin structural slabs.

Examination of bar placing tolerances and concrete dimensional tolerances indicates no serious problem

* Tolerances suggested in ACI 347-68 are listed on p. 332.

of additive tolerances at critical dimensions for spandrel beams, ordinary interior members, and exterior members not designed to minimum size. Special spacers on spandrel beams are sometimes used, however, to maintain the desired cover.

In spacing slab or other bars, chalk marks may be made on the forms, but a soluble gypsum chalk is desirable because regular keel or wax crayon will leave marks on the finished concrete.

It is sometimes necessary or desirable to move an entire mat of steel into a better position by sliding it along the form, or a layer of slab bars may be lifted as a unit to permit the insertion of bars underneath. This moving may be done with a crow bar, or for larger units with a freight car lever or "incher." This powerful piece of equipment requires that the fulcrum bear against something solid enough to take the heavy thrust. If bars are being raised from slab formwork, a temporary shore may be needed under the fulcrum point. Care should also be taken not to damage the surface of forms for concrete which will be exposed.

Preparation for Concreting

Forms must be thoroughly cleaned of all dirt, mortar, and other matter such as chips, blocks, sawdust, or ice before each use. If the bottom of the form cannot be reached from the inside, access panels, preferably at the end of the form rather than the side, should be provided to permit thorough removal of all foreign matter before placing the concrete. A jet of air, water, or steam may be used effectively to remove debris. All cleanout openings must be carefully closed after washing out the forms.

Some specifications prohibit cutting washout holes in the forms. In such cases, pumps, air-lifts, or siphons may be required to remove washings.

Oil and Other Coatings

Before concrete is placed, form surfaces should be wetted, oiled, or coated with satisfactory materials that will not stain or soften the concrete. The form coating or treatment must serve as a *parting compound* or *release agent,* to prevent sticking of the concrete to the forms and thereby aid in stripping. It may also act as a *sealer* or *protective coating* for the form, preventing absorption of water from the concrete into the form material. Numerous form coating materials available perform one or both of these functions to varying degrees; some offer additional benefits of improved surface finish of the concrete as well as longer form life through the improved weathering and wearing qualities of the forms. A few types of coatings make possible several reuses without recoating the form.

Considering the range of materials currently in use as the contact surface of forms, it is apparent that some, like steel or glass-reinforced plastic, require a coating which acts primarily or solely as a parting compound, while others like wood and plywood will benefit from a coating that seals the form against moisture penetration. A form oil or coating must be carefully chosen to be suitable for the sheathing material being used. A few materials like the plastic liners (p. 43) actually require no release agent. Application of plain water (discussed below) in some cases is the only form treatment needed to facilitate stripping.

Numerous substances *—including water repellent materials, set retarders, and oils, greases, and waxes of varied origin—have been used either alone or in combination with other materials as parting compounds and form sealers. Oils and oil compounds have been the most widely used form release agents for wood, metal, and concrete form surfaces. Some oil compounds also aid in sealing form surfaces against inroads of moisture. Many excellent proprietary products are available, but since it is not possible to cover all of them, remarks here will be limited to information on general types of form coatings and treatments. If any new material or proprietary product is being considered, it is suggested that the user test small quantities under actual use conditions, and that he secure full information from the manufacturer as to the kind of form surface for which the product is intended as well as the proper method of application.

Forms should not be coated with any material that will interfere with subsequent wetting of surfaces to be cured, or with the functioning of sealing compounds used for curing. For surfaces to be plastered or painted, the form contact area should be treated with materials which leave no oily or waxy residue that will interfere with adhesion of the paint or plaster. Some contractors consider wetting the forms with water sufficient where surfaces are to be plastered; if the stripped surface is slightly rough plaster will adhere better.

10-4 Water jets are used to clean out this dam form resting on irregular rock surface.

Wood and Plywood Forms

For wood forms most of the commercial oils are satisfactory; light colored petroleum oils and oil emulsions of various types have been successfully used, and these same oils have also proved satisfactory for concrete molds. The oil should be capable of penetrating the wood to some extent, while leaving the surface only slightly greasy to the touch. Linseed oil cut with kerosene has also been reported satisfactory for plywood forms; if the plywood is mill oiled, it should be used once without oiling, then coated lightly for each reuse.

Occasionally lumber or hardboard material contains sufficient tannin or other organic substance to cause retarded set of concrete surface. When this condition is recognized, it can be remedied by treating the form surfaces with whitewash or lime water before applying the form oil or coating.[8,9]

Products other than oil are sometimes used for treating plywood and wood forms to seal and preserve the material as well as to make stripping easier. Plywood may be coated with shellac, lacquer, resin base products, or plastic compounds which offer almost total exclusion of moisture from the plywood. This prevents wet concrete from raising the grain and detracting from surface smoothness of finished concrete. When such coatings are used, only a very light oiling prior to use of the form is generally needed; some coating manufacturers suggest no oiling with their products.

Metal Forms

Sticking of concrete to steel forms may result from:
  (1) Abrasive cleaning that exposes bright metal
  (2) Abrasion opposite openings or other areas where entering streams of concrete are directed against forms
  (3) Unsuitable form oil.

* In addition to the various oils, soft soap, talcum, whitewash, finely ground calcium stearate powder, silicones, plastics, lacquers, resins, and sodium silicate are a few that have been successfully used. In lift slab and tilt-up work, a membrane-type curing compound frequently also serves as a release agent. It is impossible to give a complete listing; more information can be found in Reference 7 which reports on comparative ease of stripping with a number of different form coating materials.

10-5 Dip tank used for treating plywood panels with sealing compound, showing how panels are stacked on edge to drain and dry. Tank is shaded to reduce evaporation of sealer.

Form oils that are satisfactory on wood are not always suitable for steel forms, especially where there is a sliding movement of concrete against the forms as in tunnel lining. If one oil does not work as well as desired, others should be tried since there are a number of satisfactory compounded oils available. Paraffin base form oils and blended oils consisting of a petroleum base along with synthetic castor oil, silicones, graphite, or other substances have been successfully used. Some marine engine oils have also given good results on steel tunnel forms. A heavier form oil should be used in hot weather if difficulty is encountered with concrete sticking to forms when they are stripped early.

Rough surfaces on steel forms where sticking occurs may be conditioned by rubbing in a liquid solution of paraffin in kerosene, or the forms may be cleaned and oiled with a non-drying oil, then exposed to sunlight for a day or two.

Plaster Molds

When the plaster waste molds used for architectural concrete are thoroughly dry, they should be given two coats of shellac or equivalent waterproofing coating before leaving the shop. After these molds are set in place, and all joints patched and touched up with shellac or other waterproofing, they should be greased with a light yellow cup grease which may be cut with

kerosene if too thick. Grease should be wiped into all crevices and recesses, and all surplus carefully removed. Grease and shellac must be kept off any hardened concrete or reinforcing steel in the area.

Applications of Coatings

Surfaces to which coatings are applied should be clean and smooth. Application may be by various methods: roller, brush, spray, wiping, etc., depending on the type of coating being placed on the form. The important consideration is to make coverage *complete* and *uniform* if good stripping and good appearance are to be attained. There should be no excess coating to stain the concrete or leave undesirable residue on finished surface. If oils or greases are used, the excess can be wiped off; some other types must be applied more carefully because wiping is not permitted.

Whenever possible, form panels or form materials should be coated before erection; this sometimes is necessary because special coatings may require several days drying or curing. It is also desirable because it permits dipping of plywood panels and various other techniques for faster coating. (Forms subject to continuing reuse are generally coated just after stripping and cleaning.) When coatings are applied after forms are erected, the application must precede steel placement so that no form coating gets on reinforcing bars. Construction joint surfaces should also be kept free of form coating.

Use of Water on the Forms

An effective way of keeping untreated board forms tight is to soak them continuously with water for about 12 hr before concreting. This also stops absorption of water from the fresh concrete, and thus prevents warping and swelling of form members after the concrete is placed. If forms are badly dried out, soaking with water at least twice daily for 3 days prior to concreting may be necessary. Untreated wood inserts should also be soaked well in advance of concreting; otherwise they may swell and cause concrete to split.

Thorough wetting of untreated wood forms just before concreting also facilitates stripping, but increasing use of oils or sealants which protect wood from absorption of moisture tends to reduce the importance of wetting. Wider use of plywood which has greater dimensional stability than board sheathing has also often eliminated the need for wetting; protective sealant coatings for the plywood forms and form panels are more widely used because they contribute to extended form life as well as aid in stripping.

Many contractors wet forms just before concreting, in addition to using protective coatings or release agents. Cooling of forms and reinforcing steel by sprinkling with cool water inside and outside just before concreting has been recommended by ACI Committee 605 [4] to help lower the temperature of freshly placed concrete in hot weather. Shading forms and steel from the hot sun is also suggested.

Where concrete is placed against earth forms of dry sands or absorbent material, the soil should be wetted to prevent the too-rapid absorption of water from the freshly placed concrete.

Inspection and Form Watching

Before concreting is permitted to progress, forms should be inspected to see that they are in the correct location and properly built to produce concrete of the required finish and dimensions, with adequate safety for the workmen on the job. Job specifications should state clearly by whom, when, and for what features the owner desires an inspection of formwork, and what approvals, if any, are required by his representative before concreting can begin. Local building codes like that of the City of New York, for example, may also require a certification of inspection and approval of the formwork * to be filed by the architect or engineer with the proper government official before concreting can begin, or after concreting is completed for a permanent record.

If the owner's representatives or local building officials do not require inspection of the formwork, the contractor will bear the sole responsibility. It is clearly to the interest of the contractor as well as the owner to make an inspection for accuracy, stability, and satisfactory workmanship before concrete is placed; however, the contractor is not likely to leave all this until the last minute. There is too much detail, and too much of it hidden by the time forms are ready for concreting. The foreman or superintendent probably will maintain a continuing check, closely watching each phase of form erection as it progresses. The contractor is also concerned with a continuing check of the forms *during and after concreting* by experienced form watchers.

* The New York code requirement applies to forms over 12 ft clear height.

Before Concreting

A competent inspector must be thoroughly familiar with the entire job and its requirements, and also have a general knowledge of good concrete construction practices. The *ACI Manual of Concrete Inspection* [2] is a valuable pocket reference guide for any inspector. Approaching the problem from the point of view of the owner, this inspection manual suggests a three-stage inspection as the work advances:

Preliminary—When excavation has been completed or forms built. If dimensions and stability are satisfactory, contractor may then clean foundation or oil the forms and may install any reinforcement and fixtures.

Semi-final or cleanup—When *everything* is in place for concreting, a detailed inspection of forms, reinforcement, foundations, and all equipment or parts to be embedded in the concrete. If the installations are satisfactory, the work is ready for final cleanup.

Final—Immediately before concreting to see that forms, reinforcement, and fixtures have not been displaced. Surfaces must be clean and wetted if so specified.

Some of the points that must be considered, whether the inspection is performed in these three stages by the owner's representative, or done by the contractor as the job advances, are listed in the following sections.

Overlapping Inspections

Inspectors for different features—structural, electrical, mechanical, or others—should coordinate their work. If the architect-engineer's representative cannot make the inspection for all trades or all parties concerned, he must make certain that no changes re-

10-6 Epoxy-resin plastic coating is applied by brush to a large made-up form panel. Two coats of this material were used to achieve greater smoothness and longer protection of the plywood sheathing.

quired by others affect structural features he has already approved. The final inspection should cover structural requirements.

Alignment, Location, and Dimensions

Forms should be checked for accuracy of line and grade as early as possible so that delays for any necessary adjustments can be minimized. Location and dimensions of the forms after they are filled with concrete may not be the same as when they were built, since loading may cause them to settle, sag, or bulge. To insure that line and grade of *finished work* be within the required tolerances, forms should be built to elevation or camber shown on the formwork drawings. If settlement of supports or sagging of spans is to be expected, the form designer generally will have planned for this and included compensating allowances in establishing his dimensions. Any indicated elevations and cambers should allow for joint closure, settlement of mudsills, dead load deflection, and elastic shortening of form members as well as any camber specified on structural drawings.

Various means of checking location and alignment are used. Governing points of line and grade will

10-7 Check of forms and reinforcement for correct position and alignment. Contractor's foreman or superintendent maintains continuing inspection as the job progresses.

have been set by the engineering staff, but the inspector will need to make additional measurements from and between these points. Transit and level may be used along with direct observation and measurement by the inspector; plumb lines and stretched wires may be necessary in some locations. An accurate straightedge should always be on hand, and in many cases homemade templates will serve as convenient and accurate means of checking dimensions.

In pavement construction, the alignment and crown of screeds should be checked. Screeds for floor and roof slabs should be set to assure the desired thickness of the member; for example, if a slab form is cambered to compensate for dead load deflection after form removal, screeds should also be cambered to give a uniform slab thickness of the member.

After the final check of alignment and location is made, telltale devices should be installed on supported forms and elsewhere to facilitate the detection and measurement of formwork movements during concreting. Wedges or jacks should be secured in position after the final check of alignment, but there should be some positive means of realignment or readjustment of shores if excessive settlement occurs after concrete is placed.

Adequate Strength and Stability

In addition to the obvious verification of position and dimensions, the question must be asked—are the forms likely to keep the proper position and dimensions during concreting? The strength and stability of the formwork depend in large measure on a properly developed form design, but there are a number of details the inspector can check closely to see that the designer's plan is being properly executed:

1. Are the bracing and tying of the formwork adequate? Are all the necessary tie rods or clamps in the proper location and properly tightened? This point is critical since it is usually impossible to force a form back into position after it has bulged while being filled.

2. Are the shores properly seated and adequately braced? Is the bearing under mudsills adequate? *Sills or spread footings should not rest on frozen ground.*

3. Are the shores adequately connected to formwork at the top to resist any upward movement or torsion at the joints?

4. Does the concrete placing crew know the placing rates and sequence planned for the job?

Quality and Cleanness of the Formwork

Joints and seams in the forms should be checked for tightness to prevent accumulation of dirt before concreting, or formation of fins of mortar when the concrete is placed. The final inspection should include examination of formwork and construction joints for cleanness and to see that necessary fittings and reinforcement are attached in the proper location.

The inspector should check to see that the form sheathing or lining can reasonably be expected to yield the desired or specified finish. He should also be sure that wetting, oiling, or other specified form treatment has been adequately performed before concreting, and that there is no form coating on the reinforcing steel.

During and After Concreting

Formwork should be continuously watched during and after concreting by a competent man or men (depending on size of the job) stationed below or alongside the forms being filled. Precautions should be taken to protect the formwork watchers and maintain an area of safety for them during concreting. Some means of communicating with placing crews in case of emergency should be planned in advance.

The form watchers will use previously installed telltale devices to maintain a constant check of elevations, camber, and plumbness of the formwork system. They should tighten wedges and promptly make appropriate adjustments of elevation by jacking or wedging wherever necessary. All adjustments must be made before the concrete takes its initial set.

If bulging of *vertical formwork* goes beyond tolerated amounts as work progresses, the superintendent should be notified and the filling of the form slowed down, possibly even stopped, until additional bracing or other corrective measures can be taken. As previously noted, it is almost impossible to push back these bulges in the filled forms without removing some of the fresh concrete, in contrast to the considerable leeway possible in adjusting jacks and wedges for horizontal forms.

If any serious weakness develops during concreting, such as would endanger workers or cause undue settlement or distortion, work should be halted while the formwork is strengthened (or concrete removed to permit form adjustments). If the affected construction is permanently damaged, it may be necessary to remove a portion of it, but this requires approval of the engineer-architect, since it may affect the safety and stability of adjoining construction.

Although a most critical stage has passed once the concrete is in the forms, the form watchers should remain on duty until the concrete has been screeded and telltale devices show that deflection has ceased. An impending form failure often gives warning by gradually increasing deflection.

Placing and Vibrating—Effect on Formwork

Properly designed formwork of good quality will not be adversely affected by proper internal vibration or normal placement of concrete, although it is advisable to watch for loosening of nut-washers and wedges during vibration.

For good form performance, rate of rise of concrete in the forms should not exceed that for which they were designed, and any limits set by the designer on vibration should be followed. Necessary depth of vibration varies somewhat with the depth of layers in which concrete is placed. When not provided for in the design of the form, revibration of previously placed layers should be avoided because vibrator action in the stiffened concrete can cause overloading of normal forms. Forms designed in accordance with the recommendations of Chapter 5 will be adequate for vibration limited to depths not exceeding 4 ft below the top of the concrete surface.

If forms are not designed for external vibration, extreme caution should be used in applying or attaching vibrators to the outside of the forms. It has been repeatedly found that external vibration can destroy the strongest form. For this reason, some agencies prohibit its use except when forms are specially designed for such external vibration.

Vibration should be used for the purpose of consolidation only, not for lateral movement of the concrete. Reasonable care by the operator is necessary to avoid scarring or roughening the forms by operating vibrators against them.

Runways for moving equipment (Figure 10-8) should be provided with struts or legs as required, and should be supported directly on the formwork or a structural member. They should not bear on or be supported by reinforcing steel unless special bar sup-

10-8 Power buggies in motion on a runway which is properly supported from the form deck at an elevation to keep it clear of the reinforcing steel. Runways should never rest on the reinforcing steel unless special bar supports are provided.

ports are provided. Formwork must be suitable for support of such runways without intolerable deflection, vibration, or lateral movement.

Abrasion of forms caused by an entering stream of concrete can be prevented by use of protective sheets of metal, plywood, or rubber belting. For forms over 10 ft high tremies or chutes should be used to avoid impact on forms as well as segregation of concrete.

Removal of Forms and Shores

Although the contractor has general responsibility for design, construction, and safety of the formwork, the time of removal of the forms and shores should be specified by the architect-engineer in the contract documents, or made subject to his approval, because of the danger of injury to concrete which may not have attained full strength or which may be overloaded in the stripping or subsequent construction operations. Where reuse of forms is planned it is vital to the interest of the contractor to remove forms and shores as early as possible. In warm weather, early stripping is sometimes desirable because it permits specified curing to begin. Another advantage of early form removal is that the necessary surface repair or treatment can be done while the concrete is "green" and favorable to good bond. In cold weather, curing requirements and the danger of thermal shock to the concrete make early removal less advantageous.

Stripping Time Based on Concrete Strength

Since early form removal is usually desirable so that forms can be reused, a reliable basis for determining the earliest proper stripping time is necessary. When forms are stripped there must be no excessive deflec-

tion or distortion and no evidence of cracking or other damage to the concrete, due either to removal of support or to the stripping operation. Supporting forms and shores must not be removed from beams, floors, and walls until these structural units are strong enough to carry their own weight and any approved superimposed load. Such approved load should not exceed the live load for which the member was designed unless provision has been made by the engineer-architect to allow for temporary construction loads, as for example in multistory work (see p. 75). Generally forms for vertical members such as columns and piers may be removed before those for beams and slabs.

Strength of concrete necessary before formwork is stripped and the time required to attain it vary widely with different job conditions, and the most reliable basis is furnished by test specimens cured under job conditions. In general, forms and supports for suspended structures can be removed safely when the ratio of cylinder test compressive strength to design strength is equal to or greater than the ratio of total dead load and construction loads to total design load, with a minimum of 50 percent of design compressive strength being required. Some agencies specify a definite strength that must be obtained; for example, 2500 psi or two-thirds of design strength. However, even when concrete is strong enough to show no immediate distress or deflection under load, it is possible to damage corners and edges during stripping, and for excessive creep deflections to occur.

If strength tests are to be the basis for the engineer-architect's instructions to the contractor on form removal, the type of test, method of evaluating, and minimum standards of strength should be stated clearly in specifications. The number of test specimens as well as who should make them and perform tests should also be specified. Ideally, test beams or cylinders should be job cured under conditions which are similar to those for the portions of the concrete structure which the test specimens represent. (These specimens must not be confused with those cured under laboratory conditions to evaluate 28-day strength of the concrete.) Curing record including time, temperature, and method for both the concrete structure and the test specimens as well as the weather record will assist both the engineer and contractor in determining when forms can be safely stripped. It should be kept in mind that specimens which are relatively small are more quickly affected by freezing or drying conditions than concrete in the structure.

On jobs where the engineer has made no provision for approval of shore and form removal based on strength and other considerations peculiar to the job, ACI Committee 347 suggests the following minimum time forms and supports should remain in place under ordinary conditions:

Walls *	12-24 hr
Columns *	12-24 hr
Sides of beams and girders *	12-24 hr

Pan joist forms †

30 in. wide or less	3 days
Over 30 in. wide	4 days

	Where design live load is:	
	<DL	>DL
Arch centers	14 days	7 days

Joist, beam, or girder soffits ‡

Under 10 ft clear span between supports	7 days §	4 days
10 to 20 ft clear span between supports	14 days §	7 days
Over 20 ft clear span between supports	21 days §	14 days

Floor slabs ‡

Under 10 ft clear span between supports	4 days §	3 days
10 to 20 ft clear span between supports	7 days §	4 days
Over 20 ft clear span between supports	10 days §	7 days

Post-tensioned slab system ** .... As soon as full post-tensioning has been applied

Supported slab systems ** .... Removal times are contingent on reshores, where required, being placed as soon as practicable after stripping operations are complete but not later than the end of the working day in which stripping occurs. Where reshores are required to implement early stripping while minimizing sag or creep (rather than for distribution of superimposed construction loads as covered on p. 217), capacity and spacing of such reshores should be specified by the engineer-architect.

* Where such forms also support formwork for slab or beam soffits, the removal times of the latter should govern.
† Of the type which can be removed without disturbing forming or shoring.
‡ Distances between supports refer to structural supports and not to temporary formwork or shores.
§ Where forms may be removed without disturbing shores, use half of values shown but not less than 3 days.
** See p. 75 for special conditions affecting number of floors to remain shored or reshored.

These periods represent cumulative number of days or fractions thereof not necessarily consecutive, during which the temperature of the air surrounding the concrete is above 50F. If high-early-strength cement is used, these periods may be reduced as approved by the engineer. When higher cement content concretes are used, in effect yielding higher early strengths, the engineer may also approve some reduction in the required stripping time. Conversely, if low temperature concrete or retarding agents are used, then these periods may be increased at the discretion of the engineer-architect.

Recommendations for time of stripping bridge forms are given on p. 202.

Form Removal Related to Curing Needs

In warm weather, wood forms left in place furnish good protection from the sun but do not keep concrete moist enough to be acceptable as a method of outdoor moist curing. Metal forms, and wood forms that are kept thoroughly wet, provide satisfactory protection against loss of moisture if forms are loosened and the exposed top surfaces are kept wet in such a way that the water finds its way down between the concrete and the forms. Under these conditions only, the forms may be left on the concrete as long as practicable. Otherwise they should be removed as soon as concrete strength development permits, so that prescribed curing may be commenced with the least delay after placing. The U. S. Bureau of Reclamation has found [6] that the surfaces of ceilings and walls inside buildings may require no other curing than that provided by leaving the forms in place for 4 days; this period may vary, however, with the humidity and drying conditions inside the building.

In cold weather, moist curing, though important, is not so urgent, and protection afforded by forms, other than of steel, is often of greater importance. In heated enclosures, such forms serve to distribute the

10-9 Proper use of screw-type leg adjustments on shoring members makes it easier to lower forms gradually without shock to structure. Pneumatic and hydraulic jacks, sand jacks, even slowly melting blocks of ice, are also used to facilitate gradual release of forms.

warmth more evenly, and to prevent local heating. With suitable insulation, the forms, including those of steel, in many cases will provide adequate protection without supplemental heating. Therefore, in view of the reduced period of protection now required, it is usually advantageous not to remove forms until the end of the prescribed minimum period of protection (in cold weather).

Stripping Techniques

Forms and shoring should be designed for easy, safe removal in a way that permits the concrete to take its load gradually and uniformly without impact or shock. Stripping was formerly referred to as "wrecking," and this description was often given a literal interpretation when forms were removed; there was little or no salvage of materials. Today, with increasing emphasis on panel systems, modular formwork components, and economy through maximum reuse of forms, much more attention is now given to building forms that can be removed intact.

Considerable damage can be done to formwork which has not been planned for orderly dismantling. The sequence of stripping is a consideration in how the forms are to be made or assembled. For example, column forms should be made so that they can be stripped without disturbing adjacent beam and girder forms. Column panels can be pried out from the bottom so that they can drop down free of beam form. Beam and girder side forms may be made to come out before slab soffits. The designer should provide crush plates or key strips to facilitate removal at difficult form intersections or where there is danger of damage from stripping tools. Small form openings to

10-11 Careful stripping and handling pays off by keeping form panel corners and edges straight and true.

permit introduction of air or water under pressure sometimes simplify stripping.

Special considerations for stripping architectural ornament or long span thin shells and similar structures are discussed in the section on structures or techniques to which they relate (architectural concrete, p. 223; shell structures, p. 251).

Time devoted to training the stripping crew in both the order and method of form removal will be well spent. Stripping requires considerable care on the part of workmen to avoid damage to the green concrete, which can be marred by scratching and chipping even though it has sufficient structural load bearing strength. The contractor is concerned both to protect the concrete and to extend the useful life of his forms by careful handling. Not only must the forms hold together, they must remain dimensionally accurate, and edges should stay in good condition to make accurate alignment and clean joints possible.

Form panels and shoring components should not be dropped but should be handed down or lowered on stretched ropes, cables, or other devices to avoid damage. Various rigs on wheels can be devised for different kinds of stripping jobs to improve the safety and speed of the workers; traveling suspended scaffolds are particularly helpful in bridge work.

10-10 Floor slabs were cast and steel beams encased in concrete, working from the top down on this building. Slab form sections were carefully lowered on cables operated by hand winches from the completed deck above. Two men out of sight on the lower floor handle guide lines which bring the form into correct position.

Multistory Buildings

Removal of shores from multistory buildings requires special consideration because a given floor slab may be required to support one or two stories of construction live and dead loads from the work going on above, depending on the rate of progress being made on the job. The contractor's schedule of shoring and reshoring should be approved by a competent engineer or architect representing the owner. The engineer's approval should be based on strength of field cured test cylinders as well as consideration of weather, placing conditions, and time and quality of curing. The total load of the upper structure, including freshly placed concrete, formwork, workmen, placing equipment, runways, and motor driven buggies, must not exceed the live load which the lower structure is capable of carrying at the strengths then available.

For a typical multistory building with proper curing conditions, three stories of shores are usually required for progress at the rate of one story per week. However, for faster rates of construction, or with structures designed for light live loads such as 40 or 50 psf, it may be that more than three floors of shoring are required to support one floor of freshly placed concrete and construction loads (see discussion of design considerations, p. 75). *Reshoring* discussed in the following section, becomes a particularly important consideration in multistory work.

Reshoring

Reshores are shores placed firmly under a stripped concrete slab or structural member where the original formwork has been removed thus requiring the new slab or structural member to support its own weight and construction loads posted to it. Such reshores are provided to transfer additional construction loads to other slabs or members and/or to impede deflection due to creep which might otherwise occur. Reshoring is done to facilitate maximum reuse of the formwork, making use of the strength of completed construction below as well as the partial development of strength in the member being reshored.

Premature reshoring and inadequate size and spacing of reshores have been responsible for a number of construction failures. Since reshoring is such a highly critical operation, it is essential that the procedure be planned in advance and approved by the architect-engineer. Detailed instructions (or prohibitions) regarding reshoring may be written into the job specifications, or the time and sequence of reshoring may be made subject to engineer approval.

10-12 Compressed air inserted through holes at the form center aids in stripping otherwise airtight forms such as these dome pans for waffle slab construction.

When the study of form removal and reshoring is being made, the live loads for which the completed structure is designed, as well as the actual strength of the partially cured concrete, must be considered. Allowance must also be made for any additional live and dead loads to be imposed as construction continues. The reshoring system must be designed to carry all loads that will be imposed. It is important to remember that partially cured concrete deflects much more than fully aged concrete, even at the same compressive strength level, for both immediate and sustained loads. Often the critical limitation on temporary construction loads will not be strength but avoidance of excessive deflection, cracking, and inadequate bond for splice details of the reinforcement.

Locations, spacings, and the type of reshores to be used should be considered carefully. Story heights, speed of construction, type and structural design of slabs, and spacing of columns are influencing factors. Under proper conditions, metal shores, 4x4 wood shores, or 6x6 wood shores can be economically and safely used as reshores.

All reshoring members must be straight and true without twist or warp. Reshores must be plumb and adequate in capacity. When placing reshores, care should be taken not to preload the lower floor and also not to remove the normal deflection of the slab above. The reshore is simply a strut and should be tightened only to the extent that no significant shortening will take place under load. In no case should wedging or jacking be permitted to lift a slab above its formed position to the point of causing cracking.

Excessive wedging will change the load distribution to various floors supporting the shores and may easily relieve one and overload another.

Operations should be performed so that at no time will large areas of new construction be required to support combined dead and construction loads in excess of their capability as determined by design load and developed concrete strength at the time of stripping and reshoring. While reshoring is under way no construction loads should be permitted on the new construction. For high story heights adequate provisions should be made for lateral bracing of reshores during this operation. Reshores should be located in the same position on each floor so that they will be continuous in their support from floor to floor. Where slabs are designed for light live loads, or on long spans where the loads on reshores are heavy, care should be used in placing the reshores, so that the loads do not cause excessive punching shear or reversed bending stress in the slab.

Reshoring should never be located where it will significantly alter the pattern of stresses determined in the structural analysis, or where it will induce tensile stresses where reinforcing bars are not provided. Where the number of reshores on a floor is reduced, such reshores shall be placed directly under a shore position on the floor above. When shores above are not directly over reshores, an analysis should be made to determine whether or not detrimental bending stresses are produced in the slab.

Reshoring Beam and Girder Construction

When stripping forms before the structure is strong enough to carry its own weight plus any construction loads above, the forms should be removed from one girder at a time, and the girder should be reshored before any other supports are removed. After the supporting girders of a bay are reshored, the beam forms in the bay should be removed one at a time, and the beam reshored before other supports are removed. Long span beams, over 30 to 35 ft, should have at least one substantial shore that remains permanently in position during reshoring operations.

Slabs should not be reshored until supporting beams and girders have been reshored. Each slab with a clear span of 10 ft or more should be reshored along its center line at regular intervals or with continuous shoring. If a line of reshores at midspan is not in line with shores on the floor above, the slab should be checked for its capacity to resist reversal of stresses or punching shear.

Reshoring Flat Slabs

When flat slab formwork is stripped before the slabs are strong enough to carry their own dead load plus construction loads above, the shore removal and reshoring should be planned and located to avoid reversal of stresses or inducement of tension in slabs where reinforcement is not provided for design loads. Reshores should be placed along the intersection line of the column strip and the middle strip in both directions. Such reshoring should be completed for each panel as it is stripped before removing forms for adjacent panels. For flat slabs whose column spacing exceeds 25 ft, it is desirable to plan the form construction so that shores at intersections of column strips with middle strips may remain in place during stripping operations. For average flat slab work, 6x6 wood reshores are usually most economical and satisfactory.

The recent development and use of expandable horizontal shores with vertical shore lines at greater spacing (perhaps 14 ft instead of 2 or 3 ft) requires careful consideration of location of shores and reshores so that stresses are not reversed, particularly in flat slab areas where no negative (top) reinforcement is provided. Construction live loads present a greater potential problem in this type of forming because the large spacing between shore lines gives the contractor work space and loading areas for construction materials not possible with typical vertical shores placed 2 or 3 ft on centers each way.

10-13 Gasoline powered cleaner for metal form panels. Forms are placed on a conveyor belt which pulls them under a rapidly rotating steel wire brush. Form faces are cleaned and oiled, and panels emerge at the far end of the conveyor belt.

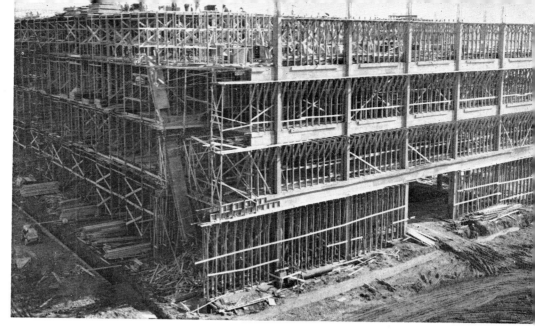

10-14 Three floors of shoring are commonly used in multistory flat slab construction. Formwork for this structure was planned so that original shores remained in place after slab soffit forms were stripped (more details on p. 187).

Removal of Reshores

Final removal of reshores is in general based on the same standards as removal of shores. Reshoring should not be removed until the slab or member supported has attained sufficient strength to support all loads posted to it. Removal of reshores should be planned so that the structure supported is not subjected to impact or loading eccentricities.

Committee 347 recommends that in no case should reshores be removed within 2 days of placing a slab above or within two floors below such a new slab.

Heavy Industrial Structures

For heavy industrial structures a "permanent" shoring system is desirable. Early stripping and subsequent reshoring may allow undesirable deflections or cause development of fine cracks that in later years create a serious maintenance problem. When quick reuse of the formwork is desired in such structures, forms should be planned so that original shores can remain in place while forms are stripped around them (several methods are shown on p. 187). Shores can then remain in place until strength tests or elapsed time indicate that it is safe to remove them.

Care and Storage of Forms

Prefabricated forms and unframed plywood panels should be thoroughly cleaned and oiled as soon as possible after stripping. Frames and metal parts if any

should be thoroughly scraped to remove any accumulated deposits of concrete. The frames should be regularly inspected for wear, and any split or damaged lumber should be replaced. After the frame has been checked the form face should be cleaned. For wood or plywood surfaces, a hardwood wedge and a stiff fiber brush are good tools. The wedge will remove any odd lumps of concrete, and the brush will remove dust with a minimum of damage to the face. Scrapers and wire brushes, unless used with great care, loosen fibers on the form face, and the "wooly" surface becomes progressively harder to strip. A hard scale of concrete may require some light tapping with a hammer, but this can be carefully done to avoid breaking fibers and damaging the form face.

Any open seams in panels should be filled, warped boards planed, metal facings straightened, and joints rematched. Plywood panel faces of prefabricated forms may be reversed on the frame or replaced if badly damaged. Tie holes may be patched with metal plates, corks, or plastic materials.

10-15 Large size panels stacked for orderly storage at the job site. Wood strips separate groups of panels to allow for circulation of air and evaporation of moisture.

10-16 Forms for a large bridge pier insulated with foamed polystyrene plastic.

Cleaning knife, steel scrapers, and wire brush are satisfactory for use on steel panels, and mechanical cleaning devices (Figure 10-13) are sometimes used on large projects. Metal forms should not be sandblasted or abraded to a bright surface as this may cause sticking.

As soon as forms are cleaned and necessary repairs made, they should be coated with a good oil or other

10-17 Insulation blanket designed primarily for use on slab forms has been wrapped around column forms and tied in place.

preservative (some of these coatings are described on p. 208). Steel forms should be oiled on the back as well as the face to prevent rusting and sticking of spilled concrete. With some coatings, a curing or drying period is required before the forms can be stacked on one another.

Following any necessary drying period for the coating material, the forms should be stacked off the ground on 2-in. or heavier lumber at a slight pitch for run-off (unless indoor storage is available). It is preferable to place strips of wood between the forms to promote evaporation of moisture. Panels should be stacked according to sizes and types to simplify handling; they should be arranged so that any code markings can be read without further moving. Old forms may be placed on top to protect the newer ones from sun and rain.

Careful techniques recommended for stripping (p. 216) should carry over into handling to prevent chipping or denting edges. Forms should be piled face to face and back to back for hauling; they must not be dumped or thrown from a truck, but should be passed from man to man for stacking. On-site stacking of panels and components varies with the superintendent and site conditions. Orderly storage will obviously do much to reduce loss and damage and to prevent panels from being used for other purposes.

Dimension lumber, as well as form panels, may be saved for reuse, in which case it should be scraped free of concrete deposits, and all nails removed. It should be sorted by sizes and stored off the ground in a location that will minimize weathering and rotting.

Reusable form hardware requires careful handling, or it will become a costly item through losses or deterioration. Boxes or buckets should be kept on hand to store small parts as they are stripped. Parts can be soaked in a special solvent to loosen hardened concrete, then brushed. Some form coatings, in their concentrated form, will soften the buildup of hardened concrete. Mechanical brushing is sometimes used where large numbers of parts are to be handled.

Insulation for Cold Weather

Full recommendations for winter concreting practices established by ACI Committee 306 [3] include the following statement regarding the value and method of form insulation:

> Arrangements for covering, insulating, or housing newly placed concrete should be made in advance of

TABLE 10-1: INSULATION REQUIREMENTS FOR CONCRETE WALLS AND FLOOR SLABS ABOVE GROUND

Concrete placed at 50F

Wall thickness, ft	Minimum air temperature allowable for these thicknesses of commercial blanket or bat insulation, °F			
	0.5 in.	1.0 in.	1.5 in.	2.0 in.
Cement content—300 lb per cu yd				
0.5	47	41	33	28
1.0	41	29	17	5
1.5	35	19	0	−17
2.0	34	14	−9	−29
3.0	31	8	−15	−35
4.0	30	6	−18	−39
5.0	30	5	−21	−43
Cement content—400 lb per cu yd				
0.5	46	38	28	21
1.0	38	22	6	−11
1.5	31	8	−16	−39
2.0	28	2	−26	−53
3.0	25	−6	−36	
4.0	23	−8	−41	
5.0	23	−10	−45	
Cement content—500 lb per cu yd				
0.5	45	35	22	14
1.0	35	15	−5	−26
1.5	27	−3	−33	−65
2.0	23	−10	−50	
3.0	18	−20		
4.0	17	−23		
5.0	16	−25		
Cement content—600 lb per cu yd				
0.5	44	32	16	6
1.0	32	8	−16	−41
1.5	21	−14	−50	−89
2.0	18	−22		
3.0	12	−34		
4.0	11	−38		
5.0	10	−40		

Insulation equivalents *

Insulating material	Equivalent thickness
1 in. cellular polyurethane foam	1.667
1 in. of commercial blanket or bat insulation	1.000
1 in. of loose fill insulation of fibrous type	1.000
1 in. cellular polystyrene foam	1.000
1 in. of insulating board	0.758
1 in. of sawdust	0.610
1 in. (nominal) of lumber	0.333
1 in. of dead-air space (vertical)	0.234
1 in. of damp sand	0.023

* NOTES to TABLE 10-1: The tables are calculated for the stated thicknesses of blanket-type insulation with an assumed conductivity of 0.25 Btu per hr per sq ft for a thermal gradient of 1°F per in. The values given are for still air conditions and will not be realized where air infiltration due to wind occurs. Close-packed straw under canvas may be considered a loose-fill type if wind is kept

placement and should be adequate to maintain in all parts of the concrete the temperature and moisture conditions recommended.

Since during the first 3 days requiring protection most of the heat of hydration of the hardening cement is developed, no heat from outside sources is required to maintain concrete at correct temperatures if heat generated in the concrete is suitably conserved. This heat may be conserved by use of insulating blankets on unformed surfaces and by insulated forms where repeated reuse of forms is possible. Temperature records will reveal the effectiveness of different amounts or kinds of insulation or of other methods of protection for various types of concrete work under different weather conditions. Appropriate modifications and selections can be made accordingly. Methods for estimating temperatures maintainable by various insulation arrangements under given weather conditions have been published.* In Table 10-1 the amount of insulation necessary for good protection can be determined from information shown for various kinds of concrete work and for several degrees of expected severity in weather. For successful use, and efficient reuse, commercial blanket or bat insulation must be adequately protected by means of tough, moisture-proof cover material from wind, and rain, snow, or other wetting. Moreover, it must be kept in close contact with concrete or form surfaces to be effective.

Several types of insulation material are suitable for or specially produced for formwork; included among these are a sprayed-on type used largely for steel forms; foamed polystyrene and polyurethane board that can be cut to fit between studs of vertical forms; and various kinds of wood and mineral bat or blanket insulation. These materials must be kept dry to maintain insulating values shown in Table 10-1. Prefabricated form panels are now available with insulation sandwiched between two plywood faces (see p. 59) or permanently attached to the outer face. Electric heating blankets have also been used to maintain desired concrete temperature during cold weather.

The several kinds of wood and mineral "wool" insulating bats for formwork come in 1- and 2-in. thicknesses, of widths designed to fit between studs spaced at 12, 16, or 24 in. The insulation itself is about 1 in. less than these widths, and the outer casing material has reinforced flanges for nailing the bats to the studs. The outer covering or encasement may be made of polyethylene plastic, asphalt-impregnated paper, or a plastic-paper laminate, meeting the general requirements of Committee 306 for weather resistance.

This insulation may be stapled or attached with batten strips to sides of the form framing. The ends of

* Tuthill, L. H.; Glover, R. E.; Spencer, C. H.; and Bierce, W. B., "Insulation for Protection of New Concrete in Winter," ACI JOURNAL, Proceedings V. 48, Nov. 1951, pp. 253-272.

out of the straw. The insulating value of a dead-air space greater than about ½ in. thick does not change greatly with increasing thickness. Handbooks or manufacturers' test data should be consulted for more detailed data on insulations.

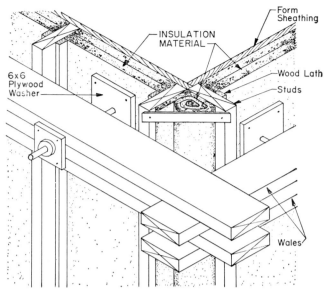

10-18 Typical method of attaching insulation bat to vertical form, showing corner detail and plywood washers used around tie rods

the blanket should be sealed by removing a portion of the blanket and bringing the paper liners (casing material) together, then stapling or battening down to form headers to exclude air and moisture. Corners and angles of forms should be well insulated (Figure 10-18) and the material held in place by battens, staples, or tie wires. For steel forms, the insulating blanket can be applied tight and held in place by wedging wood battens or by securely tying.

Where practical, the insulation or insulated form should overlay any previously placed cold concrete by at least 1 ft. Where tie rods extend through the insulated form, a 6x6-in. plywood washer can be placed on top of the insulation blanket and fastened securely.

Avoiding Thermal Shock

The need to limit excessive or rapid temperature changes before the strength of the concrete has developed sufficiently to resist temperature stresses is a factor that must be considered when planning form removal in cold weather. The problem, as outlined by ACI Committee 306,[3] is stated below:

> Winter concreting practices must be adequate to limit rapid temperature changes, particularly before strength has developed sufficiently to withstand temperature stresses. Sudden chilling of concrete surfaces or exterior members in relation to interior structure can promote cracking to the detriment of strength and durability. At the end of the required period, protection should be removed in such a manner that the drop in temperature of any portion of the concrete will be gradual and will not exceed, in 24 hr, the amounts shown below:

For very thin sections with ¾-in. maximum aggregate	50F
For thin sections with 1½-in. maximum aggregate	40F
Moderately massive sections	30F
Massive sections	20F

REFERENCES

1. *Placing Reinforcing Bars*, Concrete Reinforcing Steel Institute, Chicago, 1968, 186 pp.

2. ACI Committee 311, *ACI Manual of Concrete Inspection*, Fifth Edition, American Concrete Institute, Detroit, 1967, 270 pp.

3. ACI Committee 306, "Recommended Practice for Cold Weather Concreting, ACI 306-66 (Reaffirmed 1972)" ACI JOURNAL, *Proceedings* V. 62, No. 9, Sept. 1965, pp. 1009-1034. (Reprinted in *ACI Manual of Concrete Practice*, Part 1.)

4. ACI Committee 305, "Recommended Practice for Hot Weather Concreting, ACI 305-72," 15 pp., reprinted in *ACI Manual of Concrete Practice*, Part 1.

5. ACI Committee 304, "Recommended Practice for Measuring, Mixing, Transporting, and Placing Concrete, ACI 304-73," 40 pp., reprinted in *ACI Manual of Concrete Practice*, Part 1.

6. *Concrete Manual*, United States Department of the Interior, Bureau of Reclamation; issued by U. S. Government Printing Office, Washington, 7th Edition, 1963, 642 pp.

7. Arber, M. G.; Roberts, J. A.; and Vivian, H. E., "Concrete Form Treatments," *Constructional Review* (Sydney), V. 34, No. 6, June 1961, pp. 27-33.

8. "Tests of Form Lumber and Form Oil," Miscellaneous Paper No. 6-80, U. S. Army Corps of Engineers, Waterways Experiment Station, Vicksburg, Miss., Mar. 1954, 9 pp.

9. Feld, Jacob, "Study of Dusty Concrete Ceilings," ACI JOURNAL, *Proceedings* V. 45, No. 9, May 1949, pp. 673-678.

11: FORMWORK FOR ARCHITECTURAL CONCRETE

ARCHITECTURAL CONCRETE has a twofold purpose. Not only does it serve as the structural material, but it also becomes an architectural medium by providing the desired surface finish. Therefore, special care is needed in the design and construction of its formwork. Imperfections of all kinds will be open for inspection. Varying light conditions will emphasize fins, sheathing joint marks, crooked corners, bulges, and the like.

Although formwork quality is a critical consideration, it must be emphasized that architectural effects achieved in concrete surfaces may be vitally affected by factors other than formwork. Types or brands of cement, sources of coarse and fine aggregates, uniformity in mixing and placing techniques, slump control, and curing methods may significantly affect color and texture of the exposed surfaces despite exhaustive care in the formwork.

This chapter, along with information already presented on materials and accessories (pp. 29-72) indicates some methods of forming architectural concrete to obtain specified finishes. Most of the general principles of formwork design and construction discussed in Chapters 6 and 9 also apply to architectural concrete formwork. Only items that require special consideration for architectural reasons are discussed here.

Structural Design of Architectural Formwork

Loads and Pressures

Loads and pressures are generally the same as for structural concrete formwork. However, architectural concrete may be subjected to external vibration, revibration, set retardants, and slumps greater than those assumed for determining the lateral pressure as explained on p. 76. Particular care must be exercised in these cases to design the forms for the increased lateral pressures arising from these sources. Suggestions have already been presented for modifying the ACI formula for lateral pressure under special concreting conditions.

External vibration is the most critical of the conditions noted. In addition to making the concrete pressure greater by increasing its fluid action, external vibration sets up unusual dynamic stresses which the formwork is not usually designed to withstand. External vibration should never be used unless its effect on the formwork has been investigated and the formwork has been strengthened to withstand the added stresses.

Design Standards

Design methods discussed in Chapter 6 apply to architectural concrete, and tolerances suggested by ACI Committee 347 * for *exposed concrete members* will be satisfactory for many structures. Where more exacting tolerances are required to achieve the desired architectural effect, they should be specified by the architect, but it is not advisable to specify accuracy which the normally available craftsmen cannot attain.

Special consideration of tolerances may be necessary where precast and cast-in-place concrete members must fit together on exposed surfaces.

Deflections in the contact surface of formwork reflect directly in finished surfaces under varying light conditions, and forms for architectural concrete must be carefully planned to limit deflection. Deflection most frequently governs design rather than shear and bending considerations. Limiting deflection to $\frac{1}{360}$ of the span of formwork components is acceptable in many cases where the surfaces have a coarse or textured finish and there is little reflection of light. For

* See Appendix, Section 2.4.1, Item 2(b), for a listing of these tolerances.

smooth finishes or glossy surfaces, even less deflection may be acceptable, and it is desirable for the architect-engineer and the contractor to confer and reach a clear agreement on standards for deflections. Test panels cast against the proposed form sheathing may help to establish this agreement if they are large enough to simulate field conditions of support and span of the proposed form layout. If chipping and grinding of surfaces attained with good, standard forming practices will produce an acceptably flat architectural surface, the designer should compare the cost with that of special forming that may otherwise be needed to achieve the desired flatness or evenness.

General suggestions for design of architectural concrete forms are offered by ACI Committee 347 in their recommended practice (see Appendix). Design tables of Chapter 7 may be used for preliminary selection of size and spacing of studs and wales if $\frac{1}{360}$ span is a satisfactory limit on deflection. It must be noted, however that ACI 301-72 "Specifications for Structural Concrete for Buildings" requires a limit of $\frac{1}{400}$ of the span on deflection of facing material as well as studs and wales, unless otherwise specified by

the engineer-architect. Spans with deflection limited to $l/400$ are 96 percent of single span or continuous beam span values obtained when deflection is limited to $l/360$; they are 97 percent of two-span beam values. Since design tables in Chapter 7 show where deflection governs span length, these corrections can readily be applied to tabulated values as needed.

Where special forming systems are specified by the engineer for structural purposes (such as one-way and two-way joist systems) in areas which are considered architectural, the architect and engineer should coordinate their requirements to be sure the desired architectural effect is consistent with the forming method and material specified.

Contact Surface

The contact surface is vitally important in the forming of architectural concrete. It is usually preferable for the architect to specify the desired surface to be attained on the concrete rather than specifying the

11-1 Formwork carefully contrived to leave a distinctive board-marked pattern makes it difficult to distinguish between concrete and wood in this view of the New Lecture Theater, Edinburgh University. Vertical members and "boards" at the base are of concrete, and the end walls and infill panels between vertical frame members are sheathed with diagonal boards.

11-2 Striving for a totally different effect from that shown in Figure 11-1, this facade was cast in place against fiberglass-reinforced plastic forms to obtain a smooth surface which required only a washdown after form removal. Forms are in place at upper level where construction continues—University Apartments, Chicago.

form material. The contractor then is able to use a form lining or sheathing material familiar to him or to pick the forming method that is most economical for his operation, as long as the technique and materials selected will safely produce the required surface.

It will be helpful to the contractor if the architect can present a sample of the desired finish or indicate a similar finish on a completed structure. In turn, the contractor may submit a trial panel cast against proposed form surfacing material for the architect's inspection and approval. By working together, the architect and contractor can arrive at a surface and a method of forming it that will please the owner, meet the architect's design plan, and be economically formed by the contractor. This preliminary planning will prevent unwanted results and refinishing of the completed surface.

Contemporary architecture calls for a wide range of surface textures and treatments. A surface compatible with the architect's design may vary from a glass-smooth finish to one requiring special sculptured ornamentation. These surfaces require many different types of form sheathing and lining. Chemical retarders applied to the form surface make it possible to remove surface mortar and expose the aggregate after forms have been removed. Variations in finish may also be achieved by grinding, chiseling, hammering, and sandblasting after the concrete has set. Precast panels as forms or liners may provide the desired surface finish; sometimes a combination of several of these techniques is used.

Regardless of the finish, a non-staining form oil or coating should be used for architectural forms to prevent uneven coloring of the concrete. If there is any doubt about the release agent to be used, it should be tested. Form release agents and sealers should also be checked to be sure that they will not interfere with adhesion of specified paints or other surface treatment of the concrete, nor affect the texture of the form lining material.

11-3 Monumental curtain behind the rostrum of the Congress Hall of the UNESCO headquarters in Paris is concrete left as it was when forms were removed. Horizontal 2½-in. form boards and strongly marked lift joints at regular 4½-ft intervals were used to achieve the desired effect; tie holes also become a part of the pattern.

Since it is impossible to describe all of the methods of forming architectural surfaces, a representative sample of techniques and materials used will be discussed. Strength, stock sizes available, and other data on many of these materials are given in Chapter 4.

Form ties, control joints, and construction joints, which significantly influence the surface appearance of the concrete, are described in detail in later sections.* A thoughtful architect who plans with these necessary joints and ties in mind can often accentuate or develop them as distinctive design elements (Figure 11-3).

Smooth Surfaces

Most sheathing and lining materials are available in several different surfaces or grades, some of which are usually smooth enough that a blemish-free concrete can be formed. Proper choice of form release agent (see p. 208) is important in achieving the desired degree of smoothness. Contact surfaces of the formwork should be carefully installed to produce neat and symmetrical joint patterns unless otherwise specified. Joints should be either vertical or horizontal and, where possible, should be staggered so as to maintain structural continuity. If the surface is to be free of all marks made by the sheathing material, the joints between boards or panels must be pointed with patching plaster or otherwise filled or covered. Since this is a time consuming job, materials available in relatively large panels are of considerable value. In spite of joint filling, additional hand finishing is frequently required to bring a surface to the desired smoothness.

Nailing should be done carefully using hammers with smooth and well-dressed heads to prevent marring of the form surfaces. Box nails should be used when required on the contact surface and should be placed in a neat pattern.

Board Sheathing

If sheathing lumber is selected to build smooth-surfaced forms, dressed material is a necessity, and tongue-and-groove or shiplap is desirable. The need for dressed lumber comes from the desirability of having boards that can be easily and accurately placed. They also must fit tightly to minimize the formation of fins. A recommended method of applying the sheathing to the studs is given on p. 150.

---

* Additional information of value will be found in: "Design Details for Architectural Concrete," by J. J. Hogan, ACI JOURNAL, *Proceedings* V. 45, No. 7, Mar. 1949, pp. 529-540; and "Construction Practices for Architectural Concrete," by E. B. Oberly, also in the ACI JOURNAL, *Proceedings* V. 45, No. 7, Mar. 1949, pp. 541-552.

11-4 Accentuation rather than concealment of joints between plywood form panels provides surface interest in broad, simple masses of high walls of Northwest Airlines Engine Test Buildings in Minneapolis. Wall finishing is not yet complete in this view.

A common problem in the construction of forms with sheathing boards is the difficulty of keeping horizontal joints between the boards level. Sheathing lumber, even when dressed and matched, is not always perfectly uniform in width, and joints can easily get out of alignment. Irregularities in driving up adjoining boards may also aggravate this condition. It is therefore necessary to check the level of joint lines at frequent intervals. To do this, lines of levels may be set at 3- or 4-ft vertical intervals. The lines can be readily followed by the carpenter if they are marked on the studs about every 10 ft along the length of the form.

Other Materials

When plywood or hardboard serve as a sheathing material or liner, full size sheets are preferable whenever possible. Joints should be constructed tightly as described on p. 240. For best appearance the joints are "pointed" or filled (Figure 11–5).

Metal forms and liners give a smooth surface but the joints between the units are hard to conceal. If metal form units span the total distance between control joints or architectural features of the structure, the joints between the units will be less noticeable. The size of metal form panels can often be chosen from among a range of standard sizes available so that there is an even number of panels or a symmetrical pattern on each face of the architectural concrete. If such a pattern is acceptable, the joint marks will not require

concealment and costs are proportionately reduced.

When transverse joints are required in metal lining, the sheets can either be butted or lapped about ½ in. If a lap joint must be made in vertical form lining, the inner sheet of the lap should be the upper one so that the slight step in the concrete will not cast a shadow that calls attention to the joint.

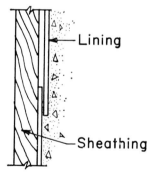

Lining materials can be attached to the sheathing with nails or a waterproof adhesive. When applying sheets of lining material, it is important to start attaching the sheet at its center and work toward the edges to prevent buckling. For hardboard liners there should be at least one 3d flat head nail in every square foot of surface and at least every 8 in. on the edges.

Very Smooth Surfaces

Nearly glass-smooth finishes are sometimes required in architectural concrete work. Normal sheathing boards and plywood do not produce this type of surface so liners must be used.

Plastic liners and glass-reinforced plastic forms can be made exceedingly smooth and they have proved excellent materials for this type of finish. After the

11-5 Patching compound between sheets of plywood obscured form joints on the lower surface of a hyperbolic paraboloid roof.

forms have been erected, joints can be filled with plastic to create a joint-free surface. Some form coating materials, among them an epoxy resin plastic, when properly applied function almost the same as plastic liners and produce glossy-smooth surfaces upon stripping. Air bubbles at the concrete surface are more common with these ultra-smooth forms than with somewhat porous materials. Another disadvantage with such a uniform finish is that any chance blemishes (including air bubbles) tend to be unduly conspicuous and may require special treatment. The glossy surfaced concrete is excellent for indoor decoration (Figure 11-7); however some reservations have been expressed regarding its use for exterior exposure because of the gradual, nonuniform loss of reflectivity.

11-6 Fiber glass reinforced plastic mold used in site casting of building components made it possible to achieve intricate shapes in precast concrete with smooth, seamless finish.

Textured Surfaces

Textured surfaces can be produced by casting against various kinds of forms and form liners; striated plywood, rubber matting, molded plastic, and many other materials can be used to achieve architectural effects. Pattern and texture of surface for units cast horizontally are also achieved by varying *finishing techniques,* but the discussion here is limited to some typical form materials and liners.

Board Marks and Simulated Wood Grain

Simulated wood grain can be made by casting concrete against plywood panels which have been wire brushed to accent the natural pattern of the wood grain. Sand blasting can also be used to reveal the grain. Special plywoods with exposed grain can be obtained from the mill where the soft grain growth has been removed to accentuate the natural swirls and contours of the face fir veneer. Sometimes the

11-7 High-gloss units precast against plastic form liners provide decorative wall treatment for a lobby. Alternating patterned and plain units are 12 in. square.

face of the concrete is dyed to make the surface resemble wood even more.

Unfinished sheathing lumber can be similarly used to produce a rough board-marked concrete.* By choosing slash grain lumber a strong grain effect is obtained. Sometimes forms are sprayed with ammonia to raise the wood fibers and accentuate grain markings. Tongue-and-groove boards may be spaced with a small gap between adjacent boards to accentuate fins, but an unbroken fin line must not be expected. Plain boards may be used to get a slight cupping that accentuates the joint lines where the scale of the structure permits a bold and rugged texture.

One advantage of a properly handled rough-board finish is that treatment after the forms are stripped is eliminated because minor defects readily blend into the general pattern. On the other hand, if honeycombing does occur, it is difficult to make the patches match the surrounding board texture.

Exposed Aggregate

To expose the aggregate on the surface of architectural concrete, two methods can be used. A set retarder can be applied to the forms so that after they are stripped the mortar between the surface aggregate particles can be washed or brushed away. The second method is the aggregate transfer method in which aggregate is attached to the form with an adhesive. After the concrete has been cast, the forms are removed, leaving the aggregate embedded in the concrete, since the bond to the concrete is stronger than the bond to the adhesive. Both methods work best when panels can be precast with the finished surface down; otherwise control becomes difficult. Care and experience are required to achieve uniform results.

Fluted Surfaces

Fluted surfaces can be easily formed by attaching wood or rubber strips to the form sheathing. If wood strips are used, they should be kerfed in the back to prevent them from swelling and breaking the concrete and to make them easy to strip. If they are lightly nailed to the forms, they will pull away when forms

* A good source of information and opinion on this technique is a 32-page brochure, "Design Notes and Specifications for Concrete from Rough-Board Formwork," issued in 1962 by the Cement and Concrete Association, 52 Grosvenor Gardens, London, S.W. 1. This is a report prepared by a subcommittee of the Wales Prestressed Concrete Development Group.

11-8 Textured surface of this structure, produced by casting against striated plywood, made possible considerable reduction in finishing labor.

11-9 Textured surface cast against rubber form liner

11-10 Wood grain simulated in concrete by casting against sand blasted plywood.

11-11 Rough surface cast against random-sized form lining boards. "Rough" applies only to the texture since considerable care in assembling forms and placing the concrete is required to achieve the desired effect of strength.

11-13 Wood strips nailed to plywood sheathing of wall forms (above) to produce fluting on the finished wall. Below, various stages of stripping, showing how nails pulled out of the plywood, leaving strips in place after form panels were taken down.

11-12 (Left) Close-up of exposed aggregate surface of precast panel. Retarder coating was applied to forms before casting. When forms were stripped 1½ days later, surface mortar was brushed and hosed off with water. Small view at the top shows panels installed in completed structure.

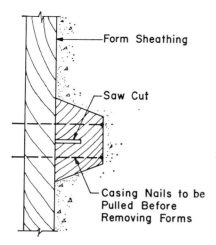

11-14 A suggested method of attaching rustication strips to the forms

are stripped, leaving the wood to be removed after the concrete is thoroughly hardened. The main advantage of rubber strips is that they can be easily pulled from the hardened concrete. Corrugated sheet metal, corrugated glass fiber building material, and corrugated asbestos cement roofing material may also be attached to forms to obtain regular fluted surfaces.

Other Over-all Decorative Patterns

An endless variety of over-all sculptured or relief patterns can be achieved by attaching specially prepared molds to the forms as liners. Plastic, glass-reinforced plastic, and rubber are among the patterned lining materials that can be nailed or attached with waterproof adhesives to the inside form surface. If the pattern is simple or geometrical, wood strips or blocks attached to the forms may be sufficient for forming the decoration. Best results are generally

achieved with a pattern or mold that is beveled and free of undercuts for easy stripping; however, even this requirement may be eliminated with some of the newer flexible materials. If patterned molds or inserts are used they should be carefully aligned and kept level to give continuity to the over-all pattern.

Air voids in concrete frequently leave "bug holes" on the formed surface. Eliminating these voids becomes increasingly difficult when complex surfaces are cast against comparatively impervious materials. Because it is easier to eliminate air voids from surfaces cast in a horizontal position, these surfaces are frequently made up of precast panels, and the job may be subcontracted to a concrete products specialist.

Precast Panels as Forms or Liners

Unusual or decorative surfaces can be incorporated in precast panels which serve as the exterior form or as a form liner which bonds permanently to the cast-in-place concrete. If the panels are to serve structurally as forms, they should be suitably reinforced to resist anticipated lateral pressures from the fresh concrete placed behind them. If they function merely as stay-in-place liners, they may be of lesser strength and thickness. Recommendations for design and fabrication of form panels of concrete are presented in Section 5.7 of ACI 347-68 (see Appendix).

The panels are fabricated with lifting inserts and anchors to attach them to the cast-in-place concrete. When the panels are to be used as exterior forms against which concrete is cast, form ties may be attached to embedded anchors, reinforcement, or inserts provided in the panels for that purpose (Figure 11-16), or they may be installed at joints between panels when suitable backing and provision for precise align-

11-15 An example of the early use of precast panels as exterior wall forms in construction of a model testing basin for the U. S. Navy at Carderock, Md., 1937-39. Bolts secured to inserts cast in the panels were used to tie the inside forms of conventional construction. Additional tie bolts passing through joints between panels were found necessary to keep the meeting edges in line.

ment of the panels is made. At the intersection of horizontal and vertical jointing, a temporary bolt through blocking is used to assure holding corners of all four slabs in the same plane during casting of concrete. Wales may be used on the concrete form face as needed to maintain alignment. Rate of rise of concrete in such forms should be limited according to recommendations of the manufacturer of the panels. Thorough consolidation of concrete behind the forms is desirable to prevent voids which would interrupt the bond of the form to structure concrete, but sufficient care must be exercised to prevent damage of concrete panels by contact with vibrators.

Precast concrete panels which serve as forms must be carefully handled during transportation and erection to prevent chipping, spotting, cracking, or other damage of the units. Where field welding of panel connections is required, the welding process should be controlled to avoid spalling and scorching of concrete. Such panel connections should not be galvanized.

Where architectural concrete form panels adjoin or are supported by other forming materials, care must be taken to use materials that will not stain the exposed concrete surface. Any concrete which is accidentally spilled on such panels must be washed off before it hardens. After concreting, precast architectural concrete form facings should be wrapped or covered with nonstaining materials to protect them from other construction materials, debris, or mechanical damage.

Joints between precast units are normally shimmed, to establish proper spacing, and then caulked, plastered, or taped on the inside or outside to prevent mortar leakage during concreting. Depending on design details, joints may require filling or caulking after concreting is completed. This filling or caulking should be done carefully to avoid damage to adjoining surfaces, and any cement-based joint filler should be adequately cured to make joints durably watertight.

Construction of Architectural Forms

Whether panel forms, built-in-place forms, or a combination of the two should be used depends largely upon the architectural treatment. Where they can produce the required surface, panel forms have numerous advantages as they do in structural concrete. Methods of building formwork for archi-

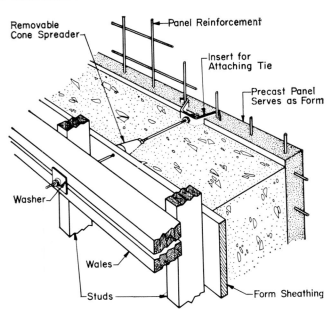

11-16 Wall form assembly showing how precast concrete panel serves as one face of the form

tectural concrete generally follow the techniques outlined in Chapter 9, Building and Erecting the Formwork. The purpose of this section is to point out additional considerations required for architectural work.

Apart from quality of contact surfaces already discussed, the main concern is for ornamental details, accurate alignment, and the prevention of disfiguring deflection. Better quality materials are usually required for architectural concrete formwork, and particular attention is given to meeting the dimensional tolerances specified by the architect.

Because the surface appearance of the architectural concrete is so important, extra vibrating or placing pockets may be needed to facilitate careful placement and consolidation of the concrete to prevent segregation, honeycomb, sanding, or cold joints.

Walls

Wall forms for architectural concrete are built the same as for structural concrete, but more attention is given to alignment, perfection of corners, and the contact surface. All wales should be constructed of two members with joints staggered to minimize deflection. Minor defects in alignment and construction, which may not be objectionable in structural work, show up badly in architectural concrete.

Any amount of care exercised in securing good alignment is time well spent. One method for aligning a long section of forms is to set points about 30 ft apart on the floor with a transit. These points may be

11-17 Typical details of straight wall forms showing one method of securing a tight corner. Vertical kick strips are attached to intersecting wales at the outside corner, and the wales are wedged tightly to prevent leakage.

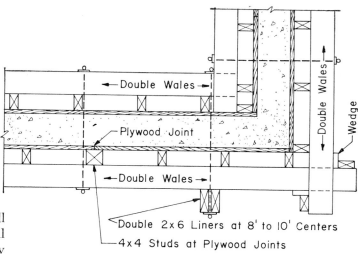

set 3 or 4 ft back from the face of the wall to be well out of the way. Control points at the top of the wall opposite the transit points are then accurately set by plumbing up from the floor points and measuring over to the wall. Intermediate points are set from a chalk line strung between the control points. Aligning of forms is best done when there is little wind. If a favorable time cannot be found, then control points set much closer together will aid in alignment.

Wall Sheathing

Unless definitely permitted or specified otherwise, board sheathing should be built in place, except that prefabricated form sections may be used if a single section will form an entire area from one reveal to another. Great care must be taken to prevent leakage through form joints. Vertical boards should have all vertical joints plumb, and horizontal boards should have all horizontal joints level and continuous. The vertical joints between horizontal boards should not be over one board wide, should be staggered at least 2 ft, and should be located at studs or girts. Each board must be driven up snug and nailed at every stud or girt with 6d box nails. Sheathing of 6-in. boards should be double nailed, and 8-in. and 10-in. boards should be nailed at both edges and at the center.

The top three boards below horizontal construction joints should be ripped to approximately one-third of the closure needed. This helps make the horizontal lines look more evenly spaced. For example, if 24 inches remain at the top of a wall formed with 10-in. boards, appearance will be better if each of the top three boards is 8 in. wide rather than having an entire wall of 10-in. material with a single 4-in. board tacked on at the top.

If plywood is used as sheathing, full size sheets are preferred and edges should be carefully butted to give tight joints. All vertical joints should be backed solidly, and the edges of abutting sheets should be

nailed to the same stud as shown in Figure 11-17. For best appearance, plywood sheets should be arranged as symmetrically as possible about the center line of each exposed surface. Grain of the outer plies should run at right angles to the studs for maximum strength.

Whenever the architect permits prefabricated form panels to be used as wall sheathing, similar care must be taken to keep horizontal joints level, vertical joints plumb, and all joints as mortar tight as possible. Panels, like plywood sheets, should be laid out symmetrically about the center line of the exposed wall face.

Form Lining

The backing for form lining should be constructed of a good grade of form lumber that is solid, straight, and free from defects which might impair its strength, but need not be of the quality used for contact forms.

11-18 Bad tie hole after stripping, showing spalled concrete, compared with a clean break-back achieved at the right. Additional impressions (right) left by fillers at panel corners where no ties were used.

Square edged, sized lumber may be used for backing. Form backing should be securely nailed and the edges of the boards should be in contact to prevent any bulging of the lining.

Joints in the lining should be offset from those in the backing. The lining material should be attached beginning at the center of the board or sheet and working toward the edges to prevent buckling. Nails should have thin flat heads, 2d for ¼-in. plywood and 3d for fiberboard, and should be spaced not more than 8 in. on centers at edges of lining material. There should be at least one nail in every square foot.

All lining material should be used in the widest size possible. Areas less than 4 ft wide should be lined with a single width of fiberboard, plywood, or other lining material. Edges of abutting sheets should be nailed to the same backing board, just as for sheathing. Joints between sheets of lining materials should be approximately ⅟₁₆ in. wide and should be filled to prevent leakage.

Ties

Form ties for architectural concrete require special consideration since the marks left by the ties can detract from the finished surface. Tie holes should be bored from the inside of the forms whenever possible to prevent the formation of burrs on the contact face. The smallest possible hole should be used to prevent mortar leakage. Special care should be taken during stripping so the concrete is not broken around the tie holes.

11-19 End view of glass-fiber-reinforced plastic form for cross-shaped architectural concrete column. Wood bracing elements are embedded in and coated with the plastic resin, so that the forms are relatively weatherproof.

Ties for architectural concrete should have the same factor of safety as for heavy formwork (Section 1.3.1. of 347-68). The ties should be adjustable to permit tightening of forms and should leave no metal closer than 1½ in. to the surface for steel ties and 1 in. for stainless steel ties. Any lugs, cones, washers, or other fittings, if permitted, should not leave depressions of a diameter greater than their depth at the exposed surface of the concrete if the hole is to be patched. Twisted wire or band iron ties should not be permitted. If ties do not fit tightly, holes should be pointed to prevent leakage. Tie layout should be planned so as to be symmetrical with the member formed, and wherever possible ties should be located at rustication marks, control joints, or other points where the visual effect will be minimized.

In some cases the architect may specify pencil rods, taper ties, or other tie bolts which are pulled out after use, and loose wood spreaders that are removed as concreting progresses. Such ties should be coated with non-staining bond breaker or encased in oiled paper sleeves to facilitate removal. Occasionally the architect may call for externally braced forms to avoid objectionable blemishes in the finished surface, or he may go to the other extreme and emphasize tie hole depressions as part of the surface design.

Corners and Openings

Forming corners in architectural concrete is a critical operation. The formwork must be unusually tight and braced so that no movement occurs since imperfections in construction and alignment are most noticeable at corners. A slight opening of a corner will cause bleeding that may result in sand streaks or an irregular line of honeycomb and a fin that cannot be easily removed or covered. One way of forming corners for architectural concrete is shown in Figure 11-17. Methods are generally the same as for structural concrete (p. 155), except that greater precision and attention to detail are required.

Forms for wall openings are built as described in Chapter 9. Precision is again the main consideration, especially at the joint between the wall sheathing and the opening form. Many difficulties can be avoided if the lumber used is selected for straightness so that it will fit accurately between the forms, leaving no blemishes in the concrete.

Columns

Modern architectural designs often require that structural columns be left exposed for architectural effects. Round or rectangular columns are formed much the same as regular structural concrete columns (p. 162), except for the attention required for surface finishing and ornamental details. Smooth sheathing or lining and carefully patched joints are essential, unless other provisions are made for a textured surface.

Columns are often sculptured or ornamented and require special fabrication of details. Glass-fiber-reinforced plastic has recently been used with good results in forming decorative columns. Figure 11-19 shows such a column form; the two halves are bolted together and when ready for concreting, this form will also be tied with steel straps or clamps on the lower third to withstand concrete pressure.

Precast concrete panels which stay in place permanently as a decorative facing have also been used as forms for architectural columns (Figure 4–50).

Pilasters

Generally, the face form for a pilaster can be made as a panel. Accuracy in forming is important, as such details are frequently the focus of attention in the facade of the building. Corners and sheathing joints must be straight and true, and marks of the edge grain of the form sheathing should not be visible from the front.

Figure 11-20 shows a typical pilaster form. Note that the edge grain of the form sheathing is either covered or is located so its imprint will not be visible

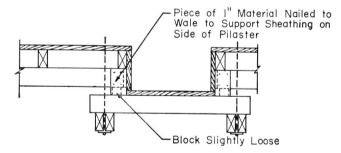

11-20 Typical detail of pilaster form where the projection is greater than the depth of the studs. Sheathing for the face laps over the corners, and wall sheathing butts against the pilaster sides.

from the front of the building. The front panel of the pilaster form laps the side panels so that if a fin is formed, it can be removed without touching the face of the pilaster.

The sides of the pilaster form should not be nailed to the studs because nailing from two sides will make the studs impossible to strip without tearing them apart. The blocks between the wall and pilaster wales should be slightly loose so that when the ties are tightened they will pull the face form tight.

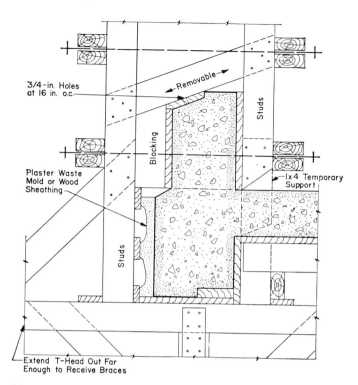

11-21 Ornamental spandrel beam form supported on T-head shores. This design is suitable for casting in two stages because face design would tend to hide construction joint at the top of the floor slab.

Spandrels and Parapets

Spandrels are often decorative features of a building and may require the use of molds if they are complicated in design. The spandrel can be cast in one or two parts depending on the location of the floor slab and the design of the spandrel. If the spandrel is to be cast in two parts, it is desirable to have the joint obscured by placing it at some architectural detail.

Two methods of forming a spandrel are shown in Figures 11-21 and 11-22. These forms can be used whether the spandrel is to be cast in one or two operations. The inside wall form is supported on 1x4's resting on the floor slab form if casting is a single operation. These supports are withdrawn before the floor slab concrete has hardened. Fabricated metal adjustable supports are available for the same purpose, or precast concrete block supports left in the floor slab can be used as shown in Figure 12–16.

Usually forms for the inside of parapet walls are made in panels erected as a unit. Panels 10 to 12 ft long are convenient for the average job. The method of support is the same as pictured for spandrel forms.

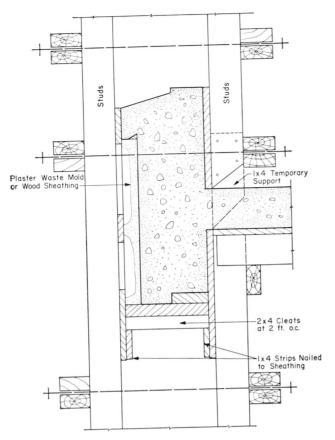

11-22 Spandrel form supported by studs extended past wall opening and sheathing also extended part way across the opening.

Ornamental Detail

Molds for casting concrete ornament can be constructed from wood, plastic, plaster, rubber, concrete, glass fiber, metal, and other materials. The type of material selected for the mold depends upon the shape to be formed, desired number of reuses, cost of making the mold, and ease of erection and stripping.

The molds should be carefully set in the forms and securely held in position to reproduce the design shown on the drawings. Where wood forms adjoin molds, the wood should be neatly fitted to the profile of the mold and all joints should be carefully pointed. The molds and the adjacent wood forms should be so detailed that the wood forms can be stripped without disturbing the molds. A slight draft on the edge of molds or pattern strips will permit removing the detail material without damaging the concrete. Special provisions should be made for early form removal and/or retardation when sand blasting, wire brushing, or other treatments are required.

Wood molds are best used for ornaments that have straight lines with no undercuts, such as fluting and molding on pilasters and cornices. Complex ornaments with curved surfaces and undercuts should be cast against molds made of materials such as plaster, plastic, and rubber which can be formed around a pattern for a true reproduction of the shape desired. Sheet metal can be rolled to shape molds for cylin-

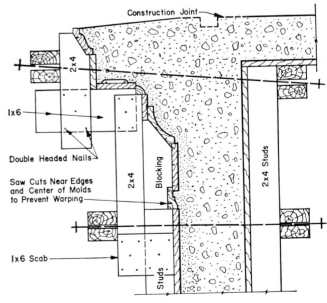

11-24 Wood mold for cornice, showing how longitudinal joints are made by overlapping the pieces, rather than butting or mitering. Brackets of 2x4 and 1x6 material cut to the approximate shape of the cornice are preassembled, scabbed to studs. Cornice form parts are then attached.

11-23 Details at the cornice and below windows and the fluting between windows were formed with wood molds.

drical sections. Precast concrete ornamentation is also used; components may be placed inside the form and concrete cast against or around them. At times it is attached after the forms are stripped.

Wood Molds

Wood molds are made of white pine, soft vertical-grain Douglas fir, or other softwood run to size and shape in a commercial mill, or in the job mill if the job is large enough to warrant installation of the necessary shapers. Molds of wood are especially well adapted to ornamentation on belt courses, cornices, and other long details; for such purposes the mold is made up of several long moldings or strips run to proper shape commercially or on the job site. It should be made of material that does not warp or split easily.

Special attention must be given to joint construction. Objectionable fins will be formed in the concrete if the mold joints are not mortar tight. Each joint should be pointed up with patching plaster before the concrete is cast.

Longitudinal joints between the mold members should be made by overlapping at reveals or returns whenever possible (Figure 11-24). If butt or miter joints are used, alternate shrinking and swelling may open them to cause fins in the finished concrete. When joints occur where there is no return or reveal, tongue-and-groove lumber or shiplap should be used. Joints may also be splined. Butt joints can be used when the pieces are attached to a solid backing which prevents distortion of the mold due to swelling or shrinkage of the pieces.

11-25 Intricate figures are cast against plaster molds that are modeled the same as a piece of sculpture. Ornament shown is on the Ector County Courthouse, Odessa, Texas.

If transverse joints between successive pieces on a long wooden mold all occur at the same place, they are easily detected in the finished concrete, and there will be a distinct break in continuity that weakens the mold. Staggering joints overcomes both of these problems, and small joints can be made almost invisible by careful pointing.

Since wood swells when wet, the mold must be built so that this property will not distort the mold or open joints. Swelling may also break the newly formed concrete. Thin, narrow boards should be used because they warp and swell less than thick, wide boards. They also save lumber. Saw cuts in the back of the mold members (Figure 11-24) will also reduce warping and wedging caused by swelling and will make the forms easier to strip.

Perfectly square pieces will bind in a formed recess and will have to be cut out with a chisel. To avoid this extra labor and possible damage to the concrete, make wood inserts with a slight bevel or draw and with saw cuts in the back.

Much time can be saved in erecting and stripping forms for a detail involving many pieces of run moldings if brackets are made in the shop to the approximate profile of the proposed mold. The brackets can be fastened to a major part of the formwork and the mold pieces attached without excessive blocking.

Plaster Molds

Plaster molds for casting intricate ornamentation are called "waste" molds because they are broken in stripping and can be used only once. However, where elements of the design are repeated a number of times, many duplicate molds can be cast from the same master pattern or model.

These molds are usually built by the ornamental plasterer who applies plaster reinforced with jute fibers to a pattern of wood, clay, or other material. The pattern is made to the exact form of the proposed ornament. When the mold has hardened sufficiently, it is taken off the pattern and finished to the texture of the form sheathing that is to surround the mold so the concrete finish of the decorative detail will match the surrounding concrete. The contact side of the mold is then waterproofed with several coats of shellac or other compound. This prevents the mold from absorbing water from the fresh concrete which would weaken the mold and the concrete, as well as possibly discoloring the concrete.

A ¼-in. layer of colored plaster placed next to the pattern when forming the mold will aid in the stripping operation by indicating when the plaster has been chipped close to the concrete surface. The coloring must be such that the concrete will not be stained if the waterproofing agent fails or is chipped off the contact surface of the mold.

The contractor and plasterer should work together in developing a mold that is strong enough to withstand the pressure of the fresh concrete. The mold maker must be given complete instructions as to how the mold will be attached to the formwork so that extensive blocking will not be necessary. The mold must also be able to withstand handling during erection.

The shape of the back of the mold varies according to the size and shape of the ornamentation to be formed. For small molds or flat surfaces with shallow ornamentation, the back of the mold will be made flat to bear directly against the studs or wales. Molds for deep ornamentation would be too heavy if the plaster were brought out to a flat surface in back, so they are made 1½ to 2 in. thick with the back of the mold made to approximate the profile of the contact surface. The mold is then blocked out around the edges and other points with plaster reinforced with jute fibers or burlap to contact the formwork.

A wooden frame is often added to the back of a mold (Figure 11-26) to prevent deflection and cracking during transportation and erection. The frame is detached when the mold is set in place.

The edges of the mold require special attention. If possible, the joints between the mold and the form sheathing should be hidden at reveals or returns. The edges of each piece should be rabbeted (Figure 11-27) so they will fit closely with the form sheathing,

making a tight joint. All joints between pieces of the mold and the mold and sheathing should be pointed with plaster.

The molds may be attached to the formwork in various ways. They can be nailed or wired to the studs and wales. If this method is used, the nails are countersunk and the wires are pulled into the plaster until they are buried and the marks pointed up with plaster. Nails may also be driven into the mold through the formwork. To strip the formwork, the nails are withdrawn from the mold, leaving it in place to be stripped later. Special brackets and blocking can be built into the mold for attachment to the formwork.

Metal and Plastic Molds

Curved surfaces of mullions, piers, and pilasters are well suited to forming by metal molds. It is advantageous if the curved surfaces are designed so that the sheet metal can be shaped on standard rolls. The metal must be reinforced with collars or diaphragms to maintain alignment. These supports are usually spaced about 9 to 12 in. apart. Figure 11-28 shows how metal molds are assembled. Corrugated metal sheets may also be used to form fluting details.

11-26 Back of a waste mold used to form recessed ornament. Flat surface around the edge of the mold is made to bear against the form sheathing or a framework of studs. Wood strips are for handling.

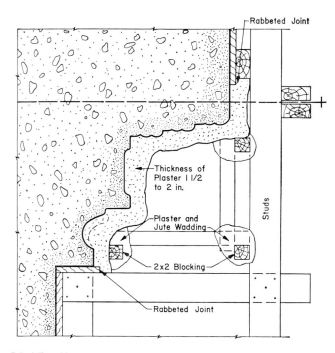

11-27 How the mold for an ornamental head jamb of a door is supported in the forms. Flat section parallel to the wall bears against studs. Jute fiber dipped in plaster is twisted about studs and blocking to secure the mold in place.

The molds should be made from black iron rather than galvanized sheets because galvanized metal may stick to the concrete even though it is well oiled. Shapes other than cylindrical can be formed with metal but this is a costly process and seldom used unless a great number of forms are needed such as metal pans for a waffle slab floor system.

Glass-fiber-reinforced plastic molds are used like wood, plaster, or metal molds for ornamentation. Like plaster molds, many duplicates can be made from a single master pattern; these molds, however, have the added advantage of reusability. They can be nailed to the form sheathing or attached with a waterproof mastic, or the shape can be built into the surface of a panel. Joints between molds and sheathing are filled to keep the joint from showing in the finished surface.

Large reinforced plastic molds are easily blocked out to a flat plane at the back for attachment to the formwork. If the ornament to be formed is complex, the mold must be made in several parts; all joints should be accurately aligned and filled with a plastic material like that of the mold.

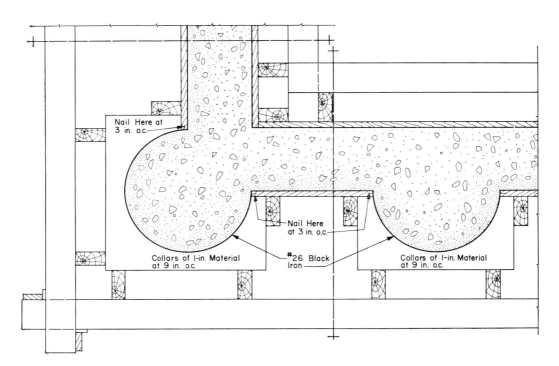

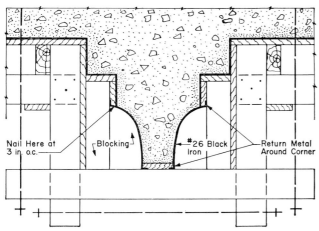

11-28 Sheet metal shaped on standard rolls used to form curved surfaces of mullions (left) and fluted corner (above). The metal is stiffened by blocks or collars cut on a band saw to the shape of the mold.

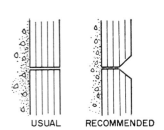 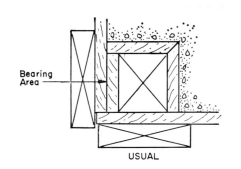 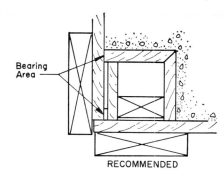

11-29 Reduced bearing area at points of contact between form members improves tightness of joints. Abutting plywood panels at the left and a recess at the corner of a column form (right) are shown.

Erection Practices

Good craftsmanship is the distinguishing characteristic of architectural concrete form construction; angles and joints must be made accurately. Corners must be sharp and straight. Leakage through the forms must be prevented. Sheathing joints and miters that are not tight must be pointed up. Molds must be accurately positioned. All of these items depend upon the skill of the form builder.

Experience indicates that if the meeting surfaces of the forms are reduced to minimum bearing areas, tightness of the joints is improved. Figure 11-29 shows two applications of this idea.

Where it is difficult to draw the form tight with only tie rods, wales, and braces, liberal use of wooden wedges driven between blocking and sheathing will often help. Studs, wales, and ties must be spaced close enough to prevent bulging of forms. In case of doubt, it is better to space supporting elements of the form closer than necessary rather than too far apart.

It is generally advisable to erect the outside form first since the exposed face is usually the exterior face. The designer should avoid requiring ornamental sculpture at opposite points in both faces. Form lining and molds are easier to apply with the outside form erected first. Tie holes can be drilled from the face side of the forms thus avoiding burrs that would mar the concrete. The completely erected outside form can be inspected and any joints or other places where leakage might occur can be corrected and pointed more easily.

Inner and outer wall forms must be carefully aligned before the ties are tightened because truss action of the tied forms will make accurate alignment difficult.

In assembling forms, one must keep in mind the steps that can be taken to aid in removing them without injury to the concrete. Boxes, molds, rustication

strips, or any insert attached to the main wall forms should be as lightly nailed as possible so they will pull loose from the forms during the stripping operation and remain in the concrete. After the lumber has dried and shrunk, these items can be easily removed. If plaster, plastic, or other molds are used, the same light nailing technique should be used since it is desirable to leave the molds in place as long as possible to protect the ornamentation.

Inserts should be attached with double headed nails driven from the outside of the forms wherever possible, because they can be pulled easily, leaving embedded parts of the form in the concrete temporarily. When applying rustication strips to the face side of a form (Figure 11-14), long casing nails which extend through the strip and sheathing may be used. Since the heads of these nails are very small the nails can be pulled through the strip and sheathing just before removing the form, thus allowing the wood strip to remain in place until it is thoroughly dry.

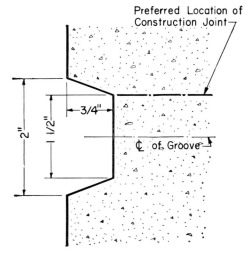

11-30 Typical dimensions of horizontal groove formed at construction joint to improve appearance of concrete. Groove is formed by strip like that in Figure 11-14.

Construction and Control Joints

Horizontal grooves at construction joints obscure the joints and may become a part of the architectural effect. Typical dimensions for such grooves are shown in Figure 11-30. These grooves permit more flexibility in form construction and reduce possible leakage of mortar onto surfaces at lower elevations. Grooves should be spaced so as to create the desired architectural pattern, and should be straight and continuous across the face being formed.

It is sometimes necessary to locate construction joints in flat wall surfaces where there are no architectural details to obscure them. By taking proper precautions, joints in such exposed locations need not be prominent enough to be objectionable. A ⅝-in. bolt or threaded internal disconnecting tie rod located not more than 4 in. below the joint should be provided to support the forms for the next lift. When re-erecting the forms, the contact surface of the sheathing should overlap the hardened concrete only about 1 in. Greater overlap provides more opportunity for leakage due to irregularities in the wall surface against which sheathing is held. When the forms above the joint are stripped, the bolt or tie end is removed from the concrete. A row of ties should always be located just above the joint to resist the pressure of the concrete rather than relying on the bolts below.

Where grooved joints are not feasible, the construction joint is kept straight by tacking a 1x2 strip along the outside form as shown. The concrete is brought slightly above the bottom of the strip. The strip should be removed after the concrete has set enough to hold its position. When the next lift of concrete is placed, there will be a straight, true joint. The next lift should be started with 1 to 2 in. of grout to avoid bottom honeycomb along this joint. A similar strip can be used on the inside form if the inside wall surface is to be exposed.

Control joints are usually required for architectural concrete to prevent haphazard cracking. The location of these joints should be specified by the architect; in some cases he may plan them as part of the decorative treatment. A straight joint of even width is formed by placing a projecting strip on the form surface that will form a depression in the concrete. Wood, metal, and plastics are suitable for such forming. It is important to keep the alignment of these joints true as any deviation from a straight line will be noticeable. Figure 11-32 shows how they can be formed. The joint may be filled with mastic after the forms have been stripped.

Stripping

Careless workmen can cancel out the value of good detailing and planning by indiscriminate use of the wrecking bar. A pinch bar or other metal tool should never be placed against architectural concrete to wedge forms loose. If it is necessary to wedge between the concrete and the forms, only wooden wedges should be used.

As a rule, wall forms should not be removed until the concrete has thoroughly hardened, but specified

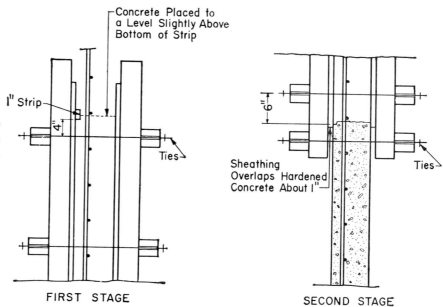

11-31 Construction joint treatment at formed surfaces. Bulges and offsets are avoided when ties are close to the joint. The 1-in. wood strip aids in producing a straight, true joint.

Concrete Placed to a Level Slightly Above Bottom of Strip

1" Strip

Ties

FIRST STAGE

6"

Sheathing Overlaps Hardened Concrete About 1"

Ties

SECOND STAGE

curing should begin as early as possible in warm weather. Ties may be removed as early as 24 hr after casting, to loosen forms slightly and permit entry of curing water between form and concrete. Ornamental molds must be left in place until they can be removed without damage to the concrete surface.

In cold weather, removal of formwork should be deferred or formwork should be replaced with insulation blankets, to avoid thermal shock and consequent crazing of the concrete surface.

When stripping forms in the vicinity of a belt course, cornice, or other projecting ornament, begin stripping some distance away from the ornament and work toward it. Thus if there is any tendency for the forms to bind around the ornament the pressure of the forms against projecting corners will be relieved so there will be less chance of spalling sharp edges.

Forms recessed into the concrete require special care in stripping. Wedging should be done gradually and should be accompanied by light tapping on the piece to crack it loose from the concrete. Never remove an embedded form with a single jerk. Embedded wood forms are generally left in place as long as possible so they will shrink away from the concrete. The embedded items should be separate from or loosely attached to the main form so that they will remain in place when the main form is stripped.

When stripping forms for a window opening, cross braces and vertical kick strips should be removed first. Next, take off top and bottom cleats and wedge out the head, using wooden wedges. The wedges should be driven in at one end, forcing the head down and away from the side member. To facilitate stripping, a

45° cut or miter through the sides of the frame is sometimes made when the form is built.

Plaster waste molds should be stripped by a man who is familiar with the detail. The plaster will usually stick to the concrete, at least in the undercuts, even with proper greasing. It must be carefully cut away with a chisel. If the mold has been made with a layer of colored plaster next to the concrete, the workman doing the chipping is warned when he has chipped close to the concrete. Plastic, steel, or rubber molds can be stripped by introducing compressed air between the concrete and the mold through an opening in the mold for that purpose. Flexible molds are peeled off.

Cleanup

After forms are stripped, all material to be reused must be throughly cleaned of hardened concrete. Some concrete will always adhere to sheathing lumber in spite of thorough oiling or other treatment. A tool made to fit the tongue and groove of matched boards will save time in cleaning the edges of boards.

All nails should be pulled from sheathing boards, plywood, hardboard, and other materials. Never bend nails over by hammering them against the face of the material if reuse for forms is planned. Holes which were bored through sheathing for form ties may be plugged by driving in common corks or foamed plastic and cutting the material off flush with a sharp chisel or fine saw. Patching plaster can also be used to fill small holes.

Cleaned lumber should be sorted by size and length and stored in neat piles. Plywood and fiberboard should be laid flat and out of the sun to keep edges from curling. Forms which are to be reused should be carefully inspected after each use to assure that they have not become distorted or otherwise unable to perform as designed.

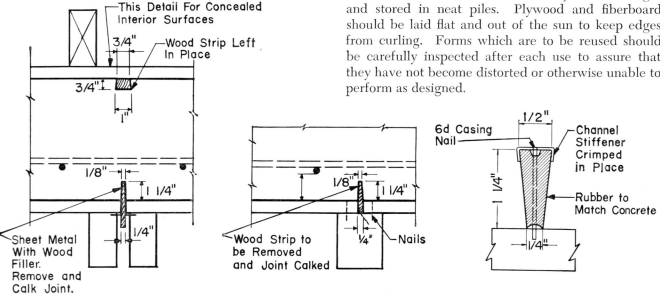

11-32 Typical details for forming control joints in architectural concrete. The rubber former is one of several types of ready-made joint forming products.

12:SHELLS, DOMES, FOLDED PLATES

CONSTRUCTION OF SHELLS, domes, and folded plates presents unique problems to the form designer and builder. Because of the relatively thin section in this type of construction, imperfections in the forms are larger in comparison with the section of the finished member than in beam and slab designs. The more complex nature of the curved and inclined surfaces and the resulting stress patterns also present difficulties not ordinarily encountered in forming rectilinear structures. Form removal is a critical operation because of the danger that formwork may bind or hang up on the shell and overload the entire new concrete structure, or the sequence of removal may concentrate loads at points not anticipated in the design of the space structure.

The key to successful formwork for shells, as in other types of construction, is careful, complete planning by the architect, engineer, and contractor. The normal procedures of form planning and building generally apply to this type of construction, but certain factors requiring special attention are pointed out in this chapter.

The most obvious deviations from other construction are the geometry of the shell structure and the resultant deflection which may require both horizontal and vertical camber. Shells can take the form of doubly or singly curved surfaces. Singly curved surfaces, such as barrels of circular cross section are relatively simple to design and build, but most of the doubly curved surfaces such as domes or the so-called free form shapes (Figure 12-1), are difficult to analyze and costly to form. One notable exception is the hyperbolic paraboloid whose doubly curved surface can be generated by the movement of a straight line. To form such a shell, joists can be spaced along the path of the generating line and the sheathing can then be warped to fit the doubly curved surface formed by the straight members (Figure 12-6).

12-1 Building the formwork for a doubly curved "free form" shell roof. Geometry of such a structure must be adequately described by structural designer, leaving the form planner free to exercise his ingenuity in deciding the best way to form it.

12-2 Costly shoring and curved formwork for domes is sometimes bypassed by using shaped and compacted earth. Surface of the earth form against which the shell is cast may be covered by a thin layer of mortar with a bond breaker, an integral acoustic or insulating material, paper, or plastic film. Dome may be cast in its final position and the earth fill removed or, as in the case illustrated, on a mound of minimum thickness, and then lifted on supporting columns by regular lift slab technique.

12-3 Underside of the dome of Figure 12-2 during lifting, showing the shaped earth form. The 2x8-ft foamed polystyrene plastic planks that lined the accurately shaped mound of earth became permanent insulation for the dome roof.

12-4 Another approach to dome forming. A temporary support tower erected at the center holds a cast-in-place solid circular center section of the dome. Remainder of the dome is cast in pie-shaped segments using a movable truss-supported form that spans from the central support tower to exterior wall framing. When all wedge segments are in place and properly joined central tower is removed and the dome becomes self supporting.

12-5 Entire form for this folded plate roof was assembled in place before concreting began. Contrast with the segmental approach pictured in 12-7.

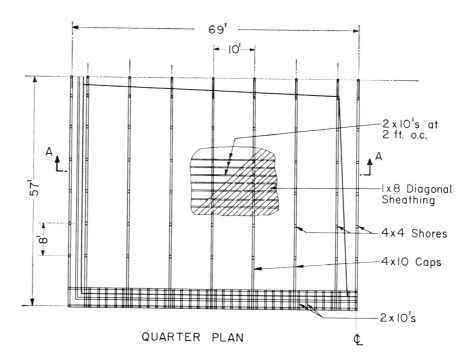

12-6 Quarter plan and elevation of formwork for hyperbolic paraboloid shell showing how straight members can be used to form the doubly curved surface. Contractor made a model of this formwork before building the full-scale structure.

69'

10'

2 x 10's at 2 ft. o.c.

A

A

57'

1 x 8 Diagonal Sheathing

4 x 4 Shores

4 x 10 Caps

8'

2 x 10's

QUARTER PLAN

℄

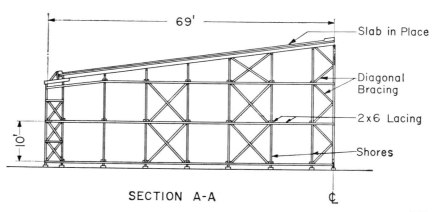

69'

Slab in Place

Diagonal Bracing

2 x 6 Lacing

10'

Shores

SECTION A-A

℄

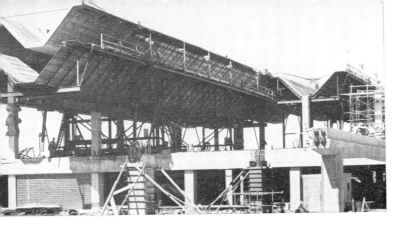

12-7 A 150 ft long form of steel, wood, and plywood was lowered and moved to a new position for concreting this folded plate, section by section. A removable unit in the form allowed it to slide past the already concreted column.

Folded plates differ from shells in geometry, but some of the same formwork problems exist. The thickness of the folded plate is like that of most shells, and the shape can be quite complex, requiring the same special care in form design and building as the shell. The slope of folded plates may be so steep as to require back forms.

Because of the high cost of forming shells and folded plates, travelers (Figure 12-7) or reusable form sections are often developed for structures having recurring elements of the same shape. Multiple cylindrical shells, groups of hyperbolic paraboloids and folded plate roofs lend themselves to this type of forming.

12-8 Multi-use barrel shell form weighing 5½ tons, lifted by cranes into new casting position where it will be supported on steel scaffold shoring already in place.

Since the concrete of shell structures is often left exposed as an interior ceiling, special attention must be given to the surface texture of the forms. If the finished surface, rather than the form material, is specified, the contractor will have enough leeway to allow him to design the most economical formwork for his resources. A test panel approved in advance by the architect or engineer may be desirable to illustrate the texture of the required surface and to provide a standard for comparison with finished work for acceptance purposes.

Shell Form Design Considerations

If the contractor is to be expected to form the shell correctly, the geometry of the finished structure must be adequately described by the structural designer. The degree of precision required should be specified, and the surface should be described by coordinates sufficiently close together to give the desired results. Due to the special shapes involved, tolerances based on functions of these shapes should be specified by the engineer-architect in the bidding documents. A contour drawing of the surface to be formed may prove helpful for irregularly curved surfaces. With the surface of the structure adequately defined the formwork designer can then employ his ingenuity and skill in deciding the best way to form it.

Thin section structures often have a large dead load deflection when the forms are removed. Edge members and free edges may have horizontal as well as vertical components of deflection. The engineer-architect should specify the correct formwork camber required to compensate for these deflections; he must also describe it in enough detail so that the form designer can interpret it correctly. This same deflection may be the cause of decentering problems, particularly where edges deflect *inward* and tend to pinch or bind the formwork.

Since a three dimensional analysis of these complex shapes is required, a competent, experienced individual should make a stress analysis of the forms and falsework. Due regard should be given to unsymmetrical or eccentric loadings which may occur in the falsework members during concrete placement. Stresses occurring during erection and decentering of the falsework or movement of traveler should also

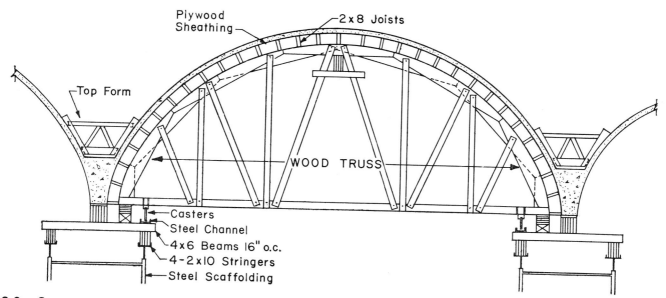

Plywood Sheathing — 2 x 8 Joists

Top Form

WOOD TRUSS

Casters
Steel Channel
4x6 Beams 16" o.c.
4-2x10 Stringers
Steel Scaffolding

12-9 Cross section through shell roof, indicating the construction of forms shown in 12-8. The 2x8 joists resting on bowstring trusses supported plywood sheathing bent to curvature of the shell.

be considered. These requirements suggest the need for planning based upon the necessary special qualifications and experience in formwork of this type.

Loads

The forms and shores for shell structures must be braced to resist all foreseeable lateral loads. Generally, the lateral loads for shell forms will be the same as for more conventional forms, but because of shell shapes and the large amount of shores necessary, a minimum wind load of 15 lb per square foot of exposed area is recommended by ACI Committee 347 instead of the 10 psf specified for wall forms. For structures such as domes, negative forces due to suction created by the wind on the leeward side of the structure should be considered. Such formwork should be anchored as a whole against uplift and all individual pieces of sheathing should be nailed down.

Construction loads must be thoroughly investigated. These loads are quite important in this type of construction because they may be large in relation to the dead load of the concrete. For example, the dead load from a 3-in. shell is about 40 psf, while the minimum recommended construction load on slabs is 50 psf. It is more important to include the estimated weight of the shell formwork as part of the dead load since it represents a larger percentage of the total than in slab forms. The engineer-architect should specify limiting values and directions of the reactive forces when the falsework is supported by the permanent structure.

As in more conventional construction, the dumping

of concrete on one section of the forms may cause upward movement of another part. The forms and falsework must be designed to resist the forces arising from the method and sequence of placement.

Another factor that can cause uplift, sagging, or warping is the mass of reinforcement required in the stiffening members of some shells (Figure 12-10). The forms near the ribs must be adequately braced to carry the load of the steel cage.

Details

Since the weight of the supporting falsework may, in many cases, be equal to or greater than the design live load, the form should be designed so it will not bind or hang up and overload the structure during decentering. The forms must not become keyed into the concrete in any way that would hinder stripping or transfer the load of the falsework to the shell. This

12-10 Heavy reinforcement for shell ribs requires additional bracing and support to prevent form deflection.

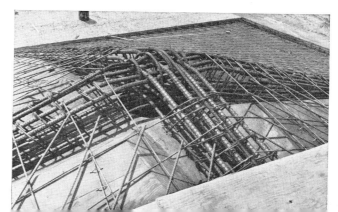

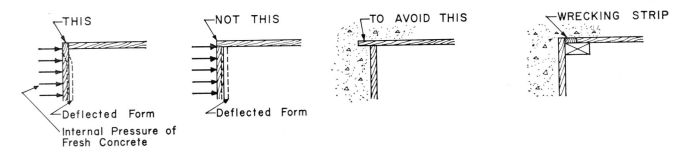

12-11 Where a horizontal form surface meets a vertical one, the vertical sheathing should be carried up flush with the top of the horizontal form so that the vertical member does not deflect and permit the horizontal one to become keyed into concrete. A wrecking strip (right) is also helpful at such an intersection.

calls for special attention to the details of formwork for shells, domes, and folded plates. Although reasonable precautions should be taken, it may not be worthwhile to eliminate all the foreseeable sources of binding. To do so might call for prohibitively expensive detailing. It is a matter of degree, and this degree should be agreed upon jointly by the contractor and the engineer-architect.

Workmen familiar with the forming of slabs, beams, and columns cannot be expected to have the same skill in building shell forms. Items ordinarily left to the man on the job will have to be set down in detail for this type of construction.

Inserts, Anchor Bolts

When inserts are nailed solidly to the form through a relatively strong ear on the insert, the nail will then pull out of the form when it is stripped. Enough of

12-12 If the shell shape is complex, or unusual forming problems are anticipated, a scale model may help both designer and field men to anticipate problems and develop a solution before construction actually begins. This model of one-eighth of a reinforced concrete dome form was built to a scale of 1 in. = 1 ft. A complete interior form for the 92-ft dome was planned, with the exterior forms (left) to be built in 16 sections. Windows in the exterior form were spaced about 10 ft horizontally to permit placing and vibrating concrete at the lower part of the dome.

these can hang up a form, and details must be arranged so that the nail *pulls out of the insert* with relative ease by weakening the ears on the insert. If possible the inserts should be anchored to the reinforcing steel rather than to the forms.

Anchor bolts and similar items which must necessarily penetrate the forms are sometimes held in place by running nuts up tight against the inner and outer faces of the form sheathing. Often nuts are run on the exposed thread of a bolt protruding below the form just to protect the threads. Of course provision must be made for removing the bottom nuts before stripping begins. If such protruding bolts are at right angles to a sloping surface where the form is expected to drop vertically, there must be adequate clearance provided in the form surface to clear the horizontal projection of the member.

Joints, Removable Panels

Joints in the forms should be planned so that no keying action can develop because of movement during the placement of concrete. For example, where a relatively horizontal surface butts a more or less vertical surface as in an arch rib below a shell, the vertical sheathing should be carried up flush with the top of the horizontal form so that it cannot move laterally as it might if the horizontal form was extended out over the top of the vertical one (Figure 12-11).

Joints that can be loosened, connections that are free to act as a hinge when a locking pin is removed, or small panels and wrecking strips that can be removed just before decentering begins often help eliminate form hang up and binding.

Drawings

The contractor should submit detailed drawings of the formwork for the approval of the engineer-architect. The formwork drawings must comply with

12-13 Actual construction of the interior dome form whose model is shown in Figure 12-12. A central tower was first erected and braced to support dome ribs and hub at the top. Steel scaffold-type shoring was substituted for the wood of the model, and horizontal sheathing was used instead of the vertical boards originally planned.

the contract drawings and specifications and meet the general requirements for good formwork to assure the integrity and stability of the structure itself. These drawings must show the recommended sequence for placing concrete. To insure that the structure can assume its deflected or loaded shape without damage, the decentering sequence should also be shown. Necessary camber, which includes allowance for settling of supports and taking up and deflection of the formwork as well as that required by the structural design, should be clearly indicated.

Drawings should show clearly how to handle sheathing joints, inserts, and any other details that might cause keying.

Building the Forms

Special care in the erection of forms and falsework for shell structures will enable the builder to meet precision requirements of the specifications and assure

that the structure will take the correct shape when loaded. If the shell shape is complex, a scale model (Figure 12-12) may help the form designer and the men in the field to anticipate problems and develop solutions before erection begins. Simpler or more regular shapes may be such that prefabricated form units will be economical. This is most apparent in singly curved shells or folded plates where prefabricated units built on truss supports can easily be used. When movable forms are used, a minimum batter of ⅛ in. per ft is recommended for vertical surfaces to facilitate form removal.

To assure ease in stripping and to prevent keying, the form builder should give special attention to the assembly of the form sheathing. Plywood, dressed lumber, and other smooth materials make for easier stripping than rough form boards, but the latter may at times be architecturally necessary. Use sealed or taped joints (Figure 12-15) wherever possible, because untaped joints leave fins that increase finishing as well as stripping difficulties, more so on sloping than on vertical surfaces. Where boards instead of sheet material are required by the shape of the shell, use the widest boards practicable and take all reasonable steps to prevent joints from opening. Narrower boards are easier to warp and may be better for

12-14 Wood trusses fabricated on a jig set up on the ground were shaped to the parabolic section of vault to be concreted pneumatically. Trusses were set at 10-ft intervals along each vault; 2-in. ribs were placed between trusses and covered with plywood sheathing.

12-15 Exacting requirements in formwork construction where doubly curved shell merges with tapered column. Plywood supported on board sheathing is cut and fitted to curves. Note taped joints on column interior.

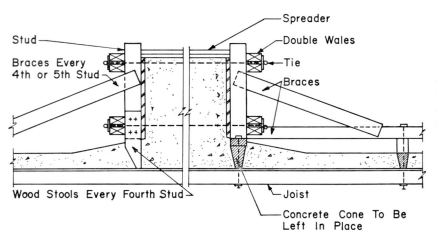

Stud

Braces Every
4th or 5th Stud

Spreader

Double Wales

Tie

Braces

Wood Stools Every Fourth Stud

Joist

Concrete Cone To Be
Left In Place

12-16 Job-cast concrete blocks in the shape of truncated cones (right) can be used to support runway and rib forms. Wood stools (left) offer another solution to rib form support. The wood stools must be removed and holes filled before the concrete hardens.

doubly curved surfaces that require *warped* sheathing.

The supports for the runways and upturned rib forms can be set on precast concrete blocks that are left in the shell, or on removable stools (Figure 12-16). The concreting operation may require that the runways be dismantled as the work progresses. This requires careful scheduling so that continuous concreting is not held up while runways are taken down.

Adequate wedges and jacking devices to adjust the form elevation before and during placing must be

12-17 Shell form ready for concreting. Runways, rib forms, and screed supports are already in position. Concreting generally proceeds symmetrically in sections or concentric rings, depending on the shape of the shell. Removal of runways and screeds must be planned to prevent interference with the continuous concreting schedule.

provided. They must have enough adjustment to allow for structural deflection during decentering.

Placing Concrete

A roof shell slab with its supporting and stiffening members is usually considered as one unit and is constructed monolithically. Except in unusual circumstances, concreting begins at the bottom and continues *up* the slope; thus the weight of the fresh concrete itself assists proper consolidation. It is usually desirable to keep the placement as symmetrical as possible to guard against unwanted deflection and stresses in the formwork. Exact sequence depends on the size and shape of the shell; e.g., concreting may proceed upward from the bottom of the slope in concentric rings, or placement may be in layers, working from both sides toward the center of the shell, as in the case of cylindrical shells. Concrete may also be placed in sections if allowed by the size and shape of the shell. Where the forming system is based on a certain placing sequence, that sequence should be clearly defined and adhered to in the field.

Top forms may be needed to keep the fresh concrete from running down or falling away from the forms on slopes steeper than about 45 degrees.* Top

* Committee 347 recommends top forms for slopes steeper than 35 degrees. However, it is difficult to set a specific slope at which back forms or top forms become necessary. Above 50 degrees from the horizontal, it is virtually impossible to place concrete by conventional methods without top forms. Below 40 degrees they are usually unnecessary. (These are general criteria which do not apply to mass concrete, shotcrete, or to concrete plastered on by hand.)

In addition to slump and method of placement, the amount of steel and the steel pattern in the shell have a considerable influence on the behavior of concrete placed on slopes. Slump alone is not an accurate index of behavior of concrete on a slope; other influencing variables include size and shape (angularity) of the aggregate, percent air, cement content, and admixtures used. There is also a marked difference between lightweight and stone aggregates.

The back form or top form need not be solid; ¼-in. hardware cloth has been successfully used. Another system is to use a series of "dams" perpendicular to the slope at intervals of 2 to 4 ft measured down the slope. Bottoms of these dams are flush with the top of the slab. Both of these methods retain concrete on a slope without the attendant disadvantages of a solid top form. A solid top form on slopes may lead to trapped air or bridging of the concrete, which leaves voids that cannot be seen until the forms are stripped. On long slopes placing pockets or windows in the top forms may be a necessary inconvenience (Figure 12-12).

forms are usually used in sets of two or three as shown in Figure 12-20. The forms should be deep enough to allow the concrete to stiffen sufficiently before they are moved up the slope for the next lift. The forms should be tied or weighted to resist the lateral pressure of the fresh concrete. If extensive use of top forms is required, prior assembling and marking may be necessary. Wherever possible, it is advantageous to avoid the use of top forms by placing lower slump concrete on the steepest parts of the slope.

The removal of top forms may be quite critical to the finishing of the shell. They should not be left in place long enough for the concrete to become too stiff for proper finishing. A proper balance between the concreting and finishing crews is important. The operation should be scheduled so the concrete is placed monolithically and finished properly.

Spacers of concrete blocks are sometimes used as a guide in areas where the slab thickness changes. Accurately placed screed supports may be required where the thickness of the shell requires special attention.

Contractors may expect a slow start in concreting when they use crews inexperienced in shell work. The rate of placing and finishing should speed up as the slope flattens and the crew becomes more experienced. Runways should be designed for maximum efficiency. Forms must be watched continuously during concreting so that any undue settlement or distortion may be promptly adjusted.

12-18 Placing concrete in one of the "corrugations" of a folded plate roof. The contractor built a screed boat that rode on steel-angle tracks at the peaks of the fold, striking off concrete to the proper grade as it was placed. A similarly shaped finishing boat was pulled along behind the screed boat to provide a working platform for finishers.

Form Removal

Removal of forms for shells, domes, and folded plates may be an extremely critical operation. As already noted, these structures are generally designed for relatively light loads; weight of forms and supporting falsework is often higher than the design live

12-19 Top forms in use during concreting of shell roof for TWA Terminal at New York International Airport. Note use of small, readily movable panels.

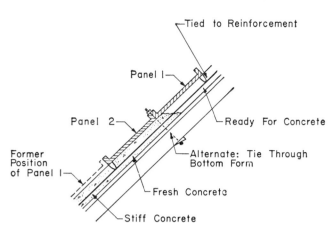

12-20 Schematic representation of top forms tied down before concreting to resist uplift pressure of the fresh concrete. As the concrete begins to stiffen, bottom form panel is moved up the slope for the next lift.

loads, because of complexity of shape and long span of structure. Thus, if for any reason the shell form clings to the shell as the supporting falsework is loosened, it may overload the new concrete structure. Further complications arise because shell and folded plate structures deflect appreciably when they become self-supporting, and the forms may be caught

or bind against the structure as it begins to deflect. These problems may be even more troublesome with prestressed shells if the shortening during prestressing has not been considered.

To meet these conditions certain precautions have already been suggested in the designing and building of the forms. Use of form joints that can be loosened, hinged joints, or small panels that can be removed *just before decentering begins* will relieve troublesome binding. Formwork must be designed so that it does not act as a dome or shell.

Special attention to the strength development of the shell concrete as well as to the decentering sequence will also help assure safe stripping. Specifications often require very high concrete strength at the time of stripping because the attendant higher modulus of elasticity minimizes deflection of the shell.

Strength Requirements

Committee 347 states that decentering and form removal should not be permitted until tests of job-cured cylinders demonstrate that the minimum concrete strength and stiffness (modulus of elasticity) specified in the contract drawings have been reached. The strength requirements for stripping are much

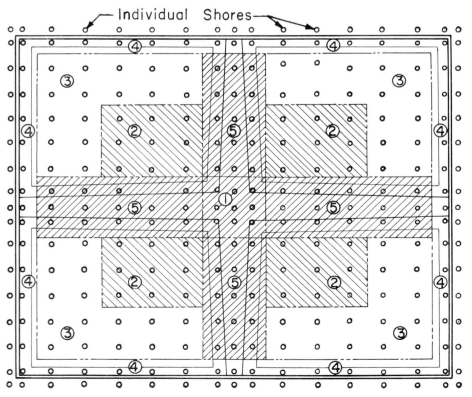

12-21 An example of the planning required for shell form removal. This shell is composed of four intersecting hyperbolic paraboloid sections cast monolithically. Small circles indicate post shores, and circled numbers indicate areas for the decentering sequence. Jacks in Area 1 were first loosened completely. Jacks in Area 2 received one turn and those in Area 3 received one-half turn, with this sequence being repeated until the shell was free of support in those areas. Then the following sequence was repeated in Areas 4 and 5 until the shell was entirely free:

Area 4—Center jacks one turn, corner jacks one-half turn

Area 5—Interior jacks one turn, exterior jacks one-half turn more critical than in conventional construction because of large deflections and high dead load to live load ratios common in shell structures.

Where elastic requirements and buckling considerations are the governing factors as to when the decentering will occur, it may be practical to make the decentering time dependent on the deflection of small test beams, reinforced to simulate the bending conditions within the roof shell.*

Decentering Schedule

Deflections in structures of this type may be such that a strict decentering procedure is necessary in order for the structure to assume its loaded shape without damage, either to the structure or the false-

work. Forms and falsework should be lowered and removed by the procedure and sequence specified on the erection or contract drawings and specifications and as approved by the engineer or architect. Decentering sequences and methods used should be planned to prevent any concentrated reaction on any part of the permanent structure. Generally decentering should begin at points of maximum deflection and should progress toward points of minimum deflection, with the decentering of edge members proceeding simultaneously with the adjoining shell.

As a convenience for the workmen, when screw jacks are used in decentering, the amount of vertical movement should be expressed as the number of turns or fractions of a turn on the jack. In some cases, the decentering instructions will be elaborate and complex; in every case, the designer should provide proper instructions. Figure 12-21 shows the form removal plan developed for one shell structure.

* This approach was described by Tedesko in "Construction Aspects of Thin-Shell Structures," ACI JOURNAL, *Proceedings* V. 49, Feb. 1953, p. 505, and recommended by ACI Committee 334 in "Concrete Shell Structures: Practice and Commentary," reprinted in *ACI Manual of Concrete Practice.*

13: MASS CONCRETE

THE TERM MASS CONCRETE generally indicates concrete used in structures which derive their strength from the weight or mass of the concrete, requiring little or no reinforcing steel. Its application is therefore limited to structures requiring minimal tensile strength, such as gravity dams, gravity retaining walls, locks, foundations, and anchorages.

Mass concrete is usually deposited in the forms by large capacity bottom dump buckets from cableways, cranes, and derricks. Because of the large plan area of most mass concrete structures, the rate of rise of concrete in the forms is usually low, although large quantities are being handled. Concrete buckets up to 12 cu yd capacity were used at Glen Canyon Dam in the United States, and rates of placement of over 1000 cu yd per shift are not uncommon when using 4-yd buckets. Such air- or hydraulically-operated buckets are capable of rapidly depositing 8 tons or more of concrete all at one time.

One major consideration facing the designer of mass concrete structures is control or elimination of thermal cracking, and in the case of hydraulic structures leakage through construction joints. Because of the large masses involved, heat of hydration of the concrete presents considerably more problems than in other structural concrete, and some of the provisions made to limit the temperature rise have a vital effect on the formwork.

In warmer climates especially, the concrete temperature is kept to a minimum during placement and hydration by the use of low-heat Type II and IV cements, fly ash or other pozzolan replacement of part of the cement, refrigeration, special curing techniques, and heat-dispersing steel forms. The type of lifts, plan, and sequence of placing the concrete are generally selected to help in controlling temperature. Form removal is also planned to avoid thermal shocks which would result in cracking of the concrete surface.

13-1 Mass concrete is used in structures whose strength depends primarily on the mass or weight of the concrete. Placement here is by crane and bucket in low lift wood cantilever forms for a powerhouse abutment.

255

Low Lift Formwork

The commonest approach to regulating shrinkage and heat of hydration in mass concrete work is to limit the height of lift. Until recently lifts were generally held to 4 to 6 ft, but the current practice on larger projects has been to use 7- to 8-ft lifts. This trend toward increased height of lift has been brought about by a common desire of contractor and engineer to reduce the number of horizontal construction joints —the engineer hoping to reduce potential leak paths without increasing residual thermal stresses in the structure, and the contractor desiring to save time and cost in joint preparation and concrete placing.

Except for the initial footing or foundation lift, most formwork used on low lift mass concrete dam and retaining wall construction is of reusable pure cantilever or tied back (propped) cantilever design. Low lifts require frequent reuse of forms, and cantilever forms are most often made of steel to withstand high loads and give long service through many reuses. Some are made of wood, however, and steel frames with wood sheathing bolted on may also be used. The latter permit greater flexibility in attaching recesses and fillings, but are expensive to align and require costly maintenance.

Types of Cantilever Forms in Common Use

The most commonly used cantilever form unit consists of a framed panel equipped with two or more strongbacks, wales, or lever arms which are attached to the panel and extend downward for ⅔ to 1⅓ times the panel height. The strongbacks are always anchored to the top of the preceding lift by proprietary

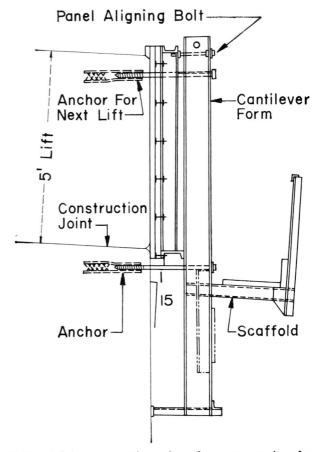

13-3 A 5-ft pure cantilever form for upstream dam face, attached by a single row of anchor bolts. Note panel aligning bolt at the top. This form slopes slightly, but the same details apply to vertical construction. Sheathing may be either wood or steel.

bolts and embedded anchors. They are generally adjustable to facilitate alignment through other means than the (tie) anchor bolt (Figure 13-3). Anchors or other holding inserts are accurately positioned in each lift by template bolts which pass through sleeves near the upper edge of the form.

For vertical faces and joints, cantilever forms follow the basic arrangement shown in Figure 13-3 or some approximation of it. The same type of forming may be accomplished by adapting heavy prefabricated panel sections and a suitable strongback as shown in Figure 13-5. For sloping faces such as in retaining walls or the downstream faces of gravity dams, it is common practice to extend each strongback so that a second anchor bolt can be attached to the bolt insert in the second preceding lift (Figure 13-4). If a sloping cantilever form does not have this two-point attachment to previously placed concrete, it must be temporarily braced from within the form until the concrete is placed behind it.

The tie back cantilever design, which uses a row of ties attached at or near the top of the form in addi-

13-2 Low lift steel cantilever forms during concreting

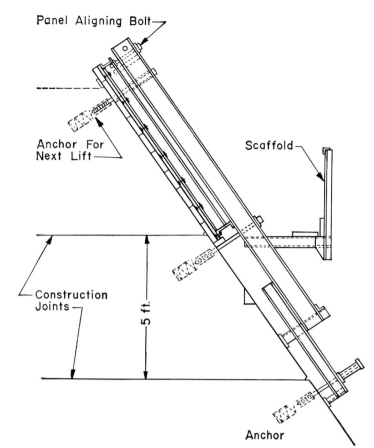

Panel Aligning Bolt

Anchor For Next Lift

Scaffold

Construction Joints

5 ft.

Anchor

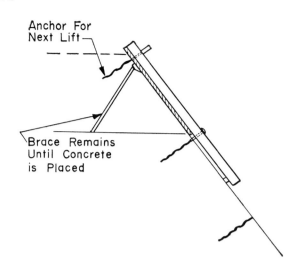

Anchor For Next Lift

Brace Remains Until Concrete is Placed

13-4 Form for 5-ft lift at the sloping downstream face of dam has two rows of anchor bolts, with considerably longer strongback than that in 13-3. Without this second row of anchor bolts, the form must be braced from within as shown in the small sketch, until the concrete is placed.

tion to anchor units at the base attached directly to the previous lift, is generally used for higher lifts, between 7 and 10 ft, to minimize form deflections and reduce the weight of the units. The tie down system may also be used with lower lift cantilever units to accomplish the same purpose of reducing weight or deflection. Cantilever forms for 7½-ft lifts may be strengthened by trussed strongbacks (Figure 13-7) or other heavy framing so that tie backs are not required.

Where cantilever forms are used on sloping surfaces with 7½-ft lifts, some United States government agencies require a special form hinged at midpoint so the top half may be swung out of the way to permit concrete to be placed as close as possible to the toe of the slope. The form must be designed to permit quick replacement and alignment during concrete placement.

For gravity arch and hollow gravity arch dams it becomes necessary to further modify the basic design to provide for curved profile and contour surfaces. Changing horizontal or vertical curvature is usually accomplished by using smaller or jointed modules with filler pieces if necessary, and inserting adjusting bolts between the strongback and the panel, or between the strongback and the surface of the preceding lift. Alternatively it can be accomplished by attach-

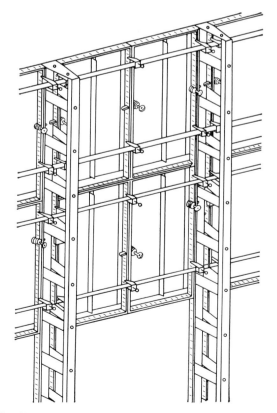

13-5 Heavy prefabricated metal panel sections with metal strongbacks have also been used as cantilever forms for mass concrete.

257

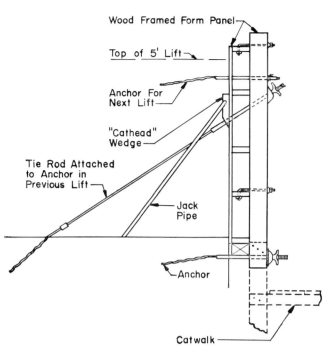

13-6 Vertical tied cantilever form for 5-ft lift. Jack pipe helps maintain alignment until concrete is placed.

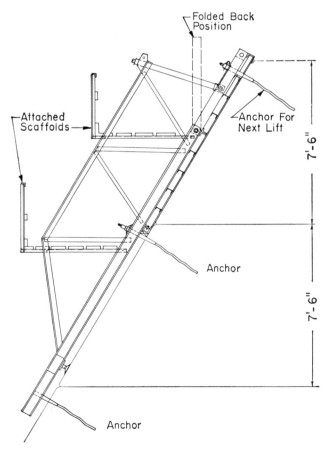

13-7 Hinged sloping cantilever form for 7½-ft lift, showing working scaffolds attached. Tilting upper portion of form makes it easier to place concrete near toe of slope.

ing the upper end of the strongback toward the middle of the panel with a combined pivot and screw combination.

Other cantilever form modifications can be made for special purposes, such as the one shown in Figure 13-11. That form has built-in slots with replaceable fillers which enable casting of lock walls containing armor steel. The armor plates curve ¼ in. out from the face of the concrete.

Cantilever form panels of precast concrete, which remain in place as the permanent facing of the structure, are technically feasible. Widespread use of such forms for mass concrete work has been reported in the Soviet Union,* but at present they do not appear economically attractive for use in North America.

Design Considerations

There is, then, a wide variation of basic cantilever form designs requiring investigation before deciding on the most suitable type for the application under consideration. However, it is general practice for most contractors to rely on the experience and recommendations of reputable form fabrication specialists who act either as vendors or subcontractors.

The factors that must be taken into consideration are:

1. Probable weather conditions that will be encountered; will insulation of construction joints or forms be needed? Will hot weather cause limit of time of day for placement of concrete?

2. Placement schedule sequence, restrictions and method of delivery, and rate of placing.

3. Number, size, height, and profile of lifts in each monolith of each gravity structure.

4. Concrete mix placing temperature and strengths during first 5 days after placement.

5. Degree of form flexibility, reusability, and methods of form handling.

6. Estimated cost.

Considering the significance of each of these factors for form design, it should be noted that even allowing for the different types of dams, there is some fundamental disagreement on placing sequences and other construction details among the various authorities under whose auspices most mass concrete structures are built.

* Ermolov, V. V., and Petrov, G. D., *Formwork for Massive Concrete Structures in Hydro Developments*, 2nd Revised Edition, 1954; published in translation for National Science Foundation, Washington, D. C., 1963. These developments are to be described in a 1969 report by Committee 347 dealing with all aspects of precast concrete formwork.

Currently one authority specifies a minimum of 5 days between lifts; another, 3 days; and yet another specifies no minimum but a maximum of 5 days. Similarly some specifications call for the minimum exposure of vertical joints (not more than three lifts), while others call for the maximum exposure of joint faces either by specifying that alternate sections be completed first or by designing the structure with narrow filler sections which are cast after completion of the main sections.

Therefore the contractor must be on guard against assuming that any specification agrees with his past experience, and by the same token, the owner must be sure that the engineering requirements are made absolutely clear.

An analysis of the conditions summarized will determine the type of form best suited to the job requirements.

Loads on the Formwork

As with all formwork, the first step in detailed design is to estimate the magnitude and distribution of pressures and loads acting on the formwork. Committee 347 has recommended the following formula for determining a value of lateral pressure to be used in design of forms, ties, tiebacks and bracing for low lift mass concrete:

$$p = 120 + \frac{7200\,R}{T}$$

where

p = maximum lateral pressure, psf
R = rate of placement or rise of concrete in forms, ft per hr
T = temperature of the freshly placed concrete in the forms, °F

Since the plan area of most mass concrete lifts is proportionally much larger than their sectional area and volumes of 500 cu yd are not uncommon, the value of R is generally 1 to 2 ft per hr. Consequently in a temperate or warm climate form pressures are substantially less than those encountered in structural concrete. However, care must be taken in vibration, and consideration must be given in design to the fact that pressures under the toe of a sloping cantilever form may locally be much greater as a result of the wedging action of the aggregate.*

When mass concrete containing fly ash or other pozzolan is placed under cold ambient conditions (below 50F), rate of hardening and consequently early

strengths are quite low. Thus, it is recommended that for these conditions the value of T be arbitrarily reduced by 20F, but not below freezing.

In addition to forces due to pressure of the concrete, the design must provide for handling of forms and dead and live loads due to exterior scaffolding, work crews, and any special form attachment. A rational design of form panel can be made for the estimated loading, following general principles outlined in Chapter 6. The required section modulus of the strongback is determined by calculating bending

13-8 Close-up view of hinged form swung back for concreting, as seen from within the formed area

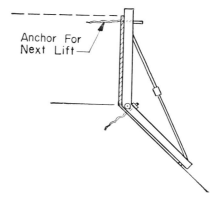

13-9 Simplified sketch indicates adjustment of cantilever form for change of direction.

Anchor For Next Lift

* Because of lack of control over field conditions, some designers prefer to use a more conservative value such as 80-100 percent of equivalent fluid pressure (based on weight of 150 lb per cu ft) plus 25 percent impact allowance.

13-10 Adjustable cantilever forms used for curved spillway of Key-stone Dam. Same forms started at the edge of the bucket and will proceed upward over the ogee.

13-10-A Close-up end view of the adjustable curve forms for 7½-ft lifts of the spillway shown in 13-10. Break point at midheight of the form panel permits the top of the form to be pulled back. Adjusting jacks are provided to make changes in curvature, and there are flexible end connections between panels.

moments and deflections for a beam supported as a tied or pure cantilever, depending on which arrangement has been chosen for the form.

As recommended on p. 86, the design stresses in structural members of a reusable form should not exceed the allowable stresses for permanent structures of the material being used, as specified in applicable building codes or trade association design specifications.

The controlling factor in design of the pure cantilever form is invariably the permissible deflection which is compatible with the specified tolerances (see p. 268).

Anchorage Accessories

The fastest placing cycles permitted in mass concrete work call for stripping and re-erection of the forms during the period 24 to 48 hr following the completion of the lift, and completing the subsequent lift within a 72-hr period. Under these conditions the form anchoring devices have to function in concrete having a compressive or bond strength as low as 15 percent of its 28-day strength. Even when successive lifts are placed as much as 5 days apart, the low-cement-content concrete requires specially designed form holding devices which will develop sufficient strength to support forms for the succeeding lift.

The design or selection of a proprietary anchorage unit of specified strength is determined by taking moments about the center of bearing at the lower end of the strongback and solving for tension or pull on the bolt, then equating this tension or pull with either the compressive or bond strength of the surrounding concrete, depending on the anchor design and the time when the force is applied. The diameter of bolt required for use with an embedded anchor is determined by bending and direct stress from the dead weight of the form and lateral pressure.

A few of the different types of embedded anchorages used in low lift mass concrete work are shown in Chapter 4, p. 55. Some estimated safe working loads on these devices when embedded in low strength concrete are also indicated. As pointed out there, the holding power of such units depends on the strength of concrete in which they are embedded, the depth of embedment, and the area of contact between the anchor and the concrete. Estimated working loads, such as those listed in Chapter 4 or presented in manufacturers' catalogs, are for guidance in making a trial selection only, since conditions and consequently the performance of the anchor vary from job to job. For any large job, or where hazard to life and property are involved, performance of the tentatively selected anchorage device should be confirmed under actual summer and winter field conditions.

Besides considering the ability of the embedded anchorage to sustain loading of freshly placed concrete, the designer must consider initial bolting stresses at the time forms are set. Although there may be a 5-day concrete placing cycle, forms are frequently stripped and reset from 24 to 48 hr after concreting, when the relatively low-strength mass concrete has gained only part of its design strength. Attaching forms for the next lift to the anchorage units in some cases cracks the concrete or partially pulls out the anchor, causing a failure later when concrete is placed. This condition may become critical at low temperatures when fly ash has been used to replace part of the cement in the lean concrete. A torque wrench with pressure cell is suggested to check the pull-out value of anchorage units when early concrete strength is in doubt. It may be necessary to set forms with anchor bolts only tight enough to support forms, and then tighten the bolts just before concreting.

Tie rods used must not be assigned design loads which exceed the ultimate strength of the anchor bar or bolt to which they are attached. Bending or welding of high tensile steel tie rods should not be permitted.

13-11 Forms and formed sections of lock wall. There are three sliding horizontal panels in each 5-ft height of form. When panel is slid out of way, modified T-section of armor is inserted through face of form, attached with clips, and bolted into place. When concrete hardens, bolts are removed and armor remains cast in concrete as it appears here installed around a floating mooring bitt.

Other Design Features

The procedure to be used for accommodating changing profile of the structure, particularly abrupt changes, and also the intersections of face and joint formwork should be fully detailed. Particular care must be taken to provide anchorage for sloping forms and wall forms tied to a rock face.

Drawings showing the form layout for each lift and the scheduled movement of the individual units are usually prepared for each elevation of each bay as the detailed designs are evaled. Many agencies require complete lift drawings in advance showing all items to be included in the particular lift of concrete. These guide the builder and various crafts involved as well as the owner's inspection forces. Form checkout cards are frequently attached to each lift form requiring initials from all the individuals connected with it preparation before placement may begin. These may include the craft represented, the inspectors for each specialty, the layout crews of the contractor as well as the owner's comparable group, and the concrete placement inspector, who checks the form for cleanliness.

Other aspects of cantilever form design include the provision of adequate external scaffolding, ladderways, and lifelines which enable the stripping and erection crews to work safely and efficiently. In this regard forms for faces with a vertical curvature or changing batter usually have self-adjusting scaffold brackets which maintain the scaffold decking in a horizontal plane. Ladderway openings in the upper scaffold deck should be provided with a snap-on guard rope at minimum and preferably a self-closing man barrier.

If catwalks are used for linking alternate bays they should be built in accordance with the appropriate design and building codes for permanent structures and be subject to regular inspection.

13-12 Scaffolding attached to steel cantilever forms

13-13 Scaffolding suspended from low lift wood formwork. Note waterstop in formed keyway.

Handling, Erecting, Stripping

Various methods have been used for handling, stripping, and erecting cantilever forms. On smaller structures, where the schedule permits, it is common practice to use the same cranes or derricks that are used for placing the concrete. When handling the forms in this fashion it is usually necessary to use a spreader beam equipped with eye turnbuckles which are attached to the form lifting lugs by shackles. The turnbuckles provide a ready means of leveling and positioning the units to facilitate the engaging of the bolts in the anchors. With this method it may be possible to move forms for an entire side of the monolith all at one time.

On large dams, the usual method of raising the forms to the succeeding lift is either by derricking devices which are attached alternately to adjoining units, or by smaller rubber-tired cranes which are landed on the top of each lift by the cableway, derricks, or larger cranes used primarily for concrete placing. The small crane moves around within the forms raising form panels. This operation is most effective where the forms exceed 3000 sq ft in plan area. Recently some forms have been equipped with self-jacking devices.

High Lift Concrete Formwork

High lift mass concrete construction has been adopted by some authorities, particularly in Canada, in an attempt to reduce potential leak paths and minimize cracking in dams built in cold and even sub-zero weather. In its extreme form, the method provides for continuous placing of lifts up to 50 ft high using wood or insulated forms with housings and steam heat. Formwork in this case is comparable to that for structural concrete, except that ties may be 20 to 40 ft long rather than 20 to 40 in. Spacing of the internal form ties usually precludes direct placement from buckets, and consequently the size of the larger aggregate is limited by the size and configuration of

13-14 Cantilever forms handled by hand. Forms are raised by chain hoists attached to light A-frames.

13-15 High lift wood formwork for gate sluice piers, showing winter protection being put into place

13-16 Early stages of construction of high lift formwork

13-17 This 50 ft lift formwork combines wood and steel framing. Vertical Bailey trusses 17 ft apart have horizontal I-beams bolted on at 5-ft intervals. Plywood panels braced by 2x4's are bolted to I-beams to make face of form.

MASS CONCRETE

hoppers, chutes, and other placing equipment. Thus, the mass concrete used in high lift work generally corresponds to that used for structural concrete and the forms are designed to withstand lateral pressures calculated in accordance with formulas in Chapter 5.

However, if the concrete contains fly ash or other pozzolan as replacement for part of the cement, and is placed under cold weather conditions, the form pressures will be considerably in excess of the values calculated from the standard formulas. Until more precise data are available it is recommended that the predicted temperature value T be reduced by 20° (but not below freezing) for pressure calculation under these conditions. Notwithstanding this precaution, the concrete placing operations require great care, and the design pressures should be confirmed by field tests made under actual ambient temperature conditions wherever practical.

Full consideration must be given to resisting the vertical components of pressures acting against forms used on sloping faces of structures such as gravity dams and retaining walls. When high lifts are placed on top of a previous lift, embedded "hairpins" or "pigtails" are used to tie down the forms, and the bottom edge of the form is held in position by the tie rods of the previous lift. Generally speaking forms used in high lift work are relatively flexible and require continuous adjustment of the tie rods to maintain the required tolerances.

The economic disadvantages of the high lift system such as the lack of vertical reuses of the formwork and the higher cement ratio of the concrete have been responsible for some recent adaptations which in-

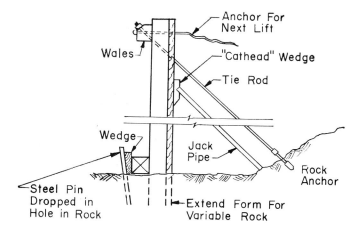

13-18 Footing form on rock or concrete surface tied to connection grouted in rock and braced with jack pipe

corporate the better features of the low lift method. These have included: (1) reusable heavy wood panel forms up to 20 ft high with widely spaced large diameter high tensile ties; and (2) tied back cantilever forms, 7 to 8 ft high, of similar construction, both of which are compatible with large aggregate concrete. Horizontal spacing of ties is large enough to permit a concrete bucket to pass between them. The significant engineering requirement for this compromise method is that successive lifts must be placed as rapidly as practicable to simulate a continuous initial placement for a height which approximates one-third to one-fourth of the base length of the gravity structure.

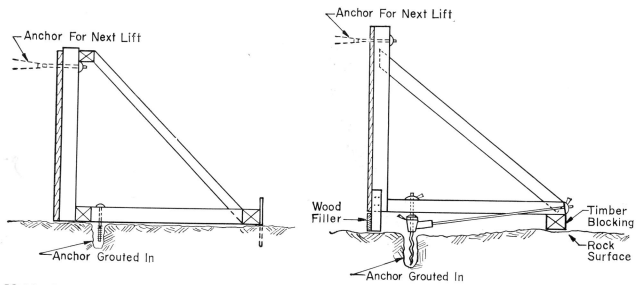

13-19 Footing form with exterior bracing, tied down to rock (left); tie down plus horizontally adjustable tie (right)

13-20 External bracing of footing form

Foundations or Starting Lifts

Initial lifts of mass concrete structures may be founded on rock or down in a rock cut, which prevents the use of cantilever forms. Special footing forms are then used, which must be tied down to pins or anchors drilled and grouted into the rock surface. Forms with vertical studs and no bottom plate may be set in place and held while extension pieces are nailed to the studs to fit the shape of the rock bottom. The

sheathing is then similarly cut to fit this irregular surface. Tie rods, sometimes called "hog rods," connect the form wales to the grouted connection in the rock. As a reaction to the pull on these rods, jack pipes or similar struts are used to resist the pull until the concrete is in place. Threaded adjustment screws or a wedge-like device called a "cathead" are used for the fine adjustment of alignment of the form through these jack pipes. The pipes are removed for reuse as the concrete is placed against the form. In some cases contractors have used the cantilever forms as footing forms to save building limited-use footing forms. However, in such a case it is necessary to invert the form so that the strongbacks stick up in the air. Problems of fitting such a form to an irregular rock surface as well as danger of damaging these expensive forms makes this practice least desirable. In some instances a special cantilever panel has been used wherein the strongback partially detaches so that it may be set at an angle to the form to serve as a brace for a footing form or where a change of direction in the concrete surface is required.

Footing forms may also be braced from the outside against kickers doweled to the rock surface. Since there is some danger of lifting a form braced this way, a tie-down may be necessary (see Figure 13-19).

On sloping footing surfaces up to a certain angle forms are not required, but the many variables preclude establishing at exactly what angle concrete may be placed without a form. An experienced individual must determine this in relation to the economics of the job. In some cases, a simple form may

13-21 Placing concrete in low lift forms. Part of the forms are enclosed with tarpaulins, and steam is being used to warm enclosures and clean frozen forms.

be placed to hold the concrete surface after it is screeded without requiring as much tie-down as a conventional form.

For high lift mass concrete, when the initial lift is cast directly on a competent rock foundation, a proportion of the tie rods are attached to rock anchors which are usually incorporated in the design of the structure, thus producing a criss-cross tie rod configuration in the lower sections of the lift.

The proportion of tie rods terminating at rock anchors will depend on the degree of slope or the ratio of vertical to horizontal forces acting against the form. Since these ties to rock anchors are generally insufficient to prevent uplift, the forms are further tied down by means of external guys and rock bolts positioned along the bottom face of the form.

Curing, Joint Cleanup, Insulation

Construction joint treatment presents special problems in mass concrete. After placement the concrete surface must be prepared by cleaning off all laitance and exposing (but not undercutting) the aggregate. This may be done before the concrete has fully set up by "cutting" it with air and water jets. Usually one or two washings are also required to complete this operation. Some agencies do not approve this method

13-22 Pre-assembly of special inserts such as this filling and emptying port form for a lock job helps keep concreting on schedule.

and, instead, require wet sand blasting of the surface shortly before the next lift is placed. In either case some way of removing waste water and cuttings must be provided. Depending on the time and method of the joint preparation, an opening may be made in the lower or upper part of the form. With a wood form, a washout hole may be neatly cut anywhere if proper care is taken in its replacement so as to prevent an unsightly finish. Where washout holes are not permitted, washout pipes and/or sumps will be required for removal of water and debris.

Curing must be maintained for certain specified periods. This is sometimes provided by installing pipe along the trailing edge of the form with spray nozzles to direct streams of water against the completed concrete. Soaker hoses or rotating sprinklers

13-23 When departures are made from conventional specifications, new forming techniques may permit greater economy. These forms for lock walls at Keokuk, Iowa, were moved horizontally. Crane is hoisting forms for complete monolith as a single unit.

for the horizontal joints are also used, as is water-soaked matting in some cases.

Providing water for curing and washing, and air for cleaning the form and vibrators is sometimes done by mounting outlets on the form with hoses connecting them to distribution lines on the ground. In other cases twin pipes (one air, one water) are carried up through the concrete the full height of the structure. These must be grouted tight at the completion of the job. They are frequently held in position by attachments on the form which hold them a foot or more back from the face of the concrete.

Insulation of mass concrete forms may be required to prevent heat loss (see also cold weather protection, p. 220). This insulation is frequently sprayed on the forms, but insulation blanket material is sometimes attached. Insulation blankets may trail from the lower edge of the form to protect concrete of the previous lift, and tarpaulin enclosures around formwork (Figure 13-21) are sometimes used together with steam under extremely cold conditions.

Planning and Supervision

Because of the large volume and numerous lifts on a large mass concrete job, there are many areas for human error in preparing forms for concreting such as:

Ties not secured
Wedges not secured
Corners not adequately tied
Wales not continuous across panels joints
Washout holes not plugged

Good supervision and well-qualified form watchers are essential to prevent such occurrences. The cost of correcting such errors may be inconsequential when compared to the expense of an interruption in production sequence which might result.

The most critical consideration in mass concrete work is the importance of maintaining continuous, uniform production rates. Therefore, monoliths which contain special recesses such as galleries, tunnels, armor steel, penstock tubes, etc., must be carefully planned so as not to slow up the whole operation. Pre-assembly of all unusual form items is of paramount importance. On a large mass concrete job, a highly efficient, well-equipped shop is necessary. Investment in labor saving tools and material handling equipment are well worth the expense. Good coordination of flow of material to the construction site is essential. In some instances intermediate placements

are made within a lift to remove a time-consuming operation such as trowel finish or tricky recesses from the over-all construction sequence.

Tolerances

Over-all quality of work in building and erecting forms must be such that specified tolerances can be maintained in the finished structure. ACI Committee 347 has suggested the following tolerances for mass concrete work:

All structures

1. Variation of constructed linear outline from established position in plan	½ in. in 20 ft ¾ in. in 40 ft
2. Variations of dimensions to individual structure features from established positions	1¼ in. in 80 ft or more (twice this amount for buried construction)
3. Variation from the plumb, from the specified batter or from the curved surfaces of all structures, including lines and surfaces of columns, walls, piers, buttresses, arch sections, vertical joint grooves, and visible arrises	½ in. in 10 ft ¾ in. in 20 ft 1¼ in. in 40 ft or more (twice above amounts for buried construction)
4. Variation from the level or from the grades indicated on the drawings in slabs, beams, soffits, horizontal joint grooves, and visible arrises	¼ in. in 10 ft ½ in. in 30 ft or more (twice these amounts for buried construction)
5. Variation in cross-sectional dimensions of columns, beams, buttresses, piers and similar members	− ¼ in. + ½ in.
6. Variation in the thickness of slabs, walls, arch sections, and similar members	− ¼ in. + ½ in.

Footings for columns, piers, walls, buttresses, and similar members

1. Variation in plan dimensions	− ½ in. + 2 in.*
2. Misplacement or eccentricity	2 percent of footing width in direction of misplacement, but not more than 2 in.*
3. Reduction in thickness	5 percent of specified thickness

Sills and side walls for radial gates and similar watertight joints

Variation from plumb and level	no more than ⅛ in. in 10 ft

*Applies to concrete only, not to vertical reinforcing bars or dowels.

14: TUNNELS AND SHAFTS

MANY TYPES OF STRUCTURES are built underground; tunnels, powerhouses, shafts, and defense installations, for example. Each structure has different formwork requirements, but their construction is similar in one respect—adverse working conditions such as high noise level, artificial lighting, restricted access, and a confined working space.

Restricted access and limited working space are major factors in the design of formwork for underground structures. The form designer must provide for maximum reuse and mobility and minimum bulk consistent with the specified concrete placing procedures.

Most of the multi-use formwork used for underground structures has been evolved over the years by a few form design and fabrication companies who have specialized in tunnel and shaft forms. The accumulated research and experience of these firms has enabled them to produce highly developed basic form arrangements which are readily adaptable to the vast majority of individual job requirements. Such companies can therefore provide contractors with precise information on proven forming arrangements at the bidding stage and can follow up by either supplying or renting forms to the successful client as and when required.

This chapter emphasizes the techniques of underground forming for tunnels and shafts. Cut and cover work—built in an excavation and later backfilled—presents less rigid space limitations than true underground construction, and the concrete placing methods are similar to those used for aboveground structures.

Tunnel Forming Components

Tunnels are usually circular or horseshoe in cross section, depending on their function and the type of ground through which they are driven. Regardless of the cross section, they are usually divided into invert and arch sections for concreting as shown in Figure 14-1; the arch section is sometimes further divided into sidewall sections which are cast separately from the upper part of the arch. Separate curbs may also be cast before the invert is concreted.

A common placing sequence for tunnel lining is to place the curbs first, and then the invert, which will serve as a base for machinery and form travelers; then the walls and arch are formed. In other cases rails for travelers and machinery are placed on excavated rock and the arch is concreted ahead of the invert. Less common is the case where the full circle of the lining is placed as work advances. The order of placement depends on many factors such as tunnel shape and size, ground and water conditions, allowable tolerances, and project schedule requirements.

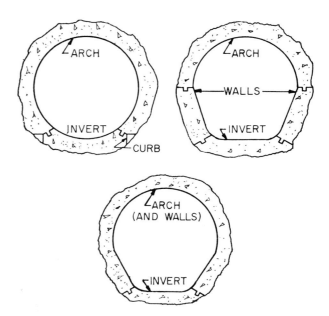

14-1 Typical circular and horseshoe tunnel sections, showing division for concreting. A curb may be used with any cross section where job conditions require it. Usual order of concreting is: (1) Curb (if any), (2) Invert, (3) Wall, and (4) Arch. Wall and arch may be concreted as a single unit. The full circle of round tunnels may also be concreted as a single unit.

Curb Forms

As noted above, it is common practice to form and place curbs along both sides of circular and modified horseshoe tunnels to provide a base for setting the invert forms (screeds) and a runway for the lead wheels of the traveling invert forming and placing bridge. Anchorages are embedded at regular intervals along the top of the curb to receive the ⅝ or ¾ in. diameter bolts used for clamping the invert forms to the curb.

Since the curb is later covered by the invert and arch concrete, the finish produced by the formwork is unimportant although the upper surface must be to the correct grade and the anchorage units accurately positioned.

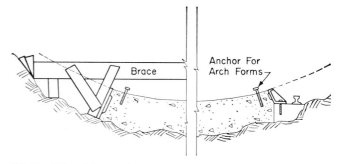

14-3 Wood invert forms without previously placed curb, and steel invert forms attached to curb.

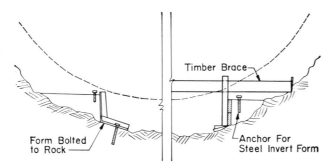

14-2 Simplified drawing shows how both wood and metal may be used for curb forms.

There are a number of different ways to accomplish this simple forming task; Figure 14-2 shows typical wood and metal curb forms. Another widely used type of curb form consists of an upper panel equipped with horizontal guides through which vertical 2x6 sheathing is driven down to the irregular excavated rock surface. The upper edge of the panel is usually supported by inclined adjustable braces which either bear against sills anchored to the rock invert or are spiked directly to the rail ties.

In designing the curb form, as with all other tunnel formwork, the prime consideration is to minimize the use of consumable lumber and form hardware or conversely to aim for maximum reuse.

Invert Forms

The invert form is another relatively simple part of the tunnel forming job, which can be built in a number of different ways, depending on local conditions (Figures 14-3 and 14-4). The invert may be placed with or without curbs as the drawings indicate.

On larger tunnel jobs, invert forming and placing is usually undertaken as a continuous process with the aid of a traveling bridge (Figure 14-5) from which the

side form handling, concrete placing, and, when required, track relaying jobs are done. Since the design and construction of such a bridge is a major cost item, it is usually adaptable for reuse with the arch form.

With this system, which produces rates of advancement of up to 1000 ft a day, the efficiency of the operation is to a large extent predetermined by the degree of workability and consistency of the concrete as well as skill of the concrete placing crew and finishers. The number of side form units needed is determined on the basis of the optimum rate of advancement, the specified stripping time (usually 12 hr), and the speed of handling of the units.

Arch forms or side wall forms are generally held in place by anchor bolts set in the previously placed invert. Special care should be taken in correctly positioning these bolts to assure rapid attachment for the arch forms. The invert side forms are usually provided with lugs or holes to which the anchor templates are attached after the slip form has passed or other screeding is done. Since the anchors are driven into the soft concrete, care must be taken to be sure that the concrete is effectively puddled around the anchors without creating surface irregularities in the surrounding concrete.

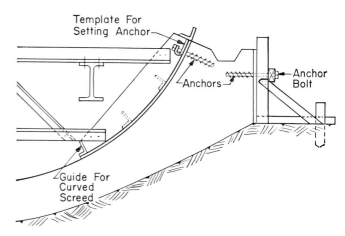

14-4 Invert forming for open cut sewer. Note anchorage units provided for exterior as well as interior forms.

14-5 Traveling bridge and typical side form arrangement used with previously placed curbs for concreting the invert of a circular tunnel. The matching invert drag screed or slip form shapes the concrete. The slip form face is usually about 8 ft long with concrete placing hoppers just behind its leading edge. Form is loaded with sandbags or scrap to about 300 to 500 psf. Finishers' platforms ride along at varying distances behind the traveling bridge.

14-6 Positioning an anchorage unit by means of template attached to invert side form. After the template has been set in the correct position (left), the anchor and bolt assembly is driven to the required depth in the soft concrete (center). The template is then removed, and finishing is completed (right).

14-7   A 41 ft diameter non-telescoping arch form used for water diversion tunnels at Glen Canyon Dam. Structural steel traveler with wheeled base resting on rails moved the 60-ft sections. Note working platform and upper working scafford supported by traveler and forms. Arrows indicate hinge points in ribs.

14-8   A 50 ft diameter non-telescoping arch form similar to that of Figure 14-7, shown assembled above ground with traveler. Chutes are in position for placing concrete in horizontal layers through access doors at various elevations around the arch. These forms were used in 50 to 90-ft lengths for "bulkhead" concreting at Sir Adam Beck Generating Station, Niagara Falls, Ont.

Arch Forms

The main structural frame for arch forms is made up of circumferential ribs and longitudinal stringers conforming to the required tunnel cross section. These ribs are braced as required and covered with wood sheathing or a steel skin. The ribs are usually hinged at their third-points and are designed to minimize obstruction of the working space. Details of typical steel arch forms are shown in Figures 14-7 to 14-12. Arch forms are partially collapsed and moved forward, usually on their own specially designed "jumbo"

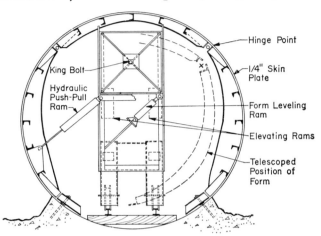

14-9-A   Telescoping steel forms for 10 ft diameter tunnel are supported on anchorages in the previously placed invert. Drawing indicates lowered, telescoped position of form.

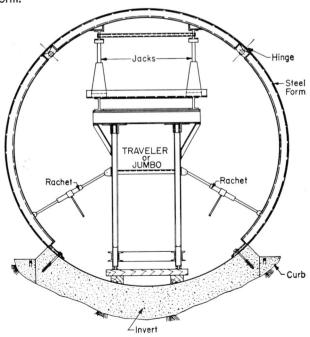

14-9-B   This telescoping form for a 15 ft diameter tunnel has a different system of raising, lowering, and collapsing the forms.

or traveler, as the arch concreting advances. Forms that can be collapsed sufficiently to move forward within an adjacent form section which remains in place are described as *telescoping arch forms;* this type of form is essential for continuous advancing slope concreting described on p. 274. *Non-telescoping* forms are those which collapse enough for stripping, then move forward beyond the just-completed tunnel section to be set in place for concreting the next section of the tunnel.

The arch forms are supported on the tunnel invert and are held in place by clamps attached to anchor bolts embedded in the previously placed invert concrete. During the initial stages of the continuously advancing slope method of placing in circular tunnels, there have been cases of the arch form developing a roll on its polar axis and also becoming out-of-round due to the inexperience of the work crews and the tolerances provided on the clamp and bolted connections. In such cases it is helpful to mark the invert with guide lines corresponding to the bottom edges of the form and to check the diagonal dimension between the hinges and the bottom edges of each unit as it is being bolted up.

Since tunnels are often driven through rock, the forms are sometimes tied to the wall, thus removing part of the load from the ribs and braces. Ties should be spaced so they do not hamper concrete placement.

14-10 Shop set-up of 17½ ft diameter telescoping steel tunnel forms with mechanized traveler. Note hinged portion of form folded back near base. The traveler includes a hydraulic system for raising, lowering, and shifting, and provides for sideways alignment. Telescopic in length, as well as diameter, the traveler can be shortened for maneuvering around tunnel curves.

14-11 Traveler operating inside the West Delaware Tunnel moves forms for the 11 ft 4 in. diameter arch section. This picture clearly shows details of form construction, including access doors which are open at the top of the section.

273

Placing the full tunnel section monolithically in one operation is restricted to full circular tunnels with forms in relatively short lengths. Form support for full-circle concreting varies with soil conditions. Forms may be supported on precast blocks set to grade in the invert excavation, or on beams that are supported outside the form at the bulkhead end (Figure 14-13). For tunnels driven through solid rock, the formwork may be positioned and held by adjustable bolts. The bolts extend out from the skin of the tunnel forms and contact the rock. The number and spacing of these bolts are determined by the dead load of concrete and forms, the lateral pressure of the concrete, and the uplift.

Concrete Placement Methods

Tunnel dimensions and the placing sequence and construction joint configuration of the lining usually determine the forming arrangement and method of concrete placement. There are two basic systems of forming and concreting the arch and sidewalls of tunnels: the advancing slope method and the bulkhead method. While the continuous advancing slope method must be an around-the-clock operation, the bulkhead method can be undertaken on two 8- to 10-hr shifts per day. Where site conditions permit, tunnel work is sometimes done in an open cut where the bulkhead method can be adapted to forms that are similar to many used above grade.

14-12 A vehicular tunnel in which sidewalls were placed separately. Advancing traveler carries only the arch (roof) forms.

14-13 Hand-handled forms used for full circle concreting of a 12 ft diameter tunnel, through soft blue clay of the Great Lakes region. Soft earth required full support until the tunnel lining gained strength.

Continuous Advancing Slope

The advancing slope method of tunnel lining is normally an uninterrupted operation, except for breakdowns or holidays. The concrete is usually introduced through one or more pipelines at or near the top of the arch. The concrete forms an advancing mass as it flows from the top of the arch around and behind the forms. This mass of concrete is in the shape of a moving wedge with a slope equal to the angle of repose of the fresh concrete. The arch form required for this method usually consists of eight or more sections ranging between 15 and 30 ft in length. The sections are successively stripped or collapsed, telescoped through other sections, and re-erected by means of a form traveler commonly referred to as a "jumbo." The operation is timed so that the rear form unit is ready to strip when it is needed at the toe of the advancing slope of fresh concrete.

This method is usually preferred for tunnels driven through competent rock. Tunnel sections between 10 and 25 ft in diameter and more than a mile long are well suited for this method.

Bulkhead Method

The bulkhead method is an intermittent placing of sections, generally of a length to suit the volume of concrete that can be placed in one shift under average conditions. Lengths vary from 50 to 150 ft. The technique of concrete placement in the bulkhead method may be similar to the advancing slope method because the concrete is often introduced at the top of the arch and the same advancing slope of concrete is present until the forms are filled. However, for larger tunnels especially, it is common practice to place the concrete in horizontal layers from internal and external chutes and elephant trunks which are fed by

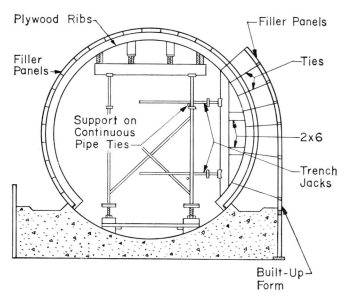

14-15   Adaptation of the filler units of a prefabricated panel system to forming a 13 ft diameter sewer in open cut.

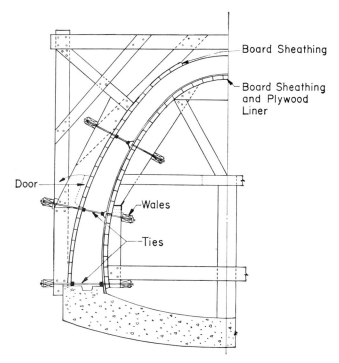

14-14   Half section through 11-ft sewer arch forms built of wood for bulkhead method of concreting in open cut.

one or more pipelines. After the concrete in the bulkheaded section has hardened, the entire form is stripped by partially collapsing the unit, moving it ahead, and re-erecting for casting the next section.

The bulkhead method is always used where poor ground conditions exist, requiring the lining to be placed concurrently with tunnel driving operations. It is also used when some factors such as the size of the tunnel, the introduction of reinforcing steel, or the location of construction joints preclude the advancing slope method.

Cut and Cover Construction

Cut and cover tunnel construction, used largely for shallow tunnels and conduits, is a variation of the other methods. The bulkhead placing technique is used for cut and cover work, but additional external wall forms are required for earth excavation. The outside forms may be braced against the excavation and the previously placed tunnel invert. The inside forms

14-16   Non-telescoping sidewall and roof forms for San Francisco Bay Area Rapid Transit District box culvert in open cut. This form assembly, adjustable for cleaning and varying with width of box, rolled forward on special casters without traveler or railroad-type rails.

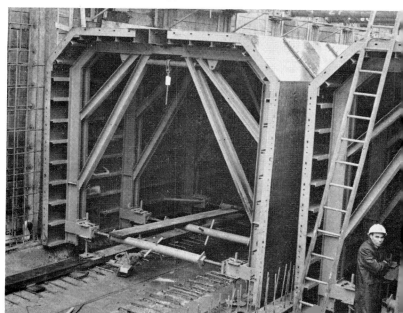

are like those used for regular underground work. Form ties are used to resist lateral pressure and spreaders maintain proper spacing and alignment.

Since the exterior of the structure is accessible from above, the outside forms for cut and cover work are usually positioned with a crane. The outer forms are often discontinued near the arch crown to leave room for the placement of concrete. This area is later finished by hand. Concrete is delivered by buckets, pipeline, or conveyor.

General Design Considerations

In planning underground formwork, the general design criteria discussed in previous chapters apply but additional considerations are important. This section will note these considerations and point out factors requiring special attention.

The design and fabrication of steel arch forms for large scale operations is frequently part of a subcontract with a company specializing in this work. In this way a complete system of prefabricated form units with integrated travelers can be designed and built to meet the project specifications. For smaller projects, the contractor can rent or purchase standard steel arch form units that meet job specifications and offer the benefit of the experience of these manufacturers. He can then design and build travelers and other form parts to use with the prefabricated units.

When renting or buying standard or special shapes and sizes of prefabricated steel form units, the following information should be furnished to the prospective supplier: drawings of tunnel lining cross section, with longitudinal dimensions and location of construction joints; proposed placing sequence; number of curves and radii; required rate of daily progress; minimum form stripping time; desired rate and method of concrete placement; underground transportation system; and services such as compressed air, and water.

The contractor who designs and builds his own arch forms should have a complete stress analysis made of the form components by a qualified engineer. He must investigate all loading conditions, including those induced by handing and surcharged concrete pressures. The proposed method of handling the form units during erection, transportation, and stripping together with proposed methods of bracing and anchorage should be clearly indicated on the drawings. Methods of supplemental strutting or bracing for abnormal conditions should also be indicated.

Influence of Placing Equipment

Tunnel arch concrete is usually placed by pneumatic gun or positive displacement pump. The fresh concrete is forced into the forms through a 6 to 10 in. diameter pipeline, the end of which is embedded at least 5 to 10 ft within the fresh concrete to prevent segregation and minimize voids. The line is withdrawn as the cavity is filled.

Various methods of mixing and transporting concrete to the pump or gun can be devised depending upon the method of tunnel lining selected. The concrete is usually batched or mixed outside the tunnel and transported to the pump by ready-mixed concrete trucks or by modified ore cars or agitator cars running on rails laid on the completed tunnel invert. Tunnel concrete pumps are equipped with barrel type agitators which are usually fed by a short rubber-belted conveyor.

The entire concrete handling and placing system is frequently positioned on a traveling bridge which moves ahead as the arch form is filled. Figure 14-17 shows one system of transporting and placing concrete in tunnel work. In cut and cover projects the concrete is usually mixed outside the excavation and deposited in the forms by buckets and chutes.

With small aggregate and high slump concrete such as might be used in a heavily reinforced tunnel lining, the localized pressure induced by a displacement pump can reach a theoretical maximum of at least 150 psi (21,600 psf) less line losses.*

When the air gun is used, compressed air at a nominal pressure of 100 psi blasts slugs of high slump concrete into the cavity, and the form must withstand the pressure due to the impact of the concrete and surges of compressed air.

When placement by pumping or pneumatic methods is anticipated, the capacity and working pressure of the prime mover and the size, length, and maximum embedment of the discharge line should be assumed in the design and specified on the drawings. If the formwork design provides for a method of placement other than by sustained pumping through a buried slick line, it should be clearly stated on the drawings that design pressures would be exceeded if sustained pumping were adopted.

---

* Rule of thumb for 8-in. pump lines is that the discharge point should not exceed either 100 ft above the elevation of the pump, or 1000 ft horizontally distant from it. There can be any combination of these figures; for example, 50 ft up and 500 ft distant. Thus 1 ft vertically equals 10 ft horizontally, or alternately friction losses should approximate 15 psf or 0.1 psi per ft of run. Even at these extremes the pump must provide additional residual pressure to discharge the concrete into the form, and thus a figure of 150 psi is considered reasonable.

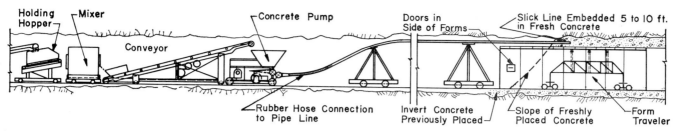

14-17 Arrangement of equipment for arch concreting within the tunnel. Here dry-batched ingredients are mixed near the concrete pump. Some jobs use ready mixed concrete delivered by chute from above grade.

Loads and Pressures

Formwork for tunnel linings placed pneumatically or by concrete pump is subjected to abnormal vertical and horizontal pressures which, in accordance with ACI Committee 347 recommendations, should be determined by engineers having firsthand knowledge of tunnel lining operations. Pressures of 3000 psf and higher can be induced at the crown of a tunnel arch form, and in practice many forms have been designed to withstand a working pressure of this magnitude.

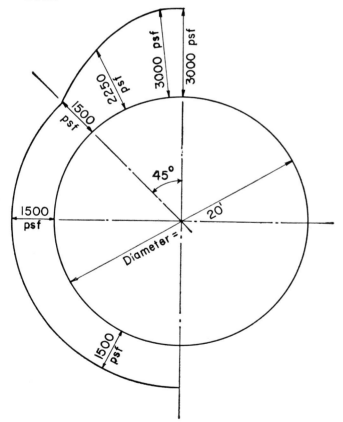

14-18 Pressure diagram used for design of circular tunnel forms where rate of filling of tunnel sides will be 6 to 7 ft per hr and concrete temperature is estimated at 50F. The 45-degree line separates wall and arch for purposes of estimating pressure.

For guidance purposes only, Committee 347 recommends that the pressure assumed for design be *at least 1000 psf* acting normal to the forms, plus the dead weight of concrete in the arch section, unless the tunnel side walls are placed separately. In this latter case, and for shafts, the lateral design pressures may be calculated the same as for wall forms above grade.*

Experience has shown that when the arch and side walls are placed in a single operation as in the case of the advancing slope method, or successively as is usually the case with the bulkhead method, the shape of the pressure diagram approximates that of the example shown in Figure 14-18.

In determining such a cross sectional pressure distribution the designer assumes that the wall section extends up to a point 45° from the vertical center line, and that the arch spans between these points on either side of the center line. Lateral pressure acting on the wall form section may be calculated from the general equation for wall forms

$$p = 150 + \frac{9000R}{T}$$

but no less than 1000 psf should be used for design. Pressure acting on the arch form section is assumed to reach a maximum at the crown, and to be a minimum, corresponding to the pressure established for the wall section, at the 45° point. Arch pressure magnitude and distribution are determined from an analysis of actual job conditions, including the size of the cavity, incidence of rock support ribs and lagging, reinforcing steel, the required degree of filling of the cavity, the method and rate of placement, plus significant characteristics of the concrete, such as temperature and workability.

Live loads produced by concrete mixers and pumps, agitator cars, muck cars, conveyors, pipelines,

---

* Continuing studies may make possible more precise estimates of pressure values required for tunnel form design. German tests made on a horizontal cylindrical tunnel form 10 meters long and 3.4 meters in diameter recorded uplift pressures appreciably less than the full fluid equivalent. See "Schalungsdruck beim Betonieren," by Otto Graf and Ferdinand Kaufmann, published in Berlin, 1960, by Wilhelm Ernst and Son, as *Heft* 135 of the Deutscher Ausschuss für Stahlbeton.

and other equipment must be considered wherever applicable in designing tunnel forms.

Except for tunnel linings and similar underground structures which are placed pneumatically or by a positive displacement pump, the design loads and pressures for underground formwork are similar to those for surface structures. Lateral bracing is required for slabs and walls, much the same as for above-grade work, despite the absence of wind.

Vibration and Form Access

External vibration is often required because of the cramped, curved space within the form, and forms must be able to withstand forces set up by this vibration. Several vibrators may be attached to the forms and moved ahead to follow the advancing slope of fresh concrete.

Access to the space behind the forms should not be overlooked. Access doors and holes should be placed in the form at convenient locations. Most commercial forms come equipped with doors that are dogged or wedged tight and opened as needed for concrete placement, vibration, and inspection. Smaller holes are needed for the insertion of bolts and grout pipes. These holes are usually closed off by a bolt with an insert plate attached at the end, the bolt being held in place by a yoke arrangement.

Form Construction

On most jobs, the forms are erected aboveground to assure proper fitting of parts when the units are taken underground (Figure 14-8). If any modification is

necessary, it is better to do it before the forms are in the tunnel where working space is at a premium.

The choice of materials for underground formwork is usually based on the shape, degree of reuse, and mobility of the forms and the magnitude of pump or pneumatic pressure to which they are subjected. Usually, tunnel and shaft forms are made of steel, or a composite of wood and steel. When reuse is not a factor, plywood and tongue-and-groove lumber can be used for exposed surface finishes.

Wood is seldom used in large underground projects unless the section being formed is of an irregular shape such as found in transition sections and draft tubes. In such sections, form surfaces are often too complicated for economical steel fabrication unless several reuses of the forms are possible.

Wood forms have one obvious advantage for tunnel jobs. The consistently high humidity in underground construction alleviates the problem of shrinkage and warping that often occurs in wood formwork, making it an excellent material for underground formwork. Since wood does not hold up as well as steel under repeated use, tunnel length is a factor to be considered when determining its suitability as a formwork material. Figure 14-14 shows a simple wood arch form design.

Stripping Time

Although the minimum stripping time for tunnel arch forms is usually established on the basis of experience, it can be safely predetermined by tests in the laboratory. It is recommended that at the start of a tunnel arch concreting operation, the minimum stripping time be 12 hr for exposed surfaces and 8 hr for construction joints. If the specifications provide for a reduced minimum stripping time based on site expe-

14-19 Wood may be used for forming underground structures where the section is of irregular shape such as found in draft tubes and transition sections.

TABLE 14-1: GENERAL TOLERANCES FOR UNDERGROUND STRUCTURES

Type of structure	Maximum departure from line and grade
Free-flow tunnels and conduits	1 in.
High velocity tunnels and conduits	½ in.
Railroad (or other vehicular) tunnels	1 in.
Allowable variation in thickness	
Tunnel lining Conduits	minus 0 minus 2½ percent or ¼ in., whichever is greater or plus 5 percent or ½ in., whichever is greater
Variations from inside dimensions	
Tunnel linings or cast-in-place conduits	½ of 1 percent

rience, such reductions should be in time increments of 30 min or less and should be established by means of laboratory tests and visual inspection and surface scratching of sample areas exposed by opening the form access doors. Hardness of the concrete may also be determined by the impact hammer method of testing under certain circumstances; some field experience indicates that this method is not too satisfactory because of the "softness" of concrete at such an early age, and should be limited to concrete with strengths in the 2000-3000 psi or higher range.

Special attention should be given to the stripping time for arch forms when there is a possibility that unvented ground water seepage could become trapped between the rock surface and the concrete lining.

Tolerances

Tolerances in underground construction depend on the use of the finished structure. High velocity conduits, for instance, require close tolerances to assure correct behavior of the fluid and to prevent erosion of concrete. Table 14-1 gives general values recommended by ACI Committee 347 for tolerances for underground structures.

Conventional application of these tolerances does not require them to be related to any specific distance. For example, the actual alignment or grade of a free-flow tunnel can be 1 in. from established alignment or grade throughout its whole length or any segment of length and meet these requirements. Tunnel forms are usually at least 20 ft long and devia-

14-20 Interior of shaft with forms suspended by heavy chains from anchor bolts set in previous lift. These 20 ft diameter steel forms were assembled in sections to form 30 ft high unit of shaft for concreting. Forms could not rest on loose muck in this case because job schedule called for excavation and blasting to go on below while concrete was hardening in forms.

tions from alignment or grade are thus gradual over at least 20 ft.

Control over both gradual and abrupt irregularities may be included in the finish requirements which vary for different types of work, depending on the function of the underground structure. The Corps of Engineers (Class B) finish required for tunnel linings limits "abrupt" irregularities to ¼ in. and gradual irregularities to ½ in.* For finishes in structures where evenness of surface for water passage is essential, the maximum abrupt irregularity allowed is ¼ in. for irregularities parallel to the direction of flow water, and ⅛ in. for irregularities not parallel to the flow direction. Maximum allowable gradual irregularity is ¼ in. for these latter finishes.

* As defined by the Corps of Engineers, "abrupt" irregularities include, but are not limited to, displaced, misplaced, or improperly matched sheathing, lining, or form sections, and loose knots which will result in surface blemishes. "Gradual" irregularities are those which result from warping, nonplanar surfaces, and similar more or less uniform variations from the true surface as designed. Gradual irregularities are checked by means of templates or straightedges 5 ft long.

Shafts

Shafts are usually required to provide ventilation and speed construction of tunnels which are greater than 3 or 4 miles in length. They may also be an integral part of the design, such as surge or intake shafts in an hydraulic tunnel, or mine shafts which are built apart from any tunnel lining operation. If the shaft is to be permanent, a lining of concrete is usually specified. This construction must be carried out within a very limited space just as in tunnel work, but with the added hazard of exposure to falling objects and loose rock. Work often must be done from hanging scaffolds, depending on the lining and excavation procedure.

Most shaft lining is done while the shaft is being sunk because state or local regulations often give a maximum depth beyond which the shaft cannot be sunk without timbering or lining. Usually when a depth of about 30 ft has been reached, the excavating is discontinued while the shaft section is lined, the forms being supported on a platform laid on top of loose muck. A variation from this practice is shown in Figure 14-20.

Shafts may also be lined from the bottom upward. When this method is adopted, the forms for each successive lift are supported on anchors in the previously placed lift. Slip forms (Chapter 15) can also be used in shaft lining when it is possible to excavate full depth before beginning the lining operation.

Care must be taken to assure an accurate circular cross section of the forms because strength of the form may be impaired considerably by an out-of-round configuration. Forms must be designed to permit the setting of anchors in the lining to support forms for the next lift, and as attachments for the structural bracing elements of the finished shaft. When the shaft form relies on the single shear value of embedded anchors as a means of support, the minimum time lapse between successive lifts and maximum allowable loading in addition to the dead weight of the forms should be specified.

15: SPECIAL TECHNIQUES IN CONCRETE CONSTRUCTION

UNUSUAL CONCRETING PRACTICES frequently impose special form requirements; an unusual type of form like the slip form may itself make departures from conventional concreting methods practical as well as advantageous. For the most part, these unusual techniques are handled by specialists. The discussion of this chapter focuses only on the special aspects of each type of construction which influence the formwork needs. No attempt is made to fully describe the construction methods.* In some of these techniques, such as tilt-up work, the forms are virtually eliminated, while in others the form is extremely important. Thus, some of the following sections are extensive in detail, while others are quite brief.

* Many excellent books and articles are available to those interested in reading the full construction story. A few of these are listed at the end of the chapter.

Slip Forms

Slip form construction, also frequently referred to as sliding form construction, is similar to an extrusion process. Plastic concrete is placed or pumped into the forms, and the forms act as continuously moving dies to shape the concrete. The rate of movement of the forms is regulated so that the forms leave the concrete after it is strong enough to retain its shape while supporting its own weight. Although uninterrupted slides are desirable, particularly in vertical work, it is possible to stop and later resume the sliding operation with resulting joints no different from those between lifts of fixed-form construction.

Slip form construction is normally used for vertical structures such as silos, storage bins, bridge piers,

15-1 Around-the-clock operation typical in slip form work requires adequate lighting for night work. Note chute from hopper on hoist tower for depositing concrete to be placed in the moving forms.

15-2 Vertical slip forms near the top of a 10-story apartment building whose eight upper floors were slip formed in an around-the-clock operation lasting 115 hr. All exterior and major interior walls were cast simultaneously and continuously.

shaft-type buildings, underground shafts, and water tanks, or for horizontal structures such as tunnel inverts, water conduits, drainage channels, canal linings, and highway pavements.

Vertical slip forms (Figure 15-2) are moved by continuous screws operated by hand, or by jacks which ride on smooth steel rods or pipe embedded in the hardened concrete. Horizontal slip forms (Figure 15-3) generally move on a rail system or a shaped berm. For either type, the working deck, concrete supply hoppers, and finishers' platforms or scaffolding are attached to and carried by the moving formwork. In some cases fixed forms such as sheathing, rock, earth, or existing masonry may be on one side, with the sliding form on the other. For vertical structures below grade, slip forming may be similar to above grade work, or where job and surface conditions favor erection of adequate supporting structures, jacks may climb on cables or rods suspended from above.

Major advantages of slip forms are speed and economy, plus the fact that continuous sliding produces a monolithic structure. In many cases the cost of materials and building of the slip forms is about the same as for fixed forms that would do the same job. The economy comes from the shorter construction time; for vertical construction, savings often do not develop unless the structure is about 40 ft or taller.

Efficient slip form construction is limited to work where there are few projections transverse to the sliding direction. It must also be remembered that the process requires a more experienced crew at all levels —forms should be designed and built by individuals experienced in slip form work, and the sliding operation must be carried out under careful, experienced supervision. Slip forms used for underground construction or mass concrete structures should comply with applicable requirements for those types of con-

15-3 Horizontal slip forming is common for long canal lining operations. From the foreground in this picture are seen the trimmer, sliding form lining machine, finishing jumbo, and curing jumbo. All four ride on rail supports at the top of the embankment.

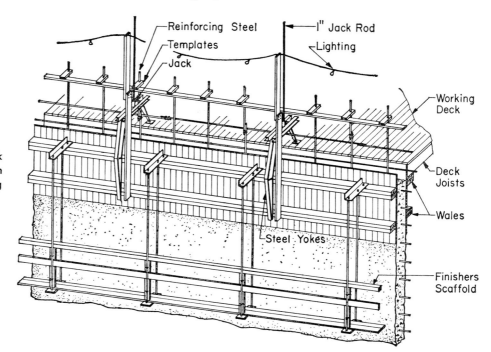

15-4 Typical slip form with deck and finishing scaffold supported on wales. Templates for positioning reinforcing bars are indicated.

struction in the "Recommended Practice for Concrete Formwork, ACI 347-68," as well as provisions therein for sliding forms.

Vertical Slip Forms

Vertical slip forms are moved upward by jacks which ride on smooth rods or pipes embedded in the hardened concrete. These jacks may be manual, pneumatic, electric, or hydraulic. Working decks and finishers' scaffolds are attached to and carried up with the forms, as shown in Figure 15-4.

The forms themselves can be considered in three sections—yokes, wales, and sheathing. The yokes have two primary functions: to keep the forms from spreading and to transfer the load of the forms to the jack. The wales stiffen the forms and are braced to carry the load to the yokes. Finishers' scaffold and working deck are connected to the wales, and the wale-yoke connections should be designed to withstand these loads. The sheathing is attached to the wales in a vertical position so as to cause a minimum of drag.

Design and Construction Considerations

Vertical Loads

In addition to any dead loads, live loads assumed for the design of working decks should not be less than 75 psf or concentrated buggy wheel loads (whichever is the greater) for sheathing and joists; 40 psf for beams, trusses, and wales.

Where working decks are also to be used as a bottom form for cast-in-place construction, the deck must be designed for the dead load of the concrete construction plus any superimposed loads, and should comply with usual slab forming practice (Chapter 9). The computed deflection of the working deck should not exceed $\frac{1}{8}$ in. or $\frac{1}{360}$ of its span, whichever is greater.

Vertical loads and possible torsional forces resulting from deck loads and friction of concrete on the forms must also be considered since the forms must act as trusses for the vertical loads between jacks. Braces should be provided for top wales where span between jacks exceeds 6 ft or where vertical loads are unusually heavy.

Lateral Pressure of Concrete

The lateral pressure of fresh concrete to be used in designing forms, ties, bracing, and wales may be calculated as follows:

$$p = 100 + \frac{6000\,R}{T}$$

where p = maximum lateral pressure, psf; R = rate of concrete placement, ft per hr; T = temperature of concrete in the forms, °F. Lateral pressure is lower in vertical slip form work than in conventional construction because vibration is slight,* concrete is placed in shallow layers, and there is no revibration.

* Current trends favor more mechanical vibration in slip form work; the use of immersion type vibrators allows the use of relatively low slump concrete and has done much to reduce honeycombing and to insure proper compaction of the concrete. If full internal vibration is used, refer to pressure formula for walls, p. 77.

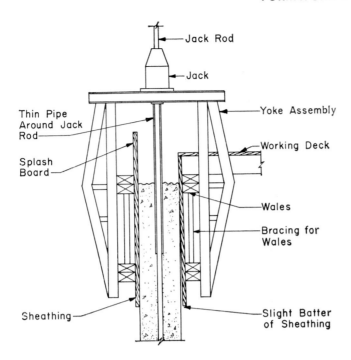

Jack Rod

Jack

Thin Pipe Around Jack Rod

Yoke Assembly

Splash Board

Working Deck

Wales

Bracing for Wales

Sheathing

Slight Batter of Sheathing

15-5 Cross section (schematic) of slip form. If the jack rod is to be salvaged, a thin pipe encasing the rod, attached to yoke or jack, moves up with the forms and prevents bonding of the rod to concrete. This leaves the jack rod standing free in a hole in the hardened concrete and it can be pulled when the slide is completed. Slight batter of sheathing helps to make the forms self clearing.

Wales must be adequately nailed or bolted together to transmit shear due to lateral pressure of concrete. Vertical posts should be placed between wales at lift points to distribute the lifting load.

Tolerances for Completed Work

The sliding operation must be conducted with sufficient care to maintain the necessary or specified tolerances in the finished structure. ACI Committee 347 recommends that variation of wall thickness be limited to $\pm \frac{3}{8}$ in. for walls up to 8 in. thick, or $\pm \frac{1}{2}$ in. for walls thicker than 8 in. The total deviation of any point on the slip form measured in a horizontal plane with respect to the projection of a corresponding reference point at the base of the structure should not exceed 1 in. per 50 ft of height. ACI Committee 313 has recommended less restrictive tolerances for construction of vertical concrete storage bins.*

Jacking System

Lifting jacks should be carefully placed so that they carry nearly equal vertical loads that do not exceed the jack capacity. The steel rods on which the jacks

* See report of ACI Committee 313, "Bin Wall Design and Construction," ACI JOURNAL, *Proceedings* V. 65, No. 7, July 1968, pp. 499-506.

climb should be especially designed for the purpose. The rods must be properly braced where not encased in concrete. If they are to be used as reinforcement, consideration must be given to splices and their low bond value as plain bars.

If the jacking rods are to be salvaged, they must not bond to the concrete. Usually a thin pipe sleeve about 3 or 4 ft long is placed around the jacking rod and attached to the yoke or jack so that it is carried upward with the forms (Figure 15-5). Since the short length of pipe is pulled upward with the forms, the rods are left standing in a small hole in the concrete and can easily be pulled out after the slide is completed.

A jacking system which provides for the precise simultaneous movement of the entire form in small preselected increments of approximately 1 in. at 5 to 10 minute intervals (6 to 12 in. per hr) is especially suited for large structures, particularly when single units are involved. To avoid unplanned cold joints, especially when such an occurrence would adversely affect the integrity of the structure, reserve jacking and placing equipment and standby construction service equipment should be immediately available to maintain a continuous operation. If it is not feasible to keep duplicate equipment on standby, then all materials needed to halt placement just as at a preplanned joint should be kept constantly in readiness. Such materials might commonly include wood joint strip, extra dowels, and for water-retaining structures, waterstop joint material.

Yokes

The yokes may be made of steel or wood and should be stiff enough to adequately resist lateral pressure from the concrete. They must transfer the full load of the forms, finishers' scaffolding, and working deck to the jacks. They should be designed with enough clearance above the forms to allow the horizontal reinforcement and embedded items to be installed in the correct location prior to being submerged in the rising concrete.

Frames called false yokes are sometimes placed between yokes to resist lateral loads by holding the wales in place. They are called false yokes because they are placed between jack rods and do not transmit their vertical load directly to the jacks. These frames are commonly used to support the forms at wall intersections or wherever the wales on one side are more easily supported than those on the other side. Hence the false yokes are generally constructed to transmit their load through the wales to the nearest main yokes on the side which is most easily supported.

15-6 Slip forms may be raised by manually operated screw jacks, as shown in this early construction view of multiple silos. (Arrows indicate jack operators.) Hydraulic-electric systems which provide for precise simultaneous movement of the entire form are preferred today for many larger jobs.

Wales

The timber or steel members making up the wales must be stiff enough horizontally to withstand the lateral pressure of the concrete tending to make the forms bulge out between the yokes. They must also be stiff enough vertically to transfer the weight of the forms and the friction force to the yokes without excessive deflection. When the span between jacks reaches about 10 ft the wales should be braced to act as a truss in a vertical plane between the yokes. Timber wales should be of 2- or 3-ply lumber (Figure 15-8), at least one ply of which is 2-in. material. The minimum depth of segmental wales for curved walls should be 4½ in. at the center after cutting.

Sheathing

The forms should be constructed of at least 1-in. board, ¾-in. plywood, 10-gage steel sheets, or other approved material. The 1-in. boards should be straight grained and center matched, and placed and finished in such a manner as to present a minimum of drag. Quarter sawn lumber may be of some advantage. Sheathing joints should be vertical so the form will slide upward without a transverse drag component.

As in other types of construction, swelling of wood forms must be controlled. Swelling may present a greater problem in slip form work because forms are in continuous contact with moist concrete for a much longer period than in conventional construction. Presoaking either in water or in a waterproofing preparation will reduce swelling during the sliding operation. A small gap at the joints between sheathing boards may be left to take up the swelling.

The forms should provide some working space

above the level of the fresh concrete but should not be so high that they interfere with the placing of horizontal reinforcing. The outside panel of the exterior wall forms should be somewhat higher than the inside panel (Figure 15-5). This provides a splash board to protect the finishers working on the scaffolding below.

Batter

The forms should be constructed with a slight batter so that they will be self-clearing as they slide. The top of the forms should be slightly smaller than the required wall thickness and the bottom of the forms

15-7 Close-up of yoke assembly showing jack climbing on jack rod. Note clearance of yoke above forms, allowing room for placing horizontal reinforcement.

15-8 Another type of yoke assembly, all wood. Three-ply construction of wales can be seen clearly.

slightly larger (Figure 15-5). In this way the concrete can take its final shape about halfway down the form and is completely free of the form at the bottom. The amount of batter is a question upon which many successful supervisors differ. A range from ⅛ in. to ½ in. in 4 ft is representative of current practice. Sometimes the form for the outside face of an exterior wall is left vertical.

Bracing

Over-all lateral and diagonal bracing of forms must be provided to insure that the shape of the structure will not be distorted beyond allowable tolerances during the sliding operation. When slip forms are used for single unit structures in excess of 50 ft diameter, they are usually segmental and are provided with a substantial center guide made of steel or concrete to maintain alignment of an otherwise unguided form.

Form Depth

The depth of the forms depends on the rate of slide and the time required for concrete to stiffen enough to be self-supporting. The minimum depth of forms is 3½ ft, with the most commonly used depth being

15-9 Carpenter attaching vertical tongue-and-groove 1x4 boards to double 2x8 wales. Slight draft to this form was obtained by nailing a strip of ¼-in. hardboard to the upper wale (visible on right side of picture).

15-10 Prefabricated slip form "machines" are commercially available in diameters from 6 to 30 ft for such standard shapes as the grain silo shown here during erection.

about 4 ft. Forms up to 6½ ft have been used successfully in winter weather or when greater sliding speed is desired.

Standard Slip Form Machines

When a number of standard shapes such as farm silos or chimneys are to be cast, prefabricated slip form construction units may prove useful. These machines are commercially available in a variety of sizes from 6 to 30 ft in diameter, and the thickness of wall cast can be adjusted. The forms are usually fabricated from steel and are easily assembled at the job site. All lifting equipment is supplied, and various built-in features are available.

Sliding Operations

Since the economic success depends primarily on attaining the highest possible rate of slide * consistent with good construction practice, careful planning and supervision are necessary to minimize delays. An

---

* Until quite recently a slide rate of 12 in. per hr (24 ft per day) was considered fast and was expected only under ideal conditions. Today 12 in. per hr is a median figure rather than an optimum one. Sliding form operations have been conducted at average speeds of 18 in. per hr or more, and the trend seems to be toward even higher rates of slide. Increased speeds have been made possible by using high early strength cements; by using admixtures which accelerate setting and improve workability; by increasing form heights to 6 ft or more; by improving jacking equipment and form design; and most importantly, through better job planning.

adequate supply of concrete to maintain the planned rate of slide is required. Materials should be conveniently stockpiled.

Rate of slide should not be greater than the rate the forms were designed to travel. Although the maximum rate of slide must be carefully predicted and planned for, the actual rate must be controlled by an experienced field superintendent who is qualified to make such adjustments as changing field conditions inevitably require. The superintendent must see that the slide operation is not proceeding so fast as to cause "blowouts" or soft concrete falling out from under the forms, nor so slow as to cause "lifts" or concrete sticking to forms and ripping away from the concrete below.

Forming Openings, Recesses

Since slip form construction is like an extrusion process, no projections beyond the face of the forms are possible because they will foul the moving forms. Any necessary structural concrete projections or decorative projections of other material may be added after the slip formed portions are completed. Although projections are not feasible during the actual slide, continuous vertical flutings and various changes in cross section are possible within the confines of the forms. Entire sections or partial inserts may be blocked out and resumed as required using stationary or moving bulkheads that fit between the forms. Window and door frames may be set in place right in the walls as the slide proceeds, and normally no difficulties are encountered in placing piping or electrical conduits in walls or columns. Horizontal features can be incorporated at the bottom and top of the structure with little difficulty.

Pockets to take beams, keys with dowels, and anchor slots for masonry attachment are also placed during the slide. Dowels for future connections may be bent to fit within the forms and later straightened, but only structural grade bars are advisable for such use. Another method is to use dowel stubs that fit within the forms for future attachment by welding; only bars of weldable grade should be specified for this purpose.

Reducing Wall Thickness

The thickness of a wall can be reduced in steps as the slide proceeds upward. When concreting is completed to the level of the step, the forms are jacked free of the concrete and the inside sheathing is rebuilt or a filler piece is inserted inside the forms. When the reduction in thickness is on one face only, the jack rods will not be in the center of the section after the reduction in wall thickness, and the pull on the yokes must be balanced. Before it is decided to reduce wall

15-11 Details of large wall openings formed at the beginning of a slide. Workers at the top place reinforcement as the slide continues.

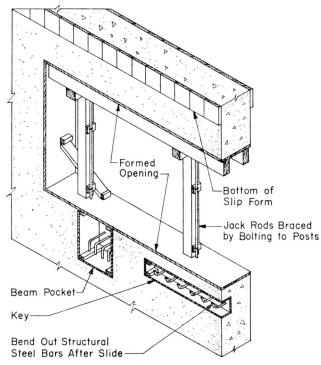

15-12 Typical forming details to allow for openings, beam pockets, concrete brackets, etc. Where jack rods extend through formed openings, bracing must be provided for their support.

287

thickness by this method, a study should be made to determine its economic feasibility. The saving in concrete may be offset by the expense of adjusting the forms and the time lost during the interruption of the sliding operation.

Maintaining Level and Alignment

Special care must be taken in building the forms and arranging the jacks so that the forms will draw straight and true without strain or twist. Care must be taken to prevent the forms from drifting from plumb or designed dimensions and to prevent torsional movement.

The best way to prevent drifting is to start with adequately braced, carefully plumbed forms, and then to keep the deck level throughout the slide. The deck may be checked for level by: (1) Checking the level of the jacks against marks on the jacking rods; (2) Using a water-level system which consists of a central reservoir and plastic tubes placed at strategic locations and connected to the reservoir by hose; (3) Checking by transit on the deck; and (4) Vertical tape measures from fixed points. The two latter methods cannot be used when the forms are in motion.

Alignment and plumbness of structure should be checked at least once during every 8 hr that the slide is in operation and preferably every 4 hr. In work that is done in separate, intermittent slipping operations, a check on alignment and plumbness should be made at the beginning of each slipping operation.

Plumbness of the structure can be verified by plumb bobs, or a transit may be used to check targets painted on several sides of the form against corresponding targets on the base of the structure. Adjustment of forms that are out of plumb is difficult and can be made only under the supervision of a man highly experienced in slip form work.

Curing and Finishing

If the forms are constructed properly and kept clean, the concrete emerges ready for a float and brush finish. The finishers work on a scaffold hung from the forms. Equipment for the application of curing compound is also carried by the scaffold. If water is to be used in curing, care must be taken to insure that it does not erode the freshly finished concrete. Water lines can be attached to the finishers' scaffold to apply a continuous fog spray to the concrete. A shield may be attached to the forms to protect the concrete from drying winds.

15-13 Central reservoir for water level system of maintaining level deck throughout the slide

15-14 With properly constructed, clean slip forms the concrete emerges ready for a float and brush finish. Workmen use scaffold suspended from the moving form assembly. Lights are available for night work.

Form Stripping

When the forms have reached the top of the slide and jacking is finished, the weight of the forms is generally transferred from the jack rods to the finished wall. This is usually done by bolts or bearers inserted through holes left in the walls below the wales. The location of these holes must be carefully planned for the particular method of supporting the forms. When the weight of the forms has thus been taken off the jacks, the yokes, jacks, and jack rods may be removed if they are needed elsewhere on the job, before the roof slab is concreted.

The working deck frequently serves as the form for casting the roof slab. If the yokes have been left in position, small boxes are set around the vertical members of the yokes so they will not be keyed into the concrete of the roof slab. After the yokes have been removed, the boxes are stripped and the holes filled with concrete.

Unless stripping is properly organized it may prove to be very expensive. The removal of the outside forms presents no great difficulties or special features, but it is usual to leave holes in certain planned positions in the roof slab in order to facilitate the suspension of a stripping scaffold inside the structure. The cost of labor in stripping and the value of the used material should be carefully investigated before it is decided to drop and waste any sections.

Winter Concreting

The rate of slide is an important factor in winter concreting. Since the setting time of the cement is increased at low temperatures, the concrete must stay in the forms longer. This can be accomplished by reducing the rate of slide or increasing the depth of the forms. To protect the concrete from the cold, a shield of lightweight rigid panels (plywood, hardboard, insulating board, etc.) attached to the forms can be constructed (Figure 15-15).

In addition to providing protection for the concrete, the shield also gives the finishers shelter from winter winds. The shield should be attached directly to the forms rather than to the finishers' scaffold to prevent unnecessary vibration of the scaffold which may make the finishers' work hazardous. Tarpaulin enclosures have been used satisfactorily on many jobs, but they tend to flap in the wind and mar the finish of the concrete.

Heat may be applied to the fresh concrete by steam pipes attached to the finishers' scaffold using a steam source at the base of the slide within the structure. Steam is recommended because it will not dry the concrete. The warm, moist air inside the structure provides excellent curing conditions. Every effort should be made to equalize the temperatures on the inside and outside faces of green walls to prevent temperature cracks.

Horizontal Slip Forms

Since most horizontal slip forming is against a fixed form support such as rock or earth, the operation is essentially a consolidating-screeding-finishing operation. The slip form machine usually moves on rails or a shaped berm. The intake of the machine is a trough designed to distribute concrete uniformly to all parts of the form. The concrete is consolidated by a vibrating tube parallel to and a few inches ahead of the leading edge of the form. The fresh concrete can also be consolidated by hand vibrators. Monolithic cast-in-place pipe is also produced by horizontal slip form methods.

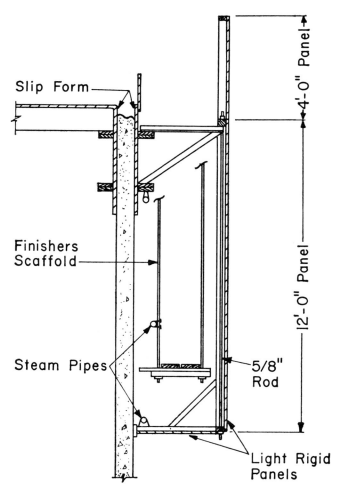

15-15 Simplified drawing of rigid enclosure with steam pipes for winter slip form work. Finishers' scaffold within the enclosure may be supported either from yokes (not shown) or wales.

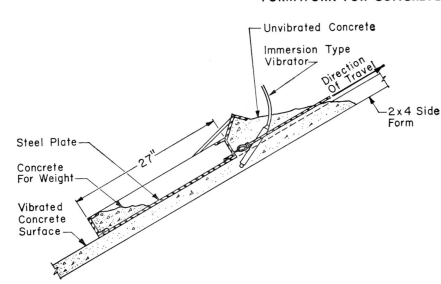

15-16 Slip form screed for placing unformed concrete on slopes is steel faced and weighted. Concrete is vibrated ahead of the slip form.

Design Considerations

For the large slip form pavers or canal liners, complete structural analysis including stress diagrams of the machine must be made to insure satisfactory performance. Consideration should be given to unsymmetrical and eccentric loading and the fact that the machine must be regularly disassembled and reassembled as it encounters siphons, bridges, chutes, etc., along the waterway or highway. Some of the larger machines are hinged so that sections may be passed through or beneath structures. Vertical or lateral deflections, particularly of long span machines, must be investigated, and sufficient rigidity provided to insure that concrete tolerances will be met.

Construction and Operation

Vibration may be used ahead of the slip form, but consolidation must be completed as the concrete passes under the form. Vibration of the slip form itself does not provide proper consolidation, apparently due to lack of means to supply additional concrete needed to fill the voids. The trailing edge of the slip form is usually adjustable to positions somewhat lower than that of the leading edge. This improves consolidation and tends to mold the concrete more closely to the subgrade. Too low a setting of the trailing edge causes tearing, rather than smoothing, of the surface. On some machines, the slip form is followed within a few feet by an "ironer" plate 18 to 20 in. wide, which, under favorable conditions, leaves a surface that requires little or no hand finishing.

Tunnel Inverts

Linings for tunnel inverts often are placed in a continuous longitudinal strip. The transverse section of the invert usually is curved to a prescribed shape. The best way to hold such a shape and at the same time obtain good vibratory consolidation of the higher areas along the side forms is to use a heavily weighted slip form supported on the fixed side forms and having a length equal to or greater than the width of the invert. The slip form is moved forward by winches, or under its own power on larger jobs. The concrete is delivered by means of pump and pipeline or conveyor belt and is placed and vibrated immediately ahead of the slip form (see also tunnels, p. 271).

Concrete on Slopes

Efficient placement of concrete on slopes may be accomplished by use of a weighted, unvibrated steel-faced slip form screed. The most efficient screed width has been found to be about 27 in. in the direction of movement. The screed may be pulled up the slope by equipment located on the berm or by air hoists mounted on the slip form. The concrete vibrators should be manually operated just ahead of the slip form rather than mounted on the form. If the form is vibrated, it will cause a swell in the finished surface emerging from the trailing edge. Figure 15-16 shows the cross section of a typical slip form screed.

Channels and Canals

For small unreinforced channels and canals, a simplified type of slip form machine has been used with good results. This machine is held to grade and line by a steel pan, shaped to fit the previously prepared excavation section, and is pulled forward by an external source of power. Behind the pan and immediately preceding the slip form is a transverse, compartmented trough for uniformly distributing the mix

15-17 On the left, a front view of slip form for lining 2.5 ft wide at the base, showing propelling winch. Rear view (right) of same form shows bucket filling the trough, and finishing work in progress.

(Figure 15-17). Internal vibration of the concrete in the trough may be used to improve the flow of concrete under the slip form, thus eliminating vibration of the form itself, and also decreasing the need for hand finishing.

For reinforced linings and also for medium-sized canal linings, more elaborate slipform machines are required. A framework, traveling on rails (Figure 15-18), or a tractor crawler assembly on the berm of the drainage channel or canal, supports the working platform, the distributor plate or drop chutes, the compartmented supply trough, vibrator tube in the bottom of the trough, and the slipform. The slipform is a steel plate, curved up at the leading edge, extending across the bottom and up the slopes of the canal and shaped to conform to the finished surface of the lining. When a distributor plate is used, it is fastened to the leading edge of the slipform and extends upward on a steep incline to the working platform. On some of the machines, a continuous row of hoppers in the working platform feeds into drop chutes, each supplying one compartment of the trough below. Concrete is dumped, usually from a shuttle car on the working platform, and is guided to the trough below by the distributor plate or the drop chutes.

As the concrete passes out at the bottom of the trough and under the slipform, it is consolidated by a vibrating tube parallel to and a few inches ahead of the leading edge of the form. Consolidation must be accomplished as the concrete passes under the slipform. Proper consolidation cannot be obtained by vibrating the slipform of a lining machine, apparently

15-18 View from in front as advancing canal liner places concrete over gravel blanket. Buggy at right carries concrete to vertical tubes for even distribution.

15-18a Part of the crawler-mounted equipment used to slipform side slopes of a large canal. From the left are the slope paver; the slope joint jumbo, from which workmen cut and set plastic transverse joint forms; the slope finishing jumbo; and the curing jumbo.

due to lack of means to supply additional concrete needed to fill the voids. The trailing edge of the slipform is usually adjustable to positions somewhat lower than that of the leading edge. This improves consolidation and tends to mold the concrete more closely to the subgrade. Too low a setting of the trailing edge causes tearing, rather than smoothing, of the surface. On some machines, the slipform is followed within a few feet by an "ironer" plate 18x20 in. wide, which, under favorable conditions, leaves a surface that requires little or no hand treatment.

For large channels (bottom widths of 50 to 110 ft) it is impractical to build machines to span the entire waterway. The slope paver is a crawler-mounted slipform which places the concrete lining on one side slope and the adjacent 8-10 ft of the invert. After the opposite side slope is similarly completed, the invert is finished by horizontal pavers. All three operations are kept on line and grade electronically through sensors probing guide wires.

Highway Pavers

The slipform used for highways is similar in principle to the slope form pavers. No fixed side forms are required as the side forms of the machine slide forward with the paver, leaving the slab edges unsupported. The concrete is deposited either on the subgrade ahead of the paver or into a hopper box.

Following spreading by a dozer-type strike-off, the concrete is consolidated by vibration and shaped by an extrusion plate or meter. Flat, parabolic, or hip roof crowns can be provided with a quick change device for transitions in and out of horizontal curves. Surface elevations can be maintained by electronic controls.

Cast-in-Place Pipe

Cast-in-place pipe is a continuous nonreinforced concrete conduit having no joints or seams except as necessitated by construction requirements. It is built in a previously excavated trench which has a semicircular bottom and vertical or nearly vertical sides. The outside lower portion of the pipe is formed by the trench and the corresponding inside is formed by a specially designed slipform commonly called a boat or a sled, or by a more complex slipform machine. The inside of the remainder of the pipe is formed by either metal forms or an inflated tube. Three construction methods are described in the report of ACI Committee 346: *

1. Two-stage construction by hand
2. Two-stage construction by machine
3. Single-stage construction by machine.

* Publication planned for 1969; report will be reprinted in *ACI Manual of Concrete Practice.*

Traveling Forms

Traveling form construction is based on reusable forms mounted on movable frames or scaffolding called travelers. After the concrete of one section of the structure has cured sufficiently, the forms are released and moved along the structure to the next section to be concreted. Traveling form construction offers maximum reuse of forms with minimum labor.

Traveling forms are suitable for many types of structures: bridges, sea walls, floor systems, shell roofs, tunnel linings, culverts, and segmented or multiple domes. Local job conditions including the design of the structure itself generally determine whether traveling forms are feasible or economical. They are generally used for building structures that have a constant section or a recurring shape.

There is no standard traveler design for any given structure. Each set of forms and travelers must be designed for the job at hand. This, of course, does not rule out reuse of major components of the forms and travelers on a similar job in the future. A great deal depends on the ingenuity of the form designer and builder as the forming systems compared in Figure 15-19 show. The three folded plate structures were essentially alike in shape and dimensions, but the systems for traveling the forms were entirely different.

The basic principles of traveling form construction are relatively simple, although details may become complex for large, long span travelers. Forms are attached to a traveler which is mounted on skids or wheels, which in turn travel on rails, a concrete pad, or any suitable surface. Movement may be by hand, crane, tractor, or any means compatible with the size of the traveler, design of the structure, and the available equipment. The traveler must be able to move freely and easily in order to obtain the maximum benefits from this type of operation.

The traveling form is built to be backed off from the hardened concrete, moved to a new position, and precisely adjusted for concreting the next section. Jacks between the traveler and forms are usually used to back off the forms and make adjustments. Care in planning and building is necessary so that form units do not become keyed into the concrete and complicate this stripping operation. After the bond with the hardened concrete has been broken and the forms have been backed off slightly, additional movement of the forms may be necessary to clear beams, columns, and other architectural features.

There are various ways for the traveler to get around architectural and constructional obstructions; sections may be cut out to clear obstructions and later inserted before concreting, or folding form sections like those in Figure 15-22 may be used. In the case of suspended travelers used in bridge work (Figure 15-23) an entire section of form and traveler may be swung out together to clear piers or other obstructions. For forms like those for the folded plates shown in Figure 15-19, a straight vertical drop of a few feet was sufficient to free the forms for lateral movement.

When the traveler has been moved to the next location, the forms must be positioned to receive the

15-18b Machine used to form cast-in-place pipe by single stage process using metal forms. Aluminum forms 6 ft long are fed into machine over rollers attached to mandrel. Metal struts to support upper forms are shown leaning against the machine.

fresh concrete. If a long rise is necessary, they are approximately positioned by jacks. The load can then be taken off the traveler wheels or jacks by blocking the structure. Sand jacks, steel chairs, wood blocks, or any device or material that will not crush under the load of traveler, forms, and concrete can be used. Final adjustments are made with screw heads or wedges and the forms are ready to receive reinforcement and concrete.

Design Considerations

When traveling forms are used for shell form construction, as they frequently are, the special requirements for shell forms outlined on pp. 246-249 should be observed. Where travelers are used for more or less conventional structural systems and on short spans, there are few special requirements and the general principles of form design prevail. Where large travelers are built for long span structures some additional factors must be considered, and it is to these conditions that the following paragraphs apply.

The large traveler for a long span structure becomes itself a major structure, and the nature of its usage makes it necessary to design it as a more or less permanent structure. Many such travelers remain in use for periods measured in months or years, not days or weeks, and are loaded and unloaded repeatedly. They must be designed to keep distortions to a minimum throughout a series of loading cycles.

Frequently, due to unsymmetrical loading and lateral pressures developed during concreting, very considerable lateral deflections of parts or of the entire traveler have occurred. This has happened on travelers of light, relatively long span construction as well as very heavily framed travelers. In many cases this lateral deflection, as well as some vertical deflection is inelastic, and the traveler does not recover its true shape after decentering. Where tolerances on the dimensions of the structure have been relatively tight this has necessitated repacking of joints to restore the falsework to its proper alignment. In general, distortions of this type, especially lateral distortions are due not to inadequate strength, or even to an inherent deficiency in stiffness, but rather to poor detailing at connections. These troubles are commonly due to large eccentricities in the connections which permit distortions (if not failure) of the members and especially the lateral bracing system before they can take any stress. Large amounts of material are often wasted due to inadequate fastenings at the connections.

These deficiencies of detailing are sometimes deliberate, in order to simplify fabrication and disassembly, and to increase salvage value of the materials used. While there may be no real harm in such practices, their implications must be realized.

Another common problem is a failure to appreciate and provide for the variety of partial and eccentric loading conditions which may be encountered during concreting and decentering operations. This is critical when the traveler itself has trusses of appreciable span. Often such trusses are designed as simply supported, but then redundants are added which enforce continuity between trusses or between trusses and columns. At other times continuous trusses or beams are used with little regard for the effect of uneven decentering which may result in complete stress reversal in many members. This may be especially serious where tie rods with little compressive strength are used as tension members.

With the foregoing problems in mind, the following suggestions are made:

1. Use a safety factor in the design of such travelers at least equal to those used in permanent construction.

2. Establish the placing sequence on any traveler in advance and follow it closely, with the falsework designed accordingly. If this is impractical, then design falsework for a number of alternate placing sequences, which will cover all conditions likely to be encountered.

3. Plan the decentering procedure during the design of the traveler and check the design for stresses during decentering, assuming reasonable tolerances in the actual performance of the decentering operation.

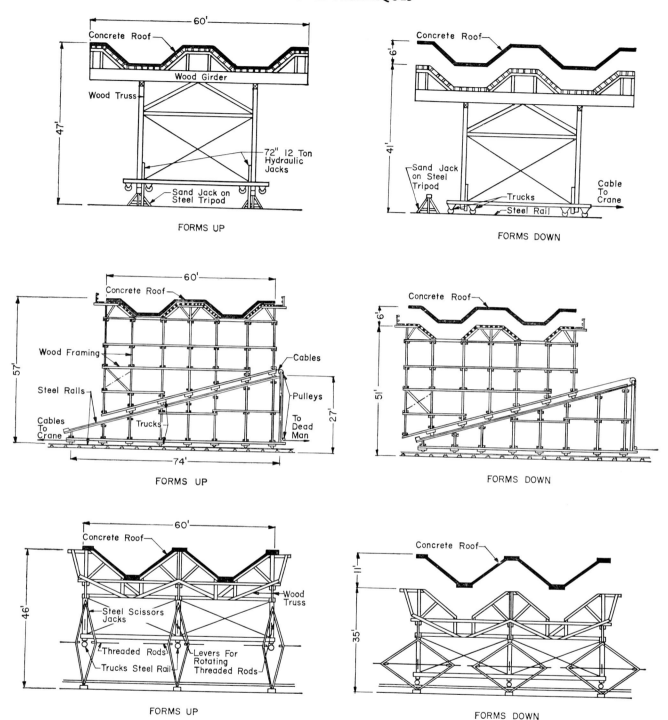

FORMS UP

FORMS DOWN

FORMS UP

FORMS DOWN

FORMS UP

FORMS DOWN

15-19 Traveling formwork designs vary widely, as shown by three different methods of vertical form movement for essentially similar folded plate hangar roofs. TOP—Glue-laminated wood falsework was raised 6 ft with 12-ton hydraulic jacks, one on each of eight columns, then shored on tripods during concrete placement. Forms were lowered the same way, except that the first 4½ in. of drop was made by draining sand jacks atop the tripods. CENTER—Wood framed traveler made in two parts with an inclined plane as the common face between top and bottom sections. To raise the roof forms 6 ft, the bottom section was forced under the top section which was guyed to prevent lateral motion. BOTTOM—Wood falsework raised and lowered about 12 ft with scissors jacks which carry total load including fresh concrete when the forms are up. With forms down, the structure rests on wood posts and jacks hang free. (Reprinted from *Engineering News-Record*, 1958, McGraw-Hill Publishing Co., Inc.)

15-20 A gantry-type traveler facilitated stripping, moving, and erection of vertical forms for wall of constant cross section. Steel-framed gantry traveled on rails on the ground. Note heavy strongbacks on the wall form.

15-21 Close-up of form support for folded plate traveler. Manually operated winches move the form forward along rails resting on the concrete floor slab.

15-22 Traveling flat slab forms with panels that fold down to clear drop heads of columns. These forms were supported on sectional steel scaffolding that rode on skids or sills directly against the concrete floor beneath. Liquid soap under the skids provided lubrication and prevented damage to the floor. Motive power was supplied by tractor.

15-23 Gantry riding on rails supported on precast bridge girders carries steel deck and curb forms forward as a unit, half a span at a time, and raises them into position. Platforms swing out to bypass piers.

15-24 Four sets of forms were sufficient for building 36 domes of a shopping center roof, as forms traveled for reuse. The dome in the foreground has been moved into place on roller mounted frames, now is being hoisted to correct elevation for concreting.

Tilt-Up Construction

Tilt-up construction is a method of casting wall panels on a completed floor slab and then tilting or lifting them into a vertical position. The main advantage of this type of construction is the elimination of vertical formwork for the walls.

The floor slab which serves as a casting bed is the bottom form for the precast wall panels, and special attention to its design and construction are necessary. It must meet all the normal requirements of the finished floor slab as well as special provisions for efficient application of the tilt-up method. For good tilt-up work, the floor should be level to a tolerance of $\frac{1}{4}$ in. in 10 ft; the slab should be smooth, hard, and free of blemishes. A steel trowel finish is preferred, because the surface texture will usually be transferred to the underside of the tilt-up panel.

The floor slab should also be designed to withstand truck crane loads if the method of lifting requires the presence of the crane on the slab. Over-all speed and efficiency are generally improved when the crane does work on the slab, so the decision will probably rest on whether or not the working area of the slab is large enough for the crane.

A compacted fill or temporary slab may be used in place of the floor slab for the casting of tilt-up units as long as it meets specifications for construction loads and smoothness. After the casting surface is completed and covered with a parting compound, the tilt-up units are cast directly on the floor slab. Often successive panels may be cast one atop the other, thereby reducing the area required for temporary casting slab and working space. Only edge forms and frames to form windows, doors, or other openings are needed. Occasionally plans may call for a half pilaster to be cast along each edge of the wall panel. Collins, who has written extensively on tilt-up construction, describes these edge and insert forms in considerable detail.[7,8]

Curing and Bond Breaking Compounds

Proper curing of the base slab is extremely important for its use as a casting bed as well as being critical for its service life as a floor. Liquid membrane curing compounds have been found practical for tilt-up work because they will allow early usage of the slab for casting, and they can also serve as parting compounds or bond breakers. Among the commercially available

15-25 Wall panel being tilted into position from its place on the casting bed. Window frames were positioned before casting.

15-26 Edge forms and reinforcing steel in place ready for casting tilt-up panels. Concrete is being placed for panels in the background.

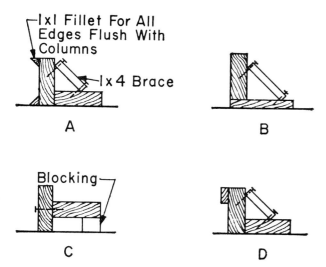

15-27 Typical construction of edge forms for tilt-up work, using 2-in. lumber. Extra strips are added as in D when offset edges are desired.

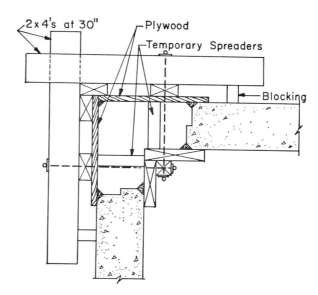

15-28 One type of corner column form for use when tilt-up panels are flush with column sides

curing and bond breaking compounds, there are chemical base, chemical resin base, resin base,* and wax base types which are usually sprayed on at a coverage of about 300 sq ft per gallon for the curing coat, and up to 600 sq ft per gallon when they serve only as bond breakers. The initial curing coat should not be expected to serve also as a bond breaker, particularly if the tilt-up panels are cast several weeks later than the floor slab.

Carpenters can begin layout and forming of wall panels as early as the morning after casting the base slab and applying curing compound. When edge forms for the wall panels have been completely laid out, before any steel or inserts have been placed, the base slab should be swept clean of all dust and debris. A second coat of the bond breaking agent is then applied at about half the intensity of the curing coat. Wooden edge forms can be sprayed at the same time to seal them from moisture and make their removal easier.

Lift Method of Construction

The lift method of construction, popularly described as lift slab, is based on casting reinforced concrete floor and roof slabs one on top of the other at or near ground level. Then, after proper curing, the slabs are lifted to their final position by the use of jacks and

fastened to the previously placed columns which supported them during the jacking operation.

In this layer method of precasting, the slabs are commonly of the flat soffit type. Other uniform depth types of framing such as ribbed or waffle slabs can also be used, with or without prestressing. Roof slabs sometimes utilize upturned beam framing. Patented methods, equipment, and materials for the lifting operations are available.

Forming and Casting

The forms for lift slab construction are relatively simple. The only forms needed for flat soffit type design are edge forms for the slabs and forms for blocking out openings in the slabs. The bottom form for each slab is the previously placed slab. The architect or engineer should remember that the ground floor slab and/or the soil supporting it are required to carry the dead load of the stacked slabs.

The forming techniques for ribbed or waffle slabs, or slabs with voids requiring filler blocks, cardboard tubes, or similar formwork components, are much the same as for conventional slabs discussed in Chapter 9. Void forms require tie-downs, but metal pans or domes are held satisfactorily by their dead weight plus the action of reinforcing steel.

The first step after completing the specified subgrade and edge forms is to place the bottom floor slab. The slab may be placed before or after the columns, according to the design. Since the slabs are cast in layers one on top of the other, special care must be taken in the finishing of a slab if the ceiling of the

---

* Some resins inhibit the set of cement they contact, and these of course are not suitable for use in curing or bond breaking compound.

floor above is to be exposed. Any imperfections or uneven surfaces will be transferred to the underside of the slab above.

As soon as the separating medium is dry and the slab has set, the forms, lifting collars, and reinforcement for the next slab may be placed. Care must be taken in locating collar keyholes or other lifting attachments to assure their vertical alignment after the slabs have set. Collars can be held in correct alignment by wedges inserted between the columns and the collar. Blockouts should be provided to prevent concrete from entering spaces between collar and column or lifting attachment openings.

Slab Separation

Bond breaking media should be carefully placed since the slabs may be damaged if they bond together and have to be separated by wedges or other mechanical means. After the slab is sufficiently set, the separation compound is mopped, sprayed, or brushed onto the slab. This compound should be properly cured or dried before reinforcing steel and other items are placed. It should be free of wax if the slabs require a separate finish, tile adhesives, or paint as a later application. Manufacturer's specifications for application and coverage of the separating media should be followed.

Another method of preventing bond between slabs is to spread a sheet of polyethylene film over the slab. The plastic must be kept flat against the slab

and must not be torn during the placement of steel. If the ceiling is to be exposed the plastic film should not be allowed to wrinkle.

Preplaced Aggregate Concrete

Preplaced aggregate concrete, also referred to as grout intrusion or prepacked aggregate concrete, is made by injecting or intruding mortar into the voids of a preplaced mass of clean, graded aggregate. This method of construction is used in the repair of damaged concrete structures, new construction, underwater concreting, and mass concrete structures.

The injected mortar may consist of sand, portland cement, and water, sometimes mixed in specially designed high-speed mixers which reportedly impart colloidal properties to the mix; or it may be a combination of water, fine sand, portland cement, pozzolanic filler, and a chemical additive designed to increase the penetration and pumpability of the mortar. The special qualities of the additive inhibit early stiffening of the grout, enhance fluidity, and hold the solid materials of the grout in suspension. The additive may also curtail shrinkage or cause expansion of the grout. The coarse aggregate is similar to coarse aggregate for conventional concrete. It is well washed and graded from $\frac{1}{2}$ in. to the largest size practicable. After compaction in the forms, it usually has a void

15-29 Lift slabs raised to final position (foreground); jacks at top will be moved to next group of 10 columns to raise the three slabs still stacked as cast.

15-30 Lifting collar and reinforcement in place ready for slab concreting. Wedges between collar and columns help maintain correct alignment for later lifting.

Lateral Pressure

Due to the method of placement, the lateral pressure on formwork is considerably higher than developed for conventional concrete construction. All formwork members should be designed to resist the sum of the pressures from the dry aggregate and the intruded mortar.

Pressure from Aggregate

The pressure of the aggregate on the formwork is converted to an equivalent lateral fluid pressure by using a reliable bin action theory or the Rankine or Coulomb theories for granular materials. Using the Rankine or Coulomb theory the maximum equivalent lateral fluid pressure from the aggregate is:

$$p(\text{aggregate}) = w\,h\!\left(\frac{1 - \sin\phi}{1 + \sin\phi}\right)$$

content ranging from 35 to 40 percent. Higher void ratios are possible, and the contractor should check this thoroughly in selecting his aggregate to avoid expense of extra cement for grout.

For normal construction the preplaced aggregates are wetted and kept wet until the injection of mortar into the voids is completed. The mortar is usually injected by horizontal or vertical perforated pipes (Figure 15-31) which are gradually withdrawn as the voids are filled. In underwater construction, the mortar displaces the water and fills the voids. If construction is to be interrupted for any length of time, the injection pipes should be withdrawn and washed out. The depth of mortar intrusion may be determined by measuring the level of mortar in preplaced inspection pipes with a float designed to sink in water but float on the rising mortar.

where w = unit weight of aggregate in packed condition, lb per cu ft; h = height of forms, ft; and ϕ = angle of internal friction of the aggregate in degrees. Approximate values of ϕ are 45° for crushed stone and 40° for rounded gravel. No distinction need be made for larger size aggregate since the volumes in such construction are so large that the size can have little effect.

Pressure from Mortar

The lateral pressure of the injected mortar is the same as the pressure of an equivalent fluid weighing 130 lb per cu ft. The time required for the initial set of the mortar (from 6 to 24 hr) should be determined by standard test methods. The rate of rise (1 to 2 ft per hr) will then be planned according to setting

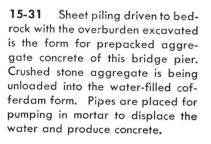

15-31 Sheet piling driven to bedrock with the overburden excavated is the form for prepacked aggregate concrete of this bridge pier. Crushed stone aggregate is being unloaded into the water-filled cofferdam form. Pipes are placed for pumping in mortar to displace the water and produce concrete.

time and other job requirements. The maximum height of fluid to be assumed in determining the lateral pressure of the mortar is the product of the rate of rise and the time of initial set. Thus the pressure from the grout is:

$$p(\text{mortar}) = 130 \, R \, t$$

where R = rate of rise in ft per hr and t = time of initial set in hr.

Total Pressure on Forms

The lateral pressure for the design of formwork at any point is the sum of the aggregate and mortar pressures as determined above.

$$p(\text{total}) = p(\text{aggregate}) + p(\text{mortar})$$

If prepacked aggregate concrete is to be placed under water, the effect of water pressure on the value of aggregate pressure on the forms must be taken into consideration.

Form Construction and Materials

In addition to the requirements outlined in Chapter 9 for conventional form construction, the forms must be completely mortar tight. The mortar is as capable of penetrating small holes in the forms as filling the voids in the preplaced aggregate. The greater lateral pressures usually require that the workmanship and details of formwork be of better quality than formwork for conventional concrete.

15-32 Pneumatic placement of concrete for this shell roof eliminates top forms that might otherwise be needed for the steep slope.

Tongue-and-groove lumber is preferred for exposed surfaces; the joints between boards permit the escape of traces of water. For unexposed surfaces, mortar tight forms of steel or plywood are acceptable. Prefabricated panel-type forms usually are not suitable because of the difficulty in making mortar tight seals between panels. Absorptive form linings are not recommended because they permit the coarse aggregate to indent the lining and form an irregular surface. Form linings, such as hardboard on common sheathing, are not successful because they do not withstand the external form vibration normally required.

Finishing

At finished surfaces, a surplus of mortar is brought to the top of the coarse aggregate, and sufficient fine aggregate is worked into the grout to produce a topping mix ready for screeding and floating. The forms are usually vibrated for exposed work to bring the mortar in contact with all parts of the form to produce a smooth surface. Since the preplaced aggregate particles are already in contact before the mortar is added, there is little drying shrinkage.

Shotcrete

In the shotcrete method of placement, concrete is projected by an air jet directly onto various types of surfaces in any desired thickness. Shotcrete can be used in numerous ways: for example, to repair dams, retaining walls, and concrete and masonry structures; to build walls, slabs, and shells; to coat existing brick, concrete, steel, and masonry structures; to encase structural members for fireproofing; and to line tunnels and sewers.

There are two shotcrete processes: wet and dry. In the dry process, sand and cement are dry-mixed and charged into a special pressurized feeder. The pressurized dry mix passes through a delivery hose to a special nozzle where water is introduced. The moistened mix jets directly onto the surface to be shotcreted. In the wet process, sand, cement, and water are mixed in a pressurized chamber and fed wet into the delivery hose. Compressed air forces a jet of the wet mix onto the surface to be shotcreted.

Shotcreting techniques simplify forming problems since only a single forming or support surface is required. Vertical walls can be built by shotcreting with only one backing or forming surface required to support the fresh concrete. Even soffits can be built up from below against a horizontal surface.

For repair or coating of existing structures, there is no formwork; the pressurized mix is supported adequately by the surface being covered. Because the final structural value of a shotcrete repair depends upon its bond with the surface on which the mortar is shot, this surface must be sound and thoroughly cleaned. All coated, scaly, or unsound concrete or masonry should be removed and dressed down to a solid, newly exposed surface.

Forms and Ground Wires

Forms, where required for support of the full weight of shotcrete, should conform in workmanship and material to supporting forms for conventional concrete, but should be so designed as to permit the escape of placing air and rebound during the gunning operations. Provision for escape of air and rebound is particularly important for thicker structural members. Columns should be formed only on two adjacent sides wherever practicable; however, satisfactory results may be obtained where three sides are formed provided the width is at least one and one-half times the depth. Pilasters may be formed on two adjacent or opposite sides. The soffit and one side of beams should be formed; this provides the maximum area of escape for air and rebound during the shotcrete buildup. Forms need be placed for only one side of a wall.

Forms or backing against which shotcrete is placed should be thoroughly secured to line and dimensions and sufficiently rigid to prevent excessive vibration from impact of the shotcrete. Form surfaces should be thoroughly cleaned and oiled before application of shotcrete; if constructed of wood, they may be wetted with water prior to application of shotcrete.

Adequate ground (gaging) wires should be used to establish the thickness, surface planes, and finish lines of the shotcrete. Ground wires should be taut, secure, and true to line and plane.

Scaffolding should be built so that the nozzleman can hold the nozzle at the optimum angle and distance from the surface for all parts of the work. The scaffolding should also give easy access to the shotcrete surface for screeding and finishing, if such is specified. Scaffolding should be constructed to permit

15-33   Vertical walls can be built by shotcreting against a single form surface such as the wire mesh and foamed plastic insulation board combination shown here. Insulation remains a permanent part of the wall.

uninterrupted application of the shotcrete wherever possible. For full details on the placing operation, refer to ACI 506-66 [19] and to the shotcrete machine manufacturer's specifications.

Tremie Concrete

Tremie concrete is placed under water by gravity feed through a vertical pipe with one end above water for charging with concrete and the bottom immersed in the concrete being placed. This type of placement is used for sealing cofferdams and caissons, for building underwater structures, and for holding tunnel sections and other objects in place underwater.

The tremie pipe is first plugged and lowered into position. After the pipe is filled with concrete, the

15-34   Foamed polystyrene planks plus steel reinforcement, top and bottom, served as the "form" and permanent insulation for this folded plate roof. Concrete was placed pneumatically on both top and bottom surfaces, completely encasing the form.

plug is pushed out by the concrete as the tremie pipe is gently lifted. The concrete flows out and forms a seal around the bottom of the pipe so that fresh concrete passing through the pipe does not contact water until it is in its final position underwater. Once the seal at the bottom of the pipe is made, the pipe is kept continuously immersed in the fresh concrete.

If the pipe is lifted out of the concrete by accident or to move the pipe to a new position, the tremie seal is lost and the original pipe plugging operation must be repeated. To prevent loss of the tremie seal and to prevent stiff concrete from obstructing the flow of fresh concrete, continuous placement is desirable. For best results, the forms are filled rapidly to minimize laitance formation and the tremie pipe is kept immersed in concrete until the forms are full.

Forms for Tremie Concrete

Tremie forms must confine fresh concrete until it has set. Ordinarily the forms are placed on a gravel blanket. The seal between the forms and the blanket must prevent concrete from flowing out under the forms. Inspection by a diver is usually necessary to insure a proper seal.

Good tremie concrete depends upon a smooth, gentle flow of concrete into the forms. Any turbulence will result in laitance. To produce gentle flow, concrete consistency, concrete head, and pipe spacing must be in proper balance. The forms must be designed to arrest water movement that would disturb the concrete before it has obtained its set.

In addition to the pressure from the concrete, the forms must withstand forces produced by waves and currents and unbalanced pressures due to non-uniform concrete placement.

Accurate knowledge of the behavior of concrete placed underwater is difficult to obtain, and therefore fewer facts are available than for other concreting techniques. For this reason, the form designer not familiar with this type of construction should consult an individual with tremie experience.

REFERENCES

NOTE: Reference material includes information on construction techniques as well as formwork.

SLIP FORMS
1. Camellerie, J. F., "Slip-Form Details and Techniques," ACI JOURNAL, Proceedings V. 55, No. 10, Apr. 1959, pp. 1131-1140; addenda published in ACI JOURNAL, Proceedings V. 59, Aug. 1962, pp. 1109.

2. ACI Committee 608, "Sliding Form Work," ACI JOURNAL, Proceedings V. 29, No. 5, Jan. 1933, pp. 201-240.
3. Robinson, W. J., and Tuthill, L. H., "Better Concrete in Slope Paving by the Use of Slip-Forms," ACI JOURNAL, Proceedings V. 52, No. 1, Sept. 1955, pp. 1-12.
4. Hunter, L. E., Moving Forms, Concrete Publications Ltd., London, 1951, 56 pp.
5. Ray, Gordon K., and Halm, Harold J., "Fifteen Years of Slip-Form Paving," ACI JOURNAL, Proceedings V. 62, No. 2, Feb. 1965, pp. 145-160.

TILT-UP CONSTRUCTION
6. Clark, C. A., "Development of Tilt-Up Construction," ACI JOURNAL, Proceedings V. 44, No. 9, May 1948, pp. 813-820.
7. Collins, F. Thomas, "Tilt-Up Construction in Western United States," ACI JOURNAL, Proceedings V. 48, No. 2, Oct. 1951, pp. 133-144.
8. Collins, F. Thomas, Manual of Tilt-Up Construction, Know How Publications, Box 7126, Landscape Station, Berkeley, Calif., 6th Edition, 1965, 150 pp.

LIFT METHOD OF CONSTRUCTION
9. Engineering Manual, U. S. Lift Slab Corp., Dallas, Texas, 1955.
10. Minges, James S., and Wild, Donald S., "Six Stories of Prestressed Slabs Erected by Lift-Slab Method," ACI JOURNAL, Proceedings V. 53, No. 8, Feb. 1957, pp. 751-768.
11. Rice, Edward K., "Economic Factors in Prestressed Lift-Slab Construction," ACI JOURNAL, Proceedings V. 55, No. 3, Sept. 1958, pp. 347-358.
12. Sefton, W., "Multistory Lift-Slab Construction," ACI JOURNAL, Proceedings V. 54, No. 7, Jan. 1958, pp. 579-590.
13. Smith, Eberle M., "Architectural Integration of Lift Slab Techniques," ACI JOURNAL, Proceedings V. 52, No. 1, Sept. 1955, pp. 35-46.
14. Youtz, Philip N., "'Lifting' Huron Towers," ACI JOURNAL, Proceedings V. 57, No. 12, June 1961, pp. 1537-1548.

PREPLACED AGGREGATE CONCRETE
15. Davis, Raymond E.; Jansen, E. Clinton; and Neelands, W. T., "Restoration of Barker Dam," ACI JOURNAL, Proceedings V. 42, No. 10, Apr. 1948, pp. 633-668.
16. Davis, R. E., Jr. and Haltenhoff, C. E., "Mackinac Bridge Pier Construction," ACI JOURNAL, Proceedings V. 53, No. 6, Dec. 1956, pp. 581-596.
17. Kelly, Joe W., and Keats, B. D., "Two Special Methods of Restoring and Strengthening Masonry Structures," ACI JOURNAL, Proceedings V. 42, No. 8, Feb. 1946, pp. 289-304.
18. Davis, Raymond E., "Prepacked Method of Concrete Repair," ACI JOURNAL, Proceedings V. 57, No. 2, Aug. 1960, pp. 155-172.

SHOTCRETE
19. ACI Committee 506, "Recommended Practice for Shotcreting (ACI 506-66)," American Concrete Institute, Detroit, 1966, 26 pp.; also reprinted in the ACI Manual of Concrete Practice.
19a. Reading, T. J. et al, Shotcreting (a symposium), American Concrete Institute, Detroit, 1966, 224 pp.

TREMIE CONCRETE
20. Halloran, P. J., and Talbot, K. H., "The Properties and Behavior Underwater of Plastic Concrete," ACI JOURNAL, Proceedings V. 39, No. 6, June 1943, pp. 461-492.
21. Angas, W. Mack; Shanley, W. M.; and Erickson, J. A., "Concrete Problems in the Construction of Graving Docks by the Tremie Method," ACI JOURNAL, Proceedings V. 40, No. 4, Feb. 1944, pp. 249-280.

16: PRECAST CONCRETE

PRECAST CONCRETE has gained increasingly wide acceptance in recent years. Beams, roof slabs, window sills, joists, wall panels, and other architectural and structural elements are now often precast. Many designs are now based on the use of precast elements, and structures built entirely of precast elements are not uncommon.

Precast elements may be produced in a factory or at the job site. On projects where specifications permit a choice between field casting or ordering factory-cast members, the contractor's decision depends upon such considerations as availability of producers; transportation costs; and number, size, and shape of members to be cast. Factory production (often with pretensioning) of precast elements has become a specialized operation, beyond the scope of a manual on formwork.

The discussion of this chapter is limited to precasting at the job site, where it is the work of the concrete contractor or subcontractor. The scope of such work may range in scale from the casting of a few complex shapes to the exceptionally large job where the contractor in effect sets up his own precasting plant at or near where the members will be used. Tilt-up and lift slab construction, which are specialized forms of site precasting, have been described in Chapter 15.

Advantages of Precasting

Precasting of structural and architectural elements at the job site has several advantages over normal cast-in-place concrete construction:

1. Formwork costs are reduced by precasting. Less scaffolding is required, and fewer forms are needed because reuse is easier to schedule. Forms are frequently simpler; in some cases they are almost entirely eliminated. This method of construction also makes more efficient use of the labor force with crews working at or near ground level.

2. Concrete placement is easier and better controlled. Finishing operations are simplified because workers have easy access to the forms, and improved control of finish quality is possible. For example, thin wall sections can be cast flat at or near ground level making it very easy to control placement, and the exposed face of the concrete can be hand finished. "Water gain" and decreasing strength of concrete with vertical depth of placement are eliminated by casting in a horizontal position.

16-1 Site precasting in segments was elected by contractor who built folded plate roof for ACI headquarters building. This precasting technique permitted placing and finishing at ground level, made numerous reuses of the set of three forms possible. Note three stages of production: one section is completed and coated with curing compound, one section is being concreted, and the third form has steel in place ready for concreting. Finished sections stored on the ground (background).

16-2 Precision casting is necessary when units are joined for decorative exterior treatment. Workman (right) eases large casting into position.

3. Vertical transportation is simpler; only the completed piece and a minimum of scaffolding need be lifted.

4. Reinforcing steel is easier to place accurately and to maintain in position. The steel is placed at ground level rather than being lifted to its position in the structure. Preformed cages of reinforcement can be easily dropped into the forms. Ground level pieces are easier to prestress.

5. Precasting is a time-saver. Precasting operations can go on during construction of the foundation, basement, etc. Cold weather and rain need not interfere with production schedules. Precast structural elements are ready to carry a load as soon as they are set in place and joined, thus eliminating the waiting period required for cast-in-place beams and slabs to gain strength.

With the foregoing advantages in mind, the architect-engineer is wise to give the contractor the option to precast whenever structural and architectural considerations make it feasible.

Formwork Requirements

Apart from requirements that differ because of the different location of forms at the time of casting, general considerations for the design and construction of formwork for precast concrete are the same as for cast-in-place work. However, since the finished units are assembled to form the structure, accurate dimensions are more vital because the pieces must fit properly. These small tolerances require special attention during construction of the forms and the actual casting of the units. As forms are reused, special attention is needed to guard against dimensional changes. A self-checking system should be established where possible if many identical units are to be cast.

16-3 Forms made of concrete used for precasting combination beam and slab deck units for a bridge. To facilitate removal of units, metal sheathing is provided for surfaces that are not horizontal. Ends of the forms are removable to permit forming variations in end details.

Suggested Tolerances

The following tolerances suggested by ACI Committee 347 (in the absence of other controlling specifications) apply to the finished precast product at the

16-4 Close-up view of metal form for casting double-T slab; a form similar to this one is shown ready for casting in Figure 16-5.

16-5 Metal forms ready for casting double-T slab; note positioning of bulkhead to adjust form to desired length for member being cast.

time of placement in the structure. The forms must be constructed to give a casting well within these limits because later shrinkage and warping caused by unequal drying or prestressing may occur.

1. *Over-all dimensions of members* should not vary more than $\pm \frac{1}{8}$ in. per 10 ft of length, with a maximum of $\pm \frac{3}{4}$ in.
2. *Cross-sectional dimensions* should not vary more than the following:
   $\pm \frac{1}{8}$ in. for sections less than 6 in. thick
   $\pm \frac{3}{16}$ in. for sections over 6 in. and less than 18 in. thick
   $\pm \frac{1}{4}$ in. for sections 18 to 36 in. thick
   $\pm \frac{3}{8}$ in. for sections over 36 in. thick
3. *Deviation from the straight line* in long sections should not be more than $\frac{1}{8}$ in. per 10 ft
4. *Deviation from specified camber* should not be more than $\pm \frac{1}{16}$ in. per 10 ft of span, and the difference in camber in adjacent units should not be more than $\frac{1}{4}$ inch in their erected position. This tolerance is especially important in prestressed concrete (see Chapter 17).

Reason and judgment are urged in the application of tolerances; the function of the member should be considered. The foregoing tolerances are intended primarily for structural units which must fit with other materials in the direction in which the dimension is measured. Exposed architectural concrete such as precast panels for walls, columns, and spandrels may require closer tolerances, which should be specified by the architect-engineer.

Materials

Forming material should be rugged, leakproof, rigid, and require little or no maintenance. Maximum reuse with minimum repair is perhaps the most important consideration when selecting materials. If the forms have to be repaired after only a few castings some of the advantages of this method of construction have been lost.

Untreated wood forms for complex shapes are satisfactory for limited reuse, but for large production they are difficult to strip and costly to keep in repair. A plastic coating or a lining material such as plywood or hardboard will improve the stripping of wood forms and lengthen their life. Form grade plywood and plastic overlaid plywood are also suitable as sheathing for these forms.

Metal molds are well suited to this work. They can be fabricated from sheets or die pressed. The stamping method is seldom used unless a great many molds of the same shape and size are to be made. A wide range of metal forms for standard sizes and shapes of structural units is available from manufacturers who specialize in this field. Many of these ready-made forms have provisions for adjustment to varying sizes.

Concrete molds may be cast from a wood, plaster, sand, or concrete master mold. Special care must be taken in finishing the concrete mold so that it will have a surface compatible with the desired finish of the precast units. Concrete molds with metal or wood side forms are well suited for the casting of ribbed slab units.

Plastic and glass-reinforced plastics are also suitable for precast concrete forms and form linings. These

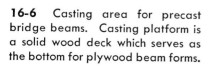

16-6 Casting area for precast bridge beams. Casting platform is a solid wood deck which serves as the bottom for plywood beam forms.

16-7 Elevated form for slab casting. Note vibrator attached to screed.

16-8 Folded plate roof sections cast one on top of the other were separated by layers of polyethylene film. Heavy supporting formwork carried the 44-ton load of the stacked sections.

16-9 Wood beam forms supported on a timber casting platform. Bulkheads adjust for beams of different lengths. Blocks at the end of the forms (foreground) are used to mold shear keys at top surfaces of beams.

materials, like concrete and metal, will give prolonged service with proper care. The method of making plastic molds is discussed in Chapter 4.

Layout of Casting Area

Efficiency in the use of materials and labor will reduce costs in any type of construction. This is especially true in precast work. One of the primary considerations is a well planned casting area at the job site; even for relatively small jobs, an orderly and efficient layout saves time and labor.

The forms should be arranged for assembly line operation. There must be enough space to allow the passage of transit-mix trucks and lifting equipment. Concreting of one set of forms must not hold up the stripping of another set and vice versa. Material storage area must be close, yet not hamper the operation. Storage of completed units must be planned for. Consideration of the layout of the yard area and scheduling of the casting operation will be time well spent.

Casting Bed

Special attention should be given to the casting bed. The type of bed used will depend upon the items to be cast and the type of forms used. For shapes to be cast using the bed as a bottom form, the surface should be level, smooth, hard, and free from cracks, holes, or crevices. A concrete slab can be used effectively—sometimes the completed floor slab of the structure. For some items, the bed is raised to table height for more efficient concrete placing and finishing. In all cases, the bed must be watertight and rigid so that the weight of the concrete will not deform it and passing equipment will not cause movement of the forms. Units such as beams may be cast in individual forms that require no special bed (Figure 16-4). The foundations for casting beds which carry heavy loads such as stacked castings should be designed to prevent differential settlement. Prestressed precast work presents special problems, as noted in Chapter 17.

Form Construction

The forms can be built in various ways depending on the shape of the piece to be cast, the material used, the space available, and the number of reuses required. For instance, panels can be cast individually or one on top of the other. Where the precast

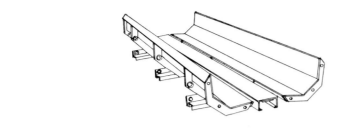

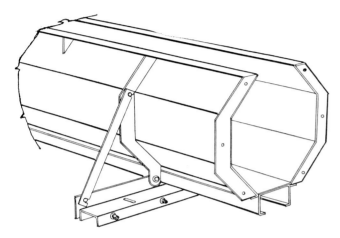

16-10 One of the many prefabricated metal forms for precasting. This one, for piling, has tilting sides (smaller picture) for easy stripping.

units are to be stacked as cast (Figure 16-8), the form must be designed to carry the total load of stacked units, and the subgrade or supporting bed must also be adequate for the total load. (This precaution must be remembered when a completed driveway or floor slab on grade is to be the casting bed.) Beams or other long members with a constant cross section can be cast individually in long forms in which the length of the members is regulated by adjustable diaphragms (Figure 16-5).

Prefabricated forms ready-made for most common shapes or custom-made for special shapes are used in field as well as factory casting. They are usually made so that the form section can be modified by bolting on diaphragms, moving side forms, or blocking. Some (Figure 16-10) have special features that speed stripping.

Since an economical precasting operation frequently depends on early stripping of forms for reuse, provision for adequate curing without the forms should be made. The vacuum and steam curing techniques used in factory precasting may be adaptable to some exceptionally large site precasting operations, but generally more conventional methods must be relied on. Any equipment needed for curing should be arranged so that it will not interfere with

placing and stripping operations. Form dimensions should take into account any shrinkage caused by the curing process.

Some precast elements such as box girders require inside forms. Inside forms must be properly located and anchored to reinforcement and side or deck forms with wire ties to prevent flotation or displacement during the placing of concrete. It is important for these interior forms to remain in the correct position at all times to prevent reduction or change in the critical cross section as the concrete is placed.

Inside forms made from cardboard are often used and left in place to eliminate stripping the interiors of hollow sections. If forms for interior openings are made of wood, they should be equipped with a knock-out or release device to provide for loosening the forms after finishing is completed. A removable or

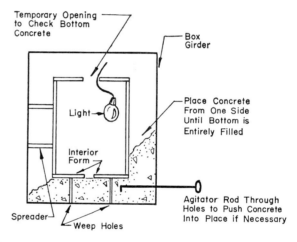

16-11 One preferred method of concreting box girders. Place from one side until concrete completely fills bottom of form and comes out on the other side. It is sometimes possible to place bottom concrete before the inside form is set in place.

adjustable relief section prevents swelling of the forms from cracking the concrete. It is desirable to leave openings in both the top and bottom of interior forms to check placement of concrete in the bottom (Figure 16-11) of the girder. Weep holes should be provided for hollow girders, whether they are formed with stay-in-place cardboard interior units or with removable wood forms.

Stripping

All forms must be designed so that they are easily stripped. Side forms are usually hinged so they can be folded down, or fastened by clamps or pins for easy removal. When the stripping operation is ac-

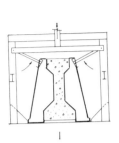 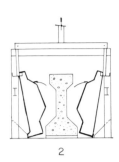 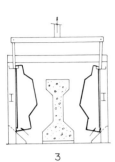

| 1 | 2 | 3 |

16-12 A lifting frame is sometimes used to remove beam or girder side forms when large quantities are being cast. For fewer units the same operation may be performed manually.

complished by lifting the casting out of the form, the design of the form should be such that it cannot become keyed or wedged to the concrete. Since the units are usually stripped as soon as possible, to free the forms for casting another piece, the green concrete may be damaged if the mold hangs up on the casting. Some small draft or "draw" in the forms is required

Cover to Keep Concrete Out of Opening

Air or Water Inlet   Form Sheathing

16-13 Air or water under pressure may be introduced through special form openings to speed stripping.

since friction on a surface exactly parallel to the movement may damage the surface of the casting.

Forms should be well oiled or otherwise treated to facilitate stripping. When precast members are cast one on top of the other, appropriate separating membranes are required. These may be sheet materials or films of plastic, but many favor the liquid type that can be applied with power spray equipment.

16-14 Metal hanger supported on wood blocks carries bottom form for cast-in-place joint between precast bridge deck units.

Any separating membrane or form oil should be of a clear, nonstaining type and should not interfere with the adhesion of paint or plaster if any is to be applied to the concrete surface after the unit is erected. Air or water introduced between casting and mold by a water or air pipe will aid stripping (Figure 16-13).

Molds can be tied down with wire to pull them from the casting as it is lifted. In the event of sticking, wire strength should be such that it will break before the concrete casting is damaged by splitting away from the mold.

Erection and Joints

All precast units must be safely and adequately shored and braced in position immediately after erection.* Shores and braces should be left in place until final connections are made and cured (if cast-in-place concrete forms part of the joint). Shoring and bracing should be installed as detailed in the plan drawings or as approved by the architect-engineer.

If the precast units are only 7 to 10 days old at the time of erection, as is frequently the case, a considerable portion of the drying shrinkage remains to be taken. Connections must be designed to accommodate this shrinkage, or else the designer should specify a longer drying period after curing or that restraining connections be made later, to allow time for shrinkage to take place.

A preferred method of connecting precast units is by doweling bars from the units into a cast-in-place joint. Use of relatively wide joints between adjacent panel units permits screeding out or compensating for minor differences in surface alignment. Forms are sometimes required for joints between adjacent panels or units.

Forms for a comparatively wide longitudinal joint in a bridge deck are shown in Figure 16-14 where the wood blocks with attached hangers support bottom forms for the 9 in. wide joint.

* A detailed discussion of erection practices presented in "Design and Construction Guide for Precast Structural Concrete," by J. L. Peterson, may be of interest. See ACI JOURNAL, *Proceedings* V. 59, No. 9, Sept. 1962, pp. 1179-1204.

Useful information on joint details is available in "Connections in Precast Concrete Construction," by Philip W. Birkeland and Halvard W. Birkeland, ACI JOURNAL, *Proceedings* V. 63, No. 3, Mar. 1966, pp. 345-368. See also "Connection Details for Precast-Prestressed Concrete Buildings," Prestressed Concrete Institute, Chicago, 1963.

17:PRESTRESSED CONCRETE

PRESTRESSED CONCRETE MEMBERS are composed of high strength concrete and steel. Design stresses are closely controlled, but behavior in service depends upon the specified concrete being properly placed in forms of the correct dimensions around accurately positioned prestressing steel or ductwork for steel. Construction requires accuracy and care. Deviation from careful workmanship may result in an unsafe structure and should not be condoned.*

There are two general methods of prestressing concrete: pre-tensioning and post-tensioning. Pre-tensioning is accomplished by stressing steel tendons to a predetermined amount and casting concrete around them while the stress is maintained. After the concrete has hardened, the end anchorages of the tendons are released. The stress in the tendons is transferred by their bond to the concrete, producing the prestressing force. In post-tensioned construction, concrete is cast around unstressed tendons enclosed in flexible metal or plastic ducts or otherwise coated to prevent bond with the concrete. In some cases the tendons are added later in spaces between or within the concrete members. After the concrete has hardened, the unbonded tendons are stressed and anchored to the ends of the member, thus prestressing the concrete. Post-tensioned tendons are then often bonded to the concrete by grouting the space around them.

Post-tensioning is commonly regarded as a job-site technique, and pre-tensioning most commonly is a method of manufacturing prestressed concrete in permanent precasting plants. However, post-tensioned beams are often made in precasting plants, and temporary pre-tensioning plants may be set up at or near the job site by the contractor who has a very large project. In keeping with the scope of this manual, discussion of both methods will be limited to work done at the construction site. Only linear prestressing

—prestressing of elongated structures or elements such as beams, slabs, piles and the like—will be discussed since most circularly prestressed structures are built by a few contractor specialists using patented methods.

Forms for Post-Tensioning

Since post-tensioning is applied without the use of a special tensioning bed or bench, this method of prestressing is applicable to both cast-in-place and precast construction. It is the method most likely to be used by the contractor, who may apply it to both cast-in-place and job-site precast members. Post-tensioning is particularly economical on projects where only a few prestressed members of special cross section are needed. For example, on a bridge job where a dozen beams of non-standard design are needed, it may prove more economical for the general contractor to make them on the job than to order from a precasting plant and transport them to the site. Or, analysis may show that cast-in-place work like that of Figure 17-1 is more efficient than site precasting.

Because of the relatively few form uses, non-adjustable wood forms are frequently used in post-tensioning operations. Well built wood forms properly coated and cared for may often be used 10 times or more before reconditioning is required. If unprotected dry wood is used, its expansion must be controlled to prevent damage to the forms and the concrete casting. Figure 17-3 shows one side of a wood girder form ready for the installation of reinforcing steel and prestressing tendons.

Steel forms are used whenever the number of re-uses is great enough to justify their added cost, and they may be made adjustable. Aside from the considerations of materials related to the anticipated

* This passage is from "Tentative Recommendations for Prestressed Concrete," reported by ACI-ASCE Joint Committee 323, published in the ACI JOURNAL, *Proceedings* V. 54, No. 7, Jan. 1958, pp. 545-578.

17-1 Formwork for cast-in-place monolithic post-tensioned slab and girder bridge was supported by heavy steel trusses. Concrete set was retarded 10 hr to permit complete formwork deflection before hardening of any part of the concrete.

17-2 Forms for bridge in Figure 17-1 being floated by barge into position for reuse on next span.

17-3 Plywood sheathing used on this form for a post-tensioned girder. One side is erected with ties already in place along the center line. Side forms were used for seven beams; only three soffit forms were required.

number of reuses of the forms, the following characteristics * are desirable in forms for post-tensioned concrete:

1. *Precision of the form units and dimensions.* Since the forms for precast work are generally made in panels which can be connected together to form a large member, it is essential that the panels fit together precisely.

2. *Ease of handling.* It is essential that the individual pieces of the form which must be handled are not awkward to handle and remain in a generally upright position. This characteristic makes it easy to adjust the forms in the precise position required during erection, and to lay them on their backs for cleaning.

3. *A design that permits one side to be erected in the final position independently of the opposite side.* This facilitates layout of the member and simplifies forming special blockouts and transverse holes through the member, as well as making it easier to secure web reinforcing and post-tensioning units in the proper location (Figure 17-4).

4. *Form vibration.* The forms should be sufficiently strong to withstand the effects of form vibration, and brackets or rails to facilitate placing form vibrators should be supplied with the forms (precast members

* From a listing by James R. Libby in *Prestressed Concrete*, Ronald Press Co., New York, 1961, pp. 331-332. (Reprinted by permission of the publisher.)

only). Fewer vibrators are needed when the soffit form is mounted on anti-vibration mountings.

5. *Rigid, structural soffit form.* The soffit form must be rigid to resist deflection under load of fresh concrete. In addition, the soffit form should be a structural element to which the side form can be securely attached to prevent the side forms from moving upward or outward during placing of the concrete. This latter requirement is particularly significant in the manufacture of members with large bottom flanges since the uplift may be great under such conditions.

In spite of the need for rigidity during concrete placement, the form assembly must be planned so that it does not restrain elastic shortening, deflection or camber resulting from application of the post-tensioning force.

6. *A minimum of joints.* All joints should be as tight as possible in order to minimize leakage and bleeding.

Some of these properties are applicable only to pre-cast post-tensioned members, and many, of course, are similar to requirements for formwork for conventional concrete.

Erection and Removal

The soffit form and one side form for a post-tensioned member are generally set in place first as shown in Figure 17-3. Then bearing plates, anchorage assemblies, prestressing steel, conduits, tube enclosures, and lifting devices to be set in the concrete must be accurately located with formwork templates and securely attached before setting the other side form. Information on the location of these devices should be given in the contract documents.

Several systems of post-tensioning are available, each with different installation and stressing techniques. Detailed information on a given system can be obtained from the supplier. The engineer who designs post-tensioned concrete should specify any camber required in forms as well as the required strength for various stages of prestressing.

As in all formwork, special attention should be given to provisions for stripping. Side forms are usually designed to be stripped before post-tensioning to prevent wedging of the forms.

Form supports and soffit forms for cast-in-place members cannot be removed until sufficient prestressing has been applied to carry dead load, any formwork supported by the member, and anticipated construction loads. The length of time that the forms are to remain in place should be specified by the architect-engineer along with any required decentering schedule. Each job has its own problems, and any generalization in this regard will tend to restrict the combinations of approaches that are possible with post-tensioned concrete.

17-4   Draped tendons showing a method of suspending from top of the form. After steel is placed, the other side form for this post-tensioned girder will be set in place, tied, and braced.

17-5   Close-up of forms for post-tensioned girder cast on the ground between two double columns, then jacked into position on supporting columns. Small clearance between reinforcement, tendons, and forms points up need for precision of alignment and construction of forms.

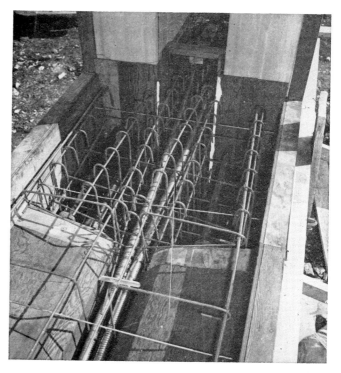

The structural designer should indicate in the contract documents any special construction requirements for prestressed construction. For example, it may be necessary to provide appropriate means of lowering or removing the formwork before full prestress is applied, to prevent damage due to upward deflection of resilient formwork. Care should be exercised with post-tensioned slabs to assure that supporting shores do not fall out due to lifting of slab during tensioning.

For large structures where the dead load of the member remains on the formwork during prestressing, displacement of the dead load toward end supports should be considered in design of the forms and shoring including sills or other foundation support. The concreting sequence for certain structures must also be planned so that concrete in the process of hardening is not subjected to bending stress caused by deflection of the formwork.

Effect of Post-Tensioning on Forms

Although the forms are quite similar to those for conventional reinforced concrete, there are several items that require special consideration. In addition to normal shrinkage, post-tensioned members will shorten when the prestress is applied. Forms can absorb part of the prestress if they resist this shortening; therefore, they must either be stripped before the prestressing operation, provided with removable sections for stress relief, or designed to allow proper movement of the casting.

Another consideration in form design for this method of construction is the deflection of the member during the post-tensioning operation. Long girders, for example, may be lifted off the soffit form at midspan when post-tensioned. The soffit form and its supports must withstand the concentrated loads at the ends of the deflected girder.

When post-tensioned members are cast in place,

17-6 Edge form for prestressed lift slab. Anchorage cones for post-tensioned tendons tied to form. Note also various inserts attached to form.

17-7 Forms for end diaphragm of bridge span shown in Figure 17-1 erected around precast end blocks for the bridge girder. The 7-ft high end block cast in a horizontal position well in advance of bridge concreting had developed minimum strength of 6000 psi at time of post-tensioning.

with relatively long clear formwork spans, the designer must camber the formwork to compensate for its deflection under load, taking into consideration the upward deflection that will occur in the member when the prestress is applied, as well as any net camber desired in the finished structure. Form removal must be planned in relation to stages of the post-tensioning operation. For example, in the case of the bridge forms shown in Figures 17-1 and 17-2:

Supporting steel trusses were built with a 2-in. camber and the forms were set for a 3-in. camber. After the deck was cast, a 1-in. camber remained, showing a 2-in. formwork deflection. Tendons were tensioned in two phases. After the first eight cables were tensioned, the falsework was lowered and moved to its next position for reuse. Prestressing was then completed. Since the bridge was much stiffer than the falsework, upward deflection from the full tensioning amounted to only about half the downward deflection of the trusses under the weight of the concrete. If the formwork had not been lowered, the upward force from the elastic recovery of the truss would have overstressed and possibly cracked the deck.

This example is representative of problems that may occur in such construction. Because of innumerable

17-8 Pre-tensioning bed with steel forms in place for hollow box girders. Form is 257 ft long with internal bulkheads which divide it for casting four 60-ft units.

variables such as site conditions, type of formwork support, and individual features of the structural design, it is difficult to make general recommendations for forming cast-in-place post-tensioned work. Each case must be planned carefully in advance by the structural designer.

Forms for Pre-Tensioning

Pre-tensioning tendons must remain stressed until the concrete-tendon bond and the concrete strength are capable of accepting prestress. Stress in the tendons may be held by anchoring them to individual steel molds designed to withstand the prestressing force as well as loads from the freshly placed concrete. Individual stress resisting molds are highly specialized equipment and will not be discussed here. More commonly the stressed tendons are held by massive end anchorages on devices called pre-tensioning beds or benches which also provide a level surface on which the members may be cast. The pre-tensioning bench is usually a permanent installation, and for this reason pre-tensioning is well suited to the factory production of precast prestressed members. However, for large jobs, site pre-tensioning may prove economical.

There are a number of types of *universal benches,* that is, benches designed to produce a variety of pre-tensioned members rather than a single standardized product. No attempt will be made here to de-

scribe all of these, but Figure 17-9 shows schematically a bench that may be practical for contractors whose projects require large quantities of pre-tensioned members in areas where there are no permanent pre-tensioning plants. This bench (Figure 17-9) is a partially portable abutment and strut type; the major parts of the prestressing equipment and a part of the abutment can be moved; counterweights and strut must be constructed at the job site.

The contractor who decides, for reasons of economy peculiar to his job or special site location away from factory facilities, to undertake the production of pre-tensioned members will be well advised to secure the services of a consultant thoroughly familiar with pre-tensioning techniques. Since the typical contractor will not be concerned with the design and construction of forms for pre-tensioned concrete, the desirable characteristics of pre-tensioned concrete forms will only be summarized briefly:

1. *High resistance to damage due to rough handling.* This requirement normally eliminates the use of wood

17-9a A movable head installation for pre-tensioning bench, bolted to foundation, can be moved from one job site to another. Over-all grid of locations for prestressing wires permits production of a variety of members on a single bench.

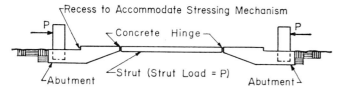

17-9 Elevation (schematic) of abutment and strut pre-tensioning bench. Reproduced from *Prestressed Concrete* by James R. Libby, by permission of the publisher, Ronald Press Co.

forms, which do not perform well under repeated use, particularly if exposed to steam curing. Although concrete forms have been used successfully, the lighter steel forms are generally preferred.

2 Adjustability. The forms, or components of the forms, should be adjustable in such a manner that members of several shapes can be made from the form or form components. (See Figure 17-10.)

3. Precision of form units and dimensions.

4. Ease of handling (see Figure 17-11), and a design that permits one side to be erected in the final position independently of the opposite side.

5. Provision for form vibration.

6. Rigid, structural soffit form.

7. A minimum of joints.

Items 3 through 7 are the same as for post-tensioned concrete forms and are discussed more fully on p. 311.

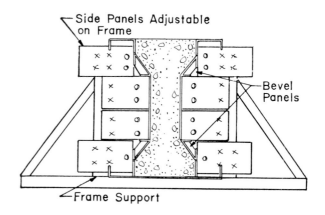

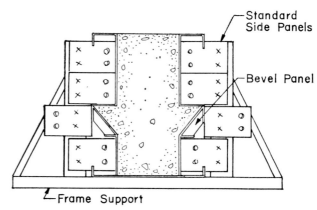

17-10 Adjustable rectangular side panels are moved to different positions on frame support to form members of various cross sections. Special inserts are added to form inclined surfaces.

17-10a Adjustable beam form has removable longitudinal insert; top flange depth can be varied by changing the screeding level.

In addition to the foregoing characteristics,* provisions should be made for the deformation and movement of the casting during the prestressing operation, and for movement of the member without damage during release of the prestressing force. Usually the forms are partially or wholly stripped before tendons are released to stress the member because short-

ening, bending, and shrinkage will occur to some degree. Where the side forms cannot be conveniently removed, they must be designed for additional axial and/or bending loads which may be superimposed on them during the prestressing operation. Adequate horizontal and vertical movement of the casting should be allowed during stress transfer to prevent the casting or forms from being damaged. Provision in the soffit for attaching tie-down devices to hold the prestressed tendons at desired depths is also required for many pre-tensioned members. Committee 347 recommends a safety factor of 2 for expendable strand deflection devices, and 3 for reusable deflection devices.

Safety shields should be provided and end anchorages of prestressing beds to protect workmen and equipment against the possible breakage of prestressing strands, cables, or other assemblies during the prestressing or casting operations.

Prefabricated forms that meet all or many of the above characteristics are available from several manufacturers. Custom-designed forms can be ordered

---

* Based on a list given by James R. Libby in *Prestressed Concrete*, Ronald Press Co., New York, 1961. Reprinted by permission of publisher.

from these same companies or may be made by sheet metal fabricators.

Suggested Tolerances for Precast Prestressed Members

ACI Committee 347 recommends that forms for *prestressed members precast at the job site* be constructed to produce a finished product within the following tolerances:

1. *Overall dimensions of members* should not vary more than ± ⅛ in. per 10 ft, with a maximum deviation of ± ¾ in.
2. *Cross-sectional dimensions* should not vary more than the following:
   ± ⅛ in. for sections less than 6 in. thick
   ± 3/16 in. for sections over 6 in. and less than 18 in.
   ± ¼ in. for sections 18 to 36 in.
   ± ⅜ in. for sections over 36 in.
3. *Deviation from the straight line* in long sections should not be more than ⅛ in. per 10 ft.
4. *Deviation from specified camber* should not be more than ± ⅛ in. per 10 ft of span. The difference in camber between adjacent units should be no more than half the allowance for deviation from specified camber.

In the application of specified tolerances, the function of the member should be considered. In some cases the function and use of a particular member will

17-11 Typical ready-made form for pre-tensioned concrete girder. Quick stripping toggle device on the left side, and a fixed panel is on the right.

not be impaired by some dimensional excess over specified tolerances. In other cases, a combination of errors within specified tolerances may render a member impractical for use. Reason and judgment are urged in the application of tolerances.

Less stringent tolerances may be acceptable for cast-in-place prestressed members because the problem of fitting members together is eliminated. Tolerances for cast-in-place work should be specified by the structural designer, taking into consideration the function of the cast-in-place structure.

ACKNOWLEDGMENT

Cooperation of form builders, contractors, engineers, and architects as well as suppliers of formwork, materials, and accessories has been of incalculable value in preparation of *Formwork for Concrete*. Although it is not possible to list individually everyone who has participated, we do wish to acknowledge illustrations contributed by the following individuals and organizations:

Acme Steel Company—Figures 4-30 and 9-65
Acrow Corporation of America—Figures 4-56, 9-29, 9-94, 9-95, 10-10, and 10-11
Baker-Roos, Incorporated—Figures 4-32, 4-55, and 9-85
Banning, J. P.—Figure 10-6
Barton-Malow Company—Figures 8-3 (in part), 9-38, 9-55, 9-74, 9-77, 9-78, 9-80, 9-96, 9-100, 9-104, 10-1, 10-2, and 10-15
Binghamton Metal Forms Division, Vega Industries—Figure 1-3
Blaw-Knox Company—Figures 4-43, 4-52, 9-121, 13-11, 14-7, 14-10, 14-20, and 17-8
Burke Concrete Accessories, Incorporated—Figure 10-5
Ceco Steel Products Corporation—Figure 9-90
Cement and Concrete Association (London)—Figures 11-1, 11-3, and 11-10
Civil Engineering—Figure 9-112
Concrete Construction—Figures 12-2 and 12-3
Concrete Forms Corporation—Figure 4-31 (in part)
Construction Equipment and Materials—Figure 10-16
Construction Methods and Equipment—Figures 9-66 and 9-109
Constructor—Figures 9-3 and 10-7
Contractors and Engineers—Figures 9-127, 9-134, and 12-18
Corbetta Construction Company—Figures 9-57, 9-60, 9-120, 9-123, 9-124, and 9-125
Council of Scientific and Industrial Research Organizations (Australia)—Figure 4-15
Dextone Company—Figure 11-15
Dixie Form and Steel Company—Figures 4-53, 9-113, 9-116, 9-119, 12-4, 13-8, 13-10, 13-10-A, 13-12, 13-23, 15-23, and 17-11
American Plywood Association—Figures 4-4, 4-5, 9-44, 9-122, 11-4, 11-5, 12-7, 15-21, and 15-24
Dow Chemical Company—Figures 4-12, 4-21, 9-9, 15-33, and 15-34
Dravo Corporation—Figures 2-5, 2-8, 3-2, 3-4, 3-5, 9-106, 9-107, 9-108, 9-111, 9-114, 9-115, 9-118, 13-14, 13-22, and 15-20
Economy Forms Corporation—Figures 4-34-C, 9-30, and 10-14
Elgood Concrete Services—Figure 4-44
Ellis Manufacturing Company, Incorporated—Figure 4-54
Engineered Concrete Forms Corporation—Figures 4-13, 4-14, and 11-2
Feld, Jacob—Figures 2-3 and 2-4
Gateway Erectors, Incorporated—Figures 4-38 and 9-88
Giffels and Rossetti—Figures 9-5, 9-99, 10-8, and 10-13
Granco Steel Products Company—Figures 4-48 and 9-129
Hausman Steel Company—Figure 4-47
Heede, B. M., Incorporated—Figures 15-6 and 15-10
Hico Corporation of America, Aluminum Division—Figure 4-63
Hurd, M. K.—9-1, 9-11
Hydroelectric Power Commission of Ontario—Figures 2-6, 9-32, 9-42, 9-48, 13-1, 13-2, 13-13, 13-15, 13-16, 13-17, 13-20, 13-21, 14-5, 14-8, and 14-19
Irvington Form and Tank Corporation—Figures 16-4 and 16-5

Jayhawk Fiber Form Company—Figure 4-41
Johnson, Drake and Piper—Figure 14-11
Jones and Laughlin Steel Company—Figure 9-93
Kirkland Industries, Incorporated—Figure 15-26
Korab, Baltazar—Figures 9-54, 12-1, and 12-15
Kreier, George, Jr.—Figure 9-53
Mabie Bell Company—Figure 11-16
Mayo Tunnel and Mine Equipment Company—Figure 14-13
Molded Fiber Glass Company—Figures 4-42 and 10-12
Nasser, Andrew—Figures 12-14 and 15-32
National Garages, Incorporated—Figures 4-1, 5-1, 9-41, and 9-101
National Gypsum Company—Figure 10-17
New England Construction—Figures 17-1 and 17-2
No-Joint Concrete Pipe Co.—Figure 15-18b
Owens Corning Fiberglas Corporation—Figure 4-19
Patent Scaffolding Company, Incorporated—Figures 2-2, 4-60, 4-61, 9-117, 9-138, and 15-22
Portland Cement Association—Figures 1-4, 4-16, 4-17, 9-23, 9-24, 9-27, 9-39, 9-43, 9-45, 9-47, 11-7, 11-14, 11-17, 11-20, 11-21, 11-22, 11-23, 11-24, 11-25, 11-26, 11-27, 11-28, 12-8, 16-2, 16-3, 16-6, 16-9, and 16-14
Proctor, Joseph R.—Figures 3-8, 3-9, 3-10, and 9-1
Puget Sound Bridge and Drydock Company—Figure 9-133
Rex-Spanall, Incorporated—Figures 4-57 and 4-62
Reese, R. C.—Figures 9-8 and 9-26
Richmond Screw Anchor Company—Figures 4-31 (in part), 9-28, 9-92, 9-132, and 14-6
Roads and Streets—Figure 9-131
Schupak and Zollman—Figures 17-1, 17-2, and 17-7
Siesel Construction Company—Figure 8-3 (in part)
Signode Steel Strapping Company—Figure 9-62
Simplex Forms System, Incorporated—Figures 3-6 and 4-34-B
Sonoco Products Company—Figures 4-40, 4-45, 9-64, 9-83, and 10-3
Stairbuilders, Incorporated—Figure 4-51
Stelmo Ltd.—Figures 17-9a and 17-10a
Superior Concrete Accessories, Incorporated—Figure 9-126
Superior Scaffold Co., Bliss and Laughlin Industries—Figure 14-16
Symons Manufacturing Company—Figures 1-2, 3-3 (right), 4-34-A, 9-33, 9-37, and 9-52
Tectum Corporation—Figure 4-20
Timber Structures, Incorporated—Figures 9-135 and 9-139
Trans World Airlines—Figure 12-19
Tubular Structures, Incorporated—Figures 3-1, 4-59, and 9-97
Turner Construction Company—Figures 9-25, 9-36, 12-12, and 12-13
U. S. Bureau of Reclamation—Figures 15-17, 15-18, and 15-18a
United States Plywood Corporation—Figures 4-6 and 11-8
Universal Form Clamp Company—Figures 4-36 and 4-37
Universal Manufacturing Corporation—Figure 6-8
Wide World Photos—Figure 2-1
Williams Form Engineering Company—Figures 6-5 and 9-31
Wire Reinforcement Institute, Incorporated—Figures 5-2 and 9-16

Continued on p. 322.

APPENDIX

GLOSSARY

ANCHOR—form anchors are devices used to secure formwork to previously placed concrete of adequate strength; normally embedded in concrete during placement. There are two basic parts: the embedded anchoring device and the external fastener which is removed after use.

ARRIS—sharp edge or protruding corner formed by the meeting of two surfaces, whether plane or curved, applied especially to edges in moldings and to edges separating flutings

BACK FORMS—see *top forms*

BACK STAY—see *brace*

BAND IRON—thin metal strap used as form ties, hangers, etc.

BATTEN (BATTEN STRIP)—a narrow strip of wood placed over the vertical joint of sheathing or paneling, or used to hold several boards together; see also *cleat*

BATTER—inclination from the vertical

BATTER BOARDS—pairs of horizontal boards nailed to wood stakes adjoining an excavation, used as a guide to elevations and to outline the building

BEAM BOTTOM—soffit or bottom form for a beam

BEAM HANGER—a wire, strap, or other hardware device that supports formwork from structural members

BEAM POCKET—opening left in a vertical member in which a beam is to rest; also an opening in the column or girder form where forms for intersecting beam will frame in

BEAM SADDLE—see *beam hanger*

BEAM SIDE—side (vertical) panels or parts of a beam form

BENT—two-dimensional frame which is self-supporting within these dimensions. It has at least two legs and is usually placed at right angles to the length of the structure which it carries.

BLOCK—a solid piece of wood or other material used to fill spaces between formwork members

BOX OUT—to form an opening or pocket in concrete by a box-like form

BRACE—any structural member used to support another, always designed for compression loads and sometimes for tension under special load conditions

BRACKET—an overhanging member that projects from a wall (or other body) to support weight beyond the wall line

BRICK SEAT—ledge on wall or footing to support a course of masonry

BUCK—framing around an opening in a wall. A door buck encloses the opening in which a door is placed.

BUG HOLE—void on the surface of formed concrete caused by an adhering air or water bubble not displaced during consolidation

BULKHEAD—a partition in the forms blocking fresh concrete from a section of the forms or closing the end of a form, such as at a construction joint

CAMBER—a slight (usually) upward curvature of a truss, beam, or form to improve appearance or to compensate for anticipated deflection

CANT STRIP—see *chamfer strip*

CATHEAD—a notched wedge placed between two formwork members meeting at an oblique angle

CATWALK—a narrow elevated walkway

CENTER MATCHED—tongue-and-groove lumber with the tongue and groove at the center of the piece rather than offset as in standard matched

CENTERING—specialized falsework or formwork used in the construction of arches, shells, space structures, or any continuous structure where the entire falsework is lowered as a unit; also, in a general sense, supports for all forms and green concrete

CHAMFER—refers to a beveled corner, which is formed in concrete work by placing a three-cornered piece of wood (cant strip or skew back) in the form corner

CHAMFER STRIP—triangular or curved insert placed in inside corner of form to produce rounded or beveled corner; also called *fillet, cant strip, skew back*

CLAMP—see *tie*

CLEANOUT—an opening in the forms for removal of refuse; closed before the concrete is placed

CLEAT—small board used to connect formwork members or used as a brace

CLIMBING FORM—a form which is raised vertically for succeeding lifts of concrete in a given structure, usually supported on anchor bolts or rods embedded in the top of the previous lift. The form is moved only after an entire lift is placed and (partially) hardened; this should not be confused with a *slip form* which moves during placement of the concrete.

COATING—material applied by brushing, dipping, mopping, spraying, etc., to preserve the form material and to facilitate stripping. (Some coatings are so effective as to approximate the *form liner* in function.)

COLUMN CLAMP—any of various types of tying or fastening units used to hold column form sides together

COLUMN SIDE—one of the vertical panel components of a column form

CONTROL JOINT—formed, saw-cut, or tooled groove in concrete structure to regulate the location of shrinkage cracks

CONSTRUCTION JOINT—the surface where two successive placements of concrete meet; frequently with a keyway or reinforcement across the joint

CRUSH PLATE—an expendable strip of wood attached to the edge of a form or intersection of fitted forms, to protect the form from damage during prying, pulling, or other stripping operations. The term is also used to designate a *wrecking strip*.

DEADMAN—an anchor for a guy line, usually a beam, block, or other heavy item buried in the ground, to which the line is attached

DECENTER—to lower or remove centering or shoring

DECK—the form upon which concrete for a slab is placed, also the floor or roof slab itself

DECKING—sheathing material for a deck or slab form

DOME—the square prefabricated pan form used in two-way (waffle) concrete joist floor construction

DOUGHNUT (DONUT)—a large washer of any shape to increase bearing area of bolts and ties; also a round concrete spacer with hole in the center to hold vertical bars the desired distance from form

DRIP—a cutout in the underside of a projecting piece of wood, stone, or concrete to prevent water from working its way back to the wall

FALSEWORK—the temporary structure erected to support work in the process of construction. In discussion of concrete construction, the term may be used much the same as *formwork* to include shores or vertical posts, forms for beams or slabs, and lateral bracing.

FASCIA—a flat member or band at the surface of a building or the edge beam on a bridge; exposed eave of a building, etc.

FLASHING—sheet metal used to waterproof roof valley joints or roof-parapet joints

FILLER—material used to fill an opening in forms

FILLET—see *chamfer strip*

FISHTAIL—wedge-shaped piece of wood used as part of the soffit form between tapered end pans in concrete joist construction

FORM—term used interchangeably with *formwork* (see *formwork*), but also used in a more restricted sense to indicate the supporting members in direct contact with the freshly placed concrete

FORM TIE, FORM ANCHOR, FORM LINING, ETC.—see *tie, anchor, lining,* etc.

FORMWORK—the total system of support for freshly placed concrete including the mold or sheathing which contacts the concrete as well as all supporting members, hardware, and necessary bracing. *Falsework* is also used with essentially the same meaning.

GANGED FORMS—prefabricated panels joined to make a much larger unit (up to 30x50 ft) for convenience in erecting, stripping, and reusing; usually braced with wales, strongbacks, or special lifting hardware

GIRT—see *ledger;* also a horizontal brace

HAIRPIN—the wedge used to tighten some types of form ties; also a hairpin-shaped anchor set in place while concrete is plastic

HANGER—a device used for suspending one object from another such as the hardware attached to a building frame to support forms (see also *beam hanger*)

HAUNCH—a bracket built on a wall or column, used to support a load outside the wall or column; also that portion of a girder or arch which is thickened near the supports

HEAD—the top of anything, e.g., the top of a window is a window head; also difference in elevation between two points in a body of fluid, as a measure of the pressure of the fluid

HONEYCOMB—voids left at the formed concrete surface revealing coarse aggregates

HORIZONTAL SHORING—see *shoring, horizontal*

INVERT—lowest visible surface; the floor of a drain, sewer, tunnel, culvert, or channel

JACK—mechanical device used for adjusting elevation of forms or form supports. *Jack* is sometimes used in place of *jack shore.*

JACK SHORE—telescoping, or otherwise adjustable, single-post metal shore

JOIST—a horizontal structural member supporting deck form sheathing; usually rests on stringers or ledgers

JUMBO—traveling support for forms, commonly used in tunnel work

KERF—to make a cut or notch, as a beam, transversely along the underside in order to curve it; also a cut or notch in a member such as a rustication strip to avoid damage from swelling of the wood and permit easier removal

KEY—see *keyway*

KEYED—fastened or fixed in position in a notch or other recess, as forms becomed *keyed* into the concrete they support

KEYWAY—a recess or groove in one lift or placement of concrete which is filled with concrete of the next lift, giving shear strength to the joint; also called a *key*

KICK STRIP—see *kicker*

KICKER—a piece of wood (block or board) attached to a formwork member to take the thrust of another member; sometimes called a cleat

KNEE BRACE—brace between horizontal and vertical members in a building frame or formwork to make the structure more stable; in formwork it acts as a haunch.

L-HEAD—the top of a shore formed with a braced horizontal member projecting on one side forming an inverted L-shaped assembly

L-SHORE—a shore with an L-head

LACING—horizontal brace between shoring members

LAGGING—see *sheathing; lagging* usually designates heavier sheathing used as in underground work to withstand earth pressure, etc.

LEDGER—horizontal formwork member, especially one attached to a beam side, that supports the joist; also may be called girt, sill, purlin, stringer

LINING—any sheet, plate, or layer of material attached directly to the inside face of the forms to improve or alter the surface texture and quality of the finished concrete

MOLD—the cavity or surface against which fresh concrete is cast to give it a desired shape; sometimes used interchangeably with *form.* As used in this book the term designates only the more intricately detailed or finely patterned forms that produce decorative concrete; may be made of wood, plaster, plastic, etc.

MUDSILL—a plank, frame, or small footing on the ground used as a base for a shore or post in formwork

MUD SLAB—a 2- to 6-in. layer of concrete below structural concrete floor or footing over soft, wet soil

NAILER—strip of wood or other fitting attached to or set in concrete, or attached to steel, to facilitate making nailed connections

NEAT LINE—a line defining the proposed or specified limits of an excavation or structure

NOSING—a projection, such as the projection of the tread of a stair over the riser

GLOSSARY

OFFSET—a displacement or abrupt change in line, or the distance between two parallel lines

OVERBREAK—excavation beyond the neat line of a tunnel or other structure

PAN—prefabricated form unit, most commonly of steel, used in concrete joist floor construction

PANEL—a section of form sheathing, constructed from boards, plywood, metal sheets, etc., that can be erected and stripped as a unit

PARAPET—that part of a wall that extends above the roof level

PENCIL ROD—plain metal rod of about ¼-in. diameter

PERMANENT FORM—any form that remains in place after the concrete has developed its design strength. The form may or may not become an integral part of the structure.

PILASTER—column built within a wall, usually projecting beyond the wall

PILASTER FACE—the form for the front surface of a pilaster parallel to the wall

PILASTER SIDE—the form for the side surface of a pilaster perpendicular to the wall

PLATE—flat horizontal member at the top and/or bottom of studs or posts; a mudsill if on the ground

PLUMB—vertical or the act of making vertical

POST—vertical formwork member used as a brace; also shore, prop, jack

PURLIN—see *ledger*

RAKER—sloping brace for a shore head

RANGER—see *wale*

REGLET—a groove in a wall to receive flashing

RESHORING—temporary vertical support for forms or completed structure, placed after original shoring support has been removed

REVEAL—the side of an opening in a wall for a window or door

RIBBON—a narrow strip of wood or other material

RIBS—parallel structural members backing sheathing

RISER—the vertical part of the step in a flight of stairs

RUSTICATION—a groove in a concrete or masonry surface

RUSTICATION STRIP—a strip of wood or other material attached to a form surface to produce a groove or rustication in the concrete

SCAB—a small piece of wood fastened to two formwork members to secure a butt joint

SCAFFOLDING—an elevated platform for supporting workmen, tools, materials. Adjustable metal scaffolding is frequently adapted for shoring in concrete work.

SCREED—two or more strips set at desired elevation so that concrete may be leveled by drawing a straightedge over their surface; also the straightedge

SCREEDING—the operation of pulling a straightedge over the surface of screeds thus leveling concrete

SHEATHING—the material forming the contact face of forms; also called lagging, sheeting

SHEETING—see *sheathing*

SHORE—temporary vertical support for formwork and fresh concrete or for recently built structures which have not developed full design strength. Also called prop, tom, post, strut. See also *L-head, T-head shore.*

SHORING—system of vertical or inclined supports for forms; may be wood or metal posts, scaffold-type frames, or various patented members

SHORING, HORIZONTAL—adjustable span members, either beam or truss type, used to support forms over relatively long spans, thereby reducing the number of vertical supports

SHUTTERING—British term used to indicate formwork in general, or more particularly form panels in direct contact with the concrete

SILL—the lowest part of an opening in a wall such as a door sill or window sill; also horizontal bearing member (see *ledger*)

SKEW BACK—see *chamfer strip*

SLICK LINE—a one-piece arch pipe through which concrete is pumped into tunnel arch forms

SLIDING FORM—see *slip form*

SLIP FORM—also referred to as *sliding form*. A form which moves, usually continuously, *during placing* of the concrete. Movement may be either horizontal or vertical. Slip forming is like an extrusion process with the forms acting as moving dies to shape the concrete.

SNAP TIE—patented concrete wall form tie, the end of which can be twisted or snapped off after the forms have been removed

SOFFIT—the underside of a subordinate part or member of a building, such as a beam, stairway, arch, etc.

SOLDIERS—vertical wales used for strengthening or alignment

SPANDREL—that part of a wall between the head of a window and the sill of the window above it. (An *upturned spandrel* continues above the roof or floor line.)

SPANDREL BEAM—a beam in the wall of a building

SPREADER—a brace, usually of wood, inserted in forms to keep the faces a proper distance apart until the concrete is placed

STANDARD MATCHED—tongue-and-groove lumber with the tongue and groove offset rather than centered as in center matched lumber

STIFFBACK—see *strongback*

STRINGER—horizontal structural member usually (in slab forming) supporting joists and resting on vertical supports

STRIKE—to lower or remove formwork or centering

STRIP—to remove formwork; also a long thin piece of wood, metal, or other material

STRONGBACK—a frame attached to the back of a form to stiffen or reinforce it; additional vertical wales placed outside horizontal wales for added strength or to improve alignment; also called stiffback

STUD—vertical supporting member to which sheathing is attached

SWAY BRACE—a diagonal brace used to resist wind or other lateral forces; see also *X-brace*

T-HEAD—top of a shore formed with a braced horizontal member projecting on two sides forming a T-shaped assembly

T-SHORE—shore with a T-head

TELLTALE—any device designed to indicate movement of formwork

TIE—a concrete form tie is a tensile unit adapted to holding concrete forms secure against the lateral pressure of unhardened concrete, with or without provision for spacing the forms a definite distance apart, and with or without provision for removal of metal to a specified distance back from the finished concrete surface.

TEMPLATE—thin plate or board frame used as a guide in positioning or spacing form parts, reinforcement, anchors, etc.

TOENAIL—to drive a nail at an angle

TOM—see *shore*

TOP FORMS—forms required on the upper or outer surface of a sloping slab, thin shell, etc.

WALE—long horizontal member (usually double) used to hold studs in position; also called waler, ranger

WATERSTOP—thin sheet of rubber, plastic, or other material inserted in a construction joint to obstruct the seeping of water through the joint

WEDGE—a piece of wood or metal tapering to a thin edge, used to adjust elevation, tighten formwork, etc.

WRECK—see *strip*

WRECKING STRIP—small piece or panel fitted into a formwork assembly in such a way that it can be easily removed ahead of main panels or forms, making it easier to strip those major form components

X-BRACE—paired set of (tension) sway braces

YOKE—a tie or clamping device around column forms or over the top of wall or footing forms to keep them from spreading because of the lateral pressure of concrete; also part of structural assembly for slip forming which keeps the forms from spreading and transfers form load to the jacks

ADDITIONAL ACKNOWLEDGMENTS FOR ILLUSTRATIONS

Continued from p. 318.

PPG Industries, Fiber Glass Division—Figure 11-6
Wacker Corporation—Figure 5-5

Recommended Practice for
Concrete Formwork (ACI 347-68)*

Reported by ACI Committee 347

WILLIAM R. WAUGH
Chairman

MARTIN W. BOLL
GEORGE F. BOWDEN
PETER D. COURTOIS
WILLIAM R. DAVIS, JR.

JACOB FELD
DAVID E. FLEMING
VICTOR F. LEABU
JOSEPH R. PROCTOR, JR.
PAUL F. RICE

HARRY L. SCOGGIN
P. R. STRATTON
WILLIAM H. WOLF
GEORGE J. ZIVERTS

Presents brief introductory statement on the need for formwork standards based on the fact that 35 to 60 percent of the total cost of the concrete work in a project in the United States is in the formwork. A section is given on engineer-architect specifications noting the kind and amount of specification the engineer or architect should provide the contractor. Since the committee concludes that formwork design and engineering, as well as construction, must be the responsibility of the contractor, the recommendations contained in the report are directed to that group. However, an understanding of these recommendations by engineers and architects will aid these groups in their specification functions.

The report is divided into five chapters: 1. Design, 2. Construction, 3. Materials for Formwork, 4. Forms for Special Structures, and 5. Formwork for Special Methods of Construction.

Keywords: aggregates; aluminum; anchors; architectural concrete; bridges (structures); buildings; canal linings; civil defense; coatings; composite construction; concretes; construction; construction materials; culverts; drawings; falsework; fiberboard; folded plates; form removal; formwork (construction); glass fibers; hangers; inserts; insulating board; loads (forces); lumber; mass concrete; paperboard; parting agents; plastics; plywood; precast concrete; preplaced aggregate concrete; pressure; prestressed concrete; reinforced concrete; roofs; safety; safety factor; shells (structural forms); shelters; shoring; slipforms; specifications; steels; structural design; supports; ties; tolerances; tunnels (transportation); underground construction; underwater construction; viaducts.

*Adopted as a standard of the American Concrete Institute at its 64th Annual Convention, Los Angeles, Calif., Mar. 6, 1968, as reported by Committee 347; ratified by letter ballot June 15, 1968. ACI 347-68 supersedes ACI 347-63 published August 1962. Copyright © 1967 by the American Concrete Institute.

CONTENTS

NEED FOR STANDARD

Since the cost of the formwork for a concrete structure may be 35 to 60 percent of the total cost of concrete work in the project, its design and construction demand sound judgment and planning to achieve adequate forms that are both economical and safe. The engineer or architect responsible for the successful completion of any concrete structure usually will include in his specifications provisons for stripping time, reshoring of concrete in place, inspection, and approval of formwork procedure which could affect the strength and appearance of the completed structure.

Neat, well-built, heavily braced forms may still fail due to inadequately tied corners or insufficient provision against uplift. Form failures have occurred when shoring has been improperly spliced, inadequately cross braced, or was otherwise inadequate to resist all possible stresses. Shores supported on previously completed floors usually can be assumed to have equal unit bearing. However, shores supporting forms for the first level above ground often are supported on "mudsills" and may not have uniform bearing. This condition may occur when mudsills rest on soft ground, on backfill recently placed and perhaps softened by surface water, or on frozen ground which may thaw out in numerous ways.

Unequal settlement of mudsills seriously changes shore reactions, and may cause serious overloading of shores which do not settle as much as others.

Proper engineering design of formwork often saves contractors more than the saving from the use of poorly designed forms. Formwork is generally more economically constructed on the ground and under the contractor's yard inspection than in the air under field conditions. A carpenter not experienced in formwork may find it difficult to conceive of forms as pressure vessels which need to be adequately tied together, braced, and anchored to resist uplift and to be capable of resisting forces in several directions. Proper detailed instruction is therefore necessary.

If working drawings are made for formwork, the necessary detailed study of the contract drawings may uncover omissions and dimensional errors. Field work is expedited and the structural engineer can see how his design is being interpreted by the contractor. Other benefits may be shorter job duration, avoidance of delays in field operations, more efficient re-use of forms, and better utilization of material and men. There should be "notes to the erector" on such drawings to eliminate need for referring to specific field customs.

Attention is called to the legal implications of specifying in any set of contract documents, including the plans and specifications, both the method by which work is to be performed and the results to be accomplished.

Some contractors feel that "end result" or performance specifications are sufficient for a contract involving concrete construction. This simple approach may be best when bidding is restricted to highly experienced contractors and for special projects which require competitive formwork solutions. In such special instances specifications must allow freedom to improvise and to apply a choice of equipment and materials.

For the majority of formwork jobs, however, certain rules and regulations are needed such as minimum design loadings, safe unit design stresses, and tolerances. Such general minimum requirements should be clearly stated to assure the owner and his engineer or architect that formwork will provide adequate support during the placement of concrete and until it has gained sufficient strength to permit removal of forms. Adequately written and enforced specifications and contractor observance of them should lessen the need for legislation or for provisions in building construction safety codes to govern design of formwork, its erection, and its removal.

It is the conclusion of the committee that the layout and design of the formwork, as well as its construction, must be the responsibility of the contractor. This approach gives him the necessary freedom to use his skill and knowledge to produce an economical finished structure.

ENGINEER-ARCHITECT* SPECIFICATIONS

GENERAL

For any concrete structure, the specification for formwork, if written by the engineer or architect, will have much to do with the over-all economy and quality of finished work. *Such a specification must be individualized for the particular job, must indicate to the contractor exactly what will be expected from him, and must be so written as to result in economy and safety.*

A well-written formwork specification tends to equalize bids for the work, provided each bidder knows that full compliance will be required of the successful one. Unnecessarily exacting requirements may make bidders question the specification as a whole and may render it virtually impossible for them to understand exactly what is expected. They may be overly cautious and overbid or not cautious enough and underbid.

A well-prepared formwork specification is of value not only to the owner and the contractor, but also to the field representative of the engineer-architect and to the subcontractors for other trades.

This proposed standard presents recommended practices for formwork and suggests criteria for assuring proper performance.

Some requirements are so written as to allow the contractor discretion where quality of finished concrete work would not be impaired by the use of alternate materials and methods. The engineer-architect may exclude, call special attention to, or strengthen, or make more lenient any requirement to best fit the needs of his particular project.

Consideration of the applicable general requirements suggested herein will not, however, be sufficient to make the specification complete. To it there must be added requirements for actual materials, finishes, and other items peculiar to and necessary for the individual structure. Much helpful and detailed information is given in *Formwork for Concrete,* ACI Special Publication No. 4.

Formwork materials and accessories

If the particular design or desired finish requires special attention, the engineer or architect may specify in his contract plans and specifications, formwork materials and such other features he feels necessary to attain his objectives. If he does not call for specific materials or accessories the contractor will be free to use materials of his choice as long as they meet design requirements.

When structural design is predicated on the use of a commercially available form unit in standard sizes such as one-way and two-way joist systems, plans and specifications should be drawn up realistically to make use of available shapes and sizes. Some latitude must be permitted for connections of form units to other framing or centering to reflect the tolerances and normal installation practices of the form type contemplated.

Finish of exposed concrete

Finish requirements for concrete surfaces should be described in *measurable* terms as precisely as practicable.

Design, inspection, and approval of formwork

The following items should be clarified in the engineer-architect specifications and drawings:

(a) By whom formwork will be designed.

---

*The terms *engineer-architect* and *architect-engineer* are used interchangeably throughout the report to designate: the architect, the engineer, the architectural firm, the engineering firm, the architectural and engineering firm, or other agency issuing project drawings and specifications and/or administering the work under project specifications and drawings.

(b) By whom, when, and for what features formwork will be inspected.

(c) What approvals will be required for formwork drawings; for the forms before concreting and during concreting; and for form removal and reshoring; and who will give such approvals.

ACHIEVING ECONOMY IN FORMWORK

The suggestions which follow are typical of those received from contractors as to how the engineer-architect can plan his work to reduce formwork costs.

The engineer-architect should consider not only the type of formwork necessary for the quality of construction desired, but also how economy of construction can be achieved. Since the cost of formwork is a significant part of the over-all concrete cost in a structure, a saving in this item alone can result in substantial reductions in the total cost. The following points should be considered and made use of insofar as possible:

1. If column and floor form dimensions can be the same size from the lowest deck to roof, beam forms as well as column forms can be re-used from floor to floor without alteration.

2. If spacing of columns and story heights are made uniform throughout the building insofar as possible, formwork will be simplified and its prefabrication more economically feasible.

3. If interior columns are the same width as or smaller than the girders they support, the column form becomes a simple rectangular or square box without cutouts, and the slab form does not have to be cut out at each corner of the column.

4. If all beams are made one depth (beams framing into beams as well as beams framing into columns), the supporting structure for the beam forms can be carried on a level platform supported on shores.

If the engineer-architect makes widths and depths the same for beams and joists, and considers the available sizes of dressed lumber, plywood, and the various ready-made formwork components when determining the sizes of structural members, savings in labor time in cutting, measuring, and leveling the work will be achieved.

5. Where commercially available forming systems such as one-way or two-way joist systems are used, design should be based on the use of one standard size range wherever possible.

6. Structural design should be prepared simultaneously with the architectural design, so that dimensions can be better coordinated. Room sizes can often be varied a few inches to accommodate the structural design.

7. The engineer-architect should be responsible for coordinating the requirements of other trades with their effect on the concrete formwork. Architectural features, depressions, and openings for mechanical or electrical work should be coordinated with the structural system for maximum economy to the over-all job, and variations in the structural system caused by such items should be shown on the structural drawings. Wherever possible depressions in the tops of slabs should be made without a corresponding break in elevations of the soffits of slabs, beams, or joists.

CHAPTER 1—DESIGN

1.1—General

1.1.1—*Planning*—Any form regardless of size should be planned in every particular prior to its construction. The thoroughness of planning required will depend on the size, complexity, and importance (considering re-uses) of the form. In any case, all of the applicable details listed in Section 1.4.2.3. should be included in the planning.

1.1.2—*Design and erection*—Formwork should be designed, erected, supported, braced, and maintained so that it will safely support all vertical and lateral loads that might be applied until such loads can be supported by the concrete structure. Vertical and lateral loads must be carried to the ground by the formwork system and by the in-place construction that has attained adequate strength for that purpose. Formwork should also be constructed so that concrete slabs, walls, and other members will be of correct size

in dimensions, shape, alignment, elevation, and position.

1.2—Loads

1.2.1—*Vertical loads*—Vertical loads consist of a dead load plus an allowance for live load. The weight of formwork together with the weight of freshly placed concrete is dead load. The live load consists of the weight of workmen, equipment, runways, and impact, and should be taken as not less than 50 psf of horizontal projection.

1.2.2—*Maximum lateral pressure of concrete*—Forms, ties, and bracing should be designed for a lateral pressure of fresh concrete as follows:

(a) For ordinary work with normal internal vibration, in columns,

$$p = 150 + \frac{9000R}{T} \quad \text{(maximum 3000 psf or 150}h, \text{ whichever is least)}$$

in walls, with rate of placement not exceeding 7 ft per hr

$$p = 150 + \frac{9000R}{T} \text{ (maximum 2000 psf or } 150h, \text{ whichever is least)}$$

and in walls, with rate of placement greater than 7 ft per hr

$$p = 150 + \frac{43,400}{T} + \frac{2800R}{T}$$

(maximum 2000 psf or $150h$, whichever is least)

where

p = lateral pressure, psf
R = rate of placement, ft per hr
T = temperature of concrete in the forms, deg F
h = height of fresh concrete above point considered, ft

(b) For concretes weighing other than 150 lb per cu ft; containing pozzolanic additions or cements other than Type I; having slumps greater than 4 in.; or consolidated by revibration or external vibration of forms, appropriate adjustment for increased lateral pressure should be made.*

(c) Where retarding admixtures are employed under hot weather conditions an effective value of temperature less than that of the concrete in the forms should be used in the above formula.

If retarding admixtures are used in cold weather the lateral pressure should be assumed as that exerted by a fluid with weight equal to that of the concrete mix.

1.2.3—Lateral loads—Braces and shores should be designed to resist all foreseeable lateral loads such as wind, cable tensions, inclined supports, dumping of concrete, and starting and stopping of equipment. In no case should the assumed value of lateral load due to wind, dumping of concrete, and equipment acting in any direction at each floor line be less than 100 lb per lineal ft of floor edge or 2 percent of total dead load of the floor, whichever is greater. Wall forms should be designed for a minimum wind load of 10 psf, and bracing for wall forms should be designed for a lateral load at least 100 lb per lineal ft of wall, applied at the top. Walls of unusual height or exposure should be given special consideration.

Wind loads on enclosures or other wind breaks attached to the forms should be considered, as well as those applied to the forms themselves.

1.2.4—Special loads—The formwork should be designed for any special conditions of construction likely to occur, such as unsymmetrical placement of concrete, impact of machine-delivered concrete, uplift, and concentrated loads of reinforcement and storage of construction materials. Form designers should be alert to provide for special loading conditions such as walls constructed over spans of slabs or beams which exert a different loading pattern before hardening of concrete than that for which the supporting structure is designed.

Imposition of any construction loads on the partially completed structure should not be allowed except with the approval of the engineer-architect. See Section 2.8 for special conditions pertaining to multistory work.

1.3—Design considerations

1.3.1—Unit stresses—Unit stresses for use in the design of formwork, exclusive of accessories, are given in the applicable codes or specifications listed in Chapter 3, Materials for Formwork. When fabricated formwork, shoring, or scaffolding units are used, manufacturers' recommendations for allowable loads may be followed if supported by test reports or successful experience records; for materials which will experience substantial re-use, reduced values may be required.

For forms of a temporary nature with limited re-use, allowable stresses should be those specified in the appropriate design codes or specifications for temporary structures or for temporary loads on permanent structures.

Where there will be a considerable number of form re-uses or where forms to be used many times are fabricated from material such as steel, aluminum, or magnesium, it is recommended that the formwork be designed as a permanent structure carrying permanent loads.

In the design of formwork accessories such as form ties, form anchors, and form hangers the following minimum safety factors based on the ultimate strength of the accessory are recommended except that yield point must not be exceeded (see Table 1.3.1).

1.3.2—Analysis—A design analysis should be made for all formwork. Safety against buckling of any member should be investigated in all cases.

1.3.3—Shores—Shores are defined as vertical or inclined falsework support. When patented shores, patented splices in shoring, or patented methods of shoring are used, manufacturers' recommendations as to load-carrying capacities may be followed but only if supported by test reports by a qualified and recognized testing laboratory; the designer must carefully follow the manufacturer's recommendations as to bracing and working loads for unsupported shore lengths.

---

*Detailed information on the effect of these special conditions is available in the report "Pressures on Formwork," ACI Committee 622, ACI JOURNAL, *Proceedings* V. 55, No. 2, Aug. 1958, pp. 173-190, and in the discussion and committee's closure for this report, ACI JOURNAL, *Proceedings* V. 55, No. 12, June 1959, pp. 1335-1348.

Field constructed lap splices must not be used more often than for alternate shores under slabs, or for every third shore under beams, and shores should not be spliced more than once unless diagonal and two-way lateral bracing is provided at every splice point. Such spliced shores should be distributed as uniformly as possible throughout the work. To avoid buckling, splices should not be located near the midheight of the shores nor midway between points of lateral support.

Splices must be designed against buckling and bending as for any other structural compression member. The minimum length of splice material for timber shores should be 2 ft. Shores made of round timbers should have three splice pieces at each splice, and those of square timbers should have four splice pieces at each splice.

Splicing material should be not less than 2-in. (nominal) lumber or ⅝-in. plywood and no less than the width of the material being spliced.

1.3.4—*Diagonal bracing*—The formwork system must be designed to transfer all lateral loads to the ground or to completed construction in such a manner as to insure safety at all times. Diagonal bracing must be provided in vertical and horizontal planes where required to provide stiffness and to prevent buckling of individual members. Where the only bracing requirement is to prevent buckling of individual members, lateral bracing should be provided in whatever directions are necessary to produce the correct l/r ratio for the load supported. Such a laterally braced system should be anchored in such a manner as to insure stability of the total system.

1.3.5—*Foundations for formwork*—Proper foundations on ground, mudsills, spread footings, or pile footings must be provided. If soil under mudsills is or may become incapable of supporting superimposed loads without appreciable settlement, it should be stabilized with cement or lean concrete, or by other adequate methods. Mudsills should never be placed on frozen ground.

1.3.6—*Settlement*—Falsework should be so constructed that vertical adjustments can be made to compensate for take-up and settlements, and so that settlements under full load will be a minimum consistent with economy. Where wood timbers are used, the number of horizontal joints and particularly the number of joints where end grain bears on side grain should be kept at a practical minimum. The unit compressive stress across the grain should not exceed that recommended in Section 3.2. The probable settlement of the falsework, exclusive of foundations, may be approximated as follows: (1) by computing the columnar shortening c in in., by the formula $c = 12SL/E$, in which S is the unit compressive stress per sq in., L is the length of column in ft, and E is the modulus of elasticity; (2) by allowing an assumed value of settlement for each horizontal joint for "taking up" and an additional value at each joint where end grain bears on side grain for "biting" of the end grain into the side grain. For normal carpentry work each assumed value may be taken as 1/16 in.; where particular care is taken, each may be taken as 1/32 in. The total estimated settlement should approximate the sum of (1) and (2).

Wedges may be used at the top or bottom of shores, but not at both ends, to facilitate vertical adjustment, to correct uneven settlements, or to facilitate dismantling of the formwork.

Screw jacks for pipe shores or scaffold-type shoring may be used at both top and bottom so

TABLE 1.3.1—DESIGN CAPACITIES OF FORMWORK ACCESSORIES*

Accessory	Safety factor	Type of construction
Form tie	1.5	Light formwork; or ordinary single lifts at grade and 16 ft or less above grade
	2.0	Heavy formwork; all formwork more than 16 ft above grade or unusually hazardous
Form anchor	1.5	Light form panel anchorage only; no hazard to life involved in failure
	2.0	Heavy forms—failure would endanger life—supporting form weight and concrete pressures only
	3.0	Falsework supporting weight of forms, concrete, working loads, and impact
Form hangers	1.5	Light formwork. Design load including total weight of forms and concrete, with 50 psf minimum live load is less than 150 psf
	2.0	Heavy formwork; form plus concrete weight 100 psf or more; unusually hazardous work
Lifting inserts	2.0	Tilt-up panels
	3.0	Precast panels
Expendable strand deflection devices†	2.0	Pretensioned concrete members
Re-usable strand deflection devices†	3.0	Pretensioned concrete members

*Design capacities guaranteed by manufacturers may be used in lieu of tests for ultimate strength.
†These safety factors also apply to pieces of prestressing strand which are used as part of the deflection device.

long as they are secured by the shore or scaffold leg against loosening or falling out. A minimum of 8 in. embedment in the pipe leg or sleeve should be required, or manufacturers' recommendations based on test results may be followed.

1.4—Drawings

1.4.1—*Discussion*—Should the engineer-architect wish formwork drawings submitted for his approval, he should so state in the specifications. In any case, the contract plans and specifications should include and cover all points necessary to the contractor for his formwork design and in the preparation of his formwork drawings, such as:

(a) Number, location, and details of all construction joints, contraction joints, and expansion joints that will be required or permitted for the particular job or parts of it.

(b) Sequence of placement, if critical, should be indicated.

(c) Locations of and details for architectural concrete. When architectural details are to be cast into structural concrete, they should be so indicated or referenced on the structural drawings as they may play a key role in the structural design of the form.

(d) Intermediate supports under permanent forms (such as metal deck used for forms, and permanent forms of other materials), supports required by the structural engineer's design for composite action, and any other special supports.

(e) The location and order of erection and removal of shores for composite construction.

(f) Special provisions essential for formwork of the special structures and special construction methods such as shells and folded plates.

The basic geometry of such structures, as well as the required camber, must be given in sufficient detail to permit the contractor to construct the form. Camber should be stipulated for measurement after initial set and before decentering.

(g) Special requirements for post-tensioned concrete members. The effect of load transfer during tensioning of post-tensioned members may be critical, and the contractor should be advised of any special provisions that must be made in the formwork for this condition.

(h) If camber is desired for slab soffits or structural members to compensate for elastic deflection and/or deflection due to creep of the concrete, the contract drawings must so indicate and state the amounts. Measurement of camber attained should be made *after* initial set and *before* decentering.

The question of allowable camber for precast members, especially prestressed precast members, is an important one. The engineer-architect must specify the amount of camber for any member and the difference in camber between adjacent members which will be acceptable in finished work. Any devices (such as clips to be embedded in edges of members and to be field welded together) desired to reduce or control differential camber should be indicated on the design drawings.

(i) Where chamfers are required on beam soffits or column corners, they should be specified.

(j) Plans and specifications of the engineer-architect must cover in detail any requirements for inserts, waterstops, built-in frames for openings, holes through concrete, and similar requirements were work of other trades will be attached to or supported by formwork.

(k) Where architectural features, embedded items or the work of other trades will change the location of structural members such as joists in one-way or two-way joist systems, such changes or conditions should be indicated on the structural drawings.

(l) The ACI Building Code requirement that structural drawings shall show the live load used in the design should always be followed.

1.4.2—*Recommendations*

1.4.2.1—General—Before constructing forms, the contractor, if required, will submit detailed drawings of proposed formwork for approval by the engineer. If such drawings are not in conformity with contract documents as determined by the engineer-architect, the contractor will make such changes as may be required prior to start of work.

1.4.2.2—Design assumptions—All major design values and loading conditions should be shown on formwork drawings. These include assumed values of live load, rate of placement, temperature of concrete, height of drop, weight of moving equipment which may be operated on formwork, foundation pressures, design stresses, camber diagrams, and other pertinent information, if applicable.

1.4.2.3—Items included—In addition to specifying types of materials, sizes, lengths, and connection details, formwork drawings should provide for applicable details such as:

1. Sequence of removal of forms and shores (when this is critical for placing loads on new concrete)

2. Design allowance for construction loads on new slabs should be shown when such

allowance will affect the development of shoring and/or reshoring schemes (see Section 2.8)

3. Anchors, form ties, shores, and braces

4. Field adjustment of the form during placing of concrete

5. Waterstops, keyways, and inserts

6. Working scaffolds and runways

7. Weepholes or vibrator holes where required

8. Screeds and grade strips

9. Crush plates or wrecking plates where stripping may damage concrete

10. Removal of spreaders or temporary blocking

11. Cleanout holes

12. Construction joints, control joints, and expansion joints to conform to design drawings [ACI Building Code (318-63) Section 704]

13 Sequence of concrete placements and minimum elapsed time between adjacent placements

14. Chamfer strips or grade strips for exposed corners and construction joints

15. Camber [see Section 2.6.1 (d)]

16. Mudsills or other foundation provisions for falsework

17. Special provisions such as protection from ice and debris at stream crossings, fire, and safety

18. Formwork coatings

19. Notes to formwork erector for conduits and pipes embedded in concrete according to ACI Building Code (318-63), Section 703

1.5—Approval by the engineer or architect

Although the safety of formwork is the responsibility of the contractor, the engineer or architect may, under certain circumstances, wish to review or approve the formwork design. If so, the engineer-architect will include provisions for such review or approval in his specifications.

Approval might be required for unusually complicated structures, for structures whose designs were predicated on a particular method of construction, for structures in which the forms impart a desired architectural finish, for certain post-tensioned structures, for folded plates, for thin shells, and for long-span roof structures.

The engineer-architect's approval of the drawings as submitted or as corrected in no way relievese the contractor of his responsibility for adequately constructing and maintaining the forms so that they will function properly. Such approval indicates that the assumed design loadings in combination with design stresses shown; proposed construction methods, rates, equipment, and sequence; the proposed form materials; and the overall scheme of formwork are deemed capable of producing the desired concrete in an approved manner.

CHAPTER 2—CONSTRUCTION

2.1—Safety precautions

In addition to the very real moral and legal responsibility to maintain safe conditions for workmen and the public, safe construction is in the final analysis more economical, irrespective of any short-term cost savings from cutting corners on safety provisions. Attention to safety is particularly significant in form construction as these structures support the concrete during its plastic state and as it is developing its strength, at which time it is unstable. Following the design criteria contained in this standard is essential to assuring safe performance of the forms. All structural members and their connections should be carefully planned so that a sound determination of loads thereon may be accurately made and allowable stresses calculated.

In addition to the adequacy of design of forms, multistory work requires further consideration of the shoring of newly completed slabs below which support the weight of fresh concrete as well as other construction loads (see Section 2.8).

Many form failures can be attributed to some human error or omission rather than basic in-

adequacy in design. Careful direction and inspection of formwork erection by qualified members of the contractor's organization can prevent many accidents.

Some common construction deficiencies leading to form failures are:

(a) Inadequate diagonal bracing of shores

(b) Inadequate lateral and diagonal bracing and poor splicing of "double-tier shores" or "multiple-story shores"

(c) Failure to control rate of placing concrete vertically without regard to drop in temperature

(d) Failure to regulate properly the rate and sequence of placing concrete horizontally to avoid unbalanced loadings on the formwork

(e) Unstable soil under mudsills

(f) Failure to inspect formwork during and after concrete placement to detect abnormal deflections or other signs of imminent failure which could be corrected

(g) Insufficient nailing

(h) Failure to provide for lateral pressures on formwork

(i) Shoring not plumb and thus inducing lateral loading as well as reducing vertical load capacity

(j) Locking devices on metal shoring not locked, inoperative, or missing

(k) Vibration from adjacent moving loads or load carriers

(l) Inadequately tightened or secured form ties or wedges

(m) Form damage in excavation by reason of embankment failure

(n) Loosening of reshores under floors below

(o) Premature removal of supports, especially under cantilevered sections

Some common design deficiencies leading to failure are:

(a) Lack of proper field inspection by qualified persons to see that form design has been properly interpreted by form builders

(b) Lack of allowance in design for such special loadings as wind, power buggies, placing equipment

(c) Inadequate reshoring

(d) Improperly stressed reshoring

(e) Improper positioning of shores from floor to floor which creates reverse bending in slabs which are not designed for such stresses

(f) Inadequate provisions to prevent rotation of beam forms where slabs frame into them on only one side

(g) Inadequate anchorage against uplift due to battered form faces

(h) Insufficient allowance for eccentric loading due to placement sequences

Specific safety provisions which should be considered are:

(a) Erection of safety signs and barricades to keep unauthorized personnel clear of areas in which erection or stripping is under way

(b) Providing form watchers during concrete placement wherever there is danger to life or property from forms failing or distorting during placement

(c) Furnishing extra shores or other material and equipment that might be needed in an emergency by form watchers

(d) Incorporation of scaffolds, guard rails, etc., into form design where feasible

2.2—General practices

Construction procedures must be planned in advance to insure the unqualified safety of personnel engaged in formwork and concrete placement and the integrity of the finished structure.

Forms should be inspected and checked before the reinforcing steel is placed to insure that the concrete will have the dimensions and be in the location shown on the drawings.

Forms should be sufficiently tight to prevent loss of mortar from the concrete.

Forms should be thoroughly cleaned of all dirt, mortar, and foreign matter and coated with a release agent before each use. Where the bottom of the form is inaccessible from within, access panels should be provided to permit thorough removal of extraneous material before placing concrete. If surface appearance is important, forms should not be re-used after damage from previous use has reached the stage of possible impairment to concrete surfaces.

Bulkheads for control joints or construction joints should preferably be made by splitting along the lines of reinforcement passing through the bulkhead so that each portion may be positioned and removed separately without applying undue pressure on the reinforcing rods which could cause spalling or cracking of the concrete. When required on the engineer-architect's drawings, beveled inserts at control joints must be left undisturbed when forms are stripped, and removed only after the concrete has been sufficiently cured and dried out. Wood strips inserted for architectural treatment should be kerfed to permit swelling without pressure on the concrete.

Sloped surfaces in excess of 35 deg from the horizontal (1.5 horizontal to 1 vertical) should be provided with a top form to hold the shape of the concrete during placement, unless there is a continuous mat of bars or mesh sufficient to keep concrete in place.

Loading of new slabs should be avoided in the first few days after placement. Loads such as aggregate, timber, boards, reinforcing steel, or support devices, must not be thrown on new construction, nor be allowed to pile up in quantity.

Building materials must not be thrown or piled on the formwork in such manner as to damage or overload it.

2.3—Workmanship

To insure good workmanship the following points warrant careful attention:

(a) Proper splices of studs, wales, or shores

(b) Staggering of joints or splices in sheathing, plywood panels, and bracing

(c) Proper seating of shores

(d) Proper number and location of form ties or clamps

(e) Proper tightening of form ties or clamps

(f) Adequate bearing under mudsills; *in no case should mudsills or spread footings rest on frozen ground*

(g) Connection of shores to joists, stringers, or wales must be adequate to resist uplifts or torsion at joints

(h) Form coatings must be applied before placing of reinforcing steel and must not be used in such quantities as to run onto bars or concrete construction joints

(i) Details of control joints, construction joints, and expansion joints.

2.4—Suggested tolerances

Tolerance is a specified permissible variation from lines, grades, or dimensions given in contract drawings.

Tolerances should be specified by the engineer-architect so that the contractor will know precisely what is required and can design and maintain his forms accordingly. The suggested tolerances herein are similar to those specified on important work or major structures by many public agencies and private firms.* In specifying these tolerances or some modifications of them, it should be remembered that specifying tolerances more exacting than needed may increase construction costs.

Contractors are expected, and should be required, to establish and maintain in an undisturbed condition until final completion and acceptance of a project, control points and bench marks adequate for their own use and for reference to establish tolerances. (This requirement may become even more important for the contractor's protection when tolerances are not specified or shown.) The engineer-architect should specify tolerances or require performance within generally accepted limits. Where a project involves particular features sensitive to the cumulative effect of generally accepted tolerances on individual portions, the engineer-architect should anticipate and provide for this effect by setting a cumulative tolerance. Where a particular situation involves several types of generally accepted tolerances, i.e., on form, on location of reinforcement, on fabrication of reinforcement, etc., which become mutually incompatible, the engineer-architect should anticipate the difficulty and specify special tolerances or indicate which controls.

The engineer-architect should be responsible for coordinating the tolerances for concrete work with the requirements of other trades whose work adjoins the concrete construction.

This section suggests tolerances that are consistent with modern construction practice, considering the effect that permissible deviations will have on the structural action or operational function of the structure. Surface defects such as "blow holes" and "honeycomb" concrete surfaces are defined as "finishes" and are to be distinguished from tolerances described herein.

Where tolerances are not stated in the specifications or drawings for any individual structure or feature thereof, permissible deviations from established lines, grades, and dimensions are suggested below. The contractor is expected to set and maintain concrete forms *so as to insure completed work within the tolerance limits.*

No tolerances specified for horizontal or vertical building lines or footings should be construed to permit encroachment beyond the legal boundaries.

2.4.1—*Tolerances for reinforced concrete buildings*†

1. *Variation from the plumb*
   (a) In the lines and surfaces of columns, piers, walls, and in arrises ¼ in. per 10 ft, but not more than 1 in.
   (b) For exposed corner columns control-joint grooves, and other conspicuous lines

   In any bay or 20 ft maximum .... ¼ in.
   In 40 ft or more .... ½ in.

2. *Variation from the level or from the grades indicated on the drawings*
   (a) In slab soffits,‡ ceilings, beam soffits, and in arrises

   In 10 ft .... ¼ in.
   In any bay or 20 ft maximum .... ⅜ in.
   In 40 ft or more .... ¾ in.

   (b) For exposed lintels, sills, parapets, horizontal grooves, and other conspicuous lines

   In any bay or 20 ft maximum .... ¼ in.
   In 40 ft or more .... ½ in.

3. *Variation of the linear building lines from established position in plan and related position of columns, wall and partitions*

   In any bay or 20 ft maximum .... ½ in.
   In 40 ft or more .... 1 in.

4. *Variation in the sizes and locations of sleeves, floor openings, and wall openings* .... ¼ in.

5. *Variation in cross-sectional dimensions of columns and beams and in the thickness of slabs and walls*

   Minus .... ¼ in.
   Plus .... ½ in.

---

*Designers employed by federal agencies required to follow Building Research Advisory Board recommendations are advised that the BRAB tolerances on formwork are often much more restrictive than those suggested herein.
†Variations from plumb and linear building lines on upper stories of high rise structures (above 100 ft high) are special cases which may require special tolerances.
‡Variations in slab soffits are to be measured *before* removal of supporting shores; the contractor is not responsible for variations due to deflection, except when the latter are corroboratory evidence of inferior concrete quality or curing, in which case only the *net* variation due to deflection can be considered.

6. *Footings*

  (a) Variation in dimensions in plan

    Minus .... ½ in.

    Plus ....2 in.*

  (b) Misplacement or eccentricity

    2 percent of the footing width in the direction of misplacement but not more than ....2 in.*

  (c) Reduction in thickness

    Minus ....5 percent

              of specified thickness

7. *Variation in steps*

  (a) In a flight of stairs

    Rise .... ⅛ in.

    Tread .... ¼ in.

  (b) In consecutive steps

    Rise .... 1/16 in.

    Tread .... ⅛ in.

2.4.2.—*Tolerances for special structures*

1. *Concrete canal lining*

  (a) Departure from established alignment

    2 in. on tangents

    4 in. on curves

  (b) Departure from established profile grade ....1 in.

  (c) Reduction in thickness of lining

    10 percent of specified thickness: *provided*, that average thickness is maintained as determined by daily batch volumes

  (d) Variation from specified width of section at any height

    ¼ of 1 percent plus 1 in.

  (e) Variation from established height of lining

    ½ of 1 percent plus 1 in.

  (f) Variations in surfaces

    Invert ¼ in. in 10 ft

    Side slopes ½ in. in 10 ft

2. *Monolithic siphons and culverts*

  (a) Departure from established alignment ....1 in.

  (b) Departure from established profile grade ....1 in.

  (c) Variation in thickness

    At any point: minus 2½ percent or ¼ in., whichever is greater

    At any point: plus 5 percent or ½ in., whichever is greater

  (d) Variation from inside dimensions

    ½ of 1 percent

  (e) Variations in surfaces:

    Inverts ¼ in. in 10 ft

    Side slopes ½ in. in 10 ft

3. *Bridges, checks, overchutes, drops, turnouts, inlets, chutes, and similar structures*

  (a) Departure from established alignment ....1 in.

  (b) Departure from established grades 1 in.

  (c) Variation from the plumb or the specified batter in the lines and surfaces of columns, piers, walls, and in arrises

    Exposed, in 10 ft .... ½ in.

    Backfilled, in 10 ft .... 1 in.

  (d) Variation from the level or from the grades indicated on the drawings in slabs, beams, horizontal grooves, and railing offsets

    Exposed, in 10 ft .... ½ in.

    Backfilled, in 10 ft .... 1 in.

  (e) Variation in cross-sectional dimensions of columns, piers, slabs, walls, beams, and similar parts

    Minus .... ¼ in.

    Plus .... ½ in.

  (f) Variation in thickness of bridge slabs

    Minus .... ⅛ in.

    Plus .... ¼ in.

  (g) Footings: Same as for footings for buildings

  (h) Variation in the sizes and locations of slab and wall openings .... ½ in.

  (i) Sills and side walls for radial gates and similar watertight joints. Variation from the plumb or level

    Not greater than ⅛ in. in 10 ft.

4. *Tolerances in mass concrete structures*

  (a) All structures

    1. Variation of the constructed linear outline from established position in plan

      In 20 ft .... ½ in.

      In 40 ft .... ¾ in.

    2. Variations of dimensions to individual structure features from established positions

      In 80 ft or more .... 1¼ in.

      In buried construction

      .... Twice the above amounts

    3. Variation from the plumb, from the specified batter, or from the curved surfaces of all structures, including the lines and surfaces of columns, walls, piers, buttresses, arch sections, vertical joint grooves, and visible arrises

      In 10 ft .... ½ in.

      In 20 ft .... ¾ in.

      In 40 ft or more .... 1¼ in.

      In buried construction

      .... Twice the above amounts

    4. Variation from the level or from the grades indicated on the drawings in slabs, beams, soffits, horizontal joint grooves, and visible arrises

      In 10 ft .... ¼ in.

      In 30 ft or more .... ½ in.

      In buried construction

      .... Twice the above amounts

*Applies to concrete only, not to reinforcing bars or dowels.

5. Variation in cross-sectional dimensions of columns, beams, buttresses, piers, and similar members

Minus .... ¼ in.
Plus .... ½ in.

6. Variation in the thickness of slabs, walls, arch sections, and similar members

Minus .... ¼ in.
Plus .... ½ in.

(b) Footings for columns, piers, walls, buttresses, and similar members

1. Variation of dimensions in plan

Minus .... ½ in.
Plus .... 2 in.*

2. Misplacement or eccentricity

2 percent of footing width in the direction of misplacement but not more than .... 2 in.*

3. Reduction in thickness

5 percent of specified thickness

(c) Sills and side walls for radial gates and similar watertight joints

1. Variation from plumb and level

Not greater than ⅛ in. in 10 ft

5. *Tolerances for concrete tunnel lining and cast-in-place conduits*

(a) Departure from established alignment or from established grade

Free-flow tunnels and conduits 1 in.
High velocity tunnels and conduits .... ½ in.
Railroad tunnels .... 1 in.

(b) Variation in thickness at any point

Tunnel lining .... minus 0
Conduits ....minus 2½ percent or ¼ in, whichever is greater
Conduits ....plus 5 percent or ½ in., whichever is greater

(c) Variations from inside dimensions

½ of 1 percent

2.5—Falsework and centering

2.5.1—*Falsework*—Falsework is the temporary structure erected to support work in the process of construction. It is composed of shores, formwork for the beams and/or slabs, and lateral bracing. The falsework must be supported on satisfactory foundations such as spread footings, mudsills, or piling as discussed in Section 1.3

Shoring resting on intermediate slabs or other construction already in place need not be located directly above shores or reshores below unless thickness of slab and the location of its reinforcement are inadequate to take the reversal of stresses. Where the latter conditions are questionable the shoring location should be approved by the engineer.

All members must be straight and true without twists or bends. Special attention should be given to beam and slab, or one-way and two-way joist construction to prevent local overloading when a heavily loaded shore rests on the thin slab.

Shores in multitier assemblies supporting forms for high stories must be set plumb and the separate parts of each shore located in a straight line over each other, with two-way lateral bracing at each splice in the shore unless the entire assembly is designed as a structural framework or truss. Particular care must also be taken to transfer the lateral loads to the ground or to completed construction of adequate strength (see Section 1.3.4).

Where a slab load is supported on one side of the beam only, edge beam forms should be carefully planned to prevent tipping of the beam due to unequal loading.

Shores or vertical posts must be erected so that they cannot tilt, and must have firm bearing. Inclined shores must be braced securely against slipping or sliding. The bearing ends of shores should be cut square and have a tight fit at splices. Splices must be secure against bending and buckling as provided in Section 1.3.3. Connections of shore heads to other framing should be adequate to prevent the shores from falling out when reversed bending causes upward deflection of the forms.

2.5.2—*Centering*—Centering is the highly specialized falsework used in the construction of arches, shells, space structures, or any continuous structure where the entire falsework is lowered (struck or decentered) as a unit to avoid introducing injurious stress in any part of the structure. The lowering of the centering is generally accomplished by the use of sand boxes, jacks, or wedges beneath the supporting members. For the special problems associated with the construction of centering for folded plates, thin shells, and long span roof structures, see Section 4.5.

2.5.3—*Shoring for composite action between previously erected steel or concrete framing and cast-in-place concrete* (see Section 4.4).

2.6—Adjustment of formwork

2.6.1—*Before concreting*

(a) Tell-tale devices should be installed on supported forms and elsewhere as required to facilitate detection and measurement of formwork movements during concreting.

(b) Wedges used for final alignment befor concrete placement should be secured in position after the final check.

*Applies to concrete dimensions only, not to positioning of vertical reinforcing bars or dowels.

(c) Formwork must be so anchored to the shores below that upward or lateral movement of any part of the formwork system will be prevented during concrete placement.

(d) To insure that lines and grades of finished concrete work will be within the required tolerances, the forms must be constructed to the elevation shown on the formwork drawings. If camber is required in the hardened concrete to resist deflection, it should be so stipulated on the structural drawings. Additional elevation or camber should be provided to allow for closure of form joints, settlements of mudsills, shrinkage of lumber, dead load deflections and elastic shortening of form members.

Where camber requirements may become cumulative, such as in cases where beams frame into other beams or girders at right angles, and at midspan of the latter, the engineer-architect should specify exactly the manner in which this condition is to be handled.

(e) Positive means of adjustment (wedges or jacks) should be provided to permit realignment or readjustment of shores if excessive settlement occurs.

(f) Runways for moving equipment should be provided with struts or legs as required and should be supported directly on the formwork or structural member. They should not bear on or be supported by the reinforcing steel unless special bar supports are provided. The formwork must be suitable for the support of such runways without significant deflections, vibrations or lateral movements.

2.6.2—During and after concreting—During and after concreting, but before initial set of the concrete, the elevations, camber, and plumbness of formwork systems should be checked, using telltale devices. *Appropriate adjustments should be promptly made where necessary.* If, during construction, any weakness develops and the falsework shows any undue settlement or distortion, the work should be stopped, the affected construction removed if permanently damaged, and the falsework strengthened.

Formwork must be continuously watched so that any corrective measures found necessary may be promptly taken. Form watchers must always work under safe conditions and should establish in advance a method of communication with placing crews in case of emergency.

2.7—Removal of forms and supports

2.7.1 —Discussion—Although the contractor is responsible for design, construction, and safety of formwork, it is recommended that time of removal of forms or shores be specified by the engineer-architect because of the possibility of in-

jury to concrete which may not have attained full strength or may be overloaded.

2.7.2—Recommendations

2.7.2.1—Suitable tests of job-cured specimens or of concrete in place, methods of evaluating such test results, and minimum standards of strength required should be completely prescribed. The engineer-architect also should specify who will make the cylinders and who will make the tests.

Results of such tests, as well as records of weather conditions and other pertinent information, should be recorded and used by the engineer-architect in deciding when to remove forms.

Determination of the time of form removal should be based on the resulting effect on the concrete.* When forms are stripped there must be no excessive deflection or distortion and no evidence of damage to the concrete, due either to removal of support or to the stripping operation. Where stripping time is less than specified curing time, measures should be taken to provide adequate curing and thermal protection of the stripped concrete. Supporting forms and shores must not be removed from beams, floors, and walls until these structural units are strong enough to carry their own weight and any approved superimposed load, which at no time should exceed the live load for which the floor was designed unless provision has been made by the engineer-architect to allow for anticipated temporary construction loads such as in multistory work (see Section 2.8). In general, removal of forms and supports for suspended structures can be safely accomplished when the ratio of cylinder test compressive strength to design strength is equal to or greater than the ratio of total dead load and construction loads to total design load with a minimum of 50 percent of design compressive strength being required. As a general rule, the forms for columns and piers may be removed before those for beams and slabs. Forms and scaffolding should be designed so they can be easily and safely removed without impact or shock. When quick re-use of forms is desired, formwork should be designed so that it can be removed without removal of sufficient original shores for support until such time as beam or cylinder tests indicate it is safe to remove all shores.

2.7.2.2—When field operations are controlled by the engineer-architect's specifications, the removal of forms, supports, and housing, and

---

*Helpful information on strength development of concrete under varying conditions of temperature and with various admixtures may be found in ACI 306 "Recommended Practice for Cold Weather Concreting" and ACI 605 "Recommended Practice for Hot Weather Concreting."

the discontinuance of heating and curing must follow the requirements of the contract documents. When test beams or cylinders are used to determine stripping times they should be cured under conditions which are not more favorable than the most unfavorable conditions for the portions of the concrete which the test specimens represent. The curing record (time, method, temperature) of the concrete and the weather conditions during the curing of concrete, as well as the test cylinder records, will serve as the basis on which the engineer-architect will determine his approval of form stripping.

2.7.2.3—When field operations are not controlled by the specifications, under ordinary conditions form and supports should remain in place for not less than the following periods of time. These periods represent cumulative number of days or fractions thereof, not necessarily consecutive, during which the temperature of the air surrounding the concrete is above 50 F. If high-early-strength concrete is used, these periods may be reduced as approved by the engineer-architect. Conversely, if low temperature concrete or retarding agents are used, then these periods may be increased at the discretion of the engineer-architect.

Walls*	12-24 hr
Columns*	12-24 hr
Sides of beams and girders*	12-24 hr

Pan joist forms†	
30 in. wide or less	3 days
Over 30 in. wide	4 days

Where design live load is:

	<DL	>DL
Arch centers	14 days	7 days
Joist, beam, or girder soffits‡		
Under 10 ft clear span between supports	7 days§	4 days
10 to 20 ft clear span between supports	14 days§	7 days
Over 20 ft clear span between supports	21 days§	14 days
Floor slabs‡		
Under 10 ft clear span between supports	4 days§	3 days
10 to 20 ft clear span between supports	7 days§	4 days
Over 20 ft clear span between supports	10 days§	7 days

Post-tensioned slab system** .... As soon as full post-tensioning has been applied

Supported slab systems** .... Removal times are contingent on reshores, where required, being placed as soon as practicable after stripping operations are complete but not later than the end of the working day in which stripping occurs. Where reshores are required to implement early stripping while minimizing sag or creep (rather than for distribution of superimposed construction loads as covered in Section 2.8), capacity and spacing of such reshores should be specified by the engineer-architect.

2.8—Shoring and reshoring for multistory structures

2.8.1—*Discussion*—Multistory work presents special conditions particularly in relation to removal of forms and shores. Re-use of form material and shores is an obvious economy. Furthermore, the speed of construction customary in this type of work provides the additional advantage of permitting other trades to follow concreting operations from floor to floor as closely as possible. However, the shoring which supports green concrete is necessarily supported by lower floors which may not be designed for these loads. For this reason shoring must be provided for a sufficient number of floors to develop the necessary capacity to support the imposed loads without excessive stress or deflection.

For purposes of this discussion the following definitions apply:

Shores—Vertical support members designed to carry the weight of formwork, concrete, and construction loads above.

Reshores — Shores placed firmly under a stripped concrete slab or structural member where the original formwork has been removed thus requiring the new slab or structural member to support its own weight and construction loads posted to it. Such reshores are provided to transfer additional construction loads to other slabs or members and/or to impede deflection due to creep which might otherwise occur.

Permanent shores—The original shores supporting forms which are designed for removal without disturbing the original shores or permitting the new concrete to support its own weight and additional construction loads above. Two basic systems are used:

(1) *The king stringer system.* This employs ledgers on the sides of the stringer which may released permitting the removal of the joist and form contact surfaces between the stringers.

---

*Where such forms also support formwork for slab or beam soffits, the removal times of the latter should govern.
†Of the type which can be removed without disturbing forming or shoring.
‡Distances between supports refer to structural supports and not to temporary formwork or shores.
§Where forms may be removed without disturbing shores, use half of values shown but not less than 3 days.
**See Section 2.8 for special conditions affecting number of floors to remain shored or reshored.

(2) *The king shore system.* In this system, the stringer is attached to the side of the shores so that the stringer may be removed, permitting the release of the joists and sections of the form contact surfaces. The shores and a trapped strip of contact surface are all that remain in place.

It should be kept in mind that in multistory work with permanent shores, once the lower floor of shores has been removed, the slabs are all in elastic support and therefore capable of deflection in direct proportion to their individual share of loads above as well as to their developed moduli of elasticity. For this reason, if reshores are properly installed, they serve the same function and act in the same capacity as permanent shores.

2.8.1.1—*Advantages of the two systems*

Reshores—Stripping formwork is more economically accomplished if all the material can be removed at the same time and moved from the area before placing reshores. No material is trapped which might cause unsightly offsets or joint lines in the exposed soffits. Reshores are installed to conform to the natural distribution of loading on the slab due to its own weight as well as from shores posted to the slab from above.

Permanent shores—Stripping of forms may be accomplished at an earlier age because large areas of concrete are not required to carry their own weight. The cost of the second placing of shores is eliminated. Use of permanent shores avoids the special attention required to assure that shores are placed uniformly tight under the slab. It also provides better assurance that shores are placed in the same pattern on each floor.

2.8.2—*Design* — Recommendations of Section 1.3.3 through 1.3.6 should be followed for reshores or permanent shores.

Shores in the lower stories should be designed to carry the full weight of the concrete and formwork posted to them prior to the removal of the first story of shores supported by the ground. Shores above the first level should be designed to carry a minimum of one and one-half times the weight of a given floor of concrete, forms, and construction loads.*

Where selective reduction in the number of reshores required for lower floors is made, the size of the shore should be carefully determined so as to assure its adequacy for the loads posted thereon.

In determining the number of floors to be shored to support construction loads above, the following factors should be considered:

1. Design load capacity of the slab or member including live load, partition loads, and other loads for which the engineer designed the slab. Where the engineer-architect included allowances for construction loads, such values should be shown on the structural drawings.

2. Dead weight of the concrete and formwork

3. Construction live loads involved, such as placing crews or equipment

4. Design strength of concrete specified

5. Cycle time between placement of successive floors

6. Developed strength of the concrete at the time it is required to support new loads above

7. Span of slab or structural member between structural supports

8. Type of forming systems; i.e., span of horizontal forming components, individual shore loads.

2.8.3—*Placing and removing reshores*

2.8.3.1—Reshoring is one of the most critical operations in formwork; consequently reshoring procedure should be planned in advance and approved by the engineer. Operations should be performed so that at no time will large areas of new construction be required to support combined dead and construction loads in excess of their capability as determined by design load and developed concrete strength at the time of stripping and reshoring. *While reshoring is under way, no construction loads should be permitted on the new construction.*

In no case should reshores be so located as to significantly alter the pattern of stress determined in the structural analysis or to induce tensile stresses where reinforcing bars are not provided.

When placing reshores, care should be taken not to preload the lower floor and also not to remove the normal deflection of the slab above. The reshore is simply a strut and should be tightened only to the extent that no significant shortening will take place under load.

Size and number of reshores must provide a supporting system capable of carrying any loads that may possibly be imposed on it.

Adequate provisions should be made for lateral bracing during this operation. Reshores should be located in the same position on each floor so that they will be continuous in their support from floor to floor. Where the number of reshores on a floor is reduced, such reshores shall be placed directly under a shore position on the floor above. When shores above are not directly over reshores, an analysis should be made to determine whether or not detrimental

---

*See Grundy, Paul, and Kabaila, A., "Construction Loads on Slabs with Shored Formwork in Multistory Buildings," ACI JOURNAL, *Proceedings* V. 60, No. 12, Dec. 1963, pp. 1729-1738.

bending stresses are produced in the slab. Where slabs are designed for light live loads, or on long spans, where the loads on the reshores are heavy, care should be used in placing these reshores, so that the loads on the reshores do not cause excessive punching shear or bending stress in the slab.

When stripping forms before slabs are strong enough to carry their own dead load and/or construction loads above, the following procedures should be followed during stripping and reshoring:

2.8.3.1.1—Reshoring beam and girder construction—The forms should be removed from one girder at a time, and the girder should be reshored before any other supports are removed. After the supporting girders are reshored, the forms should be removed from one beam with its adjacent slabs (unless the forms for slab have already been removed; see Section 2.7.2.3) and the beam should be reshored before any other supports are removed. Each long span slab (clear span 10 ft or more) should be reshored along the center line of the span unless the framing system itself is composed of a clear span between supports. If a line of reshores at midspan is not in line with shores on the floor above, the slab should be

checked for its capacity to resist reversal of stresses or punching shear.

Slabs should not be reshored until supporting beams and girders have been reshored.

2.8.3.1.2—Reshoring flat slabs—Shore removal and reshoring should be planned and located to avoid reversal of stresses or inducement of tension in slabs where reinforcement is not provided for design loads. Reshores should be placed along the intersection line of the column strip and the middle strip in both directions. Such reshoring should be completed for each panel as it is stripped before removing forms for adjacent panels. For flat slabs whose column spacing exceeds 25 ft, it is desirable to plan the form construction so that shores at intersections of column strips with middle strips may remain in place during stripping operations.

2.8.3.2 — Removal of reshoring — Reshoring should not be removed until the slab or member supported has attained sufficient strength to support all loads posted to it. Removal operations should be carried out in accordance with a planned sequence so that the structure supported is not subjected to impact or loading eccentricities.

In no case should reshores be removed within 2 days or 2 floors of a freshly placed slab.

CHAPTER 3—MATERIALS FOR FORMWORK

3.1—Discussion

The selection of materials suitable for formwork should be based on maximum economy to the contractor, consistent with safety and the quality required in the finished work. Approval by the engineer-architect, if required, should be based only on safety and quality of finished work.

3.2—Properties of materials

ACI Special Publication No. 4, *Formwork for Concrete*, describes the formwork materials commonly used in the United States and provides extensive related data for form design. Table 3.2 indicates other available sources of design and specification data for formwork materials. This tabulated information should not be interpreted to exclude the use of any other materials which can meet quality and safety requirements established for the finished work.

3.3—Accessories

3.3.1—*Discussion*

3.3.1.1—Form ties—A form tie is a tensile unit adapted to holding concrete forms against the active pressure of freshly placed plastic concrete. In general, it consists of an inside ten-

sile member and an external holding device, both made to specifications of various manufacturers. These manufacturers also publish recommended working loads on the ties for use in form design. There are two basic types of tie rods, the prefabricated rod or band type, and the threaded internal disconnecting type. Their suggested working loads range from 1000 to over 50,000 lb.

3.3.1.2—Form anchors—Form anchors are devices used in the securing of formwork to previously placed concrete of adequate strength. The devices normally are embedded in the concrete during placement. Actual load carrying capacity of the anchors depends on the strength of concrete in which they are embedded, the area of contact between concrete and anchor, and the depth of embedment. Manufacturers publish design data and test information to assist in the selection of proper form anchor devices.

3.3.1.3—Form hangers—Form hangers often are used to support formwork loads from a structural steel or precast concrete framework.

TABLE 3.2—FORM MATERIALS AND STRENGTH DATA FOR DESIGN*

Item	Principal use	Specification and design data sources
Lumber	Form framing, sheathing, and shoring	"National Design Specification for Stress Grade Lumber and Its Fastenings," National Lumber Manufacturers Association ACI Special Publication No. 4, *Formwork for Concrete*
		Design data: *Wood Handbook,* Forest Products Laboratory, U.S. Department of Agriculture *Wood Structural Design Data,* National Lumber Manufacturers Association *Timber Design and Construction Handbook* (in Canada) Part 4, Section 4.3, "Wood," of the National Research Council National Building Code of Canada
Plywood	Form sheathing and panels	U.S. Product Standard PS 1-66 ACI Special Publication No. 4, *Formwork for Concrete*
		Design data: ASTM, USASI CSA Plywood Manufacturers Association of British Columbia American Plywood Association *Plywood: Properties, Design and Construction*
Steel	Heavy forms and falsework	*Manual of Steel Construction,* American Institute of Steel Construction *Light Gage Cold-Formed Steel Design Manual,* American Iron and Steel Institute Manufacturer's specifications and recommendations
	Column and joist forms	Simplified Practice Recommendations R87-32 and R 265-63, U.S. Department of Commerce Manufacturers' specifications and recommendations
		Design data: Manual of Standard Practice, Concrete Reinforcing Steel Institute
	Permanent forms	American Iron and Steel Institute and individual manufacturer's recommendations
	Welding of permanent forms	*Specification:* American Welding Society *Design data:* American Iron and Steel Institute
Aluminum†	Lightweight panels and framing; bracing and horizontal shoring	Manufacturers' handbooks *Aluminum Construction Manual,* the Aluminum Association
Hardboard‡	Form liner and sheathing; pan forms for joist construction	Manufacturers' data CSA

Insulating board:
  Wood fiber
  Glass fiber
  Foamed plastic
	Permanent forms	Manufacturers' data
		CSA

Fiber or laminated paper pressed tubes or forms	Column and beam forms; void forms for slabs, beams, girders, and precast piles	Manufacturers' specifications and recommendations
Corrugated cardboard	Internal and under-slab voids; voids in beams and girders (normally used with internal "egg crate" stiffeners)	Manufacturers' specifications and recommendations
Concrete	Footings	ACI Building Code, ACI 318-63
	Permanent forms	ACI Building Code, ACI 318-63
	Precast floor and roof units	ACI 711-58
	Molds for precast units	—
Fiber-glass-reinforced plastic	Ready-made column and dome pan forms; custom-made forms for special architectural effects	ACI Special Publication No. 4, *Formwork for Concrete* and manufacturers' specifications

*Since handbooks, standards, and specifications of the type cited here are frequently rewritten or updated, the latest available version should be consulted.
†Shall be readily weldable, nonreactive to concrete or concrete containing calcium chloride, and protected against galvanic action at points of contact with steel.
‡Check surface reaction with wet concrete.

(continued on next page)

TABLE 3.2 (cont.)—FORM MATERIALS AND STRENGTH DATA FOR DESIGN

Item	Principal use	Specifications and design data sources
Plastics: Polystyrene Polyethylene Polyvinyl chloride	Form liners for decorative concrete	Manufacturers' data
Rubber	Form lining and void forms	Manufacturers' data
Form ties, anchors, and hangers	For securing formwork against placing loads and pressures	Manufacturers' specifications; see Section 1.3 of this standard for recommended safety factors ASTM
Plaster	Waste molds for architectural concrete	Manufacturers' recommendations
Coatings	Facilitate form removal	Manufacturers' specifications
Steel joists	Formwork support	"Standard Specifications and Load Tables for Open Web Steel Joists," Steel Joist Institute
Steel frame shoring	Formwork support	"Recommended Steel Frame Shoring Erection Procedure," Steel Scaffolding and Shoring Institute; also manufacturers' data
Form insulation	Cold weather protection of concrete	ACI 306-66 and manufacturers' specifications

3.3.2—Recommendations

3.3.2.1—Recommended factors of safety for ties, anchors, and hangers are given in Section 1.3.1. Yield point of the material should not be exceeded.

3.3.2.2—The rod or band type form tie, with supplemental provision for spreading the forms and a holding device engaging the exterior of the form, is the common type used for light construction.

The threaded internal disconnecting type is more often used for formwork on heavy construction such as heavy foundations, bridges, power houses, locks, dams, and architectural concrete.

Removable portions should be of a type which can be readily removed without damage to the concrete and which leave the smallest practicable holes to be filled.

Where ties are permitted in construction of water-retaining structures, they should be designed to prevent seepage or flow of water along the embedded tie.

Although there is no general uniformity at the present time, a minimum specification for form ties should require that the bearing area of external holding devices be adequate to prevent severe crushing of form lumber.

3.3.2.3—Form hangers must support the dead load of forms, weight of concrete, and construction and impact loads. Form hangers should be symmetrically arranged on the supporting member to minimize twisting or rotation of supporting members.

3.3.2.4—Where the concrete surface is to be exposed and appearance is important, the proper type of form tie or hanger which will not leave exposed metal at the surface is essential.

3.4—Form coatings or release agents

3.4.1—*Form coating*—Form coatings or sealers are usually applied in liquid form to contact surfaces either during manufacture or in the field to serve one or more of the following purposes:

(a) Alter the texture of the contact surface

(b) Improve the durability of the contact surface

(c) In addition to (b) above, to facilitate release from concrete during stripping

(d) Seal the contact surface from intrusion of moisture.

3.4.2—*Release agents*—Form release agents are applied to the form contact surfaces to prevent bond and thus facilitate stripping. They may be applied permanently to form materials in manufacture or applied to the form before each use. When applied in the field before each use, care must be exercised to prevent coating adjacent construction joint surfaces or reinforcing steel.

3.4.3—*Manufacturers' recommendations*—Manufacturers' recommendations should be followed in the use of coatings, sealers, and release agents, but independent investigation of their performance is recommended before use. Where surface treatments such as paint, tile adhesive, or other coatings are to be applied to formed concrete surfaces, be sure that adhesion of such surface treatments will not be impaired or prevented by use of the coating, sealer, or release agent.

CHAPTER 4—SPECIAL STRUCTURES

4.1—Discussion

In general, formwork for all structures should be designed, constructed, and maintained in accordance with recommendations in Chapters 1, 2, and 3. This section deals with the additional requirements for formwork for several special classes of work. Attention is directed to the work of ACI Committee 344, Circular Prestressed Concrete Structures, which has in preparation a proposed recommended practice for the design and construction of circular prestressed concrete structures.

4.2—Architectural concrete

4.2.1—*General*—Architectural concrete is any concrete of which one or more surfaces will be permanently exposed to view and the appearance of these surfaces is important from an architectural standpoint. Particular care must be taken in the selection of materials for and in the design and construction of the formwork, as well as in the placing and consolidation of such concrete, to eliminate bulges, offsets, or other unsightly features in the finished surface and to maintain the integrity of the surface texture or configuration. The character of the concrete surface to be produced must also be considered when the form materials are selected. Special attention should be given to closure techniques or concealing joints in formwork materials.

Location, number, and details of such items as openings, control joints, construction joints, and expansion joints should be shown on the design drawings and form details developed on formwork drawings when they are required (see Section 1.4.2.3).

It should be emphasized that architectural effects achieved in concrete surfaces may be vitally affected by factors other than formwork. Types or brands of cement, sources of coarse and fine aggregates, uniformity in mixing and placing techniques, slump control, and curing methods may significantly alter the desired visual effect on the exposed surfaces despite exhaustive care in the formwork.

4.2.2.—*Design*

4.2.2.1—Lateral pressure of concrete—Architectural concrete may be subjected to external vibration, revibration, set retardants, and slumps greater than those assumed for determining the lateral pressure as noted in Section 1.2.2. Particular care must be exercised in these cases to design the forms for the increased lateral pressures arising from the aforementioned sources as noted in Section 1.2.2. Since deflections in the contact surface of the formwork reflect directly in finished surfaces under varying light conditions, forms for architectural concrete must be designed carefully to minimize deflections. Deflections may govern design rather than bending (flexural stress) or horizontal shear.

4.2.2.2—Design of wood forms—Only stress-graded lumber free of twists and warps should be used for structural members. Form materials should be sized and positioned to prevent deflections detrimental to the surfaces formed. End joints of sheathing materials should be backed with structural members to prevent offsets.

Joints or corner connections should be designed so that they may be tightened to prevent leakage of mortar. Joints in wales or strongbacks should be designed for continuity of support.

Where tolerances closer than those suggested in Section 2.4 are deemed necessary, they should be clearly specified in the job specifications.

4.2.2.3—Approval of proposed form materials and finish—Sample mock-ups of concrete of prescribed size should be prepared and finished by the contractor for approval by the architect using proposed form materials and form surface treatments, such as wetting, oiling, or lacquering. To avoid later controversies, such mock-ups should be approved before formwork for architectural concrete is built.

Where a special effect is to be derived from the pattern of the joints in sheathing boards or plywood, the architect should include as much information as possible in the bidding documents to define the surface texture desired.

Proposed construction joint locations should be drawn up and submitted to the architect for approval.

4.2.3—*Construction*

4.2.3.1—General—Forms should be carefully built to resist the pressures to which they will be subjected and to limit deflections to a practicable minimum within the tolerances specified.

Joints in structural members should be kept to a minimum and, where necessary should be suitably spliced or otherwise constructed so as to maintain continuity.

Vibrating or placing pockets should be planned to facilitate careful placement and consolidation of the concrete to prevent segregation, honeycomb, sanding, or cold joints in the concrete.

Attachment of inserts, rustication strips, ornamental reliefs, etc., should be planned so that forms may be removed without exerting pressure on these attachments.

Where special forming systems are specified by the engineer for structural purposes (such as one-way and two-way joist systems) in areas which are considered architectural, the architect and engineer should coordinate their requirements to be sure the architectural effect is consistent with the forming method and material specified.

Forms which are to be re-used should be carefully inspected after each use to assure that they have not become distorted or otherwise unable to perform as designed.

4.2.3.2—Form sheathing—Contact surfaces of the formwork should be carefully installed to produce neat and symmetrical joint patterns unless otherwise specified. Joints should be either vertical or horizontal and, where possible should be staggered so as to maintain structural continuity.

Nailing should be done with care using hammers with smooth and well-dressed heads to prevent marring of the form surfaces. Box nails should be used when required on the contact surface and should be placed in a neat pattern.

Wherever possible, sheathing or panel joints should be positioned at rustication strips or other embedded features which may conceal or minimize the joint.

Where construction joints are necessary, they should be formed with a grade strip attached to the form to define a clean straight line on the joint of the formed surface. Formwork should be tightened at a construction joint before the next placement to prevent seepage of grout between the form and previously placed concrete surfaces.

Forms should be carefully cleaned and repaired between uses to prevent deterioration of the quality of surface formed. Film or splatter of hardened concrete should be thoroughly removed.

Form oils or releasing agents should be applied before reinforcing steel is placed and should be applied carefully to avoid contacting adjacent construction joints or reinforcing. No form oil should be used unless it can be guaranteed not to stain the concrete or impair the adhesion of paints or other intended surface treatments.

Form sealers should be tested to assure that they will not adversely affect the texture of the form lining material.

Joints in form lining material should be so fitted, pointed, or backed as to prevent loss of mortar causing sanding or streaking.

4.2.3.3—Ornamental detail—Ornamental concrete usually is formed by rubber, wood, plastic, or plaster waste molds. Members making up wood molds should be kerfed on the back wherever such members may become wedged between projections in the ornament. Molds must be so constructed that joints will not be opened by slight movement or swelling of the wood. Joints in the molds should be made inconspicuous by pointing.

The molds should be carefully set in the forms and securely held in position to reproduce the design shown on the drawings. Where wood forms adjoin molds, the wood should be neatly fitted to the profile of the mold and all joints should be carefully pointed. The molds and the adjacent wood forms should be so detailed that the wood forms can be stripped without disturbing the molds. A slight draft on the edge of molds or pattern strips should be provided to permit removing the detail material without damaging the concrete. Special provisions should be made for early form removal and/or retardation when sand blasting, wire brushing, or other treatments are required.

4.2.3.4—Form ties—Form tie assemblies for architectural concrete should be adjustable so as to permit tightening of forms and be of such type as to leave no metal closer to the surface than 1½ in. for steel ties and 1 in. for stainless steel ties. They should not be fitted with lugs, cones, washers, or other devices which will leave depressions larger in diameter than the depth at the exposed surface of the concrete. Removable ties should be of such design as not to leave holes through the concrete larger than ⅞ in. Twisted wire ties or band iron should not be permitted. Ties should be tight fitting or holes sealed to prevent leakage at the holes in the form.

Ties that are to be pulled from the wall must be coated with nonstaining bond breaker or encased in oiled paper sleeves to facilitate removal. Ties for architectural concrete should have the same factor of safety as for heavy formwork in Section 1.3.1. Tie layout should be planned so as to be symmetrical with the member formed and, wherever possible, ties should be located at rustication marks, control joints, or other points where the visual effect will be minimized.

Externally braced forms may be used instead of any of the above mentioned methods to avoid objectionable blemishes in the finished surface.

4.2.3.5—Forms for control and construction joints (see Section 2.2)—In architectural concrete, control and/or construction joints should, where feasible, be located at the junction of the formwork panels, and should be solidly backed to prevent leakage. At control joints in forms built in place, projecting strips should be provided and fastened to the face of forms.

4.2.3.6—Removing forms—Forms and molds should not be removed until the concrete has sufficiently hardened to permit removal without damaging the concrete surfaces. If removed before the specific curing period is completed, measures must be taken immediately after removal to apply and maintain satisfactory curing. In hot, dry climates, wood forms remaining in place should not be considered adequate curing but should be removed or loosened so that the concrete surfaces may be kept moist or coated with a curing agent.

In cold weather, removal of formwork should be deferred or formwork should be replaced with insulation blankets, to avoid thermal shock and consequent crazing of the concrete surface.

4.3—Bridges and viaducts, including high piers

4.3.1—*Discussion*—For bridges, the construction and removal of forms and falsework must be planned in advance. Forms and supports should be sufficiently rigid to assure that the finished structure will fulfill its intended structural function and that exposed concrete finishes will present a pleasing appearance to the public.

4.3.2—*Recommendations*

4.3.2.1 — Falsework — Follow recommended practice in Section 2.5.

4.3.2.2. — Falsework removal — Falsework should not be released until the concrete has attained 70 percent of its design strength, and in no case until at least 5 days have elapsed after the concrete has been placed. In continuous structures, falsework should not be released in any span until the first and second adjoining spans on each side have reached the specified strength.

4.3.2.3—Forms—Forms may be of wood or metal and must be built mortar tight of sound material sufficiently strong to prevent distortion during placing and curing of the concrete.

4.3.2.4—Form removal—Forms for ornamental work, railings, parapets, and vertical surfaces which require a surface finishing operation should be removed not less than 12 hr, nor more than 48 hr after casting the concrete, depending on weather conditions. Bulkheads at construction joints should not be removed for a period of 15 hr after casting adjacent concrete. Forms under slab spans, beams, girders, and brackets must not be removed until the concrete has attained at least 70 percent of its design strength.

4.3.2.5—Composite construction—Where composite construction is used, forms and shores, as well as removal of forms and shores, should follow the recommended practice in Section 4.4. If required by the design for composite action for both dead and live load, any temporary shores required for this purpose must be shown or specified in the plans or specifications.

4.4—Structures designed for composite action

4.4.1—*Recommendations*—Structures or members thereof which are designed so that the concrete portions act compositely with other materials or with other parts of the structure present special problems of forming which should be anticipated in the design of the structure. Requirements for shoring or other deflection control of the formwork should be clearly presented by the engineer in the specifications. Where successive placements are to act compositely in the completed structure, deflection control becomes extremely critical to prevent preloading reinforcing steel before imposition of live load.

Shoring, with or without cambering of portions of the structure during placement and curing of the concrete, should be analyzed separately for the effects of dead load of wet concrete and for the effect of other construction loads which may be imposed before the concrete attains its design strength.

4.4.2—*Design*—Formwork members and shores should be designed to limit deflections to a practical minimum consistent with the structural member being constructed.

Where camber is specified for previously installed components of the structure, allowance should be made for the resultant preloading of the shores before application of the dead load of concrete.

In members constructed in several successive placements, such as box girder structures, formwork components should be sized, positioned and/or supported to prevent progressive increases in deflection of the structure which would excessively preload the reinforcing steel or other portions of the composite member.

In multistory work where shoring of composite members is required, consideration should be given to the number of stories of shores necessary, in conjunction with the speed of construction and concrete strengths, to prevent excessive deflections due to successive loadings. Distinction should be made in such analyses for shores posted to relatively unyielding support such as foundations instead of to structures or members already in elastic support (see Section 2.8).

4.4.3—*Erection*—Construction and/or erection of formwork for composite construction follows basic recommendations contained in Chapter 2. Shoring of members which will act compositely with the concrete to be placed should be done with great care to assure sufficient bearing, rigidity, and tightness as to prevent settlement or deflections beyond allowable limits. Wedges, shims, jacks, etc., should be provided so as to permit adjustment if required before or during concreting as well as to permit removal without jarring or impact of the completed construction. Provision should be made for readily checking the accuracy of position and grade during placement.

Where camber is required, distinction should be made between that part which is an allowance for settlement or deflection of formwork or shoring and that which is provided for design loadings. The former should generally be the responsibility of the contractor who designs the forms and supports unless such camber is stipulated by the engineer-architect. Measurement of camber provided for design loadings should be made after hardening of the concrete but before removal of the supports [see also Section 1.4.1 (g)].

4.4.4.—*Removal*—In addition to meeting the provisions of Section 2.7, forms and/or supports should be removed only after field-cured cylinder tests and specified curing operations indicate to the satisfaction of the engineer that the most recently placed concrete has attained the strength required to develop composite action, and then only after stated approval of the engineer-architect. The sequence of such removal should be approved by the engineer-architect.

4.5—Folded plates, thin shells, and long span roof structures

4.5.1—*Discussion*—For long span and space structures requiring a complex, three-dimensional design analysis and presenting three-dimensional problems in formwork design, erection, and removal, formwork planning should be done by engineers having the necessary special qualifications and experience. These men should consult and cooperate with the engineer-architect to make sure that the resulting surfaces will conform to his design. The contractor should obtain written approval by the engineer-architect of the formwork drawings prior to erection of falsework.

4.5.2—*Recommendations*
4.5.2.1—Design
(a) The engineer-architect should specify limiting values and directions of the reactive forces when the falsework is supported by the permanent structure.

(b) When applicable, the engineer-architect should include a decentering sequence drawing with the bidding documents as a basis for the design of the forming and support system to be used by the contractor.

(c) Lateral loads—In determining the lateral forces acting on the formwork, the wind load should be calculated on the basis of a minimum of 15 psf of projected vertical area in lieu of the 10 psf specified for wall forms in Section 1.2.3. For structures such as domes, negative forces due to suction created by the wind on the leeward side of the structure should be considered.

(d) Analysis — The provisions of Sections 1.3.1 and 1.3.2 should be closely adhered to in such formwork planning.

Assumed design loads should be shown. Complete stress analyses should be prepared by competent structural engineers, and the maximum and minimum values of stress, including reversal of stress should be shown for each member for the most severe loading conditions. Due regard should be given to unsymmetrical or eccentric loadings which might occur during concrete placement and during erection, decentering, or moving of traveler. The vertical or lateral deflection of the moving forms or travelers as well as the stability under various loads should be investigated to insure that the formwork will function satisfactorily and that the concrete tolerances will be met.

Particular care must be taken in the design and detailing of individual members and connections. Where trussed systems are used, connections must be designed to keep eccentricities as small as possible to minimize deflections or distortions.

Since the weight of the forms and falsework may, in many cases, be equal to or greater than the design live load of the structure, form details should be so designed as to avoid hanging up the form and falsework and thus overloading the structure itself during decentering.

(e) Due to the special shapes involved, tolerances based on functions of these shapes should be specified by the engineer-architect in the bidding documents.

4.5.2.2—Drawings—When required, the contractor should submit detailed drawings of the formwork for approval of the engineer-architect.

These drawings should show the proposed placing sequence and alternate placing sequence of concrete and the resulting loads. To insure that the structure can assume its deflected shape without damage, the decentering or handling sequence of the falsework and forms should be shown on the drawings.

Deflection of these structures may cause binding between the form and the concrete during decentering. Falsework drawings and form details must be planned to prevent binding and to facilitate stripping of forms. Drawings must show such details as type of inserts and joints in sheathing where spreading of the form may result in the form becoming keyed into the concrete.

4.5.2.3—*Approval*—The formwork drawings and procedures must comply with the contract drawings and specifications and meet the general requirements for formwork to assure the integrity and stability of the permanent structure itself. The engineer-architect should check the design and shop drawings for the formwork to insure that these requirements are met and approve them in writing.

4.5.2.4—*Construction*—In planning and erecting formwork, provision should be made for adequate means of adjustment during placing where necessary. Tell-tales should be installed to check alignment and grade during placement.

When movable forms are used, a minimum batter of $\frac{1}{8}$ in. per ft is recommended for vertical surfaces to facilitate form removal. For slopes steeper than 35 deg (1.5 horizontal to 1 vertical) a top form is recommended. Greater slopes may be formed without top forms if there is a continuous mat of bars or mesh.

Where the forming system is based on a certain placing sequence, that sequence should be clearly defined and adhered to in the field.

4.5.2.5—*Removal of forms and falsework*— Forms and falsework should be removed and decentered in the procedure and sequence specified on the shop drawings or on the contract drawings and specifications. Decentering methods used should be planned to prevent any concentrated reaction on any part of the permanent structure. Due to the large deflections and the high dead load to live load ratio common to this type of structure, decentering and form removal should not be permitted until tests of job-cured test cylinders demonstrate that the minimum concrete strength and the modulus of elasticity specified on contract drawings has been reached. Moduli of elasticity may determine time of decentering although required compressive

strengths may already have been attained. Generally decentering should begin at points of maximum deflection and should progress toward points of minimum deflection, with the decentering of edge members proceeding simultaneously with the adjoining shell.

4.6—Mass concrete structures

4.6.1—*Discussion*—Mass concrete generally occurs in heavy civil engineering construction, such as in gravity dams, arch dams, gravity retaining walls, and lock walls. Special provisions usually are made to control the temperature rise in the mass by the use of cement or cementing material combinations possessing low or moderate heat-generating characteristics, by refrigeration, or by low temperature of fresh concrete.

Formwork for mass concrete falls into two distinct categories, namely, low and high lift. Low lift formwork, for heights 5 to 10 ft, usually consists of multi-use steel cantilever form units which incorporate their own scaffolding and, on occasion, lifting devices. High lift formwork is strictly comparable to the single-use wood forms used extensively for structural concrete.

Because of the large size of mass concrete structures, the rate of placement is low, the depth of each succeeding layer being from 15 to 20 in. With a large working space available behind the form and with little or no obstruction from reinforcing bars, internal vibration is easily accomplished, external vibration of the form is not ordinarily used, and the possiblility of mechanical wedging of the aggregate against the form is remote.

4.6.2—*Recommendations*

4.6.2.1—Design

4.6.2.1.1 — Lateral pressure of concrete (Type IV cement)—Forms, ties, tiebacks, and bracing should be designed for a lateral pressure of fresh concrete as given below:

$$p = 120 + \frac{7200R}{T}$$

where

p = lateral pressure, psf

R = rate of placement in ft per hr; generally 1 to 2 ft per hr, but higher for cold weather concreting

T = temperature of concrete in the forms, deg F

For concrete weighing more than 150 lb per cu ft, or more than 4-in. slump, appropriate allowance for additional lateral pressure should be made. Forms adequate for use with Type IV (low heat) cement will be adequate for use with other types of portland cement.

4.6.2.1.2 — Design considerations — Particular care must be taken to provide anchorage for forms with a batter and wall forms tied to a rock face. The ultimate strength of the tie rods must not exceed the ultimate strength of the anchor bar or bolt. The bending and welding of high tensile steel tie rods should be prohibited. Consideration should be given to form ties embedded in previously placed concrete to insure that such concrete has attained sufficient strength to sustain design loadings from the new placement as well as initial bolting stresses.

4.6.2.2—Tolerances—See Section 2.4

4.7—Underground structures

4.7.1 — *Discussion* — Underground structures comprise many types, such as powerhouses, tunnels, shafts, bomb shelters, factories, and defense installations. They differ from corresponding surface installations in that the construction takes place inside an excavation instead of in the open, thereby providing unique problems in handling and supporting formwork and in the associated concrete placing. As a result, the following four factors usually make the design of formwork for underground structures entirely different than for their above ground counterparts: First, concrete to fill otherwise inaccessible areas may be placed pneumatically or by positive displacement pump and pipeline; second, the rock sometimes is utilized as a form backing thereby permitting the use of rock anchors and tie rods in lieu of external bracing and shores; third, the limits of the excavation demand special handling equipment that adds particular emphasis to the removal and re-use of forms; fourth, rock surfaces sometimes can be used for attaching hoisting devices.

When placement is by pneumatic or positive displacement pump and pipeline methods, the plastic concrete is forced, under pressure, into a void such as the crown of a tunnel lining. This usually is done through a removable piepline. The end of the pipeline (or "slick" line) usually is embedded between 5 and 10 ft and occasionally up to 20 ft in the fresh concrete, the line being withdrawn progressively as the cavity fills. With small aggregate and high slump concrete such as might be used in a heavily reinforced tunnel lining, the localized pressures induced by the pump can theoretically reach a maximum of 150 psi less line losses, as the pump stalls or the shear pins fail. When the air gun is used, compressed air at a nominal pressure of 100 psi blasts slugs of high slump concrete into the cavity, and the form must withstand the pressure due to the impact of the concrete and surges of compressed air.

4.7.2—*Recommendations*

4.7.2.1—Loads

4.7.2.1.1—Vertical loads—Vertical and construction loads assumed in design of formwork for underground structures are similar to those for surface structures, with the exception of unusual vertical loads occurring near the crown of arch or tunnel forms and of flotation effect beneath tunnel forms.

Near the crowns of arch and tunnel forms, pressures up to 3000 psf have been induced in areas overbreak and near vertical bulkheads from concrete placed pneumatically or by positive displacement pump. Until more definite recommendations can be made, the magnitude and distribution of pressure should be determined by the design engineer. In no case should the assumed pressure be less than 1000 psf acting normal to the form plus the dead weight of the concrete placed pneumatically or by pump.

4.7.2.1.2—Lateral loads

(a) For shafts and exterior walls against rock the values listed in Section 1.2.2 should apply.

(b) When the shaft form relies on the single shear value of embedded anchors in the previous placement as a means of support, the minimum time lapse between successive placements (or minimum concrete strength) and maximum allowable loading additional to the dead weight of the form should be specified.

(c) For arch forms and for the portions of tunnel forms above the maximum horizontal dimension or spring line of the form, the pressure should be compatible with the pressures discussed under vertical loads in Section 4.7.2.1.1.

4.7.2.2—Drawings—In addition to the provisions of Chapters 1, 2, and 3, the following data should be included on the drawings for specialized formwork and formwork for tunnels:

4.7.2.2.1—All pressure diagrams used in the design of the form including diagrams for uplift, for unbalanced lateral or vertical loads, for pressurized concrete, or for any other load applicable to the particular installation.

4.7.2.2.2—Recommended method of supplemental strutting or bracing to be employed in areas where form pressures may exceed those listed above due to abnormal conditions.

4.7.2.2.3—Handling diagrams and procedures showing the proposed method of handling the form during erection or installation for concrete placement plus the method of bracing and anchorage during normal operation.

4.7.2.2.4—In the case of the tunnel arch form, whether it is intended for use with the unit or bulkhead system of concrete placement or is restricted to use with the continuously advancing slope method (see Section 4.7.2.3).

4.7.2.2.5—When placement of concrete by pumping or pneumatic methods is anticipated, the capacity and working pressure of the prime mover and the size, length, and maximum embedment of the discharge line should be as assumed in the design. Also, when the design provides for a method of placement other than by sustained pumping via a buried slick line, it should be clearly stated that the design pressures would be exceeded if sustained pumping were adopted.

4.7.2.3—Construction—The two basic methods of placing a tunnel arch entail problems in the construction of the formwork that require special provisions to permit proper re-use. These two basic methods are commonly known as the "bulkhead method" and the "continuously advancing slope" method.

The former is used exclusively where poor ground conditions exist, requiring the lining to be placed concurrently with tunnel driving operations. It is also used when some factor, such as the size of the tunnel, the introduction of reinforcing steel, or the location of construction joints precludes the advancing slope method. The advancing slope method, a continuous method of placement, usually is preferred for tunnel driven through competent rock, ranging between 10 and 25 ft in diameter and at least 1 mile in length.

The arch form for the bulkhead method is usually fabricated into a single unit between 50 and 150 ft long which is stripped, moved ahead, and re-erected using screw jacks or hydraulic rams. These are permanently attached to the form and supporting traveling gantry. The arch form for the continuously advancing slope method usually consists of eight or more sections that range between 15 and 30 ft in length. These are successively stripped or collapsed, telescoped through the other sections and re-erected using a form traveler.

Although the minimum stripping time for tunnel arch forms usually is established on the basis of experience, it can be safely predetermined by tests in the laboratory. It is recommended that at the start of a tunnel arch concreting operation, the minimum stripping time be 12 hr for exposed surfaces and 8 hr for construction joints. If the specifications provide for a reduced minimum stripping time based on site experience, such reductions should be in time increments of 30 min or less and should be established by laboratory tests and visual inspection and surface scratching of sample areas exposed by opening the form access covers. Arch forms should not be stripped prematurely when unvented ground water seepage could become trapped between the rock surface and the concrete lining.

4.7.2.4—Materials — The choice of materials for underground formwork usually is predicated on the shape, degree of re-use and mobility of the form, and the magnitude of pump or pneumatic pressures to which it is subjected. Usually, tunnel and shaft forms are made of steel, or a composite of wood and steel. Experience is of paramount importance in the design and fabrication of a satisfactory tunnel form, due to the nature of the pressures developed by the concrete, placing techniques, and the high degree of mobility usually required.

When re-use is not a factor, plywood and tongue-and-groove lumber sometimes are used for exposed surface finishes, but more consideration may be given to wood sheathing because the high humidity often precludes the normal shrinkage and warping.

CHAPTER 5—FORMWORK FOR SPECIAL METHODS OF CONSTRUCTION

5.1—Recommendations

The applicable provisions of Chapters 1, 2, and 3 also apply to the work covered in this chapter.

5.2—Preplaced aggregate concrete

5.2.1—*Discussion*—Preplaced aggregate concrete is made by injecting (intruding) mortar into the voids of a preplaced mass of clean, graded aggregate. For normal construction the preplaced aggregates are wetted and kept wet until the injection of mortar into the voids is completed. In underwater construction, the mortar displaces the water and fills the voids. In both types of construction this process can create a dense concrete having a high content of coarse aggregate.

The injected mortar contains water, fine sand, portland cement, pozzolanic filler, and an additive designed to increase the penetration and pumpability of the mortar. The coarse aggregate is similar to coarse aggregate for conventional concrete. It is well washed and graded from ½ in. to the largest size practicable. After compaction in the forms, it usually has a void content ranging from 35 to 45 percent.

5.2.2—Recommendations

5.2.2.1—Design considerations

5.2.2.1.1—Lateral pressure of concrete— Due to the method of placement, the lateral pressures on formwork are considerably higher than those developed for conventional concrete as given in Section 1.2.2.

Forms, ties, and bracing should be designed for the sum of

(a) The lateral pressure of the coarse aggregate as determined from the equivalent fluid lateral pressure of the dry aggregate using the Rankine or Coulomb theories for granular materials; or a reliable bin action theory; and

(b) The lateral pressure of the injected mortar as an equivalent fluid weighing 130 lb per cu ft. The time required for the initial set of the mortar (from 6 to 24 hr) and the rate of rise (1 to 2 ft per hr) should be ascertained. The maximum height of fluid to be assumed in determining the lateral pressure of the mortar is the product of the rate of rise (ft per hr) and the time of initial set in hours.

The lateral pressure for the design of formwork at any point is the sum of the pressures determined from Steps (a) and (b) for the given height.

5.2.2.2—Construction—In addition to the provisions of Chapter 2, the forms must be literally "mortar-tight" because preplaced aggregate concrete entails forcing mortar into the voids of the coarse aggregate. The increased lateral pressure usually requires that the workmanship and details of formwork be of better quality than formwork for conventional concrete.

5.2.2.3 — Materials for formwork — Tongue-and-groove lumber is preferred for exposed surfaces; the joints between boards permit the escape of traces of mortar. For unexposed surfaces, mortar-tight forms of steel or plywood are acceptable. Prefabricated panel-type forms usually are not suitable because of the difficulty in making mortar-tight seals between panels. Absorptive form linings are not recommended because they permit the coarse aggregate to indent the lining and form an irregular surface. Form linings, such as hardboard on common sheathing, are not successful because they do not withstand the external form vibration normally required.

5.3—Slipforms

5.3.1—Discussion—Placing of concrete by use of slipforms is similar to an extrusion process. Plastic concrete is placed or pumped into the forms, and the forms act as moving dies to shape the concrete. The rate of movement of the forms is regulated so that the forms leave the formed concrete only after it is strong enough to retain its shape while supporting its own weight. Formwork of this type can be used for vertical structures such as silo and storage bins, bridge piers, shaft type buildings, water tanks, and missile launchers or for horizontal structures such as tunnel inverts, water conduits, drainage channels, canal linings, and paving. Sometimes there may be fixed forms on one side (such as sheathing, rock, earth, or existing masonry) and a sliding form on the other. For other types of work, there are sliding forms on both sides.

Vertical slipforms are usually moved by jacks which ride on smooth steel rods or pipe embedded in or attached to the hardened concrete, whereas horizontal slipforms generally move on a rail system or on a shaped berm. Working decks, concrete supply hoppers, and worker's or finisher's scaffolding, where required, are attached to and carried by the moving formwork.

The vertical or horizontal movement of forms may be a continuous process carried on 24 hr of the day until the structure is completed, or in a planned sequence of finite placements.

This section is divided into two parts: *vertical slipforms*; and *horizontal slipforms* such as used on drainage channels and canal linings.

Slipforms used on such structures as tunnels and mine shafts should comply with the applicable provisions of Section 4.7. Slipforms used on mass concrete structures such as dams should comply with the applicable provisions of Section 4.6.

5.3.2—Recommendations

5.3.2.1—Vertical slipforms

5.3.2.1.1—Design considerations—Slipforms should be designed and constructed and the sliding operation should be carried out under the immediate supervision of a person or persons experienced in slipform work.

In the design of the forms in which jacks on vertical rods are used, care must be taken to place jacks in such a manner that the vertical loads are as nearly equal as possible and do not exceed the safe capacity of the jacks. The steel rods or pipe on which the jacks climb or by which the forms are lifted should be especially designed for this purpose. These rods must be properly braced where not encased in concrete. Jacking rods or pipes may be left in concrete or withdrawn as conditions permit but splices and low bond value must be given special consideration if they are to be used as reinforcement.

The design of the yokes must provide for adequate clearance to install horizontal reinforcing bars and embedments in their correct locations prior to their submergence in the rising concrete.

A Jacking system which provides for the precise simultaneous movement of the entire form in small preselected increments of approximately 1 in. at 5 to 10-min intervals is recommended for large structures, especially when single units are involved.

Lateral and diagonal bracing of forms must be provided to insure that the shape of the structure will not be distorted beyond allowable tolerances during the sliding operation.

When slipforms are used for single unit structures in excess of 50 ft diameter, they are usually segmental, or are provided with a substantial center guide made of steel or concrete, to overcome the latent uncertainty of maintaining correct alignment of an otherwise unguided form.

Drawings should be prepared by a competent and experienced engineer employed by the contractor, showing the jack layout, formwork, working decks, and scaffolds.

5.3.2.1.2—Loads

(a) *Vertical loads*

1. In addition to the dead loads, live loads assumed for design of decks should not be less than the following:

Sheathing
and joists ....75 psf or concentrated
buggy wheel loads, whichever is the greater

Beams,
trusses,
and wales ....40 psf

2. Where working decks are used as a bottom form for cast-in-place construction, the deck must be designed for the dead load of the concrete construction plus any superimposed loads, and in no case less than the design loads given in Section 1.2. The deflection of the working deck should not exceed $\frac{1}{8}$ in. or 1/360 of span, whichever is greater.

3. Vertical loads and possible torsional forces resulting from deck loads and friction of concrete on the forms must also be considered since the forms must act as trusses for the vertical loads between

jacks. Knee braces should be provided for top wales where span between jacks exceeds 6 ft or where vertical loads are unusually heavy.

(b) *Lateral pressure of concrete*—The lateral pressure of fresh concrete to be used in designing forms, ties, bracing, and wales may be calculated as follows:

$$p = c_1 + \frac{6000R}{T}$$

where

$c_1 = 100^*$

p = lateral pressure, psf

R = rate of concrete placement in ft per hr

T = temperature of concrete in the forms, deg F

Wales must be adequately nailed or bolted together to transmit shear due to lateral pressure of concrete and vertical posts should be placed between wales at lift points.

5.3.2.1.3—Construction and materials—Forms should be a minimum of 3 ft 6 in. high[†] and should be constructed of at least 1-in. board, $\frac{5}{8}$-in. plywood, 10-gage minimum steel sheets, or other approved material. The 1-in. boards should be straight grained and center-matched and placed with the grain running downward and boards spaced 1/16 to $\frac{1}{8}$ in. apart to allow for expansion when they become wet. Forms should be erected with slight draft, particularly for the inside faces so that the form is wider at the bottom than at the top.

Timber wales should be of 2- or 3-ply lumber at least one ply of which will be 2-in. material. The minimum depth of segmental wales for curved walls should be $4\frac{1}{2}$ in. at the center after cutting.

Special care must be taken in building the forms and arranging the jacks so that the forms will draw straight and true without strain or twist. To avoid unplanned cold joints, especially when such an occurrence would adversely affect the integrity of the structure, it is essential that reserve jacking and placing equipment and standby con-

---

*It is felt that $c_1 = 100$ is justified because vibration is slight in slipform work, since the concrete is placed in shallow layers of 6 to 10 in. and because there is no revibration. However, for some applications such as for gastight or containment structures, additional vibration may be required to achieve maximum density of the concrete. In such cases, the value of c_1 should be increased to 150.

†The minimum height is a function of the rate of slipping (ft per hour) and the time required for the concrete to gain sufficient strength to support itself without sagging after leaving the slipform. A slightly higher form will provide some working space in the top of the form for placing of concrete and reinforcement. Forms less than $3\frac{1}{2}$ ft high are believed to be dangerously shallow. Forms as high as 6 ft may be required when low temperature or slow setting concrete is specified.

struction service equipment is immediately available to maintain a continuous operation.

5.3.2.1.4—Tolerances—Maximum variation in wall thickness should not exceed ±⅜ in. for walls up to 8 in. thick nor ±½ in. for walls thicker than 8 in. The maximum deviation of any point on the slipform with respect to a vertical projection of a corresponding reference point at the base of the structure should not exceed 1 in. per 50 ft of height. This is the total deviation which may be composed of translational and rotational components.

5.3.2.1.5—Sliding operation—Maximum rate of slide should be limited by the rate for which the forms are designed. In addition, both maximum and minimum rates of slide must be determined by an experienced slipfrom supervisor to meet changes in weather, concrete slump, and workability, and the many exigencies which arise during a slide and which cannot be predicted accurately beforehand. A man experienced in slipform construction must be present on the deck at all times during the slide operation.

Forms must be leveled before and after they are filled and must be maintained level throughout the slide. Care must be taken to prevent drifting of the forms from alignment or designed dimensions and to prevent torsional movement.

Experience has shown that a plumb line or optical plummet used in conjunction with a water level system serviced by a central reservoir is effective in maintaining the form on line and grade and for positioning openings and embedded items.

Alignment and plumbness of structure should be checked at least once during every 8 hr that the slide is in operation and preferably every 4 hr. In work that is done in separate, intermittent slipping operations, a check on alignment and plumbness should be made at the beginning of each slipping operation.

5.3.2.2—Horizontal slipforms for tunnel inverts, drainage channels, canal linings, and highways.*

5.3.2.2.1—Tunnel inverts—Linings for tunnel inverts often are constructed in a continuous longitudinally operating method of placement. The transverse section of the invert usually is curved to a prescribed shape. The best way to hold such a shape and at the same time obtain good vibratory consolidation of the higher areas along the side forms is to use a heavy weighted slipform supported on the fixed side forms and having a length equal to or greater than the width of the invert. The slipform is moved foward by winches. The concrete is delivered by pump and pipeline or conveyor belt and is placed and vibrated immediately ahead of the slipform. If arch form anchors are inserted in the invert concrete immediately behind the slipform, care should be taken to insure that they are properly embedded in the wet concrete without despoiling the newly formed surface.

5.3.2.2.2—Drainage channels—Linings for drainage channels and canals may be constructed in either a planned sequence of finite placements or a continuous longitudinally operating method of placement. In a planned sequence of finite placements the procedures may range from hand operations for small laterals where the concrete may be dumped and spread on the sides and bottom, to the larger channels where the lining may be placed in alternate sections. In the latter, the bottom slab is placed first to provide support at the toes of the side panels.

An efficient placement of concrete on slopes is accomplished by use of a weighted, unvibrated steel-faced slipform screed about 27 in. wide in the direction of movement. The screed may be pulled up the slope by equipment located on the berm or by air hoists mounted on the slipform. The concrete vibrators should be manually operated just ahead of the slipform rather than mounted on the form. If the form is vibrated, this procedure will cause a swell in the finished surface emerging from the trailing edge.

(a) Small channels and canals—A simplified type of slipform machine has been used with good results. This machine is held to grade and line by a steel pan, shaped to fit the previously prepared excavation section, and is pulled forward by an external source of power. Behind the pan and immediately preceding the slipform is a transverse, compartmented trough for uniformly distributing the mix. This type of form which depends on the subgrade for its support is applicable for placing only unreinforced concrete lining.

(b) For reinforced linings and also for medium-sized canal linings, more elaborate slipform machines are required. A framework, traveling on rails, or a tractor crawler assembly on the berm of the drainage channel or canal, supports the working platform, the distributor plate or drop

---

*The simplified type of slipform is a relatively minor structure; its design is straight-forward and is not discussed here. The material in this subsection deals principally with the design and construction of the more elaborate slipform structures.

chutes, the compartmented supply trough, vibrator tube in the bottom of the trough, and the slipform. The slipform is a steel plate, curved up at the leading edge, extending across the bottom and up the slopes of the canal and shaped to conform to the finished surface of the lining. When a distributor plate is used, it is fastened to the leading edge of the slipform and extends upward on a steep incline to the working platform. On some of the machines, a continuous row of hoppers in the working platform feed into drop chutes, each supplying one compartment of the trough below. Concrete is dumped, usually from a shuttle car on the working platform, and is guided to the trough below by the distributor plate or the drop chutes.

As the concrete passes out at the bottom of the trough and under the slipform, it is consolidated by a vibrating tube parallel to and a few inches ahead of the leading edge of the form. Consolidation must be accomplished as the concrete passes under the slipform. Proper consolidation cannot be obtained by vibrating the slipform of a lining machine, apparently due to lack of means to supply additional concrete needed to fill the voids. The trailing edge of the slipform is usually adjustable to positions somewhat lower than that of the leading edge. This improves consolidation and tends to mold the concrete more closely to the subgrade. Too low a setting of the trailing edge causes tearing, rather than smoothing, of the surface. On some machines, the slipform is followed within a few feet by an "ironer" plate 18 x 20 in. wide, which, under favorable conditions, leaves a surface that requires little or no hand treatment.

(c) For large channels (bottom widths of 50 to 110 ft) it is impractical to build machines to span the entire waterway prism. The slope paver is a crawler-mounted slipform which places the concrete lining on one side slope and the adjacent 8-10 ft of the invert. After the opposite side slope is similarly completed, the invert is finished by horizontal pavers. All three operations are kept on line and grade electronically through sensors probing guide wires.

(d) The slipform used for highways is similar in principle to the slope form pavers. No fixed side forms are required as the side forms of the machine slide forward with the paver leaving the slab edges unsupported. The concrete is deposited either on the subgrade ahead of the paver or into a hopper box. Following spreading by a dozer-type strike-off, the concrete is consolidated by vibration and shaped by an extrusion plate or meter. Flat, parabolic, or hip roof crowns can be provided with a quick change device for transitions in and out of horizontal curves. Surface elevations can be maintained by electronic controls.

5.3.2.2.3—Design considerations—This specialized formwork should be designed by experienced, competent structural engineers employed or engaged by the contractor. A complete structural analysis, including stress diagrams of the structural members must be made to insure satisfactory performance. Due regard should be given to unsymmetrical and eccentric loadings and the fact that the machine must be regularly disassembled as it encounters siphons, bridges, chutes, etc., along the waterway. The large machines are usually hinged so that sections may be passed through or beneath structures. The vertical or lateral deflections, particularly of long-span machines, must be investigated, and sufficient rigidity provided to insure that concrete tolerances will be met. The stability of the machine under the aforementioned loading conditions must be carefully investigated to insure satisfactory performance.

5.3.2.2.4 — Drawings — The general provisions of "Drawings" in Section 1.4 should be met and the contractor should submit drawings of the slipform for review and approval by the engineer-architect. These drawings should show the handling diagrams, the placing procedure, and the provisions for insuring attainment of the required concrete surfaces.

5.4—Permanent forms

5.4.1 — Discussion — Permanent forms, as the name implies, are forms left in place that may or may not become an integral part of the structural frame. These forms may be the rigid type such as metal deck, precast concrete, wood, plastics, and various types of fiberboard; or the flexible type such as reinforced water-repellent corrugated paper, or wire mesh with waterproof paper backing.

Where the permanent form is used as a deck form it is generally supported from the main structural frame with or without an intermediate system of temporary supports.

5.4.2—Recommendations

5.4.2.1—Design considerations—If the permanent type form is not covered in the architect-engineer's specifications, (1) the manufacturer's specifications should be used; (2) the manufacturer's recommended practice* should be followed for size, span, fastenings, and other special features pertinent to this type of form, such as being water repellent and protected against chemical attack from wet concrete; and (3) the minimum requirements of Chapters 1 and 2 should be adhered to. Particular care should be taken in the design of such forms to minimize distortion or deformation of the form or supporting members under the construction loads.

Where metal deck to become an integral part of the structure is used as a permanent form, its shape, depth gage, physical dimensions, and properties should be as called for on contract drawings and specifications. If structural continuity is assumed in the design, the engineer should specify the required number of supports over which the form material should be continuous.

5.4.2.2—Installation

5.4.2.2.1—Shop drawings—The contractor should submit fully detailed shop drawings for all permanent deck forms to the engineer-architect for approval. Shop drawings should show all form thicknesses, metal gages, physical dimensions and properties, accessories, finishes, and methods of attachment to the various classes of the work.

5.4.2.2.2 — Fastenings — The permanent deck form must be properly fastened to supporting members and to adjacent sections of form, and properly lapped to provide a tight joint that will prevent loss of mortar during the placement of concrete. End closures for corrugated or fluted forms should be provided, where required, together with fill pieces around columns, openings, or other places where a tight fit is required. To prevent buckling, allowance should be made for expansion of metal deck forms.

Flexible types of forms (those that depend for lateral stiffness on supporting members) must be drawn tight for proper installation. Adequate temporary bracing or anchors must be provided in the plane of the top chord of the supporting members to prevent lateral buckling and rotation of these supports and to maintain the required tension in the flexible form.

Paper or metal forms used to form voids in concrete construction should be properly placed and anchored to reinforcement and to side or deck forms with wire ties or by other approved methods to prevent displacement or flotation during placing of concrete. End closures should be properly vented where necessary to eliminate cracking of concrete by reason of expansion of air in voids due to the heat of hydration of the concrete. Water should be prevented from entering voids. Where water intrusion is possible, weep holes should be provided to reduce its entrapment.

5.4.2.2.3—Electrical raceways—Where permanent deck forms are used as electrical raceways, units must be installed in conformance with the requirements of the National Electrical Code or similar authority having jurisdiction in such matters. Butted ends must be square and smooth on interior surfaces with no projecting edges or burrs to damage wire insulation and should be sealed against entry of concrete.

5.4.2.3—Deflections—The vertical and lateral deflections of the permanent form between supports under the load of fresh concrete should be investigated by the designer. Temporary supports should be used, if necessary, to keep deflection within desired tolerances.

5.5—Forms for prestressed concrete construction

5.5.1—Discussion—Pretensioning or post-tensioning of strands, cables, or rods may be done with or without side forms of the member in place, in accordance with Section 5.5.2.1. Bottom forms and supporting shores or falsework must remain in place until the member is capable of supporting its dead load and anticipated construction loads, as well as any formwork carried by the member. The structural designer should indicate in the contract documents any special requirements for prestressed construction. For example, it may be necessary to provide appropriate means of lowering or removing the formwork before full prestress is applied, to prevent damage due to upward deflection of resilient formwork. The concreting sequence for certain structures must also be planned so that concrete in the process of hardening is not subjected to bending stress caused by deflection of the formwork.

5.5.2—Recommendations

5.5.2.1—Design

(a) Where the side forms cannot be conveniently removed from the bottom or soffit form after concrete has set, such forms should be designed for additional axial and/or bending loads which may be superimposed on them during the prestressing operation.

*If supported by tests by a recognized commercial testing laboratory.

(b) Side forms that must remain in place during the transfer of prestressing force should be so designed as to allow for vertical and horizontal movements of the cast member during the prestressing operation. The form should be designed to minimize restraint to elastic shortening in the prestressing operation. For example, plan small components or wrecking strips that can be removed or destroyed to relieve load on side forms as well as to eliminate their restraint during prestressing. In all cases the restraint to shrinkage of concrete should be kept to a minimum, and the deflections of members due to prestressing force and the elastic deformation of form or falsework should be considered in the design and removal of the forms.

(c) Care should be exercised with post-tensioned slabs to assure that supporting shores do not fall out due to lifting of slab during tensioning. For large structures where the dead load of the member remains on the formwork during prestressing, displacement of the dead load toward end supports should be considered in design of the forms and shoring including sills or other foundation support.

5.5.2.2 — Construction accessories — Hold-down or push-down devices for deflected cables or strands should be provided in the casting bed or forms. Recommended safety factors for these strand deflection devices are given in Section 1.3.1. All openings, offsets, brackets, and all other items required in the concrete work, should be provided for in the formwork. Bearing plates, anchorage assemblies, prestressing steel, conduits, tube enclosures, and lifting devices shown or specified to be set in concrete must be accurately located with formwork templates and anchored to remain within the tolerances given on contract drawings and specifications. Quality and strength of these accessories should be as specified.

5.5.2.3—Suggested tolerances

5.5.2.3.1 — Precast prestressed individual members—Forms for this type of construction should be true to size and dimensions shown on plans and should be constructed and protected from warping so that the finished product will be within the limits given below unless otherwise noted on contract drawings and specifications. These tolerances are intended primarily for precast prestressed members produced in the field.

(a) Over-all dimensions of members
$\pm \frac{1}{8}$ in. per 10 ft, maximum of $\pm \frac{3}{4}$ in.

(b) Cross-sectional dimensions
Sections less than 6 in. .... $\pm \frac{1}{8}$ in.
Sections over 6 in. and less
than 18 in. .... $\pm 3/16$ in.
Sections 18 in. to 36 in. .... $\pm \frac{1}{4}$ in.
Sections over 36 in. .... $\pm \frac{3}{8}$ in.

(c) Deviations from straight line in long sections
Not more than $\frac{1}{8}$ in. per 10 ft length

(d) Deviation from specified camber
$\pm \frac{1}{8}$ in. per 10 ft of span
Maximum differential between adjacent units in erected position to be one-half the allowance for deviation from specified camber.

5.5.2.4—Special provisions for curing and for safety of workmen—Where required to allow early re-use of forms, provisions should be made to use such accelerated curing processes as steam curing, vacuum processing, or other approved methods.

Safety shields should be provided at end anchorages of prestressing beds or where necessary for the protection of workmen or equipment against possible breakage of prestressing strands, cables, or other assemblies during prestressing or casting operation.

5.6—Forms for precast concrete construction

5.6.1—Discussion—This type of form is used for precast concrete items which may be either load or nonload bearing members for structural or architectural uses.

5.6.2 — Construction — Exterior braces only should be used when exposed metal or filled-in pockets resulting from the use of metal ties would present an objectionable appearance.

To assure uniformity of appearance in the cast members or units, particularly in adjacent units where differences in texture and/or color would be visually apparent, care should be taken that the contact surfaces or forms or form liners are of uniform quality and texture.

Form oil or retardant coatings (nonstaining, if required) should be applied uniformly and in accordance with manufacturers' recommendations for this particular class of work.

5.6.2.1—Accessories—It is particularly important in this class of work that positive and rigid devices be used to insure proper location of reinforcement. All openings, cutouts, offsets, inserts, lift rings, and connection devices required to be set in concrete must be accurately located and securely anchored in the formwork.

The finished surfaces of members should be free of lift rings and other erection items where same will be exposed, will interfere with the proper placing of precast members or other materials, or will be subject to corrosion. Such items should be removed in such a manner that no remaining metal will be subject to corrosion.

Quality and strength of these accessories should be as required by contract drawings and specifications, but the lifting devices or other accessories not called for in contract drawings are the responsibility of the contractor.

5.6.2.2—Suggested tolerances—Forms must be true to size and dimensions of concrete members shown on the plans and be so constructed that the dimensions of the *finished product will be within the limits given below at the time of placement of these units in the structure,* unless otherwise noted on engineer-architect drawings. These tolerances are intended primarily for precast members produced in the field.

    (a) Over-all dimensions of members
        ±⅛ in. per 10 ft, maximum of ±¾ in.
    (b) Cross-sectional dimensions
        Sections less than 6 in. .... ±⅛ in.
        Sections over 6 in. and less
          than 18 in. .... ±3/16 in.
        Sections 18 in. to 36 in. .... ±¼ in.
        Sections over 36 in. .... ±⅜ in.
    (c) Deviations from straight line in long sections
        Not more than ⅛ in. per 10 ft
    (d) Deviation from specified camber
        ±1/16 in. per 10 ft of span
        Maximum differential between adjacent
        units in erected position .... ¼ in.

5.6.2.3 — Removal of forms — Precast members or units should be removed from forms only after the concrete has reached a specified strength as determined by the field-cured test cylinders or beams and job history of concrete curing.

Where required to allow early re-use of forms, provisions may be made to use accelerated curing processes such as steam curing, vacuum processing, or other approved methods.

Methods of lifting precast units from forms should be approved by the engineer-architect.

5.7—Use of precast concrete for forms

5.7.1—*Discussion*—Precast concrete panels or molds have been used as forms for cast-in-place and precast concrete, either as permanent, integrated forms or as removable, re-usable forms. They have been used for both structural and architectural concrete, designed either as structurally composite with the cast-in-place material or merely to provide a desired quality of outer surface, and in some cases to serve both of these purposes. Concrete form units may be either plain, reinforced, or prestressed, cast in the factory or at the job site. The most common use of precast concrete form units has been for forms that stay permanently in place, and the provisions of this section apply only to such forms.

As an integrated form the precast concrete unit is used in the following manner:

    (1) As self-supporting form systems requiring no external removable supports

    (2) As form facing to be supported by exterior removable framing and bracing

    (3) As architectural facing attached to the inner face of conventional forms, adding nothing to the strength or other form functions

    (4) As a part of a composite section acting with a cast-in-place slab, wall, or column.

A major reason for using integrated concrete forms is to secure a desired quality, texture, or appearance of surface which is difficult or uneconomical to achieve when using conventional forming techniques. The primary application for such forms in North America has been for architectural concrete, although some uses in mass concrete and other structural work have been reported. Under some conditions, substantial savings of time or money may be possible by building with such forms.

5.7.2—*Recommendations*

5.7.2.1—Design

5.7.2.1.1—Responsibility for design—Where the integrated form is to act compositely with the structure concrete, the form panel design will normally be prepared by the structural designer who will also indicate what additional external support is required for the forms. For permanent forms intended principally to achieve a desired architectural effect, the architect-engineer may specify surface finish and desired minimum thickness of architectural material, but design and layout of the forms and supporting systems will normally be the responsibility of the contractor-builder. The architect-engineer may require drawings of form panel design details and layout to be submitted for approval before concreting, including stated tolerances for field production.

5.7.2.1.2—Loads—Forms made of precast concrete are subject to three stages of loading: (1) loads occurring during removal of the unit from its own form and in subsequent handling, transporting, and erecting in its final position in the structure; (2) loads imposed by the placement of fresh concrete and by construction activities, during and after concreting; and (3) loads in service as part of a composite structure. Provisions of Sections 1.2 and 1.3 should be applied in relation to the first two loading stages, but the design of precast forms must also be related to the anticipated layout and setting of forms and external supports. For example, some precast forms may serve as liners or sheathing backed up by the usual formwork structure, while stronger precast forms may serve without external temporary supporting members.

When greater heights of formwork are assembled with precast units than with other forming materials, appropriate provision must be made for increased lateral loading due to wind and the pressure of freshly placed concrete.

5.7.2.1.3—Design procedure—Precast concrete form units should be designed according to currently accepted methods as set forth in ACI 318, "Building Code Requirements for Reinforced Concrete," with due regard for all stages of loading outlined in Section 5.7.2.1.2, as well as for the proposed system of support by form ties, studs, wales, or components of an existing structure and anchors or ties to develop composite action.

Deflection of concrete form panels should be held to an acceptable minimum consistent with the class of work for which the panels are being used.

Provisions for bracing, alignment, ties, and accessories should be consistent with all applicable provisions of Section 1.3.

5.7.2.1.4—Cover of reinforcement—A minimum cover of ¾ in. or 1½ bar diameters, whichever is larger, of concrete over reinforcement should be provided for all architectural concrete surfaces exposed to weather, regardless of tolerances stated elsewhere. Greater cover may be necessary for water exposure such as salt water and should be specified by the architect-engineer where needed.

5.7.2.1.5—Joints, inserts, and connections—Joints between form units should be strong, sound, impermeable, of satisfactory appearance, and should not require an excess of time and labor to complete.

Metal inserts or other embedded devices used for handling precast concrete formwork or joining it to adjacent panels or to the cast-in-place concrete should be designed for impact, shear, and bending, as well as tension loads. Inserts and connection devices should be designed so that they will not be exposed to the weather in the finished structure.

Connection details should be planned as realistically as possible to overcome problems of mating precast members to each other and to the existing or cast-in-place structure.

5.7.2.1.6—Bonding concrete form to concrete structure—Effective bond between precast form unit and the structure concrete is essential, and may be achieved by: (1) special treatment such as grooving or roughening the form face in contact with the structure concrete; (2) use of anchoring devices extending across the interface between form panel and structure concrete; (3) a combination of (1) and (2); and (4) by careful placing of the structure concrete. Lifting hooks in a form unit may be designed to serve also as anchors or shear connectors.

Where precast concrete forms are used in composite design with cast-in-place concrete, the development bond and shear should be designed according to current issues of the ACI 318 "Building Code Requirements for Reinforced Concrete," Chapter 25.

5.7.2.1.7—Size of forms—Large sizes of form panels are generally desirable to save time in erection as well as to reduce the number of joints that must be closed. However, local hauling restrictions, available handling equipment, and structural and architectural requirements must be considered in determining the size of form panels used.

5.7.2.2—Fabrication

5.7.2.2.1—General—Precast concrete form units may be cast at the job site or in the factory. Fabrication should be governed by all applicable provisions of Sections 5.5 and 5.6 for precast or prestressed units, including stated tolerance for the field production of such units.

5.7.2.2.2—Materials—Precast forms should be made of concrete having a minimum design strength in the 4000-5000 psi range. Wherever the form unit will be exposed to weathering in cold climates, air-entrained concrete should be used.

Metal inserts and connections are preferably made of a ductile material such as steel or malleable iron. If any embedded metal must be exposed to the elements after construction is completed, it should be made of noncorrosive material such as stainless steel or hot-dipped galvanized steel which has been galvanized after fabrication of the component parts. Metal reinforcement for precast forms should conform to ACI 318, Section 405.

5.7.2.3—Handling, storage, and erection

5.7.2.3.1—Storage—Precast forms should be stored so as to avoid uneven drying (warping), staining, or structural damage. Covered storage with ventilation permitting equal access of air to all sides is the best practice.

5.7.2.3.2 — Handling — Transporting and handling of precast form units should be planned to prevent damage or staining of facing material of the panels as well as to prevent structural damage.

5.7.2.3.3—Erection—Concrete form panels should be erected and braced to proper grade and alignment in such a way that the tolerances specified in Section 2.4 can be met, except where more restrictive tolerances are specified by the engineer-architect. Form ties may be attached to embedded anchors, reinforcement, or inserts provided in the panels for that purpose, or they may be installed at joints between panels when suitable backing and provision for precise alignment of the panels is made.

Where field welding of panel connections is required, the welding process should be controlled to avoid spalling and scorching of concrete. Such panel connections should not be galvanized.

Where architectural concrete form panels adjoin or are supported by other forming materials, care must be taken to use materials that will not stain the exposed concrete surface.

5.7.2.4—During and after concreting

5.7.2.4.1 — Vibration — Thorough consolidation of concrete behind the forms is desirable to prevent voids which would interrupt the bond of the form to structure concrete, but sufficient care must be exercised to prevent damage of concrete panels by contact with vibrators.

5.7.2.4.2—Protection of architectural finish —Care should be taken to avoid spilling fresh concrete on exposed surfaces, and any spilled or leaked concrete must be thoroughly removed before it has hardened. After concreting, precast architectural concrete form facings should be wrapped or covered with nonstaining materials to protect them from other construction materials, debris, or mechanical damage.

5.7.2.4.3—Filling joints—Depending on design details, joints may require filling or caulking after concreting is completed. This filling or caulking should be done carefully to avoid damage to adjoining surfaces, and any cement-based joint filler should be adequately cured to make joints durably watertight.

5.8—Forms for concrete placed under water

5.8.1—*Discussion*—Underwater placement may be made either by tremie pipe or underwater bucket. Placement by tremie—a pipe extending from above the water surface to the bottom of the form—is more common. This pipe is charged with concrete from the surface, taking care to force any water from the pipe ahead of the concrete. Once the pipe is filled with concrete, it is kept full and its bottom is kept immersed in the fresh concrete.

5.8.2—*Design*—Forms for underwater concreting are designed with the same considerations as other forms covered in Section 1.3 except that the density of the submerged concrete may be reduced by 63 lb per cu ft. However, because of large pressures which can develop due to the head developed in the tremie pipe, loads should be evaluated by personnel experienced in this type of work.

5.8.3—*Construction*—Underwater forms should be built on the surface insofar as possible, because final positioning and fitting when done underwater by divers is slow and costly.

Forms must be carefully fitted and secured to adjacent materials and/or construction to avoid loss of mortar under pressures developed. If there is any flow past the form, small openings in the form should be avoided as they will permit washing or scouring of the fresh concrete.

When it is intended to permit concrete to overflow the form and screed it off to grade, it is essential that the form is positioned to the proper grade and is detailed so that the overflow will not interfere with the proposed method and devices for stripping.

Forms should be well detailed, and such details should be scrupulously followed so that divers employed to remove the form may visualize and plan their work before descending.

Multi-use forms may have special devices for positioning forms from above water and special stripping devices such as hydraulic jacks which permit releasing the form from the surface.

For discussion see ACI JOURNAL, *Proceedings* V. 65, No. 1, Jan. 1968, pp. 61-64.

INDEX

357

TABLE OF CONVERSION FACTORS: BRITISH UNITS TO SI UNITS[*]

Multiply	By	To Obtain
Length		
Inches.................	25.4 (exactly)......	Millimeters
Feet...................	30.48 (exactly).....	Centimeters
Yards..................	0.9144 (exactly)....	Meters
Miles (statute)..........	1.609344 (exactly)..	Kilometers
Area		
Square inches...........	6.4516 (exactly)....	Square centimeters
Square feet.............	0.092903 (exactly)..	Square meters
Square yards...........	0.836127.........	Square meters
Volume		
Cubic feet..............	0.0283168........	Cubic meters
Cubic yards............	0.764555.........	Cubic meters
Capacity		
Liquid pints (U.S.)......	0.473179.........	Cubic decimeters
Gallons (U.S.)..........	3.78543..........	Cubic decimeters
Cubic feet..............	28.3160...........	Cubic decimeters
Mass		
Ounces (avdp)..........	28.3495...........	Grams
Pounds (avdp)..........	0.45359237 (exactly)........	Kilograms
Short tons (2000 lb)......	907.185...........	Kilograms
	0.907185.........	Metric tons
Force/Area		
Pounds per square inch....	0.070307.........	Kilogram-force per square centimeter
	0.689476.........	Newtons per square centimeter
Pounds per square foot....	4.88243..........	Kilogram-force per square meter
	47.8803..........	Newtons per square meter
Density		
Pounds per cubic foot......	16.0185...........	Kilograms per cubic meter
	0.0160185........	Grams per cubic centimeter

Multiply	By	To Obtain
Bending Moment or Torque		
Inch-pounds............	0.011521.........	Meter-kilograms
	1.12985 × 10[6].....	Centimeter-dynes
Foot-pounds............	0.138255.........	Meter-kilograms
	1.35582 × 10[7].....	Centimeter-dynes
Foot-pounds per inch.....	5.4431............	Centimeter-kilograms per centimeter
Velocity		
Feet per second..........	30.48 (exactly).....	Centimeters per second
Miles per hour..........	1.609344 (exactly)..	Kilometers per hour
	0.44704 (exactly)...	Meters per second
Flow		
Cubic feet per minute.....	0.4719...........	Cubic decimeters per second
Gallons (U.S.) per minute..	0.06309..........	Cubic decimeters per second
Work		
British thermal units (Btu).	1055.06...........	Joules
Btu per pound...........	2.326 (exactly).....	Joules per gram
Power		
Horsepower.............	745.700...........	Watts
Btu per hour............	0.293071.........	Watts
Foot-pounds per second....	1.35582..........	Watts
Heat Transfer		
Btu in./hr ft² deg F (k, thermal conductivity)....	1.442............	Milliwatts/cm deg C
	0.1240...........	Kg cal/hr m deg C
Btu/hr ft² deg F (C, thermal conductance)....	0.568............	Milliwatts/cm² deg C
	4.882............	Kg cal/hr m² deg C
Deg F hr ft²/Btu (R, thermal resistance)......	1.761............	Deg C cm²/milliwatt
Btu/lb deg F (c, heat capacity).............	4.1868...........	J/g deg C
Ft²/hr (thermal diffusivity).	0.2581...........	Cm²/sec
Fahrenheit degrees........	5/9 (exactly).......	Celsius or Kelvin degrees
Fahrenheit temperature...	$t_C = (t_F - 32)/1.8$	

[*] Selected conversion factors from "ASTM Metric Practice Guide," American Society for Testing and Materials. Available from ACI headquarters.

The metric technical unit of force is the kilogram-force, which is defined as the force which, when applied to a body having a mass of 1 kg, gives it an acceleration of 9.80665 m/sec/sec. The metric unit of force in SI (Systeme International) units is the newton, which is defined as that force which, when applied to a body having a mass of 1 kg, gives it an acceleration of 1 m/sec/sec. These units of force must be distinguished from the inconstant local weight of a body having a mass of 1 kg.